ISOBARIC SPIN
IN NUCLEAR PHYSICS

CONFERENCE ORGANIZATION
The Conference was held at
Florida State University, Tallahassee, Florida

Under the sponsorship of:

U.S. AIR FORCE OFFICE OF SCIENTIFIC RESEARCH

U. S. ATOMIC ENERGY COMMISSION

THE NATIONAL SCIENCE FOUNDATION

THE AMERICAN PHYSICAL SOCIETY

FLORIDA STATE UNIVERSITY

HIGH VOLTAGE ENGINEERING CORPORATION

Organizing Committee:

J. D. ANDERSON

R. H. DAVIS

J. D. FOX (CO-CHAIRMAN)

D. ROBSON (CO-CHAIRMAN)

J. P. SCHIFFER

ISOBARIC SPIN
IN NUCLEAR PHYSICS

Proceedings of the Conference on Isobaric Spin in Nuclear Physics
Tallahassee, Florida   March 17-19, 1966

Edited by

JOHN D. FOX

and

DONALD ROBSON

Both of Department of Physics
The Florida State University
Tallahassee, Florida

1966

ACADEMIC PRESS   New York and London

539
C7475

ACADEMIC PRESS INC.
111 Fifth Avenue, New York, New York 10003

United Kingdom Edition published by
ACADEMIC PRESS INC. (LONDON) LTD.
Berkeley Square House, London W.1

LIBRARY OF CONGRESS CATALOG CARD NUMBER: 66-26254

PRINTED IN THE UNITED STATES OF AMERICA

PREFACE

The purpose of the Conference on Isobaric Spin in Nuclear Physics was to assemble scientists actively engaged in the field in order to compare techniques, ideas, and results. The rapidly growing interest in this type of work had led to considerable confusion and duplication of experiments which were conveniently solved by getting the various groups together at this conference. Although the subject appeared to be highly specialized it has become increasingly apparent that isobaric spin, in one form or another, plays a role in virtually all aspects of nuclear structure and nuclear reactions. Hopefully, these Proceedings, based on the first conference in this field, will provide an adequate compendium which will assist in laying down the ground rules for future progress.

In planning the conference the organizing committee considered it best to have mainly invited papers followed by a very limited number of contributed papers. It was hoped that this would lead to more time for discussions of the papers presented. Indeed the informality and spontaneity of the participants in the lively discussion periods did bring out features which otherwise would probably not have come to light. We believe this type of conference has advantages over the more usual ones in which most of the time is taken up by contributed papers leaving virtually no time for informal exchanges of ideas.

The editorial committee took considerable liberties in editing some of the transcripts, particularly the discussions, several of which were reconstructed according to what the editors believed the speakers really wanted to say. Since it was not possible in the time available for the preparation of these proceedings to let each participant check the final transcript, the editors apologize for any mistakes they may have made by adopting this policy. The number of errors made by attempting to publish the proceedings as quickly as possible is, in the opinion of most participants, a relatively small sacrifice to make compared to extending the publication time.

All papers for which manuscripts were received have been included in the proceedings. Those papers presented are contained in the order of their appearance on the program, the remaining contributions being included in the supplementary program. Those contributions for which manuscripts were not received have been listed by title only. However, abstracts of all research contributions are published in the Bulletin of the American Physical Society. Throughout the proceedings references to this conference are simply given, for example, as Paper C2.

v

PREFACE

We hope the conference as well as the proceedings represent a worthwile contribution to this subject and look forward to future assemblies (at a different location!) at appropriate times. Finally we would like to express our sincere appreciation to fellow members of the Conference Committee, John D. Anderson, Robert H. Davis, and John P. Schiffer.

The Editors

Tallahassee, Florida

May, 1966

ACKNOWLEDGMENTS

We would first like to acknowledge the kindness of the Air Force Office of Scientific Research, the United States Atomic Energy Commission and the National Science Foundation in granting our requests for funds to support this conference. We are grateful to the Florida State University for providing facilities and financial assistance, in particular the use of the Moore Auditorium. It is a pleasure to thank various administrative officials of Florida State University. These include President John Champion who kindly consented to open the conference with a welcoming address, Vice President Karl Dittmer and Professor Earle K. Plyler, Head of the Physics Department.

Much appreciation is due to High Voltage Engineering Corporation for their financial support of the cocktail party, the accommodation of which was generously provided by the Epsilon-Sigma chapter of the Kappa Sigma Fraternity. Thanks are due to Dr. Steve Edwards for coordinating the arrangements and the Society of Hosts who were responsible for the very enjoyable evening.

The assistance of the University Union, the Conferences Office, and the Labor and Transportation crews in providing the necessary facilities and services needed by the conference was greatly appreciated. Many of the Florida State University physics graduate students participated in assisting the participants, taking notes during the conference, and helping with the preparation of the Proceedings. All these activities disrupted their studies and their assistance is gratefully acknowledged.

The projectionist, Mr. V. Marinelli, very ably performed through all the usual "slidesmanship" demonstrations and Mr. R. Baron was responsible for the recordings which greatly facilitated the editing and transcribing of the discussions. The assistance of Mrs. Jean Van Bergen's office is sincerely acknowledged.

The real, hard core work, as it must eventually become known, was performed by the valiant staff in the Tandem Office — Mrs. Bette Sprague, Mrs. Nancy Conley, and especially Mrs. Margaret Gray and Mrs. Suzy Tebor. Adequate acknowledgment of their services is beyond the scope of this discussion.

The Conference Committee was particularly pleased by the manner in which the participants, the session chairmen, and the speakers joined in making the conference a success. Those manuscripts which were carefully prepared and rapidly submitted were a source of great joy to the editors and typists.

The Conference Committee

CONTENTS

ix

CONTENTS

CONTENTS

CONTENTS

CONTENTS

CONTENTS

CONTENTS

CONTENTS

The following papers were submitted to the Conference but no manuscripts were received. The abstracts of these papers appear in an issue of the Bulletin of the American Physical Society.

S 27 Analogue States of A^{41} in K^{41}
        M. Lambert and G. Dumazet

S 28 Evidence for an Isobaric Analogue in Mg^{25} (7.75 MeV)
        D. Dehnhard and J. L. Yntema

S 29 A Reaction Mechanism Study of the (p, n) Reaction
        J. Y. Park

S 30 An Investigation of the 16.6 and 16.9 MeV States in Be^8
        Using the 2 Li$^6 \rightarrow 3\alpha$ Reaction
        M. D. Mancusi and E. Norbeck

S 31 Resonances in As^{75} (p, p) and As^{75} (p, n) Reactions
        C. Fan, B. E. Bonner, R. B. Blake and E. B. Paul

S 32 Higher T = 3/2 States in C^{13}
        D. C. Hensley and C. A. Barnes

S 33 Isobaric Spin Potential Term with Local and Non-Local Interaction
        P. C. Sood

S 34 Cross Section for Analogue Resonances in As^{75}, Cd^{111} and
        Cd^{113} (p, n) Reactions
        R. L. Kernell and C. H. Johnson

S 35 Isobaric Analogue States in the Reaction Cr^{50,52} (He^3, α) Cr^{49,51}
        R. Bock, P. von Brentano, H. H. Duhm and R. Stock

SESSION A

H. Morinaga, Chairman

A1. CHARGE DEPENDENCE OF NUCLEAR FORCES[*]

E. M. Henley

University of Washington
Seattle, Washington

I. INTRODUCTION

The fact that we are discussing the charge dependence rather than charge independence of nuclear
forces is a sign of the advances made in the precision
of nuclear measurements over the past decade. The
evidence for the charge independence of strong forces
is overwhelming, and the deviations are generally less
than a few percent. The questions before us are:
What is the evidence for a charge dependence of nuclear
forces and can we understand this small deviation from
complete symmetry in terms of electromagnetic interaction? The interest in the small charge breaking
effects stems, for instance, from their influence on
precise determinations of the energies of isobaric spin
analogue states that have not yet been found as well as
on weak interactions, as in the conserved vector current
theory.

Before discussing the charge dependence of nuclear forces, I would like to briefly review <u>charge
independence, CI</u>, and <u>charge symmetry, CS</u>. Charge symmetry is based on the equality of n-n and p-p forces;
physically it states that, in the absence of electro-

[*]Supported in part by the United States Atomic Energy
Commission

magnetic forces, a system of mesons and nucleons (or baryons), such as $\pi^{\pm}$ + n + p behaves exactly the same as its so-called charge symmetric counterpart, e.g. $\pi^{\mp}$ + p + n in the same quantum mechanical state. Charge independence generalizes this to include the neutral pions, and equates the n-p force to that of the p-p and n-n in the same state. The isobaric spin formalism which is based on these equalities is familiar to all of you. Charge independence states that

$$[H,T^2] = 0. \tag{1}$$

Charge symmetry, on the other hand, is related to invariance under a rotation of 180° about an axis perpendicular to the z-axis; this is commonly taken as the y-axis. However, because of the direct relation of charge and T_z, we have

$$[H,T_z] = 0, \tag{2}$$

and one can equally well choose the x-axis.

In the following I shall review the present status of the small deviations from CI and CS. The discussion will be almost completely restricted to (low energy) nuclear physics, and primarily to the nucleon-nucleon system, since other speakers will deal with heavier nuclei.

Charge breaking effects are not unexpected. For reasons that will be brought out, one expects a larger deviation from charge independence than from charge symmetry. The major effect arises from (1) the Coulomb force between two point nucleons ($\tau_z|p> =+|p>$)

$$V_c(1,2) = 1/2 [1 + \tau_z (1)] \; 1/2 [1 + \tau_z (2)] \frac{e^2}{x_{12}}, \tag{3}$$

4

which breaks both charge symmetry and charge independence. Basically, one photon effects, such as those
which give rise to Eq. 3 involve both an isoscalar and
isovector. It is only the isovector part which causes
charge dependent deviations from complete symmetry.
In general, the expectation value of any charge symmetry breaking effect will involve only terms in T_z^{2n},
whereas those that break independence also have terms
in T_z^{2n+1}, where n is an integer ≥ 0.

There are smaller electromagnetic corrections
that I will refer to as "direct". These include (2)
magnetic interactions, (3) the finite charge and magnetic moment distributions of the nucleons, (4) the
mass difference between the neutron and proton, and
(5) vacuum polarization. In addition to these, there
are "indirect" electromagnetic effects which change
the <u>nuclear</u> forces between two nucleons. The theoretical treatment of these corrections will be dealt
with in the second part of this talk. For purposes of
this talk CI and CS will refer to the specific nuclear
forces after the direct electromagnetic corrections
(1) - (5) have been applied.

II.   THE EXPERIMENTAL STATUS OF
CHARGE SYMMETRY AND CHARGE INDEPENDENCE

The Nucleon-Nucleon System

The mass difference between the neutron and
proton ($\Delta M/M \approx 0.14\%$) is presumably electromagnetic
in origin; although there is great interest in understanding this difference, success has not yet been
achieved. The next simplest system is the N-N system
(N = nucleon). It is a particularly appropriate one

to study, since the concept of CI originated with it.

Since Coulomb effects are less important at high energies[1], the largest sensitivity to charge dependent effects occurs at low energies. There are further advantages to the use of low energy data: (a) only S-waves are important and accurate phase shift determinations are possible (the tensor force is absent in the $^1S_0$ state); (b) the theoretical treatment is independent of the shape of the potential to first order. Thus, we have the well-known effective range approximation ($\hbar = c = 1$)

$$k \cot\delta_0 = -1/a + 1/2\, r\, k^2 + \ldots, \qquad (4)$$

in the absence of Coulomb forces. In Eq. 4 k is the relative momentum, a the scattering length, and r the effective range. An additional advantage is (c) the $^1S_0$ state is almost bound. The resultant large scattering length causes an amplification of charge dependent interactions; that is, a small change in the force causes a large change in the scattering length.

I shall therefore concentrate first on the low energy $^1S_0$ parameters determined from experiments. Unfortunately it is not possible to take the raw data, so that an experimental and theoretical discussion is necessary. Recent accurate determinations are shown in Table I. The "amplification" effect is well illustrated by the comparison of the p-p and n-n scattering lengths.

The p-p data must first be corrected for the Coulomb force from point charges (the deviations from this will be discussed later). This correction gives rise to the numbers in parentheses in Table I; to a first approximation one has

6

$$\frac{1}{(a_{pp})} \approx \frac{1}{a_{pp}} + \frac{1}{D} \times \ell n \left(\frac{D}{r_{pp}} - 0.33 \right),$$

$$(5)$$

where D is the proton Bohr radius (28.82 F), and (a_{pp}) is the point-Coulomb corrected scattering length. The shape dependence of the correction to a_{pp} is brought out in Table II taken from Heller, Signell and Yoder[3]. The effective range is hardly altered by the Coulomb force; according to Noyes[6] it is 2.84 F, instead of 2.80 F.

The n-n low energy scattering has been the object of much recent attention. It is primarily these measurements which have refocused attention on the charge dependence problem. However, I believe that the first renewed measurements gave spurious results. The experiments have been of two types, both of which make use of final state enhancements in cross sections due to the n-n attractive force. If the two neutrons are emitted together with a third particle then, for small relative n-n energy, the cross section is multiplied by[8] $|\psi (0)|^2$, the probability of finding the two particles close together. This can be large for an attractive force and is approximately related to the S-wave phase shift by[8]

$$| \psi (0)|^2 \sim \frac{\sin^2 \delta_0}{k^2} = \frac{a^2}{1 + k^2 a^2} \qquad (6)$$

The first type of measurements has three strongly interacting particles in the final state, which complicates the analysis and makes the results dependent on the reaction mechanism. The analyses omitted the effect of the interaction of the third particle with

7

either of the two neutrons. The results are summarized
in Table III. Only absolute values of a_{nn} are listed
since the sign is not determined. The most recent
measurement of Baumgartner et al. by means of the
$H^3(d,He^3)2n$ reaction has two advantages over previous
ones: They were able to show that the n-He^3 interaction was small and they made a comparison with the
$He^3(d,H^3)2p$ reaction to determine the p-p scattering
length as -7.41 $^{+ 0.39}_{- 0.49}$ F, which agrees, within statistics, with the direct determinations of this length.

The second class of measurements summarized in
Table III does not suffer from the above defects. It
uses the absorption of slow π^- mesons by deuterium.
Ryan measured the spectrum of gamma-rays, whereas
Haddock et al.[4] detected all 3 particles in coinci-
dence. It is the latter measurement which appears in
Table I.

Comparison of the n-n and point-Coulomb corrected
p-p data clearly shows consistency within statistics.
To determine the maximum charge symmetry breaking implied by the data, we need to relate a small change in
scattering length to that of the potential. This is
approximately given by[9]

$$\frac{\Delta a}{a} \approx Ma \int_r^\infty \Delta V \, u_o^2 \, dr, \tag{7}$$

where u_o is the (dimensionless) wavefunction at zero
energy and M is the nucleon mass. For an almost bound
state in a square well of radius b this is of the order
of

$$\frac{\Delta a}{a} \sim \frac{a}{b} \frac{\Delta V}{V}$$

which shows the enhancement for large scattering lengths discussed earlier. The connection between Δa and ΔV is actually shape dependent[10]; for a Yukawa potential of depth V, the error of Haddock et al. implies that charge symmetry is satisfied to within[4]

$$-1.2\% \lesssim (\Delta V/V)_{CS} \lesssim 1.6\%. \tag{8}$$

The effective range r_{nn} cannot be obtained from the above measurements; to the best of my knowledge, no direct data exists for its magnitude. Since the effective range is insensitive to the influence of electromagnetic forces, one usually takes $r_{nn} = r_{pp}$. Noyes[6] shows that the removal of Coulomb forces suggests that r_{nn} is approximately 1% larger than r_{pp}.

In order to discuss charge independence, we next consider the n-p system. Although the scattering length is well known from very low energy scattering, the effective range is still determined poorly. Recent measurements of Engelke et al.[11] at 0.4926 and 3.205 MeV give a considerably lower effective range than the average of previous work, and would cause serious questions with charge independence. Noyes[6] has analyzed the n-p data in great detail, both with and without the data from Engelke et al. This is summarized in Table IV, taken from his work[6]. The analysis labeled b) in this table assumes that the effective range, r_{np}, is $2.73 \pm .03$ F, a value that is consistent with CI to within electromagnetic corrections.

It is clear from the comparison of scattering lengths that charge independence is not valid, even after point-Coulomb corrections are taken into account.

The force is more attractive for the n-p system than for the n-n and p-p. The difference,

$$(a_{pp}) - a_{np} = 6.83 \pm 0.15 \text{ F} \qquad (9)$$

is reduced by less than 1F by other direct electromagnetic effects; we will see that indirect ones can account for the remainder. Without these corrections, Eq. 9 implies a breaking of charge independence of (for a Yukawa potential)[10]

$$[\frac{\Delta V}{V}] \lesssim 4.8 \pm 0.1\% \qquad (10)$$

Before we turn to the theory, I would like to briefly examine higher mass number systems.

Light Nuclei

After the two nucleon system, the next simplest one is that of $\text{He}^3 - \text{H}^3$, which tests CS and has the advantage that one can deal with bound states. However, the subtraction of electromagnetic effects is not accomplished as unambiguously as for the two-body system. The scattering of p and n on d exhibits CS[12], but the accuracy is not sufficient for our purposes. The electromagnetic measurements of the bound states[13], together with the static properties of the nuclei offer the most accurate information. This is summarized in Table V.

The charge distribution radius and the binding energy show clear deviations from charge symmetry. If the spatial distribution of the 3 nucleons is taken to be spherically symmetric, and we assume a uniform charge distribution, then the Coulomb correction to the binding energy of He^3 is (neglecting exchange terms)

$$E_c = \left(\frac{3}{5}\right)^{1/2} \frac{6}{5} \frac{e^2}{R_{rms}} \approx 0.66 \text{ MeV.} \qquad (11)$$

This differs from the binding energy B by about 0.1 MeV. However, the electron scattering data[13,14] indicates that the charge distribution is not uniform but rather has a shape which is peaked at small distances. This increases the Coulomb energy.

There are thus two asymmetries to explain here. The Coulomb force will tend to increase the R_{rms} of He^3 relative to H^3. Furthermore, Schiff[14] has analyzed the electron scattering data in the presence of a small percentage ($\lesssim 4\%$) an asymmetric S-state (called S' by him), for which the two like nucleons (effectively) are less tightly bound than the odd one. Since the latter is a p in H^3, this helps to explain the smaller charge radius for this nucleus. The rms radius is sensitive to the outer region of the charge distribution, where the difference in effective binding show up most strongly[15]. With a 4% S'state (with the sign predicted from the spin dependence of the N-N force) Schiff is able to account for the radius difference. With an Irving-Gunn wavefunction[14] the He^3 - H^3 difference in binding energy can then be accounted for in terms of Coulomb energy alone. Thus, this analysis shows that no charge asymmetric nuclear interaction need be invoked to understand the 3-body nuclei. In a contribution to this conference, Okamoto[16] disagrees with this conclusion and finds that a 0.5 - 1.5% breakdown of charge symmetry is required. However, I believe that he assumes a uniform charge distribution.

Okamoto's analysis of other mirror nuclei[16) reinforces his conclusion. However, the detailed treatment of the 3-body nuclei shows that one must be very careful that the exchange of a n by a p does not influence the rest of the nucleus in an unsymmetrical way such as effects due to pairing. I will not discuss this further, except to remark that for the above reason the most suitable nuclei to compare are those one particle removed from closed shells.

Tests of CI in nuclei primarily compare levels of the same isobaric spin in neighboring nuclei. Since Wilkinson, Jänecke and MacDonald, among others will discuss such states, I will not consider them.

In conclusion, the experimental data shows consistency with charge symmetry to within $\sim$ 1% and indicates that charge independence is broken by about 5%, with the n-p force stronger than the p-p or n-n forces.

III. THEORY OF CHARGE DEPENDENT FORCES

We assume that the forces which break charge symmetry and independence arise purely from electromagnetic currents. In principle, these effects can be calculated from sum rules[17) and from dispersion theory[18). However, at the present time the most accurate treatment (at low energies) is in terms of ordinary potential and field theory. This procedure has the further advantage of giving one insight into the origin of the charge dependent forces. We have already mentioned the direct electromagnetic effects and will discuss these first.

Direct Electromagnetic Effects

The Coulomb force from point charges has been

discussed in parts I and II. It remains to consider
the smaller effects. There are, first of all, the magnetic forces, which for point particles are given by[19]

$$V_{magn}(x) = 4\pi \mu_o \delta^3(x) [K_n(K_p - 1/2)(1 - \tau_z)$$

$$+ (K_p^2 - K_p + 1/2)(1 + \tau_z)] + 2\mu_o^2 p \cdot \frac{1}{x} p(1+\tau_z),$$

$$(12)$$

where μ_o is the nuclear magneton, K_p (K_n) is the magnetic moment of the proton (neutron) in nuclear magnetons, and p is the relative momentum. Since this
force gives rise to an attractive p-n force and a repulsive p-p one, it is in the right direction to remove
the observed discrepancy in scattering lengths. However, because of the repulsive short-range nuclear
force which keeps the nucleons apart, the effect is
very small[20]; less than 0.8 F of the 6.8 F scattering
length difference is removed. (The actual value depends on the hard core radius.)

Now that the electromagnetic form factors of the
nucleons are known, the replacement of the point vertex
of Fig. 1a by that shown in Fig. 1b automatically takes
into account (1) the (point) Coulomb energy, (2) the
magnetic interaction, and (3) the distribution of charge
and magnetic moment. The correction from the distribution of charge and magnetic moments was calculated by
Riazuddin[21] and by Schneider and Thaler[23]; it removes
approximately 0.3 F of the observed discrepancy of Eq. 9.

The consequence of the n-p mass difference is
negligible. The vacuum polarization is also in the
right direction (it adds a repulsion to the p-p force)

and was found by L. Heller[3,23] to account for 0.2 F of the difference noted in Eq. 9. Thus, the indirect electromagnetic effects must account for the remaining discrepancy (see Eq. 9) of

$$(a_{pp}) - a_{np} = 6.3 \pm 0.2 \text{ F}, \qquad (13a)$$

or (based on a Yukawa shape[10])

$$\frac{(V_{pp}) - V_{np}}{|V_{CI}|} \lesssim 4.1 \pm 0.1\%. \qquad (13b)$$

It must be remembered that (V_{pp}) is the purely nuclear part of the p-p potential, which is somewhat less attractive than the n-p one.

Indirect Electromagnetic Effects

The indirect electromagnetic effects are those which alter the nuclear forces themselves. They include consequences of (1) electromagnetic mass differences of the quanta exchanged between the nucleons, (2) radiative corrections to the meson-nucleon coupling constants, (3) mixing of meson states of different isobaric spin but of the same spin and parity, and (4) other radiative corrections. Unlike the direct electromagnetic influences, the results of the indirect ones cannot be computed with confidence, but can only be estimated.

The primary effect is that due to the electromagnetic mass splitting of the mesons. Of these the pions are the lightest and we have

$$\frac{m_\pm - m_o}{m} \approx \frac{4.58 \text{ MeV}}{137 \text{ MeV}} \approx 3.3\% . \qquad (14)$$

Because of the CPT theorem, which assures the equality
of positively and negatively charged meson masses, CS
is maintained, but CI is violated. Only the long range
part of the N-N force, namely that due to one pion exchange can be calculated in an unambiguous manner (see
Fig. 2)[3,21,22,24]. The p-p (or n-n) system can only
exchange the lighter π^o (m_o = 135.01 MeV), whereas the
n-p one can also exchange a charged pion (m_+ = 139.59
MeV). If g_+ is the charged pion-nucleon coupling constant and $\overline{g_o}$ that for neutral pions, one finds for the
$^1S_0$ state

$$V_{nn} (1\pi) = V_{pp} (1\pi) = - \frac{g_o^2}{4\pi} \left(\frac{m_o}{2M} \right)^2 \frac{e^{-m_o x}}{x}$$

(15)

$$V_{np} (1\pi)/V_{nn} (1\pi) = - 1 + 2 \left(\frac{g_+}{g_o} \right)^2 \left(\frac{m_+}{m_o} \right) e^{-(m_+ - m_o)x}.$$

The mass splitting has two consequences. If we put
$g_+^2/4\pi = g_o^2/4\pi$ (= 14.4), the depth of the n-p potential is lowered, but the range is shortened. Although
these two effects tend to cancel each other, the net
strength of the n-p potential is larger than for the
p-p (or n-n) interaction, which is in the right direction to explain Eq. 13. The one pion exchange ratio
obtained from Eq. 15 is able to account for about 1/2
of the difference between the n-p and p-p scattering
lengths; the exact value depends on the smallest separation for which one assumes the one pion exchange potential to be meaningful. Morrison and I have attempted
to take into account also the electromagnetic mass
differences in the 2π and ρ-exchange potentials[24,25].
We have used the boundary condition model of Feshbach,

15

Lomon and Tubis[26] who fit the N-N scattering phase shifts over a wide range of energies with a semi-phenomenological 2π exchange interaction together with 1ρ and 1π exchange. The boundary is chosen at 0.7 F. It is assumed that the percentage electromagnetic mass splitting, $\Delta m/m$, of the heavier mesons is small; thus, for most of our work the boundary condition was assumed to be charge independent, as were the coupling constants. It the electromagnetic mass splitting of the ρ meson, $m_{\rho^+} - m_{\rho^0} = \Delta m_\rho$, is taken to be 2 MeV then the results of the first line in Table VI are obtained. There are a variety of ways in which the remaining difference between the n-n and n-p scattering length can be accounted for within the framework of our model. For instance a Δm_ρ of -5 MeV will do so, or a 2% charge dependent boundary condition, or yet (as shown in Table VI) a 2% charge dependence of the neutral to charged pion coupling constants. In addition we have used our model to calculate the charge dependence of the effective range. The major effect occurs here due to the mass differences rather than to the further adjustment of Δm_ρ, boundary condition, or g_+/g_0. Because of the lighter π^0 mass the effective range of the n-n interaction is found to be larger than that for p-n, in agreement with experiment. The difference was found to be

$$r_{nn} - r_{pn} = 0.12 \pm 0.03 \text{ F.} \qquad (16)$$

However, one can question the omission of the exchange of 3 pions and other resonances. Furthermore, when more than one meson is exchanged the intermediate state could be the $N^*_{3/2,3/2}$ rather than the nucleon[27].

The other indirect electromagnetic effects spoil CS as well as CI. The first of these are the radiative corrections to the meson-nucleon coupling constants, such as those shown in Fig. 3a. Riazuddin[28] and Stevens[29] find that the fractional change of the pion-nucleon coupling constants are of the order of $\alpha/\pi \approx 2 \times 10^{-3}$ (α is the fine structure constant), the precise value depending on a cut-off parameter. Although this change is small, it is more effective than the same change of $\Delta m/m_\pi$ because the former directly alters the depth of the potential and leaves the range unaltered. A smaller coupling of the π^0 to the p than to the n is equivalent to a slightly increased Coulomb energy, as required by Okamoto for He^3 [16]. Eq. 13b requires $g_+ < g_0$ (π^0 to p or n), if this is the only effect.

The third indirect cause of charge symmetry and charge independence breaking is illustrated in Fig. 3b, and is referred to as isobaric spin mixing. Thus, the π^0 is not a pure $T = 1$ state because electromagnetic forces blend in a small amount of η^0. Similarly the η^0 is not a pure $T = 0$ state, since a small fraction of the π^0 is admixed to it. Such off-diagonal matrix elements are known to be present from the decay of the η to three pions. The neutral pion, $\bar{\pi}^0$, that is exchanged between two nucleons is thus a mixture of $T = 1$ and $T = 0$ states

$$\bar{\pi}^0 \approx \pi^0 + c\eta^0 ,$$

and similarly

$$\bar{\eta}^0 \approx \eta^0 + c'\pi^0 .$$

The constants c and c' have been estimated by various authors on the basis of SU(3) symmetry to be $c \approx c' \approx 0.01$[29-31]. The exchange of a $\bar{\pi}^0$ gives rise to a charge-dependent potential

$$V_{12}(\bar{\pi}^0) = [1 + (\tau_{z1} + \tau_{z2}) \frac{g_0 g_\eta}{4\pi} c] V_{12}(\pi^0)$$

where g_0 is the π^0-nucleon coupling constant and g_η is that for the η. In the SU(3) limit, the latter is $\sqrt{3/5}g$ if the D/F ratio is 1.5[29]. This charge-dependent interaction gives a correction that makes V_{pp} more attractive than V_{np} and V_{np} more attractive than V_{nn}, which is in the wrong direction for the explanation of Eq. 13 and for Okamoto[16]. However, Stevens[29] shows that the addition of the η exchange potential reverses the sign of the charge dependent effects and adds a contribution of the order of 0.1 MeV to the Coulomb energy of He^3, as required by Okamoto's analysis. Similar admixing of states also occurs for the vector bosons ρ^0, ω^0, and ϕ^0.

Among other indirect effects which give rise to charge dependent potentials, I will only cite one example. This is the exchange of a photon leading to an intermediate $N^*_{3/2, 3/2}$ and a further pion exchange.

The indirect electromagnetic effects also cause energy shifts among the isobaric spin members of a given multiplet. Morrison[32] has calculated the lowest order perturbation shift due to the $\pi^+ - \pi^0$ mass difference in the one pion exchange potential for mass 14 triplets. With harmonic oscillator wavefunctions he obtains an energy shift equal to $- 0.014 \, T_z^2$ MeV without a lower cut-off and $- 0.0014 \, T_z^2$ MeV with a lower cut-off at 1.4 F (T_z is the total z-component of the isobaric spin)[33].

IV. CONCLUSIONS

The major indirect electromagnetic effects are those due to the electromagnetic mass splittings of the mesons. These maintain charge symmetry and give corrections of the right sign and roughly of the right order of magnitude to explain the slightly more attractive n-p potential in the $^1S_0$ state. The experimental evidence for charge symmetry violation is still small[34] but effects due to isobaric spin mixing and radiative corrections to the meson-nucleon coupling constants are expected to cause a small deviation. The sign of these deviations appears to make the p-p interaction less attractive than the n-n one, in accord with a simple interpretation of light mirror nuclei.

Further progress requires renewed precise measurements of the n-p cross section at low energies and more accurate data on the low energy properties of the n-n system. Although it appears that the charge dependence of the nuclear forces can be understood, a more reliable theoretical treatment is also in order.

REFERENCES

1) G. Breit, M. H. Hull, Jr., K. Lassila, and K. D. Pyatt, Jr., Phys. Rev. Letters 15 (1960) 79 have shown that the high energy p-p and n-p scattering data is consistent with charge independence; for a pion physics test see D. Harting, et al., Phys. Rev. 119 (1960) 1716 and H. S. Köhler, Phys. Rev. 118 (1960) 1345.

2) M. L. Gursky and L. Heller, Phys. Rev. 136 (1964) B1693.

3) L. Heller, P. Signell, N. R. Yoder, Phys. Rev. Letters 13 (1964) 577.

4) R. P. Haddock, R. M. Salter, M. Zeller, J. B. Czirr and D. R. Nygren, Phys. Rev. Letters 14 (1965) 318.

5) H. P. Noyes, Phys. Rev. 130 (1963) 2025.

6) H. P. Noyes, Nucl. Phys. 74 (1965) 508; see also G. Breit, K. A. Friedman, and R. E. Seamon, Supplement Progr. Theoret. Phys., Extra Number, 449 (1965).

7) J. M. Blatt and V. F. Weisskopf, "Theoretical Nuclear Physics", (John Wiley and Sons, Inc., New York, 1952), p. 93.

8) K. M. Watson, Phys. Rev. 88 (1952) 1163.

9) J. D. Jackson and J. M. Blatt, Revs. Mod. Phys. 22 (1950) 77.

10) The percentage error is considerably less for a square well (~ 1/20) than for a Yukawa well. See M. J. Moravcsik, Phys. Rev. 136 (1964) B624.

11) C. E. Engelke, R. E. Benenson, E. Melkonian, and J. M. Lebowitz, Phys. Rev. 129 (1963) 324.

12) L. Rosen in "Nuclear Forces and the Few Nucleon

Problem", edited by T. C. Griffiths and E. A. Power (Pergamon Press, 1960) Vol. II, p. 481.

13) H. Collard, R. Hofstadter, E. B. Hughes, A. Johanson, M. R. Yearian, R. B. Day, and R. T. Wagner, Phys. Rev. 138 (1965) B57.

14) L. I. Schiff, Phys. Rev. 133 (1964) B802.

15) R. H. Dalitz and T. W. Thacker, Phys. Rev. Letters 15 (1965) 204.

16) K. Okamoto (private communication); see also Phys. Letters 11 (1964) 150; Progr. Theoret. Phys. 34 (1965) 326, Paper S4.

17) F. Lewis (private communication).

18) D. Y. Wong and H. P. Noyes, Phys. Rev. 126 (1962) 1866; H. Goldberg, Nuovo Cimento 40B (1965) 243; L. Heller and M. Rich (to be published).

19) J. Schwinger, Phys. Rev. 78 (1950) 135.

20) E. E. Salpeter, Phys. Rev. 91 (1953) 994.

21) Riazuddin, Nucl. Phys. 7 (1958) 217.

22) R. E. Schneider and R. M. Thaler, Phys. Rev. 137 (1965) B874.

23) L. Heller, Phys. Rev. 120 (1960) 672.

24) E. M. Henley and L. K. Morrison, Phys. Rev. 141 (1965) 1489.

25) See also D. L. Lin, Nucl. Phys. 60 (1964) 192.

26) H. Feshbach, E. Lomon, and A. Tubis, Phys. Rev. Letters 6 (1961) 635.

27) P. Signell (private communication).

28) Riazuddin, Nucl. Phys. 7 (1958) 223.

29) M. St. J. Stevens, Phys. Letters 19 (1965) 499.

30) B. W. Downs (preprint); Y. Nogami (private communication).

31) See also R. H. Dalitz and F. Von Hippel, Phys. Letters 10 (1964) 153; B. Barrett and G. Barton,

Phys. Rev. <u>133</u> (1964) B466.

32) L. K. Morrison (private communication).

33) See also S. Sengupta, Nucl. Phys. <u>30</u> (1962) 300,

34) See, e.g., R. J. Blin-Stoyle and C. Yalgin, Phys. Letters <u>15</u> (1965) 258.

TABLE I. Singlet S-state scattering lengths and effective ranges. References to measurements and/or analyses are given. The parenthetical numbers are corrected for Coulomb forces from point charges.

	p-p	n-n	p-n
a(F)	-7.815 ± 0.008[2] $(-16.6$ to $-16.9)$[3]	-16.4 ± 1.9[4]	-23.679 ± 0.028[5]
r(F)	2.795 ± 0.025[2] (2.84 ± 0.03)[6]	--------	2.52 ± 0.10[6] to 2.73 ± 0.03[6]

TABLE II. Neutron-neutron scattering length predictions from various potentials. (From Heller, Signell and Yoder[3]).

Potential	(a_{pp})
Square	-16.5 F
Gaussian	-17.1
Exponential	-17.5
Yukawa	-19.0
Bargmann	-17.9
Bargmann + OPEP	-19.0
Hamada-Johnston (HJ)	-16.7
HJ'	-16.8
Yale	-16.8
YS	-16.6
YS'	-16.9

TABLE III. Recent determinations of the n-n scattering length from final state interactions.

Reaction	Incident Energy (MeV)	Measurement	$|a_{nn}|$ (F)	Ref.
$n+d \rightarrow p+2n$	14.4	p spectrum	21.7 ± 1 F	a
$n+H^3 \rightarrow d+2n$	13.9	d spectrum	$23.6^{+1.6}_{-2.0}$	b
$n+H^3 \rightarrow d+2n$	14.4	d spectrum	18 ± 3	c
$d+H^3 \rightarrow He^3+2n$	$\begin{cases} 32.5 \\ 40.2 \end{cases}$	He^3 spectrum	16.1 ± 1	d
$\pi^- + d \rightarrow \gamma + 2n$	0	γ spectrum	$17^{+7.7}_{-4.3}$	e
$\pi^- + d \rightarrow \gamma + 2n$	0	γ, n, n	16.4 ± 1.9	f

a M. Cerineo, et al., Phys. Rev. 133 (1964) B948.
b V. K. Voitovetskii, I. L. Korsunskii, and Y. F. Pazhin, Phys. Letters 10 (1964) 109; Nucl. Phys. 64 (1965) 513.
c V. Ajdacic, et al., Phys. Rev. Letters 14 (1965) 442.
d E. Baumgartner, H. E. Conzett, E. Shield, and R. J. Slobodrian, Phys. Rev. Letters 16 (1966) 105. These authors find $a_{pp} = -7.41^{+0.39}_{-0.49}$ F from $He^3(d,H^3)2p$.
e J. W. Ryan, Phys. Rev. Letters 12 (1964) 564.
f R. P. Haddock, et al., Phys. Rev. Letters 14 (1965) 318.

TABLE IV. Analysis of ϵ_B, a_{nH}, σ_{tot} (0) and the eight n-p total cross section measurements below 5 MeV (from H. P. Noyes[6)]).

Data	r(F)	a_t(F)
a) ALL	2.5166 $\pm$ 0.1036	-23.679 $\pm$ 0.028
ALL-EBML	2.6393 $\pm$ 0.1259	-23.678 $\pm$ 0.028
EBML	2.4427 $\pm$ 0.1122	-23.678 $\pm$ 0.028
b) ALL	2.7134 $\pm$ 0.0288	-23.714 $\pm$ 0.021
ALL-EBML	2.7251 $\pm$ 0.0292	-23.688 $\pm$ 0.023
EBML	2.7108 $\pm$ 0.0290	-23.720 $\pm$ 0.022

TABLE V. Properties of the A = 3 nuclei.

Ref.		H^3	He^3	$(He^3 - H^3)$
a	charge R_{rms}(F)	1.70$\pm$0.05	1.87$\pm$0.05	0.17$\pm$0.07
b	[corrected R_{rms}(F)]	(1.47$\pm$0.07)	(1.66$\pm$0.07)	(0.19$\pm$0.10)
a	magn. R_{rms}(F)	1.70$\pm$0.05	1.74$\pm$0.10	0.04$\pm$0.11
c	B (MeV)	8.4819	7.7181	-0.76384 $\pm$ 0.00026

[a] H. Collard et al., Phys. Rev. 138 (1965) B57.
[b] These numbers have been corrected for the electro-magnetic structure of the nucleons.
[c] J. H. E. Mattauch, W. Thiele, and A. H. Wapstra, Nucl. Phys. 67 (1963) 1.

TABLE VI. Neutron-proton scattering length predictions for pseudoscalar coupling. The first row lists the predicted n-p scattering lengths for a charge-independent coupling and the second one the ratio of $(g_+/g_o) = (G_+/G_o)$ required to fit the experimental scattering length. We take $\eta_+^2 = \eta_o^2 = 1.668$, $r_{1n} = 0.7011$, $a_{nn} = -16.4$ F, $\Delta m = 2$ MeV, and $A_+ = A_o = 1$.

	OPEP	OPEP + TPEP	OPEP = TPEP + V_ρ
a_{np}(F)	-19.9	-20.80	-18.27
$\dfrac{g_+}{g_o} = \dfrac{G_+}{G_o}$	1.0094	0.9953	0.9832

DISCUSSION

BLOOM, Livermore: I was wondering if you could give us some simple notion as to why the effective ranges are so much the same for the n,n and n,p. You showed us the magnification of the scattering length, but why should there not be a similar magnification for the effective range? Is there some simple way of seeing this?

HENLEY: The effective range is much less sensitive to any small changes of potential because the amplification factor is not present for it. For a given percentage change in the potential, the effect on the range is of the same order of magnitude, but that on the scattering length is much larger.

This does not really answer your question, but a look at the equation for the effective range shows that the magnification is not expected for it.

DAVIS, Florida State: You mentioned the strong dependence on the shape of the potential, for the percentage deviation from charge independence. Did you explore this for other cases besides the Yukawa well?

HENLEY: This is actually Moravcsik's work rather than ours. I really do not understand why the percentage deviation is so large for a Yukawa shape; it is much less for a square well.

The results for a square well are less than those for a Yukawa potential by a factor of about 20. However, I have not checked Moravcsik's calculations.

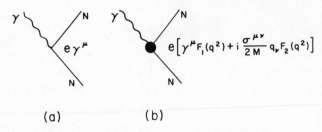

Fig. 1. (a) Bare NN$_\gamma$ vertex. (b) Renormalized NN$_\gamma$ vertex, with charge (F_1) and magnetic (F_2) form factors.

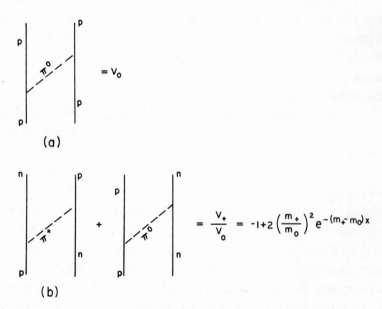

Fig. 2. One pion exchange potential (a) for p-p (or n-n) and (b) for p-n.

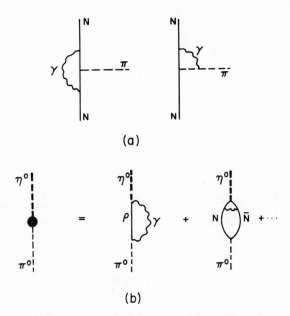

(a)

(b)

Fig. 3. (a) Typical radiative corrections to the π-N vertex. (b) Contributions to the π-η electromagnetic coupling.

A2. THE ISOBARIC MASS FORMULA AND COULOMB ENERGIES IN THE 1p-SHELL

D. H. Wilkinson

Nuclear Physics Laboratory, Oxford

INTRODUCTION

Some historical comments are made about the quadratic formula relating the masses of members of isobaric multiplets. It is remarked that the formula is still true even if the nuclear forces themselves are charge-dependent provided that the departure from charge-independence is of a two-body character and, like the Coulomb effect, may be treated as a perturbation. This means that charge-independence may be tested through the mass formula only by agreement of the coefficients of the mass formula with computations of the Coulomb energy differences. Computations of Coulomb energy differences in the 1p-shell are presented based on wavefunctions derived from a study of electron scattering and (p,2p) reactions. Good agreement between the computed Coulomb energy differences and the binding energy differences is found but the need for improvements in the computations is stressed. Weak evidence that the n-p interaction may be some 2% stronger than the n-n or p-p interaction is presented. The critical role played by the binding energy of the "last proton" in calculations of Coulomb energy differences and the related importance of the parentage spectrum are emphasized.

HISTORICAL NOTE

The isobaric mass formula says that if the wave-functions of the members of an isobaric multiplet may be regarded as identical one with another and if any charge-dependences are of a two-body character and may be treated as perturbations then the nuclear mass is given by:

$$M = a + bT_z + cT_z^2$$

without higher powers of T_z and without any odd-even alternations due to pairing or such causes.

When, in 1964, the work at Berkeley of Cerny, Garvey and Pehl began to reveal the excitation of states of $T > 1$ in light nuclei it immediately occurred to me[1] that we were at last approaching the possibility of testing the parabolic character of the mass relationship, a possibility obviously denied us while limited to multiplets of $T \leq 1$. I thought at that time that this self-evidently-correct formula was part of our general culture and was universally-known; it never occurred to me that it might be desirable, still less that it might be necessary, to give a reference for it. The difficulty I experienced in convincing some of my colleagues of the correctness of the formula, particularly of its innocence of any pairing alternation, persuaded me, however, of my lack of historical perspective.[2] It is difficult to find early explicit statements of this formula although it is, of course, implicit in the earliest work of Wigner following his introduction of the isobaric spin concept for complex nuclei.[3] Probably because of MacDonald's work on isobaric spin impurities[4] the formula was familiar to me when I heard Wigner state it explicitly at the Welch Conference[5] in Houston,

31

Texas in November 1957 in an address in which he emphasized the interest there would be in completing isobaric
quartets to test the parabolic character of the formula.
The next time I heard it discussed was by Okubo in his
address to the Canadian Association of Physicists in
Halifax, Nova Scotia in June 1964; it was probably this
last occasion that ensured that the formula came immediately to my mind on learning of the Berkeley work.
Of course the formula has also come into considerable
prominence in elementary particle physics as has received a microscopic justification.[6]

DERIVATION
Words

The meaning of an isobaric multiplet is that there
exists a series of $2T + 1$ nuclear states, $T_z = +T...-T$,
of successively increasing charge but with identical
nuclear wavefunctions such that the successive conversions of neutron into proton along the series <u>do not
distinguish neutron from proton except in the overall
charge that the nucleus carries</u>. The fact that the
electrostatic energy of a system increases quadratically
with the overall charge if the overall charge does not
change the structure of the system then establishes the
formula. (Note particularly that although pairing
forces may operate in the strong nuclear force they may
not, by definition, operate along the T-multiplet in the
successive conversions of neutron into proton in such a
way as to distinguish neutron from proton, and so do not
reflect in any odd-Z-even-Z alternation in the formula;
they may, however, be reflected in the magnitudes of the
coefficients of the formula.)

We may immediately note that if the nuclear forces themselves are charge-dependent then if that charge dependence may also be treated as a perturbation and if it, like the electrostatic force, is of a two-body character, then its contribution to the nuclear mass follows the same quadratic formula.

Symbols

If the total charge-dependent perturbation (Coulomb plus nuclear) is V then, under the assumption already stated namely that the wavefunctions themselves are unaffected by the perturbation:

$$M = \text{constant} + < TT_z \,|V|\, TT_z >$$

If V is the sum of two-body interactions only, then its tensor expansion does not go beyond the second rank:

$$M = \text{constant} + \sum_k a_k < TT_z \,|T_o^{(k)}|\, TT_z > \qquad k \leq 2$$

By the Wigner-Eckart theorem this becomes:

$$M = \text{constant} + \sum_k a_k (-)^{T-T_z} \begin{pmatrix} T & k & T \\ -T_z & 0 & T_z \end{pmatrix} \langle T||T^{(k)}||T\rangle \qquad k \leq 2$$

$$= a + bT_z + cT_z^2$$

since the successive terms in the expansion are: (i) a constant; (ii) a constant times T_z; (iii) a constant times $(T_z^2 - T[T+1])$.

CHARGE INDEPENDENCE

As has been stressed, the experimental checking of the parabolic character of the mass formula will only test for a charge dependence to the nuclear force if that charge dependence is of a three-body or higher nature; a charge-dependence of the two-body nuclear

33

force leaves the quadratic form of the formula unchanged.
Such a specifically-nuclear charge-dependence of the
two-body force would, however, change the constants b
and c of the formula from the values expected of them on
the basis of the Coulomb perturbation alone.

A realistic calculation of the b and c coefficients is therefore demanded if we are going to be able
to use the mass-splittings within the isobaric multiplets
as a test of charge-independence: are the calculated
Coulomb energy differences equal to the experimental
binding energy differences?

A great body of data on mass splittings is now ac-
cumulating and awaits analysis from this viewpoint. It
can only be done, of course, using wavefunctions and
charge densities deriving from independent evidence and
at the moment sufficient data bearing on detailed wavefunctions exist only in the 1p-shell with some small
evidence beyond.

COULOMB ENERGY DIFFERENCES IN THE 1p-SHELL

It has been customary to compute Coulomb energy
differences for a uniform charge distribution or for
harmonic oscillator wavefunctions or sometimes for wavefunctions appropriate to finite square wells. None of
these methods is acceptable any longer. As will be
shown, the Coulomb energy computed for a particle in a
realistic potential is a sensitive function of its binding energy into that potential and so wavefunctions that
reflect the effect of the binding energy and that are
computed in realistic potentials are essential if the
computed Coulomb energies are to be directly compared
with experiment. As a specific illustration from data
to be presented below, if we wish to compute the Coulomb

energy difference between C^{11} and B^{11} and consider C^{11} to be a B^{10} "core" plus a "last proton" and B^{11} to be the same B^{10} "core" plus a "last neutron", the Coulomb energy difference for an unchanging B^{10} "core", computed without correlations, changes by 0.5 MeV as we change the binding energy of the fictitious "last proton" in C^{11} from 1 MeV to 15 MeV.

This emphasizes that it is important to know what is meant by the binding energy. Clearly the simple separation energy between the state we are concerned with and the ground state of the parent nucleus - the binding energy of a proton in C^{11} to the ground state of B^{10} in the present example - is of no interest in itself since there will in general be a whole spectrum of parent states π in the A-1 system each represented in the state α of the nucleus A with which we are concerned with a probability equal to the sqaure of the fractional parentage coefficient $\langle \pi | \alpha \rangle$. The ground state of A-1 has no special role. Now there will be a different binding energy of a proton in the state α to each of the parent states π; since the Coulomb energy difference is determined by this binding energy it too will be a function of the parent state and so the actual overall Coulomb energy difference E^C will be determined by the parentage spectrum. We may write roughly

$$E^C = \sum_\pi | \langle \pi | \alpha \rangle |^2 E^c_\pi$$

where E^c_π is what the Coulomb energy difference would be if the parent state π were the unique parent. This expression is incorrect because it neglects the coherence of the parent states but it becomes more nearly correct as the parentage spectrum becomes richer and is good enough for the moment.

35

This emphasizes that not only do we want to know
the radial wavefunctions or charge distribution involved
for the "core" protons but we must also know the parentage spectrum and the associated binding energies so
as to compute for each case the range of wavefunctions
for the "last proton" and the corresponding range of
Coulomb energies to be appropriately weighted to give
the overall Coulomb energy. This must be strongly emphasized and shows that we cannot treat seriously
Coulomb energy calculations in which the "last proton"
is characterized simply by its binding energy to the
ground state of the parent nucleus. In an extreme case
a state may be unstable by many MeV against proton emission to the ground state of the parent nucleus but have
a Coulomb energy difference relative to its analogue
state appropriate to a positive "last proton" binding
energy - if the states to which proton emission with
positive Q-value can take place all have very small
fractional parentage coefficients for the state in
question as they might if, for example, proton emission
to them were forbidden by some selection rule. This is
indeed the situation with many of the isobaric analogue
states of high isobaric spin. Putting it more simply,
if an unstable state is very narrow it behaves as if it
were bound. Although this is an extreme case the effect
is always present and the right proton binding energy to
use in a Coulomb energy difference calculation is not
that for the ground state of the parent nucleus (except
perhaps in rare and accidental cases).

We shall here compute the Coulomb energy differences between $T = 1/2$ states of mirror systems and
between the $T_z = -1$ (proton rich) and $T_z = 0$ states of
$T = 1$ systems. The auxiliary data which are used to

36

obtain the wavefunctions or charge distributions come
from electron scattering and (p,2p) reactions and so
refer to the stable, $T_z = +1/2$ and $T_z = 0$ members of the
same multiplets. We must assume that the proton distributions of the parent A-1-states effective in the A-
states are the same as those determined by the electron
scattering plus (p,2p) data for the groundstates of the
A-nuclei e.g. that the effective spatial distribution of
charge in the B^{10} parent states within B^{11} and C^{11}
needed for the computations of the C^{11}- B^{11} Coulomb
energy difference is the same as that inferred for B^{11}
from the auxiliary data. This is, of course, wrong on
several grounds but we can do no better at this time.
The error on this account is probably not serious because it is unlikely that the charge distribution is
a strong function of excitation. It introduces, however,
another complication that may be more serious but that
remains an unknown quantity. This is that it is incorrect to represent C^{11}, in the above example, as a B^{10}
"core" plus a "last proton", even allowing for the correct spectrum of B^{10} parent states. The $T = 0$ parent
states of C^{11} are only found in B^{10} and so for them C^{11}
is like B^{10} plus a proton. For the $T = 1$ parent states,
however, C^{11} is like B^{10} plus a proton and, simultaneously, like C^{10} plus a neutron. In the latter case the
Coulomb energy has gone into the "core" and does not
reside in the "last proton". We will ignore this difficulty and make the (usual) charge-dependent assumption
that we can describe C^{11} as B^{10} plus a proton and B^{11} as
B^{10} plus the corresponding neutron. The error is probably not very serious since the parents of higher T tend
to lie higher than those of lower T and so to have correspondingly higher values of the binding energy: if we

37

continue our assumption that the core is given by the re-presentative mean wavefunctions as determined by electron scattering and the (p,2p) data these correspond also to high proton binding energies. Since the Coulomb energy changes more slowly with binding energy as the binding energy increases the difference between the "B^{10}+p" and "C^{10}+n" pictures for the T=1 parents is probably not large.

Critical to the computation of the Coulomb energy differences are the radial wavefunctions. We base ourselves on a recent discussion[7] in which mean lp-shell and ls-shell proton binding energies as determined in (p,2p) reactions were analyzed in terms of a static Saxon-Woods potential: $V \sim [\exp(r-R)/a+1]^{-1}$ to give, for chosen values of the diffuseness constant a, a radius R and a well-depth. The resulting wavefunction were used to compute $\langle r^2 \rangle_p^{1/2}$ for the entire (lp-shell plus ls-shell) proton distribution and this was then compared with the same quantity determined by electron scattering. The comparison showed agreement within the errors. ($\langle r^2 \rangle_p^{1/2}$ refers to the distribution, relative to the center-of-mass of the nucleus, of the centers-of-mass of the protons. It does not refer to the distribution of charge for which the finite extension of the proton's own charge distribution must be folded in.) For the present work the weighted mean $\langle r^2 \rangle_p^{1/2}$ values as given by the two methods have been used together with the effective lp-shell binding energies as seen in the (p,2p) work and used previously.[7] For each A-value the simple Saxon-Woods potential has been computed that reproduces these mean $\langle r^2 \rangle_p^{1/2}$ values and lp-shell binding energies E_p as listed in Table I. In the cases of N^{14} and O^{16}, where the $lp_{3/2}$ shell and the $lp_{1/2}$ shell are separately identified in the (p,2p) reaction, the effective lp-shell binding energy has been taken as the mean energy weighted by occupancy (no spin-orbit term is used in the Saxon-

Woods potential). Experimental values are not available
for all quantities: those bracketed are interpolated
between their neighbours.

All computations have been carried out for the
reasonable value a = 0.5 fm for the diffuseness constant.
The answers are insensitive to this choice.

With the well-parameters determined in this way
the charge distribution of the Z-proton "core" for each
A-value was computed, summing over 2 1s-proton and Z-2
1p-proton uncorrelated distributions. This "core" distribution was held constant for the rest of the computation. To calculate the wavefunction of the "last
proton" in the nucleus Z + 1 the radius R of the well
was kept constant at the value used for the "core" calculation and its depth adjusted. The Coulomb energy
between this "last proton" so described, uncorrelated
with the others, and the unchanging Z-proton "core" was
thus determined as a function of the binding energy of
the "last proton". Some typical results are displayed
in Fig. 1 where the considerable sensitivity of the
Coulomb energy to the binding energy is seen. The chief
contribution to this sensitivity is not the increasing
exponential tail as the binding energy is reduced but
rather the expansion of the wavefunction owing to its
riding further out on the sloping sides of the potential.

This gives us the Coulomb energy, without proton
correlations, as a function of the binding energy for
each A-value. It is clear that considerable uncertainty
must attach to the final answer owing to our uncertainty
as to the parentage spectrum. A detailed model will
predict a definite spectrum and will also permit the
coherence to be taken into account although the point
about the higher-T parents and the mixed neutron-proton

structure of the states will remain a tricky one in its
relation to the binding energies. As a concrete illustration the problem has been calculated in LS coupling using the standard tabulation of fractional parentage coefficients.[8] The parent states in the real
A-1 parent nuclei have been identified with states of
the model; this can be done with adequate accuracy since
the parents that cannot be identified unambiguously lie
at relatively high excitations for which the binding
energies are large and so where the Coulomb energy is
not so sharply dependent on the binding energy. Where
identification between real states and states of the
model cannot be made the calculated excitations of the
parent states in A-1 have been used. In all cases an
upper limit on the binding energy equal to the mean
binding energy E_p of the lp-shell protons as listed in
Table I has been set.

Computations have been made for those states up to
a maximum of four for each A-value that are identified
as belonging to $(lp)^{A-4}$; for the respective A-values
9.....15 these number 2, 2, 4, 2, 2, 1, 2. Table II
lists these Coulomb energy differences so computed for
uncorrelated protons as E_u^c (averaged over the states
analyzed for each A-value). Lighter nuclei were excluded because for them it is likely that strong clus-
tering is present and so their representation by the
simple Saxon-Woods potential may well be poor.

Before these values of E_u^c are compared with the
experimental values of the binding energy differences
some corrections are necessary. The first of these is
for the anti-symmetrization of the proton wavefunctions
which lowers the Coulomb energy below that for the uncorrelated proton wavefunctions used so far. This

40

correction may be taken from harmonic oscillator wavefunctions for which it is a standard exercise. Computations have also been reported using more realistic
wavefunctions[9] and these agree closely with those from
harmonic oscillator wavefunctions. The effect is to
multiply the Coulomb energy difference E_u^c computed without correlations by a factor of 0.92. It is unlikely
that this factor is in error by more than 2% at the most
for any of the states of concern here. The second correction is for the magnetic energy differences between
the neutron and proton states arising from the different
values of the neutron and proton magnetic moments; it
has been taken from an earlier work.[10]

Table II shows the result of applying these two
corrections as E^c which is therefore the final calculated figure to be compared with the corresponding
experimental binding energy difference listed as E_{exp}
and similarly averaged over the states concerned. The
percentage excess of the calculated over the experimental
figures is also shown and is seen to be small. The
agreement is in fact closer than would reasonably be
permitted by the errors in the determination of the wavefunctions from the auxiliary data even if no further uncertainties were involved - these errors would imply
uncertainties of $\pm$ 5% or more in the calculated Coulomb
energy differences. (The sensitivity of the Coulomb
energy computations to the input parameters may be seen
from material presented in the earlier publication.[7])
These results have been presented elsewhere.[11]

DISCUSSION

The close agreement between theory and experiment
revealed in Table II may indicate superficially that
charge symmetry and charge independence must be good.

We must beware of too easily drawing this conclusion.
These computations have been carried through for the
parentage spectrum given by LS coupling and should certainly be redone using more realistically-based wavefunctions. They have also been made using as "core"
wavefunctions those generated by the simple expedient
of a static Saxon-Woods well. There is no guarantee
that these wavefunctions will, for example, give the
correct momentum distributions as revealed by the angular correlations in reactions such as (p,2p) although
it may conversely by doubted whether our understanding
of all the effects operative in such reactions is yet
deep enough to allow us with confidence to use them to
revise our ideas about nuclear wavefunctions given by
the present simple model. Other obvious deficiences are
neglect of velocity-dependences, quadrupole effects and
so on. We must also remark on two effects associated
with nucleon structure: the hard core of radius ρ_1 to
the nucleon-nucleon interaction and the finite extension
ρ_2 of the proton's own charge distribution. These effects are difficult to allow for but it is clear that
they introduce a correction in the sense of lowering the
calculated Coulomb energy and that the magnitude of the
correction is of order $\rho^2/\langle r^2 \rangle$. Since $\rho_{1,2} \approx 0.4, 0.8$fm
this correction may well be of several percent, of the
same order as the uncertainty associated with the determination of the constants of the potential via the
auxiliary data. As we improve measurement and analysis
of electron scattering and (p,2p)-type reactions we
should gain more certain knowledge of the nucleon wavefunctions. This will make necessary a more realistic
treatment of the nuclear wavefunctions themselves and
will also justify a thorough examination of the two

42

roles played by the nucleon structure. In a more detailed treatment we must also consider the change in
energy associated with the nuclear forces themselves
that is brought about by the difference between the
wavefunction of the "last proton" in Z + 1 and the corresponding neutron in Z. The changes in "core" energy,
both nuclear and electrostatic, between Z + 1 and Z must
similarly be explored.

Our interim conclusion must be that it seems unlikely that calculated and experimental Coulomb energies
differ by more than perhaps 10%. The more likely sense
of the discrepancy is for the calculated Coulomb energy
difference to fall below the experimental binding energy
difference. This is the same sense as that recently
suggested by Okamoto[12] but the possible discrepancies
indicated here are much smaller than his and cannot at
this stage be regarded as significant.

The degree of charge symmetry implied by agreement
to 10% between the calculated and experimental figures
may be estimated by computing the shift in the 1p-level
for a given change in the optical model potential. A
change in depth by 1% of the Saxon-Woods potential used
in this work shifts the 1p-level by about 0.45 MeV. Ten
percent of the Coulomb energy differences of Table II is
about 0.3 MeV. It therefore seems unlikely that the
departure of the overall nucleon-nucleus interaction
from charge symmetry is as great as 1%.

We may make a further remark about charge independence. Although the "dead reckoning" approach used
here is limited by several crudities in the computation,
particularly the neglect of the nucleon structure effects, most of these deficiencies become much less important if we compare the results for even-A in which

charge independence is involved with those for odd-A
which depend only on charge symmetry. As may be seen
from Table II there is a slight suggestion that the
discrepancies may be different by perhaps 4 - 5% in
the two cases. If we assume charge symmetry of the
nuclear force this 4 - 5% difference between the two
classes of nuclei may be interpreted as indicating a
departure from charge independence. The sense is that
the n-p force is stronger than the n-n or p-p force.
The magnitude would correspond to a difference in
strength by about 2%. This figure is arrived at by
examining typical behavior of energy levels in intermediate coupling as a function of the Slater integral
K that measures the strength of the effective residual
nucleon-nucleon interaction[13]. It must be stressed
that this is a very preliminary indication only and
can have no great weight placed upon it; the sign and
magnitude of the effect are concordant with conclusions
from other evidence, particularly the comparison of
zero-energy singlet scattering lengths.

A final comment is to re-emphasize the importance of the binding energy effect brought out quantitatively in these computations and displayed in Fig. 1.
Intimately tied to this point is the importance of the
parentage spectrum. In an earlier discussion[10] the
extra Coulomb energy found empirically in mirror nuclei
of even Z was interpreted as a reflection, into the
Coulomb energy, of the pairing produced by the nucleon-
nucleon force. It was there remarked, however, that
this effect appeared to persist also in the excited
states where the pairing was presumably broken. It now
seems more likely that this alternation is a direct
binding energy effect or at least receives an important

contribution from it. The magnitude of the empirically-observed Coulomb energy alternation, 0.2 MeV or so, tallies with the change in Coulomb energy associated with the alternation of 5 MeV or so in proton binding as between odd-Z and even-Z nuclei - see Fig. 1. This remark is, of course, also valid outside the 1p-shell and is being investigated by appropriate computations there too.

CONCLUSION

There is no clear evidence that, in the 1-p shell, binding energy differences have values different from those expected on the basis of the Coulomb perturbation alone. This tallies with an earlier conclusion[10] based on a very different approach namely the relationship between the b and c coefficients of the isobaric mass formula. At the same time some small departure from charge symmetry cannot be excluded and, so far as charge independence goes, there is weak evidence for a difference of about 2% between the strengths of the n-p and n-n or p-p interactions, the former being the stronger.

The importance of using realistic proton wavefunctions for Coulomb energy calculations and the importance of the binding energy effect are manifest.

REFERENCES

1) D. H. Wilkinson, Phys. Letts. 11 (1964) 243; 12 (1964) 348.

2) I am particularly grateful to Dr. G. T. Garvey for convincing me that this formula was indeed not a case of constat inter omnes.

3) E. P. Wigner, Phys. Rev. 51 (1937) 106.

4) W. M. MacDonald, Phys. Rev. 98 (1955) 60; 100 (1955) 51; 101 (1956) 271.

5) E. P. Wigner, Proc. of the Robert A. Welch Foundation Conf. on Chemical Research. I. The Structure of the Nucleus, 1957, Houston, Texas 1958, p. 67.

6) S. Weinberg and S. B. Treiman, Phys. Rev. 116 (1959) 465.

7) D. H. Wilkinson and M. E. Mafethe, Nucl. Phys., in press.

8) H. A. Jahn and H. van Wieringen, Proc. Roy. Soc. A209 (1951) 502.

9) N. V. V. J. Swamy and A. E. S. Green, Phys. Rev. 112 (1958) 1719.

10) D. H. Wilkinson, Phys. Rev. Letts. 13 (1964) 571.

11) D. H. Wilkinson and W. D. Hay, to be published.

12) K. Okamoto, Phys. Letts. 19 (1966) 676.

13) D. Kurath, Phys. Rev. 101 (1956) 216.

TABLE I. Input data used in the computation of Coulomb energy differences. $\langle r^2 \rangle_p^{1/2}$ (in fm) is the weighted mean of values determined by electron scattering and from (p,2p) reactions and is summed over all protons in the nucleus. It refers to the distribution of the centers-of-mass of the protons not to the charge distribution. r is relative to the center-of-mass of the nucleus. E_p (in MeV) is the mean binding energy of the lp-shell protons as determined in the (p,2p) reaction (in the cases of N^{14} and O^{16} a mean figure is given for the $1p_{3/2}$ and $1p_{1/2}$ shells weighted by occupancy). Bracketed quantities are not experimentally determined but are interpolated between their neighbours.

A	Z	$\langle r^2 \rangle_p^{1/2}$	E_p
9	4	2.44	16.5
10	5	(2.31)	13.7
11	5	2.19	15.1
12	6	2.37	17.0
13	6	(2.37)	(16.4)
14	7	2.37	15.8
15	7	(2.45)	(16.3)
16	8	2.54	16.9

TABLE II. Calculated Coulomb energy differences E^c (between the Z and Z + 1 members of the isobaric multiplets) compared with the binding energy differences E_{exp}. The directly-computed quantity is the Coulomb energy difference for uncorrelated protons E_u^c. This is multiplied by 0.92 on account of anti-symmetrization of the proton wavefunctions and corrected by the column μ, the magnetic moment correction, to give E^c which is to be compared with E_{exp}. The column $\Delta\%$ gives the percentage excess of the calculated Coulomb energy difference E^c over the binding energy difference E_{exp}. All quantities are averaged over the number of states involved for each A-value and are in MeV.

A	Z	Pair	E_u^c	μ	E_c	E_{exp}	$\Delta\%$
9	4	B^9-Be^9	2.03	-0.01	1.86	1.81	+2.8
10	5	C^{10}-B^{10}	2.73	-0.02	2.49	2.61	-4.6
11	5	C^{11}-B^{11}	2.95	-0.02	2.70	2.64	+2.3
12	6	N^{12}-C^{12}	3.28	+0.03	3.04	3.11	-2.2
13	6	N^{13}-C^{13}	3.30	+0.02	3.05	2.92	+4.5
14	7	O^{14}-N^{14}	3.86	+0.07	3.62	3.62	0.0
15	7	O^{15}-N^{15}	3.74	+0.02	3.46	3.46	0.0

DISCUSSION

SCHIFFER, Argonne: I'd just like to mention
that we have done some calculations in the same spirit
of Coulomb energies in the calcium isotopes taking into
account the binding energy and calculated states in a
Woods-Saxon potential. The interesting thing is that
the difference in Coulomb energies between the 1f and
2p states is about 300 kilovolts which is just due to
the fact that they are different states. This is
beautifully reproduced in Ca^{41} and Sc^{41} Coulomb energies for the $1f_{7/2}$ state and the $2p_{3/2}$ state.

WILKINSON: You took your Woods-Saxon potential
from what - from the optical model?

SCHIFFER: From the optical model which was
adjusted to give the correct binding for all states.

WILKINSON: Yes, there is one thing about all
this which is certainly a criticism of what I have been
talking about today. I presume you used a velocity
independent potential, and there is indeed reasonable
evidence now that one should have a velocity dependence.

I have done some small checks on that in this
case, and I don't think it's a very serious factor. So
far as I can see, it does get more serious as one goes
to heavier nuclei, but how much more serious, I can't
say. It is certainly something one has to worry about.
There is also the state dependence of the form of the
Saxon-Woods potential which might have to be worried
about.

If one interprets the data on the (p, 2p) angular correlations, for example, literally, using DWBA
computations, one finds relative s and p shell sizes

in the p shell region which are somewhat different
from those given by this computation. Not very different, but ten percent or so. One should therefore
presumably get some sort of experimental handle on the
distribution of all the shells separately which you
can hope to do, I think, in the p-shell, and maybe in
the s-d-shell.

In heavier nuclei, you will probably have very
little chance of doing it, but there, equally, it may
not be so important.

BAYMAN, Minnesota: I'd like to make a comment
on what you did about parent states of the higher
isobaric spin. If we described C^{11} not in terms of
nucleons but rather as six protons plus five neutrons
and we use fractional parentage coefficients appropriate to this description, then no problem arises because we are expanding in terms of states of B^{10} plus
a proton. However, if we describe C^{11} in terms of 11
nucleons and we use fractional parentage coefficients
appropriate to this description, then we will get the
same result provided we multiply the coefficients for
the parent states of higher isobaric spin by the
appropriate vector coupling coefficients that express
the fraction of the time that this last nucleon is a
proton.

WILKINSON: Yes, I am not actually so much
worried about the formality of this as what to do with
the binding energies. If you do it in terms of just
proton parentage, maybe it's clear what you ought to
do, I don't know; if you do it the way I was doing it
here and then not worrying about the error, when you
represent C^{11} as C^{10} plus a neutron, your Coulomb
energy has gone into the core, as it were, and it's

not then clear what's happened to the binding energy of that proton that's gone into the C^{10} core.

It just gets very messy to try to think of it in this way, and as you say, it's not right to think of it this way. If the expansion is available, then one should clearly use that.

GINOCCHIO, Rutgers: It seems to me that what you are doing is to set an upper limit on this Coulomb energy by your expansion, since you haven't taken into account coherent terms in the parentage expansions. I am assuming that all the Coulomb energies in the parent state are of the same sign.

WILKINSON: Yes, but the parentage coefficients won't be all of the same sign.

GINOCCHIO: But you are taking the square.

WILKINSON: I have, yes, but if I had done it properly, I would have gotten those squares and a lot of cross terms, some of which would be positive and some of which would be negative.

GINOCCHIO: Yes, exactly. What I am surprised at is that you have differences, negative differences when you compare this to your experiment. In other words, your calculated result is smaller than the experimental result. So I am surprised; if anything, I would expect it would always be larger.

WILKINSON: Well, I don't think I am quite with you, because as I see it the correction terms to this are themselves of either sign, depending on whether the product of the fractional percentage coefficients is plus or minus.

What I have neglected is a set of terms which have randomly assorted signs, and that is why I said when the parentage spectrum gets richer, I would expect

51

this approximation to get better.

I think it's very early days to worry about this. The point that I am making is that the Coulomb energy is very sensitive to the binding energy. One has to worry about it. This is only the first step in worrying about it.

GARVEY, Princeton: Could you please say something about the magnetic corrections?

WILKINSON: They come about because one has a nucleus and one has a particle going round in it, and that particle has got a magnetic moment, and as it goes around, it sees a magnetic field because of the charge of the nucleus, and depending on what the magnetic moment is, you get either a positive or negative contribution to the mass, and then when you change your neutron into the proton, you change the magnetic moment, and so you change the correction.

So if one is in jj-coupling, this is quite easy to work out, and there are standard references for it. A handy one is Lovitch on the mass-six system, and he, in turn, gives a reference to Bethe's "Handbuch der Physik" article on the one electron atom.

It gets more tricky when you are in intermediate coupling where you can't have this simple picture of an orbit with a magnetic moment attached to it. However, what one can do there is to go to the intermediate coupling calculations which tell you the energies of levels as a function of a/k in the old-fashioned way of talking about it, and you can regard this magnetic effect as an extra $\vec{1} \cdot \vec{s}$ term that you can add in. Consequently you can get what the perturbation of the level is for the particular state that you are interested in by making the appropriate adjustment, and that is, in fact, what I have done here.

WINTER: William and Mary: Most of the methods
of determining a potential are more sensitive to
things that have to do with the overall bulk look of
things. Coulomb energies are particularly sensitive
to how the tail of the wave function behaves. Are
there dangers in that, that you could discuss?

WILKINSON: Yes, it is just that, I think, which
makes the Coulomb energies so sensitive. The reason
that the Coulomb energy changes so rapidly as one decreases the binding energy is not that the exponential
tail is getting longer and longer, but the wave function is riding up further and further on the sloping
side of the potential here.

So if the form of the Saxon-Woods is quite
wrong, then this effect will simply be quite wrongly
computed. So for that reason, the shape of the potential where its value is rather low is a very important
quantitative factor in the results that I have been
presenting here, and we really don't know.

I mean nobody is going to really believe that
they know the shape of the potential out here, and
nobody is really going to believe these numbers that
I am presenting. That's what I am saying this morning,
it is a rather tricky matter to calculate Coulomb
energies.

ZAMICK, Princeton: I'd like to make a comment
on this. If you compare, let's say, B^{11} and C^{11}, I
think a very good approximation for the proton wave
function in C^{11} would be the neutron wave function in
B^{11}.

In other words, the neutron wave function is
almost identical to the proton wave function, so if

either the proton is loosely bound, it could be the
neutron is very tightly bound, and then the wave function is very easy to calculate. It's not too sensitive
to the surface, and the wave function would be almost
99 percent the same.

WILKINSON: Oh, I am worried about that, because
I thought the point was that you had to take into
account the strongly charge dependent differences between C^{11} and B^{11} as reflected in the details of the
last nucleon's wave function.

ZAMICK: Well, the proton might be loosely
bound, but the Coulomb barrier prevents that from
allowing the tail to be diffused, and that compensates
for it.

WILKINSON: Well, I don't know if there is a
computation concerning what we have been doing here
to test that.

ZAMICK: Well, I will explain that the neutron
wave function and the proton wave function overlap is
probably better than 99 percent.

WILKINSON: But how would you know that other
than by doing a computation?

ZAMICK: I did it.

WILKINSON: I see. Well, this is presumably
the same computation. Of course, when I have drawn it
like this, I don't mean we did our calculations without
a Coulomb potential.

ZAMICK: But it might be interesting to compare
the overlap of the neutron and proton wave function.

WILKINSON: Yes, true.

SCHIFFER: As I understand it, all your calculations are for the Coulomb energies of the ground
states of nuclei.

WILKINSON: No, I did use as many excited states, up to a maximum of four, that obviously belonged to the p-shell.

SCHIFFER: And these were averages.

WILKINSON: These were averaged, yes, for experimental differences, and the calculations have been averaged.

SCHIFFER: You haven't done any calculations for states which might occur outside the p-shell, such as for excited states in C^{13}?

WILKINSON: No, strictly p-shell. We are looking at the s-, d-shell now, but I have nothing to report.

MacDONALD, Maryland: On the question of the overlap of the neutron and proton wave functions. I'd just like to make the comment that the rms radii and such things as the differences between Coulomb energies are more sensitive than the mere overlap integrals themselves because, of course, these former quantities weight the exterior portion, and one might expect to find these differences important.

The effect on electromagnetic transitions, some of which are weighted with even higher powers of the radius, may be even more pronounced because of the added dependence upon the wave function in the asymptotic region.

WILKINSON: Yes, that's true. We can look at where the Coulomb energy comes from as a function of the distance, and it isn't dramatic. Of course, the outside of the nucleus is an interesting place, but it's not a very dramatic effect.

MacDONALD: No, but here you are looking at the differences between Coulomb energies for different levels, and these are primarily the result of the R^2 dependent term in the Coulomb potential for a uniform sphere of charge.

This weights the asymptotic portion of the wave function. These Coulomb energy differences are therefore somewhat more sensitive than the absolute values of the energy shifts.

WILKINSON: That is another remark that probably ought to be made, that there is implicit in this assumption that the Coulomb energy to the B^{10} part, to continue in that language, is the same in B^{11} and C^{11}, which it won't be.

There will be a change of the core wave functions between boron and carbon, and this will be associated with Coulomb energy and nuclear energy differences. This is just another one of the many things that one has to worry about in trying to do this problem properly.

SHAFROTH, Bartol: Could I ask you the same thing about Li^{12} or F^{12}, whether the parabolic mass formula doesn't work any more?

WILKINSON: Well, the only remark I made about that I can just repeat, and that is that when the nucleus begins to fall apart, you have perturbations that cannot be represented in this first order theory.

The parabolic mass formula does depend on assuming that the nuclear wave functions are the same for all members of the same multiplet and when it falls apart, they are clearly not the same. I just do not know what to do about that. This doesn't mean to say that you can't do Coulomb energy calculations for highly unstable states. For example, the high isobaric spin states obey the mass relationship very well, and

so they should, because the parent states that have
significant fractional parentage coefficients are
bound for those states. They are unstable for decay
to low-lying states but these decays are forbidden by
isobaric spin conservation. The fractional parentage
coefficients are consequently very small, so you don't
have to worry about them.

But then if you have a nucleus falling apart,
obviously the nuclear wave function is very different
from that of the stable members of the multiplet. You
just can't talk about it in these simple terms at all.

SHAFROTH: Are there any theoretical reasons
for higher masses? Isn't it true you can't go past
the ultimate $T = 2$?

WILKINSON: I am not sure offhand why not. You
mean that all $T = 3$ states in the self-conjugate nuclei
will be ill-defined or something?

SHAFROTH: Do they follow the parabolic masses?

WILKINSON: Oh, sure they do, yes, insofar as
they exist and have the same wave functions, as long
as they remain stable, certainly.

SCHIFFER: May I just ask one more question. It
seems to me that in the excited states, by averaging,
aren't you throwing away some information? Couldn't
one learn something because the structure of each state
is different?

Therefore, they might have different Coulomb
energies.

WILKINSON: Yes.

SCHIFFER: How much difference do you get?

WILKINSON: Oh, yes, there is both experimentally and in the computations an excitation energy
dependence of the Coulomb energy in the sense that

you'd expect. The more highly excited states, leaving changes of parentage spectrum out of account, are less tightly bound, and so they slide down that Coulomb energy versus binding energy plot shown earlier and do have lower computed Coulomb energies.

For an excitation of three of four MeV, they tend to be lower than the ground state typically by perhaps 200 kilovolts, so there is a correlation in the right sense between excitation and Coulomb energy, but I consider all these computations as extremely crude. I wouldn't like to trust them more than qualitatively.

SCHIFFER: Do these fluctuations which occur between different nuclei also show up in fluctuations between excited states of the same nucleus; in other words, do you have five-percent deviations?

WILKINSON: Yes.

SCHIFFER: Do such effects also show up between excited states of the same nucleus?

WILKINSON: Those, of course, are average deviations that I put there. I think the answer is yes, yes there is a tendency, but I just wouldn't like to place any significance on looking at such a fine effect.

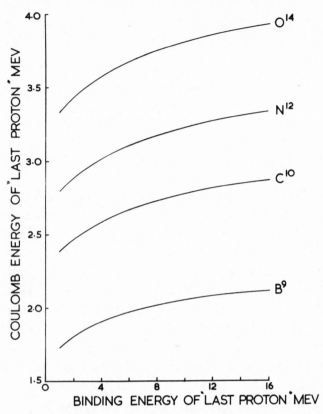

Fig. 1. The Coulomb energy of the "last proton" in a
few nuclei of the 1p-shell as a function of the binding
energy of the "last proton". The Coulomb energy is computed without exchange in the field due to the charge
distribution of uncorrelated "core" protons moving in
Saxon-Woods potentials (with a = 0.5 fm) that reproduce
the parameters of Table I for each A-value. The wavefunction of the "last proton" is computed by holding the
radius at the value used in the "core" computation and
changing the depth to give the stated binding energy.
The "core" distribution is held fixed throughout for
each A-value.

A3.   COULOMB ENERGY SYSTEMATICS*

Joachim Jänecke

University of Michigan

Ann Arbor, Michigan

Information about the charge distribution and the
charge radius of atomic nuclei can be obtained primarily
from three experimental methods: (i) elastic electron
scattering (to a certain extent also elastic α-particle
and other charged particle scattering), (ii) muon capture X-ray experiments, (iii) Coulomb energy studies.
The first two methods are more sensitive to the shape of
the distribution than the third method. On the other
hand they have the disadvantage that they can be used
only to study the ground states of stable nuclei while
the Coulomb energy method, in principle at least, is
applicable to both ground and excited states (except
those with T = 0) of any nucleus.

It is the purpose of this contribution to obtain,
from a systematic survey, information about the A dependence and, if possible, the T dependence of the
Coulomb energies over the whole range of atomic nuclei.
Whenever possible, this information will be related to
nuclear structure effects.

The Coulomb interaction between nucleons

$$H_c = e^2 \sum_{i<j} \left(1/2 - t_z^{(i)}\right) \left(1/2 - t_z^{(j)}\right) r_{ij}^{-1} = T^{(0)} + T^{(1)} + T^{(2)} \tag{1}$$

*Supported in part by the U. S. Atomic Energy Commission.

like other charge dependent two body interactions which have been proposed[1] leads to a quadratic equation[2-5] in T_z for the energetic position of the members of an isobaric multiplet

$$E_{Coul}(A,T,T_z) = E_{Coul}^{(0)}(A,T) - T_z E_{Coul}^{(1)}(A,T)$$
$$+ \left(3T_z^2 - T(T+1)\right) E_{Coul}^{(2)}(A,T). \qquad (2)$$

The scalar, vector and tensor Coulomb energies $E_{Coul}^{(0)}$, $E_{Coul}^{(1)}$ and $E_{Coul}^{(2)}$ depend on A, T and the details of the configurations. Equation 2 is obtained in first order perturbation theory (effects of T admixtures on the energy are not considered). Other effects like the Thomas-Ehrman shift[6] are also disregarded in the derivation of Eq. 2.

Since $Z = A/2 - T_z$ it follows from Eq. 2 that any Coulomb energy formula based on the above assumptions must depend quadratically on Z. This is not the case for the second and third term in the equation[7]

$$E_{Coul} = \frac{e^2}{r_o A^{1/3}} \left\{0.6\, Z^2 - 0.46\, Z^{4/3} - \left(1-(-1)^Z\right) 0.15\right\} \qquad (3)$$

which is often used in an analysis of the experimental data.

By inverting Eq. 2 one can express[5] $E_{Coul}^{(i)}(A,T)(i=0,1,2)$ in terms of the energies $E_{Coul}(A,T,T_z)$. The scalar Coulomb energy, in particular, becomes

$$E_{Coul}^{(0)}(A,T) = \frac{1}{2T+1} \sum_{T_z=-T}^{+T} E_{Coul}(A,T,T_z) \qquad (4)$$

which means that $E_{Coul}^{(0)}$ represents an average Coulomb energy for a particular multiplet. The quantity $E_{Coul}^{(0)}$

will be discussed only briefly at the end of this contribution.

A detailed discussion[5] of the A dependence of the vector and tensor Coulomb energies is possible at present only for the isobaric doublets and triplets up to $A = 43$. For $T = 1/2$ and $T = 1$ the relations between the experimentally observed Coulomb energy differences $\Delta E_{Coul}(A,T,T_z|T'_z) = E_{Coul}(A,T,T_z) - E_{Coul}(A,T,T'_z)$ and the quantities $E^{(1)}_{Coul}(A,T)$ and $E^{(2)}_{Coul}(A,T)$ are very simple

$$E^{(1)}_{Coul}(A,1/2) = \Delta E_{Coul}(A,1/2,-1/2|+1/2) \qquad (5)$$

$$E^{(1)}_{Coul}(A,1) = 1/2\Big\{\Delta E_{Coul}(A,1,-1|0)$$
$$+ \Delta E_{Coul}(A,1,0|+1)\Big\} \qquad (6)$$

$$E^{(2)}_{Coul}(A,1) = 1/6\Big\{\Delta E_{Coul}(A,1,-1|0)$$
$$- \Delta E_{Coul}(A,1,0|+1)\Big\} . \qquad (7)$$

Assuming the atomic nucleus can be considered as a homogeneously charged sphere of radius $R = r_o A^{1/3}$ one obtains

$$E_{Coul} = 3e^2 Z^2/5r_o A^{1/3} \qquad (8)$$

$$\Delta E_{Coul} = 6e^2 \bar{Z}/5r_o A^{1/3} \qquad (9)$$

$$E^{(1)}_{Coul} = 3e^2 A^{2/3}/5r_o \qquad (10)$$

$$E^{(2)}_{Coul} = e^2/5r_o A^{1/3} \qquad (11)$$

$$E^{(2)}_{Coul}/E^{(1)}_{Coul} = 1/(3A) \qquad (12)$$

The quantity $\bar{Z}$ in Eq. 9 is $\bar{Z} = 1/2(Z_1 + Z_2)$. Equations 10, 11 and 12 show that $E^{(1)}_{Coul}$ and $E^{(2)}_{Coul}$ should be independent of T and that $E^{(2)}_{Coul} \ll E^{(1)}_{Coul}$ for large A. It is clear, however, that the above assumption is an extreme simplification and is particularly poor for light nuclei. This expectation is strongly confirmed by an examination of Figs. 1, 2 and 3. In Fig. 1 the quantity $E_{Coul}^{(1)}$ is plotted as a function of $A^{2/3}$. The vector Coulomb energy $E_{Coul}^{(1)}$ is indeed roughly proportional to $A^{2/3}$, but shell closure effects and weak superimposed oscillations for the isobaric doublets are noticeable. In Fig. 2 the tensor Coulomb energy $E_{Coul}^{(2)}$ is plotted as a function of $A^{-1/3}$. The experimental values for $E_{Coul}^{(2)}$ strongly deviate from the expected $A^{-1/3}$ dependence. Instead, very pronounced oscillations become apparent. The quantity $A\, E_{Coul}^{(2)}/E_{Coul}^{(1)}$, finally, which is plotted in Fig. 3 as a function of A, also deviates strongly from the constant value of 1/3.

The preceding analysis shows that nuclear structure effects have to be taken into account. Carlson and Talmi[8] have derived an expression for the Coulomb energy of nuclei with Z' protons in a j^n configuration outside a closed shell

$$E_{Coul} = Z'C + 1/2\ Z'(Z' - 1)a + (Z'/2)b. \qquad (13)$$

It is probable that Eq. 13 holds approximately in the case that the configurations are more complicated than j^n or that there are protons and neutrons outside a core. For the latter case the pairing term $(Z'/2)$ has to be modified to comply with Eq. 2. Therefore, a quadratic dependence of the form

$$(Z'/2) \rightarrow \lambda + \mu T_z + \upsilon T_z^2 \qquad (14)$$

is suggested, which means that the pairing energy should depend quadratically on T_z and also quadratically on Z and Z'. Assuming Nilsson-like or more general fourfold

63

degenerate orbits and one can derive[5] the following expressions for μ and v,

$$\mu = 1/2 , \quad v = \frac{1}{4T}\left(1 + \frac{1}{2T-1}(-1)^{A/2 - T}\right) \quad \text{even A}$$

(15)

$$\mu = 1/2\left(1 - \frac{1}{2T}(-1)^{A/2 - T}\right), \quad v = \frac{1}{4T} \quad \text{odd A}$$

Using these expressions one obtains for the Coulomb energy difference and the vector and tensor Coulomb energies

$$\Delta E_{Coul} = E_1 \bar{Z} + E_2 + (\mu - 2v\bar{T}_z)E_3 \tag{16}$$

$$E^{(1)}_{Coul} = E_1/2 \, A + E_2 + \mu E_3 \tag{17}$$

$$E^{(2)}_{Coul} = 1/6(E_1 + 2vE_3). \tag{18}$$

For $T = 1/2$ and $T = 1$, in particular, one obtains for $E^{(1)}_{Coul}$ and $E^{(2)}_{Coul}$

$$E^{(1)}_{Coul} =$$

$$E_1/2 \, A + E_2 + E_3/2 + \begin{cases} (-1)^{(A+1)/2}E_3/2 & \text{Isobaric Doublets} \\ 0 & \text{Isobaric Triplets} \end{cases} \tag{19}$$

$$E^{(2)}_{Coul} = 1/6\left\{E_1 + 1/2\left(1-(-1)^{A/2}\right)E_3\right\} \quad \text{Isobaric Triplets.} \tag{20}$$

The energy coefficients are expected to vary from shell to shell. Within a given shell, the vector Coulomb energies for the isobaric triplets should depend linearly on A provided the radius remains approximately constant. The isobaric doublets should oscillate about the straight lines determined by the triplets. Figure 4 shows that the experimental points follow the above expectation very closely. Pronounced discontinuities can be seen at the major shell closures at A = 4, 16, 40,

and weak discontinuities appear also for A = 12, 28 and
32. The oscillations for the isobaric doublets are
easily recognized so that values for the Coulomb pairing
energy E_3 can be extracted from them. One obtains an
average value of $E_3 \approx 150$ keV; considering only values
for A > 16 one obtains $E_3 \approx 120$ keV. The coefficients
needed to predict $E_{Coul}^{(2)}$ can be evaluated from the slope
and the magnitude of the oscillatory term of $E_{Coul}^{(1)}$ (see
Eqs. 19 and 20). Figure 5 shows the experimental tensor
Coulomb energies as a function of A. The horizontal
lines were calculated using the procedure described
above. Oscillations are predicted. For A = 4n the
points should lie on the lower curve, for A = 4n + 2 the
points should lie on the upper curve. The experimental
points do indeed exhibit very pronounced oscillations
and follow the general trend of the calculated lines.

The preceding discussion has established that
Eq. 13 with the modified pairing energy term works very
well despite the approximation used in the derivation.
The experimental vector Coulomb energies are well de-
scribed and even the experimental and calculated tensor
Coulomb energies are basically in agreement.

In the intermediate and heavy nuclei many isobaric
analogue states with $T = T_z + 1$ have been observed, two
"double analogue" states with $T = T_z + 2$ have also been
reported[9] recently. The A and T dependence of the vector and tensor Coulomb energies can only be studied in
this mass region if more such data and the related Cou-
lomb energy differences $\Delta E_{Coul}(A,T,T-2|T-1)$ become
available. Then, $E_{Coul}^{(1)}$ and $E_{Coul}^{(2)}$ can be obtained from

$$E_{Coul}^{(1)}(A,T) = (T-1/2)\ \Delta E_{Coul}(A,T,T-2|T-1)$$

$$- (T-3/2)\Delta E_{Coul}(A,T,T-1|T) =$$

65

$$(T-1/2)\Big(\Delta E_{Coul}(A,T,T-2\,|\,T-1) - \Delta E_{Coul}(A,T,T-1\,|\,T)\Big) +$$

$$\Delta E_{Coul}(A,T,T-1\,|\,T) \tag{21}$$

and

$$E_{Coul}^{(2)}(A,T) = 1/6\Big(\Delta E_{Coul}(A,T,T-2\,|\,T-1) - \Delta E_{Coul}(A,T,T-1\,|\,T)\Big) \tag{22}$$

The following discussion will be concerned with the Coulomb energy differences $\Delta E_{Coul}(A,T,T-1\,|\,T) = E_{Coul}^{(1)}(A,T) - 3(2T-1)E_{Coul}^{(2)}(A,T)$ which represent a combination of vector and tensor Coulomb energies. From Eq. 9 which is obtained in the approximation of a homogeneous charge distribution (also under similar simple assumptions) it follows that ΔE_{Coul} essentially becomes a linear function of $Z/A^{1/3}$. Figures 6 and 7 show[10,11] that the gross structure of the experimental data is well described by this equation up to the very heavy nuclei. A more detailed comparison is shown[12] in Fig. 8 where the quantity $\Delta E_{Coul}A^{1/3}/Z$ is plotted as a function of $Z/A^{1/3}$. The curved line corresponds to the straight line in Fig. 6. Departures from this line are apparent over the whole range of nuclei.

Using Eq. 16 with $\bar{T}_z = 1/2\Big(T+(T-1)\Big) = T - 1/2$ one obtains

$$\Delta E_{Coul} = E_1/2 \; A - E_1 T + E_2 + 1/2\Big(1-(-1)^{A/2-T}\Big)E_3/2T \tag{23}$$

where the energy coefficients are expected to vary from one type of configuration to the next. The A dependence should be of the form $1/A^{1/3}$ due to the change in radius. Since Eq. 23 is an approximation only, one might expect that in reality all energy coefficients become in addition functions (hopefully weak) of T and A. Therefore, one should write Eq. 23 as $\qquad$ (24)

$$\Delta E_{Coul} = E_o A - E_1 T + E_2 + 1/2\Big(1-(-1)^{A/2-T}\Big)E_3/2T$$

with $E_1 \approx 2E_0$. Discontinuities in the energy coefficients due to shell crossings can be expected whenever A
or N is a magic number n_0, that is above $A = 2(n_0 - T)$
and below $A = 2(n_0 + T)$. Note that a given magic number
n_0 may lead to two discontinuities (except for $T = 1/2$)
and that the respective values of A depend on T. The
pairing term in Eq. 24 predicts a reduction in the superimposed oscillations with increasing T. The marked
difference in amplitude (factor 2) for $T = 1/2$ and $T = 1$
had been noticed[13] before but had not been explained.
For both even-A and odd-A nuclei there should be well
defined phase relations for the above oscillations. Such
effects have also been noticed[14] recently in a study of
second Coulomb energy differences. We note in passing
that the quantity ΔE_{Coul} is proportional to $Z/A^{1/3}$ only
if $E_1 = 2E_0 = const/A^{1/3}$ and $E_2 = E_3 = 0$.

In Fig. 9 the reduced Coulomb energy differences
$$\Delta E_{Coul}^{(red)}(A,T,T-1|T) = \Delta E_{Coul}(A,T,T-1|T) - 1/2\left(1-(-1)^{A/2-T}\right)E_3/2T$$
are plotted versus A with T as a parameter. The sub-
traction of the pairing term with $E_3 = 120$ keV practically
eliminates all oscillations. The experimental points
for $T = 1/2$ and $T = 1$ exhibit the well known discontinuities at the shell closures. The experimental points
for $T > 1$ were connected by straight lines and no effort
was made to display shell effects. The slope E_0 of the
various lines decreases with increasing A which is expected because all energy coefficients are related to
expectation values of $1/R$. Therefore, it appears reasonable to plot the quantity $A^{1/3}\Delta E_{Coul}^{(red)}$ as a function
of A. Figure 10 shows that the new slopes indeed become
almost constant. After subtracting a term which is proportional to A one obtains a plot which is particularly
suited to study fine structure effects.

67

The quantity $A^{1/3}\Delta E_{Coul}^{(red)}$ - (0.722 MeV) A is plotted in Fig. 11 as a function of A. The numerical coefficient for the subtracted term was taken from the best fit (Fig. 6) in terms of a homogeneous charge distribution. For a homogeneous charge distribution Fig. 11 should show parallel horizontal lines with an equal spacing of 0.722 MeV between lines which differ in isobaric spin by 1/2. This is not the case.

Pronounced discontinuities occur at the major shell closures at A = 4, 16 and 40 for both T = 1/2 and T = 1. Less pronounced breaks can also be seen for A = 32 and 56. Not enough data are available yet to establish similar shell closure effects for T > 1. There is no doubt, however, that such effects will eventually show up for at least T = 3/2 and T = 2 in the light nuclei. Small vertical lines indicate the respective values of A which were calculated for n_o = 8, 16, 20, 28 and 50.

The slope of the various lines seems to increase with j which implies that E_o is j dependent. Considering the $1f_{7/2}$, $1d_{5/2}$, $1p_{3/2}$ and $1d_{3/2}$ shells one finds $E \gtrless (0.722$ MeV$)/A^{1/3}$ for j = 7/2, 5/2, 3/2. The points in the $1p_{1/2}$ and $2s_{1/2}$ shells follow closely the trend in the preceding shells. All lines for different T are practically parallel. They are also about equally spaced in accordance with the relation $E_1 \approx 2E_o$.

The preceding analysis shows that nuclear structure effects can be seen for T ≤ 1 and for T > 1. More experimental data are needed for T > 1 to demonstrate the effects more clearly.

A theoretical study[4,15] of the A and T dependence of the Coulomb energies is presently being carried out by Hecht based on the seniority scheme. The seniority scheme is not too good an approximation when neutrons

68

and protons are filling the same shell. Nevertheless,
the result which is shown in Eq. 25 (together with the
supplementary Eqs. 26, 27 and 28) should represent a
good guideline to the true A and T dependence of the
Coulomb energies. The case $A = 4k$, T odd and $A = 4n + 2$,
T even is not yet included. The scalar, vector and
tensor Coulomb energies are represented by the expressions in curly brackets. They are functions of $n = A -$
A_0 and T. The expression for the scalar energy is identical with an expression[16) obtained previously for the
nuclear interaction. The coefficients a, b, c and d
are defined in Eq. 26. They can be calculated from the
two body Coulomb integrals which are defined in Eq. 27.
Note that $V_J = 0$ for odd J (odd J implies $t = 0$). The
coefficients b and c have a dominant effect on the variation of the vector and tensor energies. The quantity
c has "pairing character", and c/b is typically of the
order of a few percent. In the approximation $c = 0$ and
$b = \text{const}/A^{1/3}$ the expressions for the vector and tensor Coulomb energy are very similar to the ones obtained for a homogeneous charge distribution. All fine
structure effects are due to the finite value of C.
The slope of $E_{Coul}^{(1)}$ should depend slightly on the even
or odd character of A. In the latter case there should
also be a weak T dependence. Superimposed oscillations
are predicted for odd A nuclei in agreement with the
previous Eq. 17. The T dependence, however, deviates
slightly from the previously given form 1/T. The expression for the tensor Coulomb energy is somewhat more
complicated than before. Since the coefficients for the
vector and tensor energies are related one can again
compare the experimental data with the theoretical
equation and check for internal consistency. One can

69

also compare the empirical coefficients with calculated
coefficients. In such a comparison one would have to
include the electromagnetic spin orbit interaction.
Hecht[4,15] has shown that the quantities a and b are
only slightly affected, but the numerical value of c
increases considerably. The increase of c is different
in the vector energy term than in the tensor energy
term.

Equation 25 has been derived under restrictive
assumptions (seniority scheme) and more accurate calculations have been performed[17] for specific nuclei or
classes of nuclei. Nevertheless, this equation seems
to give a very good overall description of the true A
and T dependence of the Coulomb energies.

In conclusion, a brief remark about the scalar
Coulomb energies will be made. The quantity $E_{Coul}^{(0)}$ as
given for instance in the first curly bracket of Eq. 25
and the nuclear energy[16] obtained from a charge independent interaction cannot be separated because both
exhibit the same A and T dependence. The T dependence
of the combined energy, in particular, is of the form
$T(T + 1)$. Therefore, the excitation energies of the
isobaric analogue states should follow this T dependence
which is shown graphically in Fig. 12. For even A nuclei
pairing effects have to be taken into account. A systematic study[18] of the excitation energies of the isobaric analogue states has led to the conclusion that the
experimental data can indeed be reproduced with the
above T dependence. This result is not trivial because
the super-multiplet model[19], for instance, predicts a
different T dependence.

$$a = \frac{v_o + (2j-1)(j+1)\bar{v}_2}{2j+1}$$

$$b = \frac{2(j+1)\bar{v}_2 - v_o}{2(2j+1)}$$

$$c = \frac{v_o - \bar{v}_2}{4(2j+1)}$$

$$d = \frac{1}{4}\bar{v}_1$$

$$v_J = \left\langle (j^2)J \left| \frac{e^2}{3r_{ij}} \right| (j^2)J \right\rangle \qquad (26)$$

$$\bar{v}_1 = \sum_{J\ odd} \frac{(2J+1)v_J}{(2j+1)(j+1)} \equiv 0$$

$$\bar{v}_2 = \sum_{J\ even} \frac{(2J+1)v_J}{(2j-1)(j+1)} \qquad (27)$$

When including electromagnetic spin orbit interaction (and nuclear interaction) replace

$$\frac{e^2}{3r_{ij}} \longrightarrow \frac{e^2}{3r_{ij}} + \frac{1}{3}\left(g_p + \frac{1}{2}g_n\right)W_{ij} + (v^{nuclear}_{ij}) \qquad \text{iso - scalar, J even}$$

$$\frac{e^2}{3r_{ij}} \longrightarrow \frac{e^2}{3r_{ij}} + \frac{1}{3}g_p W_{ij} \qquad \text{iso - vector, J even}$$

$$\frac{e^2}{3r_{ij}} \longrightarrow \frac{e^2}{3r_{ij}} + \frac{1}{3}(g_p - g_n)W_{ij} \qquad \text{iso - tensor, J even}$$

$$0 \longrightarrow 0 \qquad + \frac{1}{2}g_n W_{ij} + (v^{nuclear}_{ij}) \qquad \text{iso - scalar, J odd}$$

$$\text{with} \quad W_{ij} = -\left(\frac{e\hbar}{Mc}\right)^2 \frac{(\vec{s}_i + \vec{s}_j)\cdot \vec{l}_{ij}}{r_{ij}^3} \qquad (28)$$

j^n Configurations

$v = 1$	$t = \frac{1}{2}$	$A = 4k \overset{+}{_-} 1$	$T = \text{any}$	$J = j$
$v = 0$	$t = 0$	$A = 4k$	$T = \text{even}$	$J = 0$
		and $\quad A = 4k + 2$	$T = \text{odd}$	$J = 0$

$$
\begin{aligned}
E_{Coul}(A,T,T_z) = \Bigg\{ & E_{Coul}(A_o,0,0) + \frac{3a}{2}_{core}\, n + \left(\tfrac{3}{2}b + c + d\right)\frac{n(n-1)}{2} + (b - 2c - 2d)\left(T(T+1) - \tfrac{3}{4}n\right) + (8c(j+1))\left[\tfrac{n}{2}\right]\left[\tfrac{n}{2}\right] \\[4pt]
& - T_z \left\{ 3a_{core} + 3a + \left(3b + \delta_{v1}\frac{3c}{2T(T+1)}\right)(n - 2j - 1) - (-1)^{\frac{n}{2} - T}\, \delta_{v1}\, 3c(2j+3)\,\frac{2T+1}{2T(T+1)} \right\} \\[4pt]
& + \left(3T_z^2 - T(T+1)\right)\left\{ b + c - c\,\frac{(n-2j-1)^2 - (2j+4-v)^2}{(2T-1)(2T+3)} + 4t(t+1) \right\}
\end{aligned}
$$

$$\tag{25}$$

REFERENCES

1) R. J. Blin-Stoyle in Selected Topics in Nuclear Spectroscopy, ed. by B. J. Verhaar (North Holland Publishing Company, Amsterdam, 1964), p. 213.

2) E. P. Wigner and E. Feenberg, Rept. Progr. Phys. 8 (1942) 274; W. M. MacDonald, Phys. Rev. 98 (1955) 60; 100 (1955) 51; 101 (1956) 271; S. Weinberg and S. B. Treiman, Phys. Rev. 116 (1959) 465; D. H. Wilkinson, Phys. Letts. 11 (1964) 243; Phys. Letts. 12 (1964) 348; Phys. Rev. Letts. 13 (1964) 571.

3) D. H. Wilkinson, Paper A2.

4) K. T. Hecht, Paper S21.

5) J. Jänecke, Phys. Rev., (to be published).

6) R. G. Thomas, Phys. Rev. 81 (1951) 148; J. B. Ehrman, Phys. Rev. 81 (1951) 412; R. G. Thomas, Phys. Rev. 88 (1952) 1109; A. M. Lane and R. G. Thomas, Rev. Mod. Phys. 30 (1958) 329.

7) S. Sengupta, Nucl. Phys. 21 (1960) 542.

8) B. C. Carlson and I. Talmi, Phys. Rev. 96 (1954) 436; A. de-Shalit and I. Talmi, Nuclear Shell Theory (Academic Press, New York and London, 1963), p. 345.

9) C. J. Batty, E. Friedman, P. C. Rowe and J. B. Hunt, Phys. Letts. 19 (1965) 33.

10) J. D. Anderson, C. Wong and J. W. McClure, Phys. Rev. 138 (1965) B615.

11) C. J. Batty, R. S. Gilmore and G. H. Stafford, Nucl. Phys. 75 (1966) 599.

12) M. Harchol, S. Cochavi, A. A. Jaffe and Ch. Drory, Nucl. Phys., (to be published).

13) J. Jänecke, Z. f. Physik 160 (1960) 171.

14) R. Sherr, B. F. Bayman, E. Rost, M. E. Rickey and
C. G. Hoot, Phys. Rev. <u>139</u> (1965) B1272.

15) K. T. Hecht, (private communication).

16) A. de-Shalit and I. Talmi, Nuclear Shell Theory
(Academic Press, New York and London, 1963), p. 465.

17) See for instance Ref. 3.

18) J. Jänecke, Nucl. Phys. <u>73</u> (1965) 97.

19) E. P. Wigner, Phys. Rev. <u>51</u> (1937) 106; J. M. Blatt
and V. I. Weisskopf, Theoretical Nuclear Physics
(John Wiley and Sons, New York, 1952), p. 222.

DISCUSSION

WILKINSON, Oxford: I would like to ask one or
two questions of the theoreticians about the pairing
term. The first question is: Would one expect to see
the pairing contribution to the Coulomb energy in excited states just as strongly as in the ground states?
Offhand, I would guess that you wouldn't because the
symmetry changes and the pairs get broken to a certain
extent. Experimentally, at least in the p- and in the
s-, d-shells, the pairing alternations are present just
as strongly in excited states as in ground states.

And the second remark is that the dependence of
the Coulomb energy on the binding energy of the last
particle which I talked about will also produce an
odd-even alternation just like the pairing energy,
because, of course, the binding energy of the last
proton shows the odd Z- even Z alternation.

And if, in fact, you look at the diagram which
I projected and read off the difference in Coulomb
energy for a change of last proton binding energy equal
to that which you see as the empirical alternation,
you get just about 150 or 200 kilovolts, in other words,
just the magnitude of the pairing alternation.

So my question is: May this alternation perhaps be due to the alternation of the last proton
binding energy and not be a pairing alternation of the
symmetry type?

Certainly there will be this binding energy
effect. I don't think one can get away from that, and
so my operative question is whether the evidence that

one has the same alternation in excited states may tell against the symmetry origin of this apparent pairing alternation.

MORINAGA: Any answers to this question? Otherwise, I think we might make it a home task for theorists because we are running out of time.

WILKINSON: Will any experimentalist answer my question then?

AXEL, Illinois: I had the impression that the odd nuclei go above and below the trend, and it isn't clear to me that Wilkinson's wave function effect for the last bound particle should show that kind of alternation. Do you think that it should? I mean there is a difference between the $4n + 1$ and the $4n + 3$ nuclei.

JÄNECKE: Yes, the alternations follow from simple pairing considerations, that were also obtained by Hecht (Eq. 25). In the plot $E_{Coul}^{(1)}$ as a function of

Figure 4, see page 82

A (Fig. 4), three points for T = 3/2 in the p-shell are included.

For these points you have a positive term for A = 4n + 3 and a negative term for A = 4n + 1, so the additional Coulomb pairing terms have opposite signs; for T = 1/2 and T = 3/2, the phases are different.

WILKINSON: This is, of course, what one would expect from the binding energy argument; the phases would be opposite also.

SCHIFFER: I'd like to comment. The pairing energy does experimentally show an effect - I learned this from Martin Rickey - the Coulomb energy between two pairs of nuclei, differing in that one has a paired set of neutrons and the other a neutron and a proton paired off and another pair with one having a paired set of protons and the other a proton-neutron pair, are different.

This is because of the Coulomb effect of two strongly overlapping protons. Are such effects in your data? Then there are effects caused by differences in binding energy which we heard from Professor Wilkinson. Are such effects included in your constants?

JÄNECKE: Well, yes, it contributes to all of them.

CERNY, Berkeley: I'd like to ask a question of either Wilkinson or Jänecke. You have a three-parameter mass equation and there are now several instances of completed isobaric quartets.

How good should such an expression be, and what should be its expected breakdown with increasing Z or A?

JÄNECKE: I don't know. This depends on the isobaric spin impurities and on the Thomas-Ehrman shift. The fine structure of the vector and tensor Coulomb energy depends mostly on the pairing quantity c (Eq. 26) and these effects decrease with increasing T and A (Eq. 25).

CERNY: Yes, but what I would like is a theoretical calculation stating, for example, how large the coefficient d of a possible term dT_Z^3 should be compared to c (of cT_Z^2)?

The only reference I know giving something like this is in the Weinberg-Treiman article (Phys. Rev. <u>116</u> (1959) 465), which implies that d would be of order $(Z^2/137)c$. The experimental data is already better than that.

WILKINSON: I might make just one comment. Of course, if you do the calculations, taking into account the change in binding energy, then you depart from the quadratic formula.

This is because the true nuclear wave function changes if you change the binding energy. So one would not expect the quadratic formula even without the higher order perturbations to hold because of the empirical change of the binding energy of the last proton. Now, one would just have to compute specific cases to see how important that was in any particular case.

CERNY: I think that such calculations would be very interesting since we have now completed the mass 9, 13 and 37 quartets and in all three cases find perfect agreement with the mass formula within the experimental errors.

WILKINSON: Yes, all that I am saying is that the very crude effect is very strong. It must simply be computed in the particular cases to see what the significance is.

I'd want to just make the qualitative point
that the remarks that I made were, in principle, in
the direction of modifying the quadratic. Now, it may
seem reasonable that the quadratic form remains valid
if one has a systematic and slow change in the binding energy of the last proton.

CERNY: Well, it does. My main reason is to see
how good the form ought to be. That is the question,
I mean the main specific question.

WILKINSON: Well, I am saying this is a trivial
effect, the one that I quoted; a more fancy effect is
the second order effect, which will certainly displace
the masses from the quadratic formula, and I think
MacDonald, in his talk, is going to mention this.

But before one can make a good analysis, one
has to take into account the crude effect that I
talked about and then the size effect. Of course, the
thing I talked about can be represented to some degree
by isobaric spin mixing with states of different T or
perhaps even the same isobaric spin e.g. T = 3/2
mixing with T = 3/2 states.

That's another way of representing the change
in the wave function between members of the isobaric
multiplet. So it's not even clear that you can separate those two effects; the one that I was talking
about and the second effect of mixing states.

JÄNECKE: In the expression derived in first-
order perturbation theory (Eq. 25) for the Coulomb
energy you can also include the nuclear interaction.

A charge independent nuclear interaction contributes only to the scalar energy, but a charge dependent
interaction would also contribute to the vector and
tensor energy (Eq. 28).

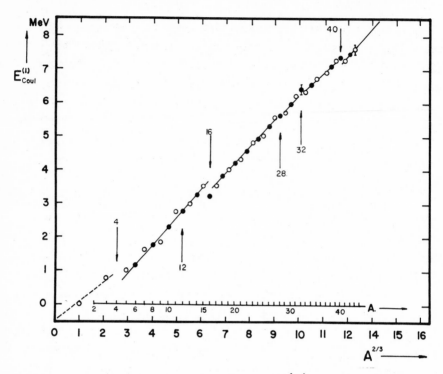

Fig. 1. Vector Coulomb energies $E_{Coul}^{(1)}$ as a function of $A^{2/3}$. The filled and open circles correspond to the isobaric triplets and doublets, respectively. Major shells and subshells are indicated.

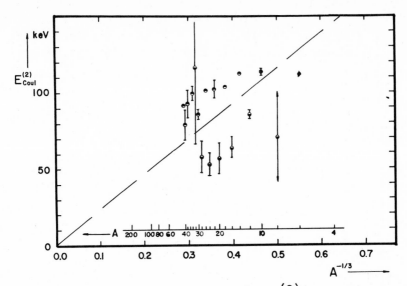

Fig. 2. Tensor Coulomb energies $E_{Coul}^{(2)}$ as a function of $A^{-1/3}$. The experimental points for the nuclei with $A = 4n$ and $A = 4n + 2$ are indicated by ● and ◒, respectively.

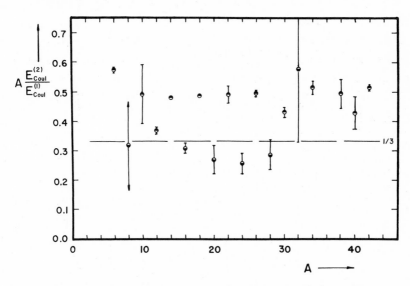

Fig. 3. Plot of A times the ratio $E_{Coul}^{(2)}/E_{Coul}^{(1)}$ as a function of A.

81

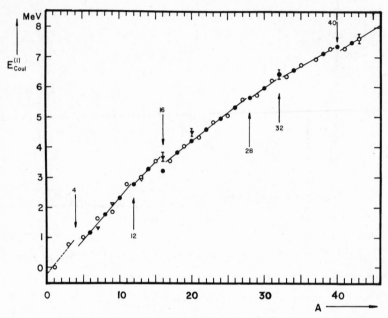

Fig. 4. Vector Coulomb energies $E_{Coul}^{(1)}$ as a function of A. The filled and open circles correspond to the isobaric triplets and doublets, respectively. Major shells and subshells are indicated. (The triangular points are not discussed).

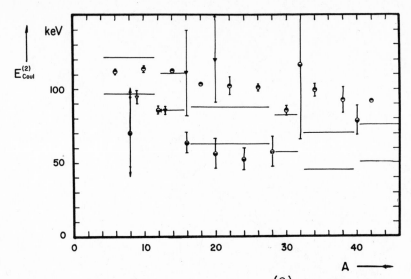

Fig. 5. Tensor Coulomb energies $E_{Coul}^{(2)}$ as a function
of A. The experimental points for the nuclei with
A = 4n and A = 4n + 2 are indicated by ⊖ and ⊖ ,
respectively. (The triangular points are not discussed.)

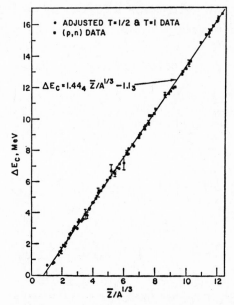

Fig. 6. Coulomb energy differences ΔE_{Coul} as a
function of $\overline{Z}/A^{1/3}$. The figure is taken from Ref. 10.

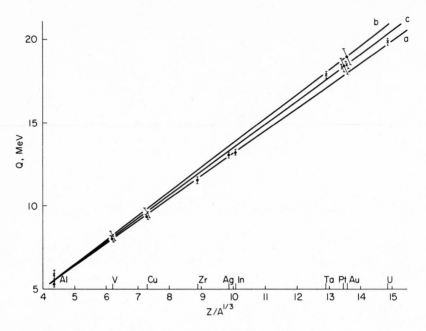

Fig. 7. Coulomb energy differences ΔE_{Coul} as a function of $Z/A^{1/3}$. The figure is taken from Ref. 11.

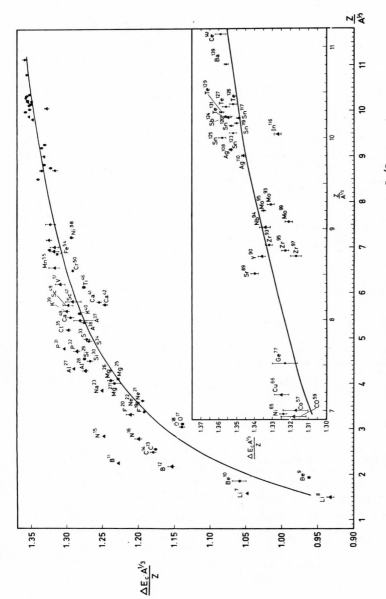

Fig. 8. Plot of the quantity $\Delta E_{Coul} A^{1/3}/Z$ as a function of $Z/A^{1/3}$. The figure is taken from Ref. 12.

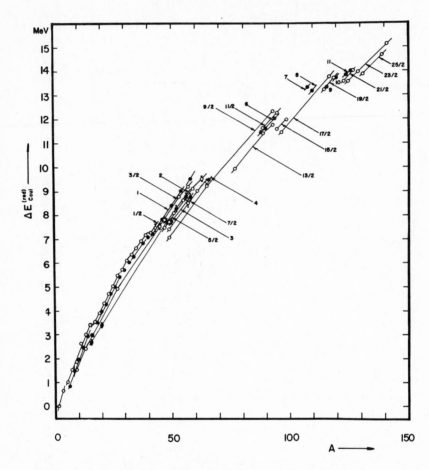

Fig. 9. Plot of the reduced Coulomb energy differ-
ences $\Delta E_{Coul}^{(red)}$ as a function of A. The experimental
values for all half-integer and integer T are shown as
open and filled circles, respectively. Uncertainties
are indicated only when $\geq$ 50 keV. The experimental
data were taken from Refs. 5, 12 and 14. (Read 23/2,
25/2 and 27/2 instead of 21/2, 23/2 and 25/2).

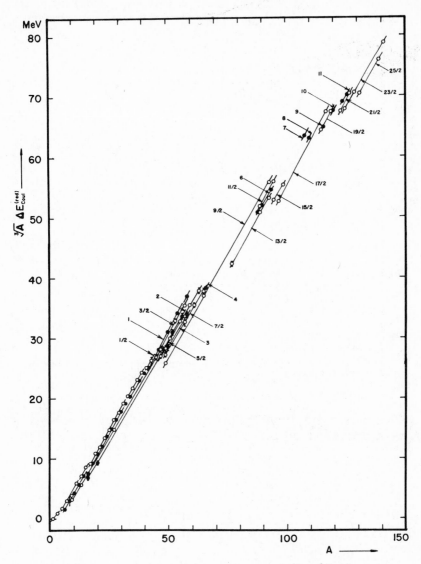

Fig. 10. Plot of the quantity $A^{1/3}\Delta E_{Coul}^{(red)}$ as a function of A. (Read 23/2, 25/2 and 27/2 instead of 21/2, 23/2 and 25/2.)

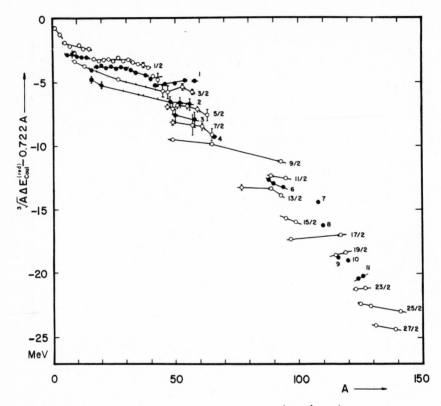

Fig. 11. Plot of the quantity $A^{1/3}\Delta E_{Coul}^{(red)} - (0.722 \text{ MeV})$ A as a function of A.

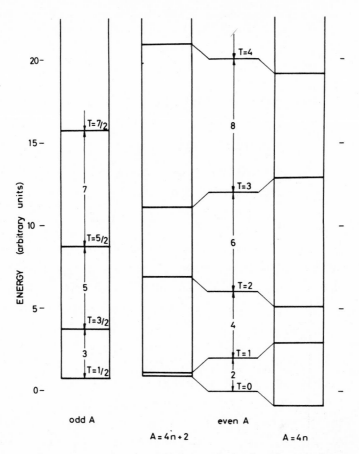

Fig. 12. Energetic position of isobaric analogue states for odd-A and even-A nuclei. The level structure resembles rotational bands. For a more detailed discussion see Ref. 18.

A4. ISOBARIC SPIN SELECTION RULES FOR ELECTROMAGNETIC TRANSITIONS[*]

E. K. Warburton

Brookhaven National Laboratory
Upton, New York

INTRODUCTION

In this talk we shall consider the isobaric-spin selection rules for electromagnetic transitions between nuclear levels and shall discuss some of the experimental evidence supporting these rules. I shall give such illustrations of their use as time permits. In the presentation of the selection rules rigor will be sacrificed to brevity and to an attempt to show the common origin of the various rules and relationships.

The early history (prior to 1957) of these selection rules has been discussed in several excellent review articles[1-3]. I shall touch only incidentally on this earlier work.

THE GENERAL RULES

The development in this section follows closely that of Morpurgo[4]. For simplicity, both charge symmetry and charge independence of nuclear forces shall be assumed and will not be discussed further. We shall neglect meson-exchange interactions and Coulomb effects of the type which (a) give rise to isobaric-spin

---

[*]Work performed under the auspices of the United States Atomic Energy Commission

impurities and (b) cause departures from the equality of wave functions for corresponding levels in conjugate nuclei.

The matrix element for an electromagnetic transition between two levels a and b with isobaric spin T_a and T_b, respectively, in a nucleus of A nucleons and with z-component of isobaric spin $T_3 = (N-Z)/2$ is customarily written in the form

$$M_{ab}(T_3) = \langle aT_a | \sum_1^A {}_i (1/2 + \tau_3^{(i)}) H_{LM}^{(i)} \text{ (neutron)}$$

$$+ (1/2 - \tau_3^{(i)}) H_{LM}^{(i)} \text{ (proton)} | bT_b \rangle \qquad (1)$$

where $\tau_3 = + 1/2$ for neutrons and $- 1/2$ for protons. The charge and magnetic moment of the neutron and proton are associated with $H_{LM}^{(i)}$ (neutron) and $H_{LM}^{(i)}$ (proton), respectively. Equation 1 can be written with an obvious notation

$$M_{ab}(T_3) = \langle aT_a | \sum_1^A {}_i (H_0^{(i)} + H_1^{(i)} \tau_3^{(i)}) | bT_b \rangle \qquad (2)$$

That is, the interaction is the sum of a part proportional to $\tau_3^{(i)}$ and a part independent of $\tau_3^{(i)}$. We can also express $M_{ab}(T_3)$ as

$$M_{ab}(T_3) = M_0(T_3) + M_1(T_3) \qquad (3)$$

i.e., explicitly separate the two parts of the matrix element implied by Eq. 2. Using the Wigner-Eckart theorem we find the following properties of $M_0(T_3)$ and $M_1(T_3)$[4]:

$$M_0(T_3) = M_0 \qquad\qquad \Delta T = T_a - T_b = 0 \qquad (4a)$$

91

$$M_0(T_3) = 0 \qquad\qquad |\Delta T| > 0 \qquad\qquad\qquad (4b)$$

$$M_1(T_3) = M_1 T_3 \qquad\quad \Delta T = 0 \qquad\qquad\qquad (4c)$$

$$M_1(T_3) = (T_a^2 - T_3^2)^{1/2} M_1 \qquad \Delta T = 1 \ (T_a = T_b + 1)$$
$$(4d)$$

$$M_1(T_3) = 0 \qquad\qquad |\Delta T| > 1 \qquad\qquad\qquad (4e)$$

where M_0 and M_1 are independent of T, but, of course, are dependent on the levels in question. The following general selection rules[4] are obtained from Eq. 4:

(1) For all multipolarities $\Delta T = 0, \pm 1$.

(2) Corresponding transitions in conjugate nuclei (i.e., opposite signs of T_3) with $\Delta T = 1$ are the same for all multipolarities.

These rules are not broken by departures from the long wavelength approximation; in fact, we have not yet assumed it. They are apparently not broken by exchange interactions. They are both broken by the Coulomb force insofar as it gives rise to isobaric spin mixing[5]. Rule (2) is based on the equality of the matrix element M_1 for corresponding transitions in conjugate nuclei. It is therefore broken by Coulomb effects which give rise to "dynamic distortion" (see Paper B4). An example of this type of effect will be given after Rule (3) is presented.

Rule (1) can be seen physically as a natural consequence of the fact that only one nucleon may change its quantum numbers in an electromagnetic transition and the nucleon has an isobaric spin of $1/2$[2].

Rule (1) was first pointed out in 1952 by

Radicati[6]. It could not be tested before the iden-
tification of levels with $T = |T_3| + 2$. Such states
have been found in recent years (as we shall hear at
this conference) and it is now quite feasible to test
or apply this rule. The most straightforward method
would be to study the (p, γ) reaction proceeding through
a $T = 2$ resonance in a $T_3 = 0$ nucleus (for instance
Si^{28}). From rule (1) we would expect to observe gamma
ray cascades through the $T = 1$ states. Any cross-over
transitions to $T = 0$ states would indicate breakdown
of the rule - presumably due to isobaric spin impurities.

Rule (2) also has not been tested or applied.
It too could conceivably be tested in the near future.

SPECIFIC SELECTION RULES

We shall now turn to a discussion of selection
rules for specific multipoles. Unlike the general
rules, (1) and (2), these specific rules are broken by
various second-order processes other than those associated with Coulomb effects[3]. They are also specific
to either conjugate or self-conjugate (N=Z) nuclei.
However, they have been extremely useful in assigning
isobaric spin and investigating isobaric spin mixing
in these nuclei.

Conjugate Nuclei

We now make the multipole expansion and the long
wavelength approximation[7]. Then we note $M_0 = 0$ for E1
transitions (conservation of total momentum) and we
have[4],

(3) Corresponding E1 transition strengths in
conjugate nuclei are equal.

This rule follows from Eqs. 4c and 4d. It is broken, at least in principle, by several second-order processes[4], the most important of which we assume to be Coulomb effects. The rule has been tested most thoroughly by comparing branching ratios in the mirror nuclei B^{11} and C^{11} and in N^{15} and O^{15}. A small departure from the rule has been noted in the former case[8] and a large one in the latter[9]. As an example the decay modes of the second $J^{\pi} = 1/2^{+}$ states in N^{15} and O^{15} are shown in Fig. 1, and a comparison of the relative transition strengths in these two nuclei is made in Table I. These results are taken from those quoted by Warburton et al.[9]. For present purposes the important conclusion to draw from these results is that the ratio of the strengths of the E1 transitions to the $1/2^{-}$ and $3/2^{-}$ states differs between the two nuclei by more than a factor of 100. This gross violation of rule (3) is probably due to two factors. First of all, the E1 ground-state branch in O^{15} is exceedingly weak (see Table I) - indicating strong interference effects in the transition matrix element. Secondly, the O^{15} $1/2^{+}$ level in question is unbound and close (280 keV) to the threshold for proton emission while the N^{15} $1/2^{+}$ state is bound by about 3 MeV against nucleon emission. This situation gives rise to a large Thomas-Ehrman shift and could also cause enough difference in the radial wave functions of the two $1/2^{+}$ states to explain the difference in the E1 transition strength ratios. This is a case, then, in which the E1 transition strengths presumably are extremely sensitive to Coulomb effects. A theoretical study of this situation might be informative.

Self-Conjugate Nuclei
A comparison of Eqs. 1 and 2 shows that

$$H_0^{(i)} = 1/2 \left[H_{LM}^{(i)} \text{ (neutron)} + H_{LM}^{(i)} \text{(proton)} \right]$$

and   (5a)

$$H_1^{(i)} = \left[H_{LM}^{(i)} \text{ (neutron)} - H_{LM}^{(i)} \text{ (proton)} \right].$$

(5b)

From Eq. 4 we see that in a self-conjugate nucleus $(T_3 = 0)$ we can write the single-nucleon operator as[10],

$$f_i(\tau_3)\left[H_{LM}^{(i)} \text{ (neutron)} + (-)^{\Delta T} H_{LM}^{(i)} \text{ (proton)} \right] \quad (6)$$

where $f_i(\tau_3) = 1/2$ for $\Delta T = 0$ and $\tau_3^{(i)}$ for $\Delta T = 1$. In this formalism it is the phase factor $(-)^{\Delta T}$ which gives rise to all the known isobaric spin selection rules for electromagnetic transitions in self-conjugate nuclei.

Electric transitions.
For electric transitions the operator $H_{LM}^{(i)}$ is proportional to the charge of the ith nucleon to which it refers. In this case the operator of Eq. 6 is proportional to[11]

$$z_n + (-)^{\Delta T} z_p \quad (7)$$

where z_n and z_p are the effective charges of the neutron and proton respectively.

For E1 transitions conservation of total momentum (the center-of-mass effect) demands that the effective charge of the proton be $+ e/2$ and that of the neutron

95

be - e/2. Thus from Eq. 7 the effective charge is 0
for $\Delta T = 0$ transitions and e for $\Delta T = 1$ transitions
and we have

(4) $\Delta T = 0$ El transitions in self-conjugate
nuclei are forbidden.

This rule is also broken by second-order processes[6,12,13]; it is the oldest and best-known isobaric spin selection rule. Rule (4) is best tested by an omnibus
comparison of El transition strengths. This has been
done by Wilkinson[2]. The histogram of Fig. 2, due to
Wilkinson, shows the results of such a comparison.
From this figure we conclude that the inhibition due
to rule (4) is not complete, but is about a factor of
30. This indicates isobaric spin impurities of the
order of 3% in intensity - presumably in the initial
(upper) states of the transitions.

For higher order electric transitions the
center-of-mass effect is not important[2] so that the
effective charge of the neutron from this source is
negligible and there is no strong inhibition of $\Delta T = 0$
transitions. However, there is a selection rule of
sorts. The collective effects responsible for the enhancement of E2 and E3 transitions have been conven-
tionally characterized by the weak surface coupling
model which endows the neutron with a charge $\beta_L e$ and
the proton with a charge $(1 + \beta_L)e$. From Eq. 7 we see
that, in this model, the effective charge for $\Delta T = 0$
transitions is $(1 + 2\beta_L)e$ while for $\Delta T = 1$ transitions
it is just e. Thus, we have the following selection
rule:

(5) $\Delta T = 1$ EL transitions in self-conjugate
nuclei can have no collective enhancement
within the framework of the weak surface

coupling approximation.

Rule (5), derived in the present fashion, expresses what can be seen rather easily on physical grounds. The evidence for or against this rule is scanty. The one authenticated $\Delta T = 1$ E2 transition of which I am aware is quite weak in agreement with rule (5)[14].

Magnetic transitions.

For ML transitions the single-nucleon operator is of the form[7]

$$\text{grad} \left[r^L Y_{LM}(\theta,\phi) \right] \cdot \left[(\mu_i - \frac{\beta_i}{L+1}) \, \vec{s}_i + \frac{\beta_i}{L+1} \, \vec{J}_i \right] \quad (8)$$

where β_i is 0 for a neutron and 1 for a proton. We define

$$\langle aT_a | \sum_i^A f_i(\tau_3) \, \text{grad}\left[r^L Y_{LM}(\theta,\phi) \right] \cdot \vec{J}_i | \, bT_b \rangle =$$

$$C_{ab}(\Delta T) \langle aT_a | \sum_1^A f_i(\tau_3) \, \text{grad}\left[r^L Y_{LM}(\theta,\phi) \right] \cdot \vec{s}_i | bT_b \rangle$$

$$(9)$$

and $G_{\Delta T} = C_{ab}(\Delta T)-1$. Then from Eq. 6 the ML transition matrix element will be of the form,

$$\left\{ \mu_n + (-)^{\Delta T}(\mu_p + \frac{G_{\Delta T}}{L+1}) \right\} < aT_a | \sum_1^A i f_i(\tau_3) \, \text{grad}\left[r^L Y_{LM}(\theta,\phi) \right]$$

$$\cdot \vec{s}_i | bT_b >. \quad (10)$$

The matrix element in Eq. 10 should not be too different, on the average, for $\Delta T = 0$ and $\Delta T = 1$

97

transitions, i.e., for $f_i(\tau_3) = 1/2$ or $\tau_3^{(1)}$. Thus the expression in curly brackets gives, on the average, the major dependence of the ML transition strength on isobaric spin. The dependence is due to the near cancellation of the neutronic and protonic magnetic moments for $\Delta T = 0$, i.e., $\mu_n + \mu_p = 0.88$ nuclear magnetons while $\mu_n - \mu_p = -4.70$ nuclear magnetons.

If we assume that the matrix element in Eq. 10 is independent of ΔT and define $< G_{\Delta T} >$ as the average value of $G_{\Delta T}$ in all self-conjugate nuclei, then we have

$$\left[\frac{0.88 + <G_0>/(L + 1)}{-4.70 - <G_1>/(L + 1)} \right]^2 \tag{11}$$

as the ratio of the average $\Delta T = 0$ ML transition-strength to the average $\Delta T = 1$ ML transition strength for given L in self-conjugate nuclei. A consideration of the expected distribution of allowed values[10] of G_0, which vary from ~ 5 to ~ -10 indicates that $< G_0 >$ should be close to -1 which is the value of G_0 for a single-particle transition with $|J_a - J_b| = L$. We take $< G_1 > = < G_0 >$, which is a similar assumption to assuming the matrix element in Eq. 10 is independent of ΔT. With $< G_0 > = < G_1 > = -1$ the ratio of Eq. 11 varies from 0.8×10^{-2} for $L = 1$ to 3.5×10^{-2} for L very large. Note that because $G_{\Delta T}$ can vary greatly from -1, it is possible that large fluctuations from this average inhibition will be encountered. We thus have the following selection rule[15]:

(6) $\Delta T = 0$ ML transition strengths in self-conjugate nuclei are expected to be on

the average weaker by a factor of about
30 - 100 than the average normal ML transition strength and should show larger
fluctuations about the average than the
normal transitions.

For M1 transitions G_0 has the definite value of
-1. This can be seen by evaluating the left-hand side
of Eq. 9 for $\Delta T = 0$ transitions. This becomes for
$L = 1$[16],

$$< a| \sum_1^A {}_i \vec{J}_i |b > = < a|\vec{J}|b > = 0 \qquad (12)$$

since $\vec{J}$, the total angular momentum, has no non-vanishing off-diagonal matrix elements. Thus $C_{ab}(0) = 0$
for $L = 1$, and the selection rule for M1 transitions,
first pointed out by Morpurgo[16], is more rigorous
than the general ML selection rule. However, it is
not greatly so since the rule still depends on the
assumption that the matrix element of Eq. 10 is not
strongly dependent on ΔT and also on the analogous
assumption that $< G_1 >$ is not greatly different from
-1. The M1 selection rule as stated by Morpurgo[16]
is,

(7) "M1 transition strengths between levels
with the same T in self-conjugate nuclei
are expected to be on the average weaker
by a factor 100 than the average M1 transition strength."

We now consider the experimental evidence bear-
ing on rules (6) and (7). For $Z \leqslant 10$, where the rules
are expected to hold best, there is experimental data

available for M1 and M2 transitions but none for higher
L. In Fig. 3 is shown a histogram of the measured
strengths of M1 transitions in Weisskopf units[2] for
light (Z ≤ 10) self-conjugate nuclei. The data in
this distribution includes all the well-authenticated
M1 transitions in self-conjugate nuclei known to the
author as of February, 1966[17]. The separation between allowed and forbidden M1 transitions in Fig. 3
is quite startling. The mean transition strengths are
0.002 and 0.6 Weisskopf units for forbidden and allowed
transitions, respectively. The most probable M1 transition strength for all light (Z ≤ 10) nuclei is about
0.15 Weisskopf units[2]. Thus the inhibition due to
rule (7) is just about as predicted. The cause of the
rather large value for the mean $\Delta T = 1$ M1 transition
strength is not clear. It is certainly partially due
to experimental selectivity, but also may contain an
effect due to a dependence on ΔT of the matrix element
in Eq. 10.

There are only 9 known M2 transition strengths
in light (Z ≤ 10) nuclei. The distribution of these
transition strengths (in Weisskopf units) is shown in
the upper part of Fig. 4. Also included in this distribution are upper limits for 3 $\Delta T = 0$ M2 transitions
in self-conjugate nuclei. The available information[17]
is seen to be quite sparse; however, that shown in
Fig. 4 is seen to be in fairly good agreement with
rule (6). The mean forbidden and allowed M2 transition
strengths are 0.04 and 0.8 Weisskopf units, respectively
(including the 3 upper limits for $\Delta T = 0$ M2 strengths).
Thus the inhibition is about 20 or more which, considering the sample available, is consistent with the
expected value of ∼50. Most of the data represented

in this distribution has only become available in the
last year. Thus it is expected that a better check of
rule (6) will be possible in the future.

The lower part of Fig. 4 shows the distribution
of M2 transition strengths in the (s,d) shell[18]. This
distribution has a mean of 0.08 Weisskopf units, considerably smaller than the mean for $Z \leq 10$, so that
there is some indication of A-dependence for M2 transition strengths. There are only two $\Delta T = 0$ M2 transitions in self-conjugate nuclei in this distribution
and the stronger is somewhat uncertain[18]. Thus this
distribution does not cast much light on the ML selection rule.

I would like to close by giving two examples of
the use of the results presented here for M1 transitions
in self-conjugate nuclei. The first involves the much
publicized isobaric spin mixing between the two 2^+
states at 16.62 and 16.92 MeV in Be^8. The Be^8 1^+ state
at 17.64 MeV decays to both of these states by M1 transitions[19] as shown in Fig. 5. The strongest $\Delta T = 0$ M1
transition included in the distribution of Fig. 3 has
a strength of 0.02 Weisskopf units. Thus it seems
quite certain that both transitions shown in Fig. 5
contain a $\Delta T = 1$ component. If the 17.64-MeV level is
pure $T = 1$ then we conclude that both 2^+ states contain
$T = 0$ components. This interpretation is not unique
but is consistent with other evidence[19]*. Various sum
rules, based on rule (7) can be constructed to make
arguments of this type more rigorous[20].

The final example involves the gamma-ray decay
of the N^{14} 3.95-MeV level. The experimental information
is collected in Fig. 6. The E2 radiative width of the

*See Paper S14.

$3.95 \rightarrow 0$ transition was determined by inelastic electron scattering[21] while the E2, M1 mixing ratio of this transition was determined by various gamma-ray correlation measurements[22]. It is not possible to choose between the two possibilities for the E2, M1 mixing ratio from studies of gamma-ray correlations, even including polarization. However, the strengths of the $3.95 \rightarrow 2.31$ and $3.95 \rightarrow 0$ M1 transitions are fixed for given x(E2,M1) by the measurement of Γ_γ(E2), and the branching ratios[22] to the ground state and 2.31-MeV level (Fig. 6). The strengths for the two M1 transitions obtained by combining this information are shown in Fig. 7 as a function of x(E2,M1). It is seen that $|x(E2,M1)| < 0.41$ corresponds to strengths greater than 9 and 0.021 Weisskopf units for the $\Delta T = 1$ $3.95 \rightarrow 2.31$ and $\Delta T = 0$ $3.95 \rightarrow 0$ transitions, respectively. These M1 strengths are both larger than any having the corresponding ΔT in Fig. 3[23]. Thus, we conclude that the solution x(E2,M1) = $- (0.36 \pm 0.04)$ can be eliminated. The solution x(E2,M1) = $- (2.75 \pm 0.30)$ is seen to give reasonable strengths for both transitions.

REFERENCES

1) W. E. Burcham, Prog. in Nuclear Phys. __4__ (1955) 171.
2) D. H. Wilkinson, in Nuclear Spectroscopy, Part B, edited by F. Ajzenberg-Selove (Academic Press, New York, 1960), p. 852ff.
3) W. M. MacDonald, in Nuclear Spectroscopy, Part B, edited by F. Ajzenberg-Selove (Academic Press, New York, 1960), p. 932ff.
4) G. Morpurgo, Phys. Rev. __114__ (1959) 1075.
5) A further generalization of Rule (1) is that

$|\Delta T| > 2$ is apparently not allowed even if Coulomb effects are included. (J. D. Walecka, private communication).

6) L. A. Radicati, Phys. Rev. 87 (1952) 521.

7) A. de-Shalit and I. Talmi, Nuclear Shell Theory (Academic Press, New York, 1963).

8) J. W. Olness, E. K. Warburton, D. E. Alburger, and J. A. Becker, Phys. Rev. 139 (1965) B512.

9) E. K. Warburton, J. W. Olness, and D. E. Alburger, Phys. Rev. 140 (1965) B1202.

10) J. M. Kennedy and W. T. Sharp, CRT-580 (1956).

11) We neglect the contribution of the magnetic moment to electric transitions since it is down by order $(v/c)^2$ where v is the velocity of the proton in the nucleus.

12) M. Gell-Mann and V. L. Telegdi, Phys. Rev. 91 (1953) 169.

13) G. Morpurgo, Nuovo Cimento, 12 (1954) 60.

14) The $16.11 \to 0$ transitions in C^{12}. (See R. E. Segel and M. J. Bina, Phys. Rev. 124 (1961) 814. The strength of this E2 transition is reported to be 0.15 Weisskopf units.

15) E. K. Warburton, Phys. Rev. Letts. 1 (1958) 68.

16) G. Morpurgo, Phys. Rev. 110 (1958) 721.

17) The list of input data is available upon request to the author.

18) I would like to thank Dr. C. van der Leun who provided me with the experimental data for this histogram.

19) J. B. Marion and M. Wilson, (to be published).

20) E. K. Warburton, Phys. Rev. 113 (1959) 595.

21) G. R. Bishop, M. Bernheim, and P. Kossanyi-Demay, Nucl. Phys. 54 (1964) 353.

22) J. W. Olness, A. R. Poletti, and E. K. Warburton, (to be published); F. Riess, W. Trost, H. J. Rose, and E. K. Warburton, Phys. Rev. $\underline{137}$ (1965) B507; S. Gorodetzky, R. M. Freeman, A. Gallmann, and F. Haas, (to be published).

23) The two strongest $\Delta T = 1$ M1 transitions included in Fig. 3 are $0^+ \to 1^+$ transitions which are intrinsically 3 times stronger than a $1^+ \to 0^+$ transition such as considered here.

TABLE I. Comparison of relative transition strengths for transitions from the N^{15} 8.312- and O^{15} 7.550-MeV levels (from Ref. 8).

J^π Final State	Multipolarity	$\Gamma_\gamma(O^{15})^a$ $(10^{-3}$ eV)	O^{15} Transition strength (Weisskopf units)	N^{15} Transition strength (arbitrary units)[b]
$1/2^-$	E1	1.3 ± 0.5	0.73×10^{-5}	$(0.3 \pm 0.05) \times 10^{-2}$
$3/2^-$	E1	23 ± 0.5	0.022	0.03 ± 0.01
$1/2^+$	M1	6.7 ± 0.5	0.024	0.20 ± 0.05
$3/2^+$	M1	9 ± 0.5	0.97	(0.97)

[a] Assuming a total gamma-ray radiative width of 40×10^{-3} eV (S. Bashkin, R. R. Carlson, and E. B. Nelson, Phys. Rev. 99 (1955) 107).

[b] Normalized to the strength of the O^{15} transition strength to the $3/2^+$ state.

105

DISCUSSION

GARVEY, <u>Princeton</u>: In the mass 15 case, isn't it true that the ground state dipole transition is very, very inhibited?

WARBURTON: Yes.

GARVEY: So that small changes could really speed it up a great deal?

WARBURTON: Yes.

GARVEY: It's kind of deceptive.

WARBURTON: Yes, that's right.

SEGEL, <u>Argonne</u>: Is there any implication that in non-self-conjugate nuclei you can get collective enhancement of transitions between states differing by one unit of isobaric spin?

WARBURTON: I don't know if you can or not. I would presume you can't, but I don't know.

SEGEL: But just intuitively, you wouldn't think you could?

WARBURTON: That rule had nothing to do with anything but self-conjugate nuclei.

HAMBURGER, <u>Pittsburgh</u>: In the $N^{15} - O^{15}$ case, you blame the discrepancy on the tails of the wave function or on the different binding energies. Is it the same thing as saying that there are admixtures of lower T-states?

WARBURTON: No. Wilkinson could comment on that. He said it after the last talk. His way of looking on this is to say that there are mixtures of other states of the same isobaric spin. That is one way of explaining it.

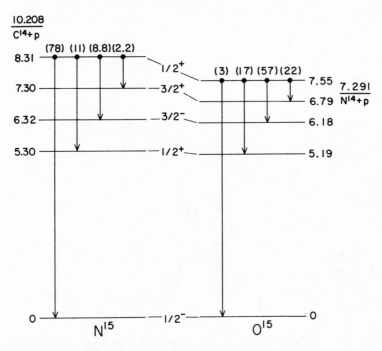

Fig. 1. Comparison of the branching ratios of the second $J^{\pi} = 1/2^{+}$ mirror levels in N^{15} and O^{15} (from Ref. 8).

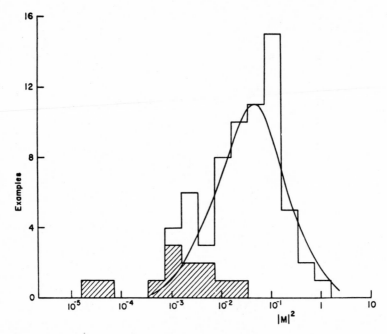

Fig. 2.   Histogram of the distribution in strength of E1 transitions in light nuclei (Z ≤ 10). $|M|^2 = \Gamma_\gamma/\Gamma_{\gamma W}$ where $\Gamma_{\gamma W}$ are the Weisskopf units defined in Ref. 2.   The cross-hatched histogram represents transitions that violate the isobaric spin selection rule. The full curve is the prediction for the distribution of transition strengths made by the full independent-particle model in intermediate coupling (from Ref. 2).

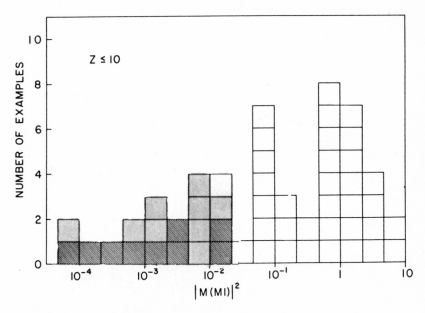

Fig. 3. Histogram of the distribution in strength of M1 transitions for light ($Z \leqslant 10$) self-conjugate nuclei. The histogram shows the number of examples which fall within a given range of $|M(M1)|^2$ (in Weisskopf units). The unmarked blocks correspond to $\Delta T = 1$ transitions, the cross-hatched blocks correspond to $\Delta T = 0$ transitions, and the stippled blocks correspond to upper limits for $\Delta T = 0$ transitions.

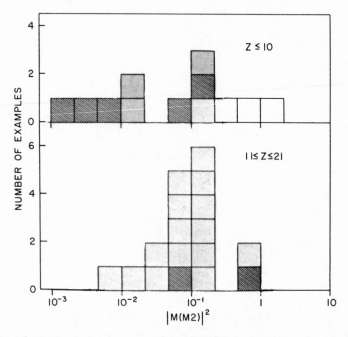

Fig. 4. Histograms of the distribution in strength (in Weisskopf units) of M2 transitions in light (Z ≤ 10) nuclei (upper) and the (s,d) shell (lower). The unmarked blocks correspond to normal transitions. The cross-hatched and stippled blocks correspond to $\Delta T = 0$ transitions in self-conjugate nuclei; the stippled blocks represent upper limits.

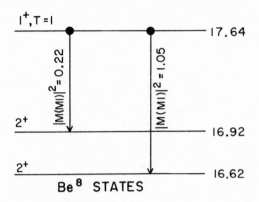

Fig. 5. Ml transitions connecting the Be^8 17.64-MeV level to the 2^+ levels at 16.62 and 16.92 MeV (from Ref. 19).

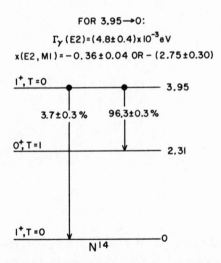

Fig. 6. Experimental information pertaining to the gamma-ray decay of the N^{14} 3.95-MeV level (from Refs. 21 and 22).

111

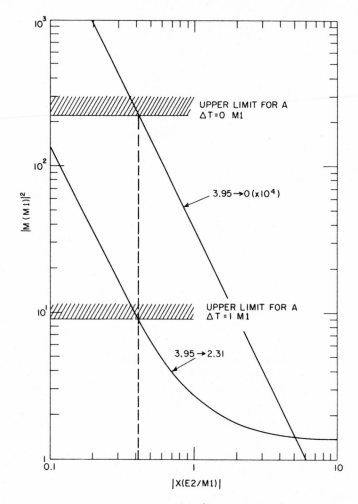

Fig. 7. Variation of the N^{14} 3.95 → 0 and 3.95 → 2.31 M1 transition strengths (in Weisskopf units) as a function of the E2,M1 mixing amplitude of the 3.95 → 0 transition. The upper limits correspond to the strongest $\Delta T = 0$ and $\Delta T = 1$ M1 transitions of Fig. 3.

A5. ISOBARIC SPIN DEPENDENCE OF THE NUCLEON-NUCLEON INTERACTION[*]

A. E. S. Green, T. Sawada and R. D. Sharma

University of Florida
Gainesville, Florida

This is a report of our first efforts to fit the nucleon-nucleon phase shifts with our relativistic meson-theoretic nuclear force. For each meson field, we use the generalized Yukawa function

$$J = (g^2/r) [\exp(-kr) - \exp(-\Lambda r)] \qquad (1)$$

suggested by old work on meson fields with higher derivative Lagrangians[1]. Here k is $mc/\hbar$ for the physical meson and $\Lambda = M_\Lambda c/\hbar$ is a convenient cut-off parameter similar to the parameter in Podolsky's[2] electrodynamics used by Feynman[3].

Among many possibilities explored by Kemmer[4] we selected[5] for detailed study direct coupling interactions due to pseudoscalar mesons and a synthesis of a scalar and vector meson. These lead to the Diracian one boson exchange potentials,

$$V^D_{ps} = \theta_T \beta_1 \gamma_{51} \beta_2 \gamma_{52} J_{ps}(r) \qquad (2)$$

and

$$V^D_{5v} = \theta_T (1 - \beta_1 \beta_2 - \vec{\alpha}_1 \cdot \vec{\alpha}_2) J_{5v}(r) \qquad (3)$$

[*]Supported in part by AFOSR Grant 902-65

113

where θ_τ is either unity or $\vec{\tau}_1 \cdot \vec{\tau}_2$, depending upon
the isobaric spin (originally called isotopic spin) of
the exchanged mesons.

The Breit-like approximations[6] for these purely
relativistic interactions are

$$V_{ps} = \theta_\tau (\hbar/Mc)^2 \left\{ (\nabla^2 J/12) \vec{\sigma}_1 \cdot \vec{\sigma}_2 + (1/12)[r \ d(r^{-1}dJ/dr)/dr]S_{12} \right\}$$

and $\hspace{10cm}$ (4)

$$V_{5v} = -\theta_\tau (\hbar/Mc)^2 \left\{ \nabla^2 J/4 + 2J\nabla^2 + 2\nabla J \cdot \nabla - (\nabla^2 J/6) \vec{\sigma}_1 \cdot \vec{\sigma}_2 \right.$$

$$\left. -2r^{-1}(dJ/dr)\vec{L} \cdot \vec{S} + (1/12)[r \ d(r^{-1}dJ/dr)/dr]S_{12} \right\}$$

$$(5)$$

These relativistic interactions are closely analogous
to magnetic interactions between spinning and moving
charged particles.

In our recent test of these interactions[7], we
used a zero parameter model in which all mesons had the
pi-meson-nucleon coupling constant ($g^2 = 14.7$) as deduced by Hamilton and Woolcock[8] from pion-nucleon
scattering experiments. We found that the net tensor,
spin-spin and spin-orbit isoscalar and isovector po-
tentials generated by the ω, η, π, and ρ mesons along
with ω_s and ρ_s, the assumed scalar mesons compared
quite favorably with the meson theoretic-phenomenolo-
gical potentials of Bryan and Scott[9], Breit, et al.[10],
and Hamada and Johnston[11]. Because of the velocity
dependent terms in Eq. 5, we could not directly compare our central potentials with the static potentials
of these three groups. However, our velocity dependent interactions compared favorably with those proposed in strictly phenomenological studies of the nucleon-nucleon force[12,13]. Subsequently, Bryan and

Scott[14] extended their meson theoretic derivation and have confirmed the velocity dependent terms in Eq. 5.

In our current work we are pursuing three calculational techniques: (1) we are exploring phase shifts using the Born approximation, which provides a reasonable way to examine the influence of many possible perturbation terms which can enter the nucleon-nucleon force even when the "effective mass" would go negative, (2) we are calculating the phase shifts associated with simple relativistic models using a Schroedinger equation program developed by Prof. Bruce Scott, which has been adapted to embody the velocity dependent terms and to accomodate various cut-off masses, and (3) we are developing a program for the direct solution of the two particle Dirac equation.

Figure 1 presents a set of phase shifts for a simple unbroken relativistic model consisting of a 5ω meson and the π meson with three adjustable parameters (g_ω^2 and Λ_π and Λ_ω). These phase shifts are shown in comparison with the experimental phase shifts recently determined by Arndt and MacGregor[15]. This π - 5ω model was chosen because:(a) it is the simplest meson theoretic model which represents the nucleon-nucleon scattering data in a semi-quantitative fashion, (b) to improve upon the π - 5ω model requires the consideration of very many possible extra ingredients, many of which cannot be fully justified at the present stage of fundamental particle physics, (c) the π - 5ω model gives results comparable to the 10 parameter Bryan and Scott[14] model which is an almost relativistic π, ω, ω_s, η, ρ, ρ_s model with derivative coupling to the ρ, and (d) the π - 5ω model contains practically all the component effects which have been observed phenomenolo-

115

gically in nuclear physics studies. Thus the nucleon-nucleon potentials represented in Eq. 4 (with $\theta_T = \vec{T}_1 \cdot \vec{T}_2$ for the π meson) and in Eq. 5, manifest themselves in corresponding nucleon-nuclear potentials used in shell model and optical model studies. Thus these terms provide a simple physical basis for the observed isobaric spin dependence, the diffuseness, the velocity and spin orbital dependence of the phenomenological nucleon-nuclear potentials explored here at Florida State University from 1953 to 1959 by Green and his students K. Lee and R. J. Berkley, P. C. Sood, N. V. V. J. Swamy, P. J. Wyatt and R. H. Lemmer[16].

In conclusion for nuclear physics, we primarily seek a single and accurate representation of the nucleon-nucleon force which might be used to explain the properties of many nucleon systems. For particle physics, we wish to identify all the fundamental ingredients of the nucleon-nucleon force. Both directions of research are currently being pursued and further progress will be reported upon at a later date.

We would like to express our sincere thanks to Prof. Bruce L. Scott for making available his phase shift program.

REFERENCES

1) A. E. S. Green, Phys. Rev. $\underline{73}$ (1948) 26, 519; $\underline{75}$ (1949) 1926.

2) B. Podolsky, Phys. Rev. $\underline{62}$ (1942) 68.

3) R. P. Feynman, Phys. Rev. $\underline{76}$ (1949) 769.

4) N. Kemmer, Proc. Roy. Soc. A166 (1938) 127.

5) A. E. S. Green, Phys. Rev. $\underline{76}$ (1949) 460A and 870L.

6) G. Breit, Phys. Rev. $\underline{51}$ (1937) 248.

7) A. E. S. Green and R. D. Sharma, Phys. Rev. Letters $\underline{14}$ (1965) 380.

8) J. Hamilton and W. S. Woolcock, Rev. Mod. Phys. $\underline{35}$ (1963) 737.

9) R. A. Bryan and B. L. Scott, Phys. Rev. $\underline{135}$ (1964) 434B.

10) K. E. Lassila, M. H. Hull, Jr., H. M. Ruppel, F. A. McDonald and G. Breit, Phys. Rev. $\underline{126}$ (1962) 881.

11) T. Hamada and I. D. Johnston, Nucl. Phys. $\underline{34}$ (1962) 382.

12) A. M. Green, Nucl. Phys. $\underline{33}$ (1962) 218.

13) O. Rojo and L. M. Simmons, Phys. Rev. $\underline{125}$ (1962) 273.

14) B. L. Scott and R. A. Bryan, Bull. Am. Phys. Soc. $\underline{II-10}$ (1965) 736.

15) R. A. Arndt and M. H. MacGregor, Phys. Rev. $\underline{141}$ (1966) 873.

16) A. E. S. Green, et al., Phys. Rev. $\underline{99}$ (1955) 772, 1410; $\underline{102}$ (1956) 1325; $\underline{104}$ (1956) 1617, 1625; $\underline{111}$ (1958) 1147; $\underline{112}$ (1958) 1719; $\underline{119}$ (1960) 1031, 1043.

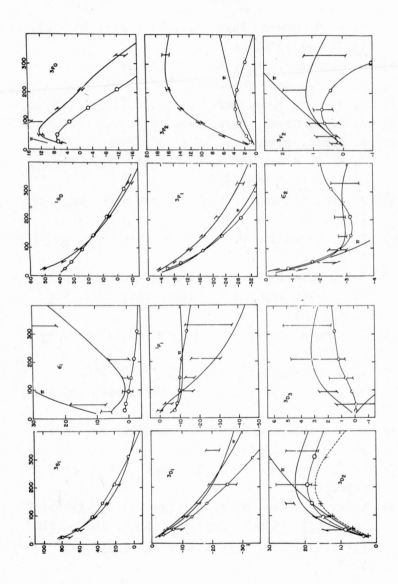

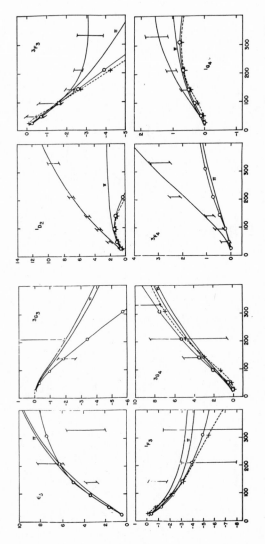

Fig. 1. Nucleon–Nucleon Phase Shifts. Solid curves represent the Arndt–MacGregor[15] energy dependent phase shift solutions for 58 parameters with $g_\pi^2 = 13$. The solid curves labeled with π are the one pion exchange phase shifts. The curves with open circles represent the Schroedinger phase shifts for the purely relativistic $\pi - 5\omega$ model with $g_\pi^2 = 14$ using adjustable constants $g_{5\omega}^2 = 3g_\pi^2$, $\Lambda_\pi = 750$ MeV and $\Lambda_{5\omega} = 1600$ MeV. The dashed curves with crosses are the Born phase shifts for several unmixed states. The phase shifts are in degrees and energy is in MeV.

SESSION B

J. B. Marion, Chairman

B1. ISOBARIC SPIN CONSERVATION AND β-DECAY*

Stewart D. Bloom

Lawrence Radiation Laboratory, Livermore, California

INTRODUCTION

The isobaric spin selection rules applying to allowed β-decay have been known for many years now[1] and since they form the basis, in large part, for what will be said here we restate them briefly:

Fermi interaction: $\Delta T = \Delta J = 0$,

No change in parity.

Gamow-Teller interaction: $\Delta T = \Delta J = \pm 1, 0$,

No change in parity,

$J = 0$ to $J = 0$ forbidden.

We have also included the spin selection rules, since they have essentially the same appearance as the isobaric spin rules, and for about the same reasons. As we now know the form of the β-interaction is (V - A),[2] where "V" stands for vector and denotes the Fermi part of the interaction, and "A" stands for axial-vector and denotes the Gamow-Teller part of the interaction. The value of the coupling constant, C_V, pertaining to the vector interaction for nuclear β-decay, has been rather precisely measured,[3]

$$C_V = (1.400 \pm 0.004) \times 10^{-49} \text{ erg-cm}^3 \qquad (1)$$

The (nuclear) Gamow-Teller coupling constant, C_A, is not quite as well-known since its constancy as a

*Work performed under the auspices of the U. S. Atomic Energy Commission.

function of atomic weight is a difficult thing to
establish due to the unreliable (or non-existent) nature
of the theoretical calculations for the Gamow-Teller
matrix element. Nonetheless it does appear clear that
C_A does exceed C_V by a definite amount,[2]

$$C_A = -C_V \ (1.19 \pm 0.03) \tag{2}$$

Because of the difficulty in predicting the value of the
Gamow-Teller matrix element as well as the less restrictive nature of the isobaric spin selection rule applying
to it the Gamow-Teller transitions give essentially no
information on isobaric spin. Quite the opposite is
true of the Fermi matrix element, which gives a great
deal of information bearing on isobaric spin, as we
shall soon see. This is already indicated in the highly
restrictive nature of the isobaric spin selection rules
in this case which is due to the particularly simple
nature of the Fermi interaction, H_V,

$$H_V = C_V \times 1 \times T_{\pm} \tag{3}$$

Where 1 is the identity operator in ordinary spin space,
$T_{\pm}$ is the raising or lowering operator in isobaric spin
space, and the lower and upper signs of $\pm$ refer to
electron decay or positron decay respectively.

The application of the Fermi isobaric spin selection rule in β-decay is surprisingly recent and this is
only partly due to the paucity of available data, at
least up until a few years ago. For instance the application to $0^+ \rightarrow 0^+$ transitions, not superallowed, was
first pointed out by Alford and French in 1961.[4] In
these cases the allowed selection rules tell us that
only the Fermi interaction can lead to β-decay. Thus,
unlike the super-allowed Fermi transitions such as 0^{14},

if there <u>is</u> a change in isobaric spin between the initial and final states we should expect a severe depression in the probability of the β-decay; in other words the ft value should be significantly higher than the allowed range, i.e. $\gtrsim 6.0$. This is tantamount to assuming that isobaric spin is well defined in both the initial and final states, and since it turns out we are specifically talking about nuclei with A > 60 (e.g., Ga^{64}) the supposition, until quite recently, has been that in this region isobaric spin is most likely very poorly defined. It is for this reason, as well as the scarcity of data, that application of the isobaric spin selection rules for β-decay had to wait so long. At any rate the breakdown of parity in β-decay not only led to our present knowledge of the (V-A) form for the β-decay interaction, but it also incidentally provided an important new experimental tool from the point of view of the investigation of the isobaric spin quantum number in nuclear physics, since it made possible the <u>experimental</u> evaluation of both the Gamow-Teller and Fermi matrix elements in mixed decays, i.e. allowed β-decays wherein both the Gamow-Teller and Fermi interactions may contribute. These decays will be of the J $\rightarrow$ J variety, J $\neq$ 0, no change in parity, and $\Delta T \approx 1$. The new experimental tool is the polarization of the residual nucleus consequent to the emission of a 100% polarized neutrino and an ~100% polarized electron in β-decay. One experimental consequence of this is the asymmetry of emission of electrons from polarized nuclei. Another one is the possibility of the observation of β-γ (CP) correlations, where CP $\equiv$ circularly-polarized. In both the first and second instances the experimental result is the determination of an asymmetry parameter, A_β for the polarized-nuclei experiments and A_γ for the $\beta-\gamma(CP)$ correlation experiments. A_β and A_γ appear in the same form of correlation expression,

$$W(\theta) = \frac{1}{4\pi}(1 + \tau \frac{v}{c} \cos\theta \ A) \tag{4}$$

where θ may represent either the angle between the direction of β-emission and direction of nuclear polarization or the angle between directions of emission of the β and circularly-polarized γ. τ represents the sense of nuclear polarization for the polarized nuclei experiments (this is over-simplified) and the sense of circular-polarization for the $\beta-\gamma(CP)$ experiments. v/c is the velocity of the detected electron in units of c. A, the asymmetry parameter, may be expressed as a function of the initial and final state spins and the ratio $y \equiv (C_V M_V)/(C_A M_A)$, where M_V and M_A are the allowed Fermi (vector) and Gamow-Teller (axial-vector) matrix elements respectively. (Actually in the $\beta-\gamma(CP)$ experiments knowledge of the multipolarity of the emitted γ-rays is required or deduced from the experimental results, as the case may be.) Thus the determination of the asymmetry parameter A plus our knowledge of the form of the β-interaction gives us one more datum besides the ft-value, namely y. It is now easy to derive a formula for $|M_V|^2$ in terms of y, ft, and C_V, where we have slightly redefined H_V by dropping C_V, so that,

$$H_V = 1 \times T_{\pm} \tag{5}$$

We absorb C_V in the measured ft-value for super-allowed Fermi transitions which now appears in the numerator of the following expression for $|M_V|^2$,

$$|M_V|^2 = \frac{(6120 \pm 20)\ y^2}{ft\ (1 + y^2)} \tag{6}$$

Thus the breakdown of parity considerably enlarges the number of cases we may investigate for evidence of isobaric spin conservation. Now we go on by expressing $|M_V|$ in a way more directly relatable to the isobaric spin conservation question. This we do below for the case of electron decay by explicitly evaluating $M_V = \langle f|H_V|i\rangle$, taking into account the possibly complex isobaric spin structure of the initial and final states $|i\rangle$ and $|f\rangle$,

$$M_V = \langle f|H_V|i\rangle = \langle f|T_-|i\rangle \tag{7a}$$

$$|i\rangle = \beta_T(T)|T,T\rangle + \beta_{T+1}(T)|T+1, T\rangle + \cdots \tag{7b}$$

$$|f\rangle = \alpha_{T-1}(T-1)|T-1,T-1\rangle$$
$$+ \alpha_T(T-1)|T, T-1\rangle + \cdots \tag{7c}$$

where the notation for the ket-vectors is, as is now usual, $|T, T_3\rangle$. The α's and β's are coefficients in the isobaric spin expansion and we shall assume $\beta_T(T)$, $\alpha_{T-1}(T-1) \approx 1$, to second order corrections.

The application of the H_V to $|i\rangle$ is exactly equivalent to the rotation of all the constituent isobaric states in charge-space, reducing T_3 by one unit and multiplying each of the ket-vectors by the appropriate numerical factor. We will consider only the effect on the state $|T,T\rangle$,

$$H_V|i\rangle \approx (2T)^{1/2}|T, T-1\rangle \tag{8}$$

127

It is now easy to see,

$$\alpha_T(T - 1) \approx M_V/(2T)^{1/2} \tag{9}$$

Substituting back in Eq. 6 we get,

$$(\alpha_T(T - 1))^2 = \frac{(6120 \pm 20) \; y^2}{ft \; (1 + y^2)(2T)} \tag{10}$$

By letting $y \to \infty$ (pure Fermi transition) this becomes the expression derived originally by Alford and French,[4]

$$(\alpha_T(T - 1))^2 = \frac{6120 \pm 20}{ft \; (2T)} \tag{11}$$

$\alpha_T(T - 1)$ is what is commonly referred to as an impurity coefficient.[1] It is important to emphasize that although the evaluation of this quantity does give us some information on isobaric spin purity we are still a very long way indeed from having any experimental idea of the degree of total isobaric spin purity of the state in question. This is because all that has been determined is the specific impurity induced in the final state via all charge-dependent elements in the nuclear Hamiltonian describing the final state nucleus by the isobaric analogue of the initial state nucleus in the final nucleus. The situation is illustrated in Fig. 1 for the case of electron decay (the case of positron decay is somewhat different). The energy separation between the two states in question is given by,

$$\Delta E = \Delta E_c - 1.29 \text{ MeV} + Q_\beta$$

where ΔE_c is the Coulomb energy difference between $|T,T>$ and $|T,T - 1>$ (see Fig. 1).[5] It is an elementary application of first-order perturbation theory to relate $\alpha_T(T - 1)$ and $< T, \; T - 1 \; |H_c| T - 1, \; T - 1 >$, where we refer to the "principal" isobaric spins in the matrix element of H_c, which is defined as the sum of all charge-dependent elements in the nuclear Hamiltonian including, of course, the Coulomb interaction,

$$< H_c > \equiv < T, \ T - 1 | H_c | T - 1, \ T - 1 > = \Delta E(\alpha_T(T - 1)).$$

$< H_c >$ is the quantity which is ultimately derivable from M_V and beyond which we cannot go (for instance to determine contributions to $< H_c >$ due to other than the Coulomb interaction) without actually inserting wave-functions into the matrix elements and evaluating them. $< H_c >$ is evidently more fundamental than α_T since that may be fortuitously large or small depending on the size of ΔE. It is also of interest in that it should be possible to relate $< H_c >$ to the Coulomb matrix elements which lead to the spreading of the isobaric analogue states.[6,7] For these reasons (and others) the discussion in the next section will be limited to the consideration of all values for $|< H_c >|$ so far deduced from the kind of β-decay results described above.

$< H_c >$ The Charge-Dependent Matrix Element

In Fig. 2 I have collected all the results leading to a definite value or at least an upper limit for $|< H_c >|$ pertaining to two particular and known levels in the same nucleus. All of these results come from β-decay using the formulas given in the last section with the single exception of the two well-known states in Be^8 at 16.6 and 16.9 MeV excitation, and insofar as I can determine no other results of this type exist in the published literature. The results represent in most instances best averages of many different experimental measurements for which detailed references may be found

129

elsewhere.[8,9,10] Only the absolute value of $|< H_c >|$
can be determined since the sign of M_A, the Gamow-Teller
matrix element, is unknown and the experimental determinations yield (for mixed transitions) only $(C_V M_V)/(C_A M_A)$.
It is not difficult to see a pattern in Fig. 2, since
the logarithmic plot of $|< H_c >|$ vs A shows quite
clearly the strong tendency of $|< H_c >|$ to have a value
somewhere between 1 keV and 40 keV. The most notable
exception is the pair of states at $\sim$16.8 MeV in Be^8,
where $|< H_c >|$ reaches the record value of 150 keV. The
recently discovered case of Ge^{72}, [11] is second largest
at 50 keV. Ga^{64}, third largest at 35 keV, also possesses the distinction of being the strongest $0^+ \to 0^+$
β-transition known (by a factor of about 10 or more)
always excepting the super-allowed β-transitions, of
course. Between 20 keV and 1 keV there now come fifteen
cases ranging in A from 24 to 240 and in isobaric spin
from 0 to 24. It seems clear that nature has set some
kind of pattern for $|< H_c >|$, though we must not forget
the thrice-measured case of Gd^{152}, [11] which apparently
exhibits the phenomenally low value for $|< H_c >|$ of
< 50 eV!

However Fig. 2 does not show the entire picture
since it tells us nothing about the ft-values for the
transitions. This could be very important because of
the possibility of 2nd forbidden transitions requiring
considerable corrections to the simple calculation of
$|< H_c >|$ given earlier. A rough way of gauging this
effect is to take the average of all known 2nd forbidden
transitions,[12]

$$<\log ft>_{2nd} = 12.0 \pm 1.0$$

and then using this to estimate the magnitude of the
interference between a "typical" 2nd forbidden matrix

element and any one of the allowed matrix elements from our tabulation. In the worst two cases, Gd^{152} and Gd^{156} (log ft = 10.6) our error in estimating $|< H_c >|$ could be as much as a factor of two in either direction. Clearly this does not seriously affect the pattern of events in Fig. 2. There is of course considerably more information[13] on the smallness of $2^{\underline{nd}}$ forbidden effects in the literature as well, to which we will not make explicit reference here. In any case it seems clear that the general trend of events in Fig. 2 is simply explained by one factor: the operation of the isobaric spin selection rule, which should be a very useful piece of information.

In a review of this brevity it is difficult to include anything like an adequate description of the various aspects of the panorama of data presented in Fig. 2 which are of interest in understanding nuclear phenomena. However one thing of possibly particular interest to this conference is the considerable theoretical effort to discover the effects of a possible charge-dependent element in the nuclear 2-body force in some of the measured values of $|< H_c >|$. So far the results are not conclusive, though they are consistent with as much as a 1% charge-dependent force.[14] The effort (both experimental and theoretical) is continuing and I believe it is quite possible a reasonably definitive answer to this elusive question may well be available within a few years.

REFERENCES

1. E.g., see W. M. MacDonald, "Nuclear Spectroscopy, Part B," F. Ajzenberg-Selove, Ed., Academic Press (New York) 1960.

2. E. J. Konopinski and M. E. Rose, "Alpha-, Beta-, and Gamma-Ray Spectroscopy," p. 1327, K. Siegbahn, Ed., (North-Holland) 1965(Amsterdam); O. Kofoed-Hansen, ibidem, p. 1517.

3. R. J. Blin-Stoyle, S. C. K. Nair, and S.Papageorgiou, Proc. Phys. Soc. $\underline{85}$ (1965) 477.

4. W. P. Alford and J. B. French, Phys. Rev. Letts. $\underline{6}$ (1961) 119.

5. J. D. Anderson, C. Wong and J. W. McClure, Phys. Rev. $\underline{138}$ (1965) B615.

6. D. Robson, Phys. Rev. $\underline{137}$ (1965) B535.

7. A. F. R. de Toledo Piza, S. Fallieros, A. H. Kerman, and R. Venter, to be published.

8. S. D. Bloom, Nuovo Cim. $\underline{32}$ (1964) 1023.

9. H. Daniel and H. Schmitt, Nucl. Phys. $\underline{65}$(1965)481.

10. P. G. Hansen, H. L. Nielsen, K. Wilsky, and J. Treheine, Phys. Letts. $\underline{19}$ (1965) 304; P.G. Hansen, private communication.

11. S. K. Bhaltacherjee, S. K. Mitra, and H. C. Padhi, Nuclear Phys. $\underline{72}$ (1965) 145.

12. C. E. Gleit, C. W. Tang, and C. D. Coryell, Nuclear Data Sheets, Nov. 1963.

13. Z. W. Grabowski, R. S. Raghovan, and R. M. Steffen, Phys. Rev. $\underline{139}$ (1965) B24.

14. R. J. Blin-Stoyle and C. T. Yap, to be published.

DISCUSSION

GARVEY, Princeton: With regard to the value shown for Be^8, I presume that the H_c was taken from the fact that the levels are 300 kilovolts apart.

BLOOM: That's right.

GARVEY: It is not clear that all of that separation is due to the Coulomb interaction.

BLOOM: That's right.

GARVEY: It is most likely due to a Thomas-Ehrman shift.

BLOOM: It could be even smaller, but how much smaller is it, does anyone know?

GARVEY: I think Don Robson knows.

ROBSON, Florida State: The Thomas-Ehrman shift, I think, is just part of the Coulomb energy shift between analogue states. However, the change from neutron to proton boundary conditions not only has diagonal matrix elements corresponding to the Thomas-Ehrman shift but also has off-diagonal matrix elements which correspond to the mixing between states of different T. This mixing produces a splitting of 300 keV for the 16.6 and 16.9 MeV levels in Be^8 as shown recently by Dalton and myself.

MARION, University of Maryland: The next speaker will also have something to say about that, I believe.

MacDONALD, University of Maryland: I wanted to ask a question of Bloom about these calculations. You said the impurity is due to the mixing of the analogue state with the state to which you are decaying.

BLOOM: That's correct.

MacDONALD: What calculations have been done to

show that?

BLOOM: Theoretical calculations?

MacDONALD: Yes. It's my impression that Blin-Stoyle's calculations do not include that mixing. That is not the mixing that he calculates. I may be mix-taken on this.

BLOOM: No, I think that is the only mixing he calculates. Moszkowski, Bouchiat and Blin-Stoyle all calculate this in the same way because that one mixes with the largest coefficient in the parent state. That's for electron decay; it's reversed for positron decay. The other mixing, the one you calculated, they didn't consider at all.

MacDONALD: Well, the mixings that he calculated also in O^{14} are not of this variety. They are always matrix elements to states which differ in the principal quantum number for one of the nucleons.

BLOOM: I guess that's right.

MacDONALD: And this was my impression, that it was also the same with these calculations, which would not be a mixing of the analogue state.

BLOOM: In this case, it's definitely a mixing of the analogue, and it's only that, it's nothing else but.

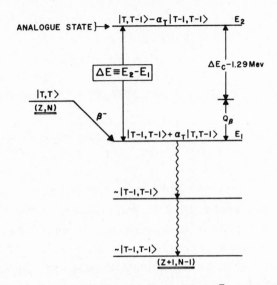

Fig. 1. Isobaric picture of β^- decay.

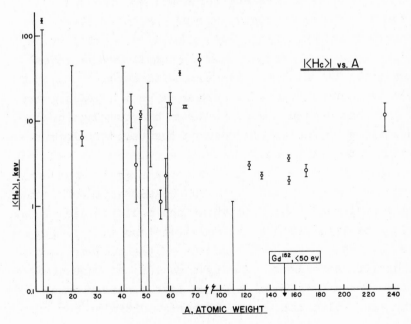

Fig. 2. $|\langle H_c \rangle|$ vs. A.

B2. ISOBARIC SPIN REACTIONS IN LIGHT NUCLEI

Cornelius P. Browne

University of Notre Dame, Notre Dame, Indiana

I.   INTRODUCTION

I shall restrict this paper to a discussion of in-
elastic scattering, (d,α) and (α,d) reactions, and Li^6-
induced reactions, on nuclei of mass number 40 or less.
The emphasis will be on even-A nuclei in the first row
of the periodic table. After some introductory remarks
about the aims of these experiments and the difficulties
involved, I shall review some of the data. Then two
experiments involving states with $J^\pi = 0^+$ will be described in some detail. Next, I shall review three
reactions in which the problems with angular momentum
are avoided and finally there will be a brief summary.

What does one hope to learn by studying (d,α)
reactions or inelastic deuteron scattering? Such reactions were first used to test the validity of selection
rules derived from the concept of charge independence of
nuclear forces.[1] The apparent conservation of isobaric
spin suggested that such reactions could be used to assign the T-value to a nuclear state and to actually
measure the charge independence of the nuclear forces
acting in a nucleus. In light nuclei the best prediction of the T-value of a given level usually comes from
the mass relations in the isobaric multiplet but reaction
data is often needed to choose between two closely

spaced levels. More recently, interest has centered on
the information to be gained on reaction mechanisms,
and on the properties of the final states. As data accumulated difficulties became apparent. The Coulomb
force destroys conservation of isobaric spin. In a
reaction this "mixing" of states of different T-value
may occur in the initial state, the compound nuclear
state, and the final state. One of the problems is to
separate these three effects. Another problem is how to
compare cross sections in order to measure the "forbiddeness" of a reaction. One would of course like to
compare the observed yield with the yield in the absence
of a selection rule. As this is impossible, people have
had recourse to several other comparisons.

The cross section of the forbidden reaction may be
compared with those of allowed reactions leading to
neighboring states, or to the cross section of another
reaction where no isobaric spin selection rule operates.
The trouble is, of course, that other effects beside
isobaric spin influence the yields. The effect of angular momentum was ignored for some years until it was
pointed out[2] that in all (d,α) reactions previously
studied, both initial and final states had $J^{\pi} = 0^{+}$.
This fact and not the operation of the isobaric spin
selection rule accounts for a large part of the observed
reduction of yield.

Another factor to be considered in comparing cross
sections of forbidden and allowed reactions is the reaction mechanism. It has generally been assumed that in a
direct reaction isobaric spin would be strictly conserved and only the mixing in the initial and final
states would contribute to a forbidden yield. If an appreciable part of the allowed reaction goes by a direct

process, the ratio of forbidden to allowed yields cannot
be taken as a measure of mixing of isobaric spins in the
compound nucleus.

I shall discuss attempts to correct for these effects later. It has been said that reactions are a poor
way to measure the isobaric spin purity of a nuclear
state. We shall see some evidence for this and then see
what has been measured.

II. SURVEY OF REACTION MEASUREMENTS

One can measure the relative cross sections for
inelastic scattering of deuterons and alpha particles
(T = 0) from T = 0 nuclei having T = 1 and T = 0 final
states. If isobaric spin is conserved the T = 1 state
will not be excited. Bombarding energies and observation angles at which inelastic scattering from T = 1
levels has been sought are shown in the first three
figures. Figure 1 shows the very meager data on inelastic deuteron scattering from Li^6 and B^{10}. A solid
horizontal line would represent an angular distribution
and thus a total cross section. Deuterons were observed
from Li^6 at two angles at 6.35 MeV,[3] one angle at
7.5 MeV[4] and one angle at 14.8 MeV.[5] From B^{10} deuterons have been measured[6] at three energies at 90°,
two angles at 10.0 MeV and one angle at 10.6 MeV,[7] and
two angles at 11.4 MeV.[8] Figure 2 shows energies and
observation angles for $N^{14}(d,d')N^{14*}$. At 90°, two bombarding energies have been used.[6] The solid dots in
this figure correspond to work now being done by our
group using the Argonne tandem accelerator.[9] A measurement that is relevant to the latter work and illustrates the problem of comparing yields of forbidden and
allowed groups is that of Oda, et al.[10] on inelastic

proton scattering from N^{14}. Here where there should be no inhibition from the isobaric spin selection rule, the cross section to the T = 1 level is only 5.5% and 15% of that to the neighboring T = 0 level, at energies of 10.5 and 14.1 MeV respectively. Similar results were obtained at 9.51 MeV. [11] One attempt was made to observe excitation of the T = 1 state in C^{12} with inelastic deuteron scattering. [12]

Some of the results of the above measurements are shown in Table I. Here the reaction, bombarding energy, excitation energy in the compound nucleus (CN) excitation energy of the T = 1 level, excitation energy of the comparison T = 0 level, ratio of cross sections, and references are given. In two cases a ratio to the cross section for proton scattering is shown. One sees only upper limits, albeit often quite low ones, at a rather random scattering of energies and angles. Much more data would be required to draw any significant conclusions. The work in progress[9] should give actual cross sections for $N^{14}(d,d')N^{14*}$ over a range of energies.

Energies and angles used for inelastic alpha scattering are displayed in Fig. 3. Using an alpha energy of 31.5 MeV, Waters[13] set an upper limit for the inelastic group from the first T = 1 level of Li^6, of 4% of the cross section to the 3.57 MeV (T = 0) level. For N^{14} a limit of 6% was set for the ratio of differential cross sections of the 2.31 MeV and 3.95 MeV levels. At 19.2 MeV and 72.5° Ploughe[14] set a limit of 5%. Elsewhere in these proceedings Chesterfield and Spicer* report on yield curves taken between 10 and 13 MeV at three angles. At 21.5 MeV and three angles Miller, et al.[15] could set a limit for the ratio of 5%. It is

*Paper S10.

pointed out[14] that this reaction is also "ℓ-forbidden." Harvey , et al.[16] using 65 MeV alphas found strong excitation of one or more levels near 13 MeV in O^{16}. There are four T = 1 levels in this region but there is also undoubtedly a wide T = 0 level underlying these[17] and with the low resolution available, these would not be separated. Here again too few data are available for meaningful conclusions.

We now turn to (d,α) reactions. Perhaps the most extensively studied reaction is $O^{16}(d,\alpha)N^{14}$, measurements on which are displayed in Fig. 4. This reaction was the first used to study isobaric spin selection rule violation over a range of energies and angles.[18] Angular distributions have been taken at 3.94 MeV,[19] 7.0 MeV,[18] 14.7 MeV,[20] 15.0 MeV,[21] 19.0 MeV,[22] and 24 MeV.[23] Four energies were used[24] at 35°. Previous data on this reaction are summarized in Table II. A report of new work was submitted to this conference by S. Messelt.* The table shows that for excitation energies in the compound nucleus ranging from 11.0 to 28.9 MeV the cross section to the T = 1 level is less than 5% of that to the T = 0 ground state. This ratio appears to decrease with increasing energy. If this reduction in cross section was the result of isobaric spin conservation the few percent violation could be understood in terms of small impurities in initial and final states, plus some isobaric spin mixing in the compound nucleus. That no such conclusion can be drawn will be seen in the next section.

Many other (d,α) reactions have been examined. A number of these including $C^{12}(d,\alpha)B^{10}$, $Mg^{24}(d,\alpha)Na^{22}$, $Si^{28}(d,\alpha)Al^{26}$, $S^{32}(d,\alpha)P^{30}$ and $Ca^{40}(d,\alpha)K^{38}$ involve

---

*Paper S20.

$J\pi = 0^+$ levels as initial and final states. New work on $Si^{28}(d,\alpha)Al^{26}$ is presented in these proceedings by Bizzeti and Bizzeti-Sona.* Two of these reactions and three other reactions will be discussed in more detail below.

The $C^{12}(\alpha,d)N^{14}$ reaction was studied by Harvey and Cerny[25] and a limit for the T = 1 state of 3% of the ground state was set. Here again we have two $J^\pi = 0^+$ levels and furthermore some of the known T = 0 states were not excited. Again in the $N^{14}(\alpha,d)O^{16}$ reaction, no T = 1 levels were seen[26] but some T = 0 levels were also not seen, so little was learned about isobaric spin effects.

A good deal of interesting work has been done with reactions induced by Li^6 ions. Some of the regions of energy and angles covered are shown in Fig. 5. Morrison[27] bombarded Li^6 and Li^7 with 2.1 MeV Li^6 and observed deuterons and tritons respectively leading to the first T = 1 state in B^{10}. In both reactions the yield to the $J^\pi = 0^+$, T = 1 state is very low. A cluster model interpretation of the isobaric spin selection rule in this case has been proposed.[27] These same reactions were run[28] at 6 MeV and 30° where the group to the T = 1 level was not seen. Angular distributions of the $C^{12}(Li^6,\alpha)N^{14}$ reaction leading to the first T = 1 state, the second excited state (T = 0) and the ground state were observed[29] at 3.8 and 4.0 MeV. A yield ratio of 1 to 29 was found at 4 MeV. All the other data indicated in Fig. 5 were obtained by the group at the State University of Iowa.[30-33]

Dr. Carlson has summarized these results[34] by stating that isobaric spin appears to be generally a

---

*Paper S16.

good quantum number for Li^6 induced reactions. In the $B^{10}(Li^6,\alpha)C^{12*}$ reaction the cross section to the 15.1 MeV, T = 1 state is about 3% of that to the 12.7 MeV, T = 0 state. In a series of measurements of Li + B reactions, no violations of isobaric spin of larger than a few percent were seen. The T = 1 states in N^{14} at 2.31, 8.06, 8.63, 8.72, 9.17, and 9.51 MeV were not seen with the $B^{10}(Li^6,d)N^{14}$ reaction but were seen with the $B^{10}(Li^7,t)N^{14}$ reaction which is allowed by the isobaric spin selection rule. The $C^{12}(Li^6,\alpha)N^{14}$ (2.31) cross section was measured[31] from 3.8 MeV to 5.5 MeV. The cross section at 5.5 MeV is about 40% of that at 4.5 MeV, whereas the cross sections for the ground state and the 3.95 MeV state increase 35% and 80% respectively over this range. At the higher energy the forbidden yield is about 0.4% of that to the 3.95 MeV state. The excitation energy in F^{18} varies from 15.7 to 16.9 MeV and the decrease in forbidden yield probably reflects the decreased mixing of isobaric spins. A report on the $Li^6(Li^6,\alpha)Be^8$ reaction leading to the 16.6 and 16.9 MeV states is to be given by M. D. Mancusi* at this conference. These results are consistent with results obtained with the $B^{10}(d,\alpha)Be^8$ reaction which will be discussed below.

III.   PROBLEM OF ANGULAR MOMENTUM EFFECTS

Let us examine the problem of other effects which influence the cross section of reactions forbidden by isobaric spin. Two experiments in which corrections were made for angular momentum effects will be discussed. In the first of these, the relative cross section expected for states of different angular momentum was

*Paper S30.

142

calculated using the statistical theory of the compound
nucleus. Jänecke[35] studied the $Ca^{40}(d,\alpha)K^{38}$ reaction
with 7.7 MeV deuterons at observation angles between 10°
and 170° for the T = 0 levels and 10° to 90° for the
first T = 1 level. The excitation energy in the compound nucleus Sc^{42} is 18.2 MeV. Figure 1 in Ref. 35
shows data obtained at 50°. The T = 1 level is seen to
be very weakly excited compared to T = 0 levels on
either side. At first sight a strong inhibition arising
from the isobaric spin selection rule is suggested.
Jänecke proceeds to show, however, that there is no inhibition whatever in the part of the reaction proceeding
via compound nucleus (CN) information. He used Hauser-
Feshbach theory and alpha particle penetrabilities to
calculate the expected cross section ratios for final
states with different spin and parity. It is assumed
that in this region of the CN there are many wide, overlapping levels and hence this theory applies. Figure 6
of Ref. 35 shows the resulting relative cross sections
expected for the low lying levels of K^{38}. Now it is
assumed that the isobaric spin selection rule holds rig-
orously for direct interaction mechanisms (DI) and hence
the observed yield to the T = 1 state is all by CN.
Using the observed yield to normalize the point for the
0^+ level in the Fig., the expected cross sections for CN
formation of the other levels in the absence of any isobaric spin selection rule, are found. The results agree
closely with the minima in the measured angular distributions for the T = 0 levels. Destructive interference
between CN and DI amplitudes is considered unlikely so
the remaining cross section to the T = 0 levels is ascribed to DI. Thus the results are consistent with a
complete mixing of isobaric spin in the CN and a large

contribution of DI to the T = 0 cross sections, but none
to the T = 1 cross section. Isobaric spin impurities
of initial and final states are quite reasonably neglected. We will see in the next example that neither
the complete inhibition for DI nor complete lack of inhibition for CN holds in general. It would be instruc-
tive to measure yield curves for the $Ca^{40}(d,\alpha)K^{38}$
reaction. A second example is a recent, very thorough
investigation[36] of the $C^{12}(d,\alpha)B^{10}$ reaction which was
carried out at the Argonne Laboratory. Here differential and total cross sections of the isobaric spin
forbidden reaction to the first T = 1 state ($J^{\pi} = 0^+$)
are compared with the cross sections of the allowed
reactions to the ground state ($J^{\pi} = 3^+$), first excited
state ($J^{\pi} = 1^+$) and third excited state ($J^{\pi} = 1^+$). The
intensity of the T = 1 group is generally less than 1%
of the intensity of the T = 0 groups. After factors for
the angular momentum difference, calculated by use of
Hauser-Feshbach theory are applied, the yield at a deuteron energy of 9 MeV, to the T = 1 level is about 10%
of that to the T = 0 levels; at 11 MeV it is 1% to 2%.
The range of CN excitation energies is 18-19.7 MeV.
Again the transition from CN to DI appears and the forbidden yield drops as excitation energy in the CN rises.
Table I of Ref. 36 summarizes the cross section ratios
found for the forbidden to ground state, first excited
state, and third excited state. Yield curves for the
four groups are shown in Fig. 10 of Ref. 36. Even after
correcting for angular momentum, there appears to be a
strong inhibition of the reaction to the T = 1 level.
At the lower end of the energy range the contribution of
the compound nucleus is surely important. Fluctuations
are seen in the yield curves of the allowed groups and

the angular distributions do not show strong forward peaking. At about 11.5 MeV an interesting effect appears. The total cross section of the forbidden group rises. Figure 5 in Ref. 36 shows the differential cross section of the forbidden group as a function of energy at several angles. A very strong forward peak (20-fold increases at 20°) is seen to occur above 11.4 MeV. The authors tentatively conclude that the reaction to the T = 1 state proceeds through a surface reaction which includes the production of the observed mixing. Possible mechanisms suggested are, Coulomb excitation during the emission of alpha particles to an allowed state, and polarization of the incoming deuteron in the Coulomb field of the target nucleus.[2]

IV. ATTEMPTS TO AVOID ANGULAR MOMENTUM EFFECTS

We have investigated three (d,α) reactions where 0^+ levels are not involved. The results are quite divergent.

The total cross section of the $N^{14}(d,\alpha)C^{12}$ (1^+, T = 1) reaction was measured[37] from 3 MeV to 12 MeV. Angular distributions to this state and to the 16.11 MeV, 2^+, T = 1 state were measured at 7.18 MeV. Angular distributions from several T = 0 levels were measured to investigate the reaction mechanism.[38] Cross section ratios were compared with those measured for the $B^{10}(He^3,p)C^{12}$ reaction.[39] For the 15.11 MeV level which is known[40] to be quite pure T = 1, the cross section is 3% of that to the 12.71 MeV, 2^+, T = 0 level at 7.18 MeV. How much DI occurs? Figure 7 of Ref. 38 shows the sum of angular distributions for a number of T = 0 states at 4 MeV and at 7.2 MeV. Figure 9 of Ref. 37 shows the yield curve for the 15.11 MeV

145

level. Similar conclusions to those given above for $C^{12}(d,\alpha)B^{10}$ may be drawn. The symmetry of the summed angular distributions and the structure in the yield curve argues for predominant CN mechanism. Some DI appears as the bombarding energy goes above 7 MeV. Above this the structure in the forbidden yield decreases and the cross section decreases. In the region of strong CN reaction and with no angular momentum factor, the forbidden to allowed ratio is small (3%), indicating small mixing in the CN at these excitation energies (23-31 MeV).

The second case to be discussed is $B^{10}(d,\alpha)Be^{8}$. The 16.62 and 16.92 MeV levels, one of which was at first assumed to have T = 0 and the other T = 1, are about equally excited at 3.9 MeV, 4.0 MeV[41] and 7.5 MeV.[42] Much work has been done on these two levels. Stephenson and Marion * point out elsewhere in these proceedings that 16 different reactions have now provided 31 separate data. The picture emerging is that these two states may be represented as nearly equal mixtures of T = 0 and T = 1 wave functions. In the absence of Coulomb forces they would be degenerate. An interesting prediction is that if only the T = 0 part of this wave function is excited, the shape of the observed alpha groups should show an interference effect. Figure 6 shows data taken recently by Erskine and myself with 12 MeV deuterons and at 30°. The curve through the points is calculated from the expression

$$f = \left| \frac{a_1}{Q-Q_1+\dfrac{i\Gamma_1}{2}} + \frac{a_2}{Q-Q_2+\dfrac{i\Gamma_2}{2}} \right|^2.$$

The arbitrary amplitudes a_1 and a_2, the Q_1 and Q_2 and

---

*Paper S14.

Γ_1 and Γ_2 were adjusted for best fit. The Q-values and widths are close to those obtained earlier with other reactions but a definite shift in the peak maxima and widths at half maximum is seen. This figure also shows the 17.64 MeV (T = 1) and 18.15 MeV (T = 0) levels, a pair of 1^+ levels. The same T-impurity does not occur here. This is true at 7.5 MeV also.[42] Another interesting pair of levels with $J^\pi = 3^+$ and T = 0 or 1 occurs near 19 MeV. The cross sections of the (d,α) reaction to these levels is being measured. Figure 7 shows the calculated interference pattern compared to the shape for no interference. Attempts to fit the data with two such single level resonance curves is not successful, and a change of sign between terms in the above formula makes the fit far worse.

Finally I would like to mention the $Ne^{20}(d,\alpha)F^{18}$ reaction leading to the second T = 1 state in $F^{18}(J^\pi=2^+)$. The alpha group's intensity is 1/4 to 1/2 of that of groups leading to neighboring T = 0 states.[43] The close lying state is now known[44] to have a different spin and the closest state of possibly the same spin is 0.29 MeV away. The question of a large final state impurity as in Be^8 remains open.

Thus in these reactions where angular momentum is not a factor we have three cases $C^{12}(15.11)$, $C^{12}(16.11)$, $Be^8(17.64)$ of T = 1 states whose excitation by (d,α) reaction is strongly inhibited and two cases $Be^8(16.2)$, $F^{18}(3.13)$ where there is little or no inhibition.

V.   SUMMARY

We have seen that (d,α) reactions can be analyzed to disentangle isobaric spin effects from angular momentum, penetrability, and to some extent, reaction mechanism effects. In general as bombarding energy increases the DI becomes more important and the isobaric spin is more nearly conserved. There is evidence that in the region where CN predominates mixing of isobaric spin in this CN varies from moderate to strong. The effect of shorter lifetime of the CN at higher energy reducing mixing is observed. There is some evidence for DI leading to an isobaric-spin forbidden reaction. In at least one case the final state is found to have an undefined T-value. Nevertheless the concept of isobaric spin has been helpful in understanding the properties of these states. The Be^8 nucleus presents a very interesting problem with three pairs of close spaced levels of the same J^π but supposedly different T. There are good questions involving F^{18} and probably several more of the light nuclei and in most cases observations should be extended over wider energy ranges.

In general isobaric spin is well conserved in reactions induced by Li^6. It is thought that in inelastic reactions proceeding mainly by DI, isobaric spin should be well conserved. The data is very meager; however, some work is in progress.

I am especially indebted to Dr. R. R. Carlson for his summary of the work with Li^6 reactions, and to Dr. L. Meyer-Schützmeister for permission to quote the $C^{12}(d,\alpha)B^{10}$ results prior to publication.

REFERENCES

1) C. P. Browne, C. K. Bockelman, W. W. Buechner, and
A. Sperduto, Phys. Rev. 90 (1953) 340A.

2) Y. Hashimoto and W. P. Alford, Phys. Rev. 116
(1959) 981.

3) G. Johnson, H. L. Joliot and P. Roussel, J. Phys.
(France) 26 (1965) 161.

4) C. P. Browne and C. K. Bockelman, Phys. Rev. 105
(1957) 1301.

5) E. W. Hamburger and J. R. Cameron, Phys. Rev. 117
(1960) 781.

6) C. K. Bockelman, C. P. Browne, W. W. Buechner, and
A. Sperduto, Phys. Rev. 92 (1953) 665.

7) B. H. Armitage and R. E. Meads, Nuclear Phys. 33
(1962) 494.

8) B. H. Armitage and R. E. Meads, Phys. Letts. 8
(1964) 346.

9) Cornelius P. Browne (to be published).

10) Y. Oda, M. Takeda, N. Takano, T. Yamazaki, C. Hu,
K. Kikuchi, S. Kobayashi, K. Matsuda and Y. Nagahara,
J. Phys. Soc. (Japan) 15 (1960) 760.

11) R. G. Freemantle, D. J. Prowse, A. Hossain, and
J. Rotblat, Phys. Rev. 96 (1954) 1270.

12) C. N. Waddell, H. E. Adelson, B. J. Moyer, and
H. C. Shaw, Bull. Am. Phys. Soc. 2 (1957) 181.

13) H. J. Watters, Phys. Rev. 103 (1956) 1763.

14) W. D. Ploughe, Phys. Rev. 122 (1961) 1232.

15) D. W. Miller, B. M. Carmichael, U. C. Gupta,
V. K. Rasmussen, and M. B. Sampson, Phys. Rev. 101
(1956) 740.

16) B. G. Harvey, E. Rivet, A. Springer, J. R. Meriwether,
W. B. Jones, J. H. Elliot, and P. Darriulat, Nuclear
Phys. 52 (1964) 465.

17) G. E. Mitchell, E. B. Carter and R. H. Davis, Phys. Rev. 133 (1964) B1434; J. D. Larson and R. H. Spear, Nucl. Phys. 56 (1964) 497; I. Mitchell and T. Ophel Congres Inter. de Physique Nucleaire, Vol. 2 (Paris 1964) p. 37.

18) Cornelius P. Browne, Phys. Rev. 104 (1956) 1598.

19) J. Jastrzebski, F. Picard, J. P. Schapira, and J. L. Picou, Nucl. Phys. 40 (1963) 400.

20) T. Yanabu, J. Phys. Soc. (Japan) 16 (1961) 2118.

21) F. Pellegrini, Nucl. Phys. 24 (1961) 372.

22) R. G. Freemantle, W. M. Gibson, D. J. Prowse, and J. Rotblat, Phys. Rev. 92 (1953) 1268.

23) J. Cerny, R. H. Pehl, E. Rivet, and B. G. Harvey, Phys. Letts. 7 (1963) 67.

24) A. W. Dalton, S. Hinds, and G. Parry, Proc. Phys. Soc. A71 (1958) 252.

25) B. Harvey and J. Cerny , Phys. Rev. 120 (1960) 2162.

26) J. Cerny, B. G. Harvey and R. H. Pehl, Nucl. Phys. 29 (1962) 120.

27) G. C. Morrison, Phys. Rev. Letts. 5 (1960) 565.

28) D. A. Bromley, K. Nagatani, L. C. Northcliffe, R. Ollerhead and A. R. Quinton, Rutherford Jubilee Conference, Manchester, J. B. Birks, Ed., Academic Press, New York (1961),p. 597.

29) R. K. Hobbie and F. F. Forbes, Phys. Rev. 126 (1962) 2137.

30) R. R. Carlson and K. G. Kibler, State Univ. of Iowa SUI 64-21 (1964).

31) R. R. Carlson and D. W. Heikenen, Phys. Letts. 17 (1965) 305.

32) R. R. Carlson and M. Throop, Phys. Rev. 136 (1964) B630.

33) R. L. McGrath, Phys. Rev. (to be published).

34) R. R. Carlson, private communication.

35) J. Jänecke, Nucl. Phys. <u>48</u> (1963) 129.

36) L. Meyer-Schützmeister, D. von Ehrenstein, and R. G. Allas (to be published).

37) C. P. Browne, W. A. Schier, and I. F. Wright, Nucl. Phys. <u>66</u> (1965) 49.

38) W. A. Schier and C. P. Browne, Phys. Rev. <u>138</u> (1965) B857.

39) C. P. Browne, W. E. Dorenbusch, and J. R. Erskine, Phys. Rev. <u>125</u> (1962) 992.

40) E. L. Garwin, Phys. Rev. <u>114</u> (1959) 143; G. L. Miller, R. E. Pixley, and R. E. Segel, Proc. Roy. Soc. <u>259</u> (1960) 275.

41) J. R. Erskine and C. P. Browne, Phys. Rev. <u>123</u> (1961) 958.

42) C. P. Browne and J. R. Erskine, Phys. Rev. (to be published).

43) G. M. Matous and C. P. Browne, Phys. Rev. <u>136</u> (1964) B399.

44) P. R. Chagnon, Nucl. Phys. (to be published); A. R. Poletti and E. K. Warburton, Phys. Rev. <u>137</u> (1965) B595.

TABLE I. Some Ratios of Cross Sections of Forbidden and Allowed Inelastic Scattering.

Reaction	E_d (MeV)	E_x^{CN} (MeV)	θ (deg)	$T = 1$ level	$T = 0$ level	$\sigma_{T=1}/\sigma_{T=0}$	$\sigma_{d,d'}/\sigma_{p,p'}$	Ref.
$Li^6(d,d')Li^6$	6.35	27.0	60	3.56	2.18	<2		Jo 65
$Li^6(d,d')Li^6$	14.8	33.4	25	3.56	2.18	<0.16		Ha 60
$B^{10}(d,d')B^{10}$	11.4	34.7	45, 60	7.48			0.02	Ar 64
$B^{10}(d,d')B^{10}$	10.0	33.5	60,90,120	5.16	"all"	<0.01		Ar 62
$B^{10}(d,d')B^{10}$	7.0	31.0	90	1.74	0.72	<0.017	<0.15	Bo 53
$N^{14}(d,d')$	10.94	30.3	20,50,80, 110	2.31	3.94	<0.015		Br 66

Note: Reference labels in the last column correspond to the labels in Figs. 1 and 2. Br 66 corresponds to text Ref. 9.

152

TABLE II. Some Ratios of Cross Sections of the $O^{16}(d,\alpha)N^{14}$ (G. S.) to the $O^{16}(d,\alpha)N^{14}$ (2.3, T = 1) Reactions.

E_d (MeV)	E_x in F^{18} (MeV)	Angular Range (deg.)	$\sigma_{T=1}/\sigma_{T=0}$	Ref.
3.9	11.0	20 - 170	~0.05	Ja 63
5.5 - 7.5	12.4 - 14.2	30		Br 56
7.1	13.8	18 - 138		Br 56
14.7	20.6	20 - 80	0.01 - 0.03	Ya 61
15.0	20.9	18 - 100	<0.03	Pe 61
19.0	24.4	20 - 160	<0.038	Fr 53
24.0	28.9	9 - 90	<0.007	Ce 63

Note: Reference labels in the last column correspond to labels in Fig. 4.

DISCUSSION

MARION, University of Maryland: I'd like to know the ratio from the spectrum that you showed of the yields to the 17.6 and 18.1 MeV states.

BROWNE: Yes, sorry I didn't get a chance to cover that. The ratio, unfortunately, is somewhat angle dependent. In general, it runs something like 1.2 to 1.3

I wanted to also mention another paper that's been presented at the meeting by Mancusi[*] on Li^6 on Li^6 to the same two states, and that same intensity ratio is observed there, and presumably again, that should excite the $T = 0$ part so it's completely consistent with the result. One of the reasons I say this is crude is the fact that the ratio does change with angle in order to get this fit.

BLOOM, Livermore: I just wanted to make a remark concerning the question of Garvey. I am talking about the separation of two states in Be^8 at 16.8 MeV, and I just assume that those states started with zero separation, and then I turn on the Coulomb interaction to get a separation of 150 keV as discussed by many people. Garvey suggested maybe I should have started with a larger separation. I do not believe that that question is at all related to what you are discussing.

BROWNE: What I wanted to say here is that we can observe the experimental spacing between the two alpha groups. Now, the question is how is this related to the actual energies of the two states?

BLOOM: Well, it's very closely related, I agree.

---

[*] See paper S30, (no manuscript submitted).

BROWNE: Well, it's no longer obvious when the groups aren't symmetrical, you see. If you have some interference effect going on, then what you want to get out of it is not necessarily what one would read directly from the data.

Now, there is the second question then, as I understand it, how is that related to what the states' separation might be in the absence of the Coulomb force?

BLOOM: That's right.

BROWNE: I was hoping that people like Robson and maybe Kurath and some others would talk about that.

DAEHNICK, University of Pittsburgh: I'd like to ask you about one of the comments you made concerning (d,α) reactions where they saw the very steep forward peaking. I don't recall whether you showed large angle data and close to 180° for this particular reaction. Were they measured?

BROWNE: Let's see, I saw Allas here a while ago. It's his data.

ALLAS, USN Research Lab, Wash., D. C.: No.

DAEHNICK: Well, in that case, unless you can show that you don't have any backward peaking, it is not at all safe to say that occasional forward peaking at a given energy proves that a direct reaction is taking place.

The conclusion which you yourself called tentative is certainly open to much doubt. I personally wouldn't think that has anything to do with the direct reaction.

BROWNE: Yes, my impression was that they had measured over a wide enough angular range to make it fairly clear that the yield had become quite asymmetric, that there was, in fact, quite a forward peak. Now, that was the way I read that paper.

ANON: The data on the slide went back to 120°.

BROWNE: Anyway, that is a point that certainly ought to be clarified in experiment before any conclusion is drawn.

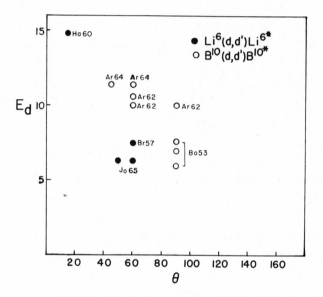

Fig. 1. Display of bombarding energies and observation angles at which inelastic deuteron scattering from $T = 1$ states in Li^6 and B^{10} has been measured. Point labels correspond to text references as follows: Jo 65, Ref. 3; Br 57, Ref. 4; Ha 60, Ref. 5; Bo 53, Ref. 6; Ar 62, Ref. 7; Ar 64, Ref. 8.

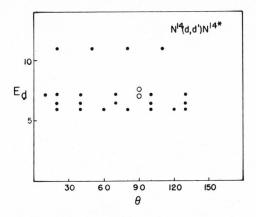

Fig. 2.   Energies and angles at which inelastic deuteron scattering from the first T = 1 state in N^{14} has been measured.   The open circles correspond to text Ref. 6, the solid dots to text Ref. 9.

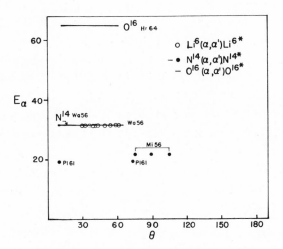

Fig. 3.   Energies and angles at which inelastic alpha particle scattering to T = 1 states has been sought. Labels correspond to text references as follows: Wa 56, Ref. 13; Pl 61, Ref. 14; Mi 56, Ref. 15; Hr 64, Ref. 16.

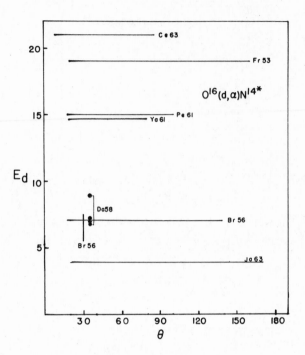

Fig. 4. Energies and angles at which the $O^{16}(d,\alpha)N^{14}$ (T = 1) reaction has been studied. Horizontal lines indicate the range of angles over which measurements were made at the indicated energy. Labels correspond to text references as follows: Ja 63, Ref. 19; Br 56, Ref. 18; Da 58, Ref. 24; Ya 61, Ref. 20; Pe 61, Ref. 21; Fr 53, Ref. 22; Ce 63, Ref. 23.

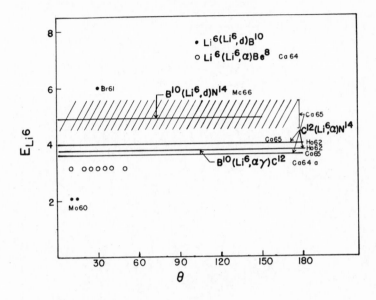

Fig. 5.   Energies and angles at which reactions induced by Li^6 ions and leading to T = 1 states in the
residual nucleus have been measured.   Horizontal lines
indicate energies at which complete angular distributions
were taken.   The cross hatched area indicates a range of
energies over which complete angular distributions were
taken.   Labels correspond to text references as follows:
Mo 60, Ref. 27; Ca 64, Ref. 30; Ca 64a, Ref. 32; Ca 65,
Ref. 31; Mc 66, Ref. 33; Br 61, Ref. 28; Ho 62, Ref. 29.

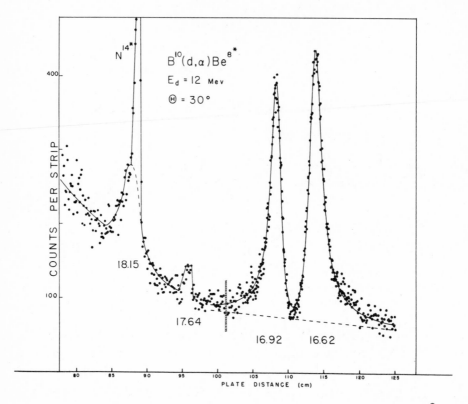

Fig. 6. Alpha particle spectrum from the $B^{10}(d,\alpha)Be^8$ reaction obtained at 12 MeV and 30°. The curve through the 16.6 and 16.9 MeV groups is calculated from the formula given in the text. Background is indicated by the dashed curve. The curve through the higher excitation region was drawn by eye.

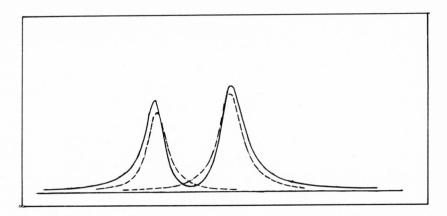

Fig. 7. Curves calculated for the 16.6 and 16.9 MeV states of Be^8 with and without an interference term. The solid curve is the same as that shown in Fig. 6. The dotted curve is the best fit using two single level resonance equations.

B3. ANALOGUE STATES OBSERVED
VIA DELAYED PROTON EMISSION[+]

R. McPherson

Chemistry Department, Brookhaven National Laboratory,
Upton, New York

To examine the validity of the isobaric mass
formula $M = a + bT_z + cT_z^2$, it was long ago suggested
that a search be made for the masses of missing members of T = 3/2 quadruplets among the light elements.[1,2]
The observation of β-delayed proton emission[3] allowed
identification of the most neutron deficient, i.e. T_z =
-3/2, member of several T = 3/2 multiplets and verified
that they were particle stable. Recently, the Q-values
for stripping and pickup reactions have allowed mass
determinations for all missing members of the mass 9,13
and 37,T = 3/2 quadruplets.[4,5] Delayed proton experiments have so far allowed identification of the
T_z =-3/2 delayed proton precursors C^9, O^{13}, Ne^{17}, Mg^{21},
Si^{25}, S^{29}, Ar^{33}, Ca^{37}, and Ti^{41}.[6-8] While the delayed
proton experiments have not been successful for direct
determination of the masses of these nuclides, the
observation of proton emission following superallowed
beta decay has allowed easy identification of the analogue states in many of the beta-decay daughters. It
is the purpose of this paper to outline the method and
collect some of the information derived by these

[+]Work performed under the auspices of the U. S. Atomic
Energy Commission.

observations. The work is largely due to the groups at McGill University and at Brookhaven. The author has participated in some of the work of both groups.

Figure 1 is a schematic level diagram showing the states involved in the decay chain. The observed de-layed proton emitters form a sequence with mass number of the form $A = 4n + 1$. The beta-decay parents are characterized by large available beta-decay energies (11 to 18 MeV) and the daughters have low proton separation energies (0.5 to 3 MeV). In general, beta decays will populate a number of the virtual excited states of the daughters. Proton emission from a virtual state may leave the final nucleus in its ground state or one of its excited states. Since the Coulomb energy difference between the analogue states is great-er than the neutron-proton mass difference, superallow-ed beta decay of the parents is possible. Proton decay of the $T = 3/2$ analogue state in the daughter, as shown in the figure, is forbidden if T is a strict quantum number. If such was the case, the state would decay by an electromagnetic transition. However, only small admixtures of isobaric spin $T = 1/2$ in the ana-logue state or $T = 1$ in the final state are necessary to provide sufficient particle width to compete success-fully with gamma decay. It was pointed out by Goldanskii [9] that for the heaviest members of the ob-served sequence, proton emission following the super-allowed beta transition would be the predominant mode of decay.

The $T_z = -3/2$ nuclides have been produced by pro-ton induced reactions and $(He^3, 2n)$ reactions on appro-priate targets. The delayed protons are observed as a proton activity decaying with the half life of the beta-decay parent. Assuming that gamma competition is negligible, the relative intensities of proton transitions reflect the relative ft values of the preceding beta transitions. Figure 2 shows a spectrum of delayed protons following the beta decay of Si^{25}.[10] This spectrum is not typical of recent, good resolution spectra but was the earliest evidence of $T = 3/2$ superallowed beta decay and shows clearly the pertinent features. The peaks of 4.89 and 3.46 MeV are due primarily to proton transitions to the ground and first excited state of Mg^{24} from a level in Al^{25} at 7.14 MeV which has been observed in resonant proton scattering. The peaks at 5.62 and 4.28 MeV represent corresponding transitions from the analogue state at 7.90 MeV. Based on relative proton intensities, the difference in log ft values for beta decay to the two Al^{25} levels amounts to 1 unit. The 7.14-MeV level would be expected to follow allowed (log ft 4 to 5) beta decay. The beta transition to the 7.90 MeV level would then have a log ft between 3 and 4.

With increasing mass number, the energy available for the superallowed decay becomes greater and proton transitions from the analogue states dominate the decay. The results are summarized in Fig. 3 and Table I. The data for mass 9 and 13 are taken from references 4 and 5 and are included for comparison. The beta-decay energies of the remaining parents are those estimated using the energy separation of $T = 1/2$ ground states in the isobaric mass formula for $T = 3/2$ states.[9,11] The superallowed beta decay of C^9 and O^{13} have not been observed and has been observed for Ne^{17} only with difficulty.[7] The excitation energies of the analogue states are listed in the last column of the table.

164

Hardy and Margolis[12] pointed out that the calculated superallowed log ft's are relatively insensitive to the model-dependent Gamow-Teller matrix elements. The square of the Fermi matrix element is 3
and squares of Gamow-Teller matrix elements calculated
from Nilsson model wave functions ranged from 0.08 to
0.3. The log ft's thus varied between 3.26 and 3.30.
The superallowed log ft's for members of the sequence
from Mg^{21} to Ca^{37} have been indirectly measured by
Hardy, et al.[13] The method adopted was production of
more than one delayed proton precursor under identical
conditions in reactions where the production cross sections were assumed to vary systematically. The yields
of delayed proton peaks from analogue states were compared with the yield of proton peaks in the Ne^{17} decay
where log ft values are known. The log ft's obtained
ranged from 2.9 to 3.6 with a possible error of 0.3, in
essential agreement with the calculations. The superallowed branches shown in Table I are those calculated
using the estimated $Q_\beta+$, the observed half life and an
assumed value of 3.3 for the log ft's.

While the analogue states are all high (3 to
10 MeV) above the threshold for proton emission they
are all bound against the isobaric spin allowed proton
emission to the lowest T = 1 states in the final nuclei
(i.e., they are quasi-bound). It is interesting to see
if the existing proton widths are sufficient to produce
significant energy displacements from the expected
positions. For the mass 9,13 and 37 multiplets this
has been shown to be not the case. The levels are well
fitted by the isobaric mass parabola.[4,5] For the remaining mass numbers, the T = 3/2 multiplets are incomplete. However, the next best thing is to compare the

double Coulomb energy difference between each quasi-bound $T = 3/2$ state and its $T_z = +3/2$ analogue with that of the $T = 1$ multiplet one neutron removed. Figure 4 shows the comparison. The mass values are derived from the analogue state excitation energies and the tables of Mattauch et al.[14] with recent revisions. Except for the mass 9-mass 8 discrepancy the displacements of the $T = 3/2$ levels appear to be consistent with those of adjacent $T = 1$ bound states and level shifts greater than a few tens of keV do not seem to occur. Information on directly measured proton widths of the $T = 3/2$ analogue states is scanty. Upper limits of 10 keV can be set for many of them because of their absence in resonant proton scattering data. A width of less than 5 keV has been observed for the $T = 3/2$ analogue state in N^{13}.[15] In another case, a level at 5.04 MeV has been observed in K^{37} which has a width of 4 keV[16] and may be the first $T = 3/2$ state. Such widths are not inconsistent with the lack of level shifts noted above.

The width is dependent on the amounts of isobaric spin mixing. From the energetics of the T-allowed analogue state decay, the $T = 1/2$ impurity in the analogue state is perhaps comparable to the impurities in nearby bound states. A reasonable amount of the appropriate $T = 1$ wave function in the $T = 0$ state of the final nucleus would account for part of the observed width.

REFERENCES

1) E. P. Wigner, in "Proceedings of the Robert A. Welch Foundation Conferences on Chemical Research, I. The Structure of the Nucleus" (Nov. 20-22, 1957), p. 86.

2) S. Weinberg and S. B. Treiman, Phys. Rev. <u>116</u> (1959) 465.

3) R. Barton, R. McPherson, R. E. Bell, W. R. Frisken, W. T. Link and R. B. Moore, Can. J. Phys. <u>41</u> (1963) 2007.

4) J. Cerny, R. Pehl, F. S. Goulding, and D. A. Landis, Phys. Rev. Letters <u>13</u> (1964) 726.

5) J. Cerny, R. Pehl, G. Butler, D. G. Fleming, C. Maples, and C. Detraz, Phys. Letters <u>20</u> (1966) 35 and references therein. Also, J. Cerny private communication re mass 37.

6) R. McPherson, R. A. Esterlund, A. M. Poskanzer, and P. L. Reeder, Phys. Rev. <u>140</u> (1965) B1513 and references therein.

7) R. A. Esterlund, R. McPherson, A. M. Poskanzer, and P. L. Reeder, Bull. Am. Phys. Soc., Ser. 11, Vol. <u>11</u> (1966) 332.

8) P. L. Reeder, A. M. Poskanzer, R. A. Esterlund, and R. McPherson, Phys. Rev. (to be published - Si^{25}).

9) V. I. Goldanskii, Nucl. Phys. <u>19</u> (1960) 482.

10) R. McPherson and J. C. Hardy, Can. J. Phys. <u>43</u> (1965) 1.

11) D. H. Wilkinson, Phys. Letters <u>12</u> (1965) 348.

12) J. C. Hardy and B. Margolis, Phys. Letters <u>15</u> (1965) 276.

13) J. C. Hardy, R. I. Verrall, and R. E. Bell, Nucl. Phys. (to be published).

14) J. M. E. Mattauch, W. Thiele, and A. H. Wapstra, Nucl. Phys. <u>67</u> (1965) 1.

15) D. J. Bredin et al., Paper D7.

16) V. E. Storizhko and A. I. Popov, Bull. Acad. Sci. USSR, Phys. Ser. <u>28</u> (1964) [translation p. 1048].

TABLE I. Summary of results of delayed proton emitters.

Parent-Daughter	Parent Half-life msec	Q_{β^+} Calculated MeV	Calculated Superallowed Branch-%	Analogue Excitation Energy MeV
C^9 B^9	127 ± 3	16.53*	0.01	14.668 ± 0.016
O^{13} N^{13}	8.7 ± 0.4	17.77*	0.01	15.068 ± 0.008
Ne^{17} F^{17}	104 ± 5	14.4	0.4	11.06 ± 0.08
Mg^{21} Na^{21}	121 ± 5	12.9	1.7	8.90 ± 0.04
Si^{25} Al^{25}	220 ± 4	12.4	7.3	7.90 ± 0.02
S^{29} P^{29}	193 ± 8	14.0	16.3	8.36 ± 0.03
Ar^{33} Cl^{33}	181 ± 4	11.5	28.3	5.54 ± 0.03
Ca^{37} K^{37}	172 ± 4	11.5	42.8	5.06 ± 0.04
Ti^{41} Sc^{41}	90.5 ± 2	12.7	30.2	5.83 ± 0.03

*Known

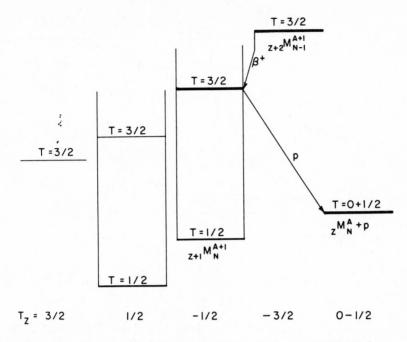

Fig. 1. Level diagram illustrating superallowed beta decay of the most neutron deficient member of a $T = 3/2$ multiplet followed by T forbidden proton emission. In the cases observed, (Z,N) of the figure is of the form $(2n,2n)$.

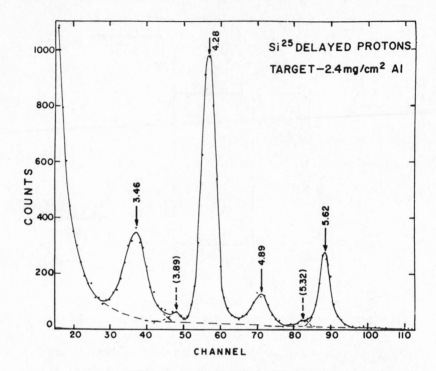

Fig. 2. Proton spectrum following Si^{25} beta decay.
The peaks at 5.62 and 4.28 MeV represent proton transitions from the analogue state in Al^{25} to the ground and
first excited state of Mg^{24}. The intensity of these
peaks relative to others in the spectrum reflects the
superallowed character of the preceding beta decay.

170

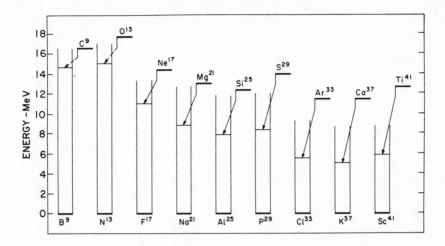

Fig. 3. The relative trend of the parent beta-decay energies and the excitation energies of the daughter analogue states. The levels for masses 9 and 13 were located by means other than delayed proton observations. The vertical bars enclosing the analogue states indicate by how much they are quasi-bound.

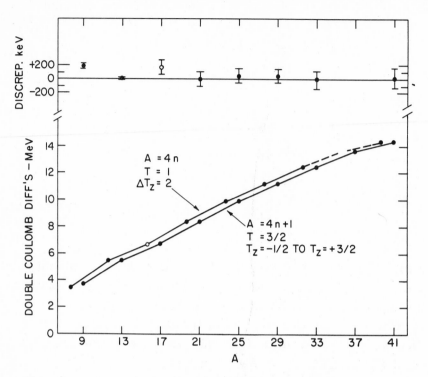

Fig. 4. The double Coulomb energy difference between each observed T = 3/2 state and its most neutron-rich analogue is compared with that of the ground states of the T = 1 multiplet, one neutron removed. The latter values have been corrected for an $A^{1/3}$ variation in radius and represent bound states except (because of F^{16}) where indicated by an open circle. The data are taken from Table I and Ref. 14 with recent revisions.

B4. ISOBARIC SPIN AND ANALOGUE SPIN*

William M. MacDonald
University of Maryland
College Park, Maryland

INTRODUCTION

The use of the isobaric spin formalism to describe nuclear forces and wave functions originated with Heisenberg[1] and was given justification by the experimental evidence for the equality of the interaction between like and unlike nucleons.[2] To Eugene P. Wigner[3] we owe the observation that this "charge independence" of nuclear forces also implies the existence of a quantum number for nuclear states--the isotopic or isobaric spin[4] as it is now called. From the validity of the isobaric spin quantum number there follow immediately a number of important consequences for both nuclear structure and reactions, for example, the multiplets of corresponding states in isobaric nuclei, selection rules on beta decay and electromagnetic transitions, and relations between the amplitudes for various nuclear particle reactions.

The validity of the isobaric spin quantum number, however, does not follow from the charge independence of the nuclear interaction alone. The Coulomb force between protons is a charge dependent interaction whose

*Research supported in part by the National Aeronautics and Space Agency under Contract No. NsG-642.

magnitude is by no means small compared to the binding
energy of nuclear forces. This interaction introduces
displacements and distortions of eigenstates of definite
isobaric spin which modify to a greater or lesser degree
all of the consequences of the existence of this quantum
number. These Coulomb effects have been investigated
both theoretically and experimentally in order to establish the general usefulness of the isobaric spin, and
a considerable amount of insight has been gained into
the way in which the Coulomb interaction distorts the
nuclear wave functions.

The principal outcome of these investigations has
been to explain why Coulomb forces do not generally produce the large violations of predictions from isobaric
spin which are expected on the basis of naive arguments.
It will be seen, in fact, that to a considerable extent
the distortions which are introduced can be included in
a wave function which possesses a more general symmetry
that the usual isobaric spin states. These wave functions are obtained from a generalization of isobaric
spin which I shall call "analogue spin". The significance of the name is that the corresponding states recently discovered in heavy nuclei which are called
analogue states are actually eigenfunctions of the
analogue spin quantum number. Eigenfunctions of analogue
spin are also appropriate in light nuclei where the
effect of the Coulomb field on loosely bound single
particle states dictates a non-perturbative treatment of
this distortion.

ISOBARIC SPIN AND COULOMB EFFECTS

In the isobaric spin formalism the wave functions
for neutrons and protons are

174

neutron: $\begin{pmatrix}1\\0\end{pmatrix}$ $g(\vec{r},\vec{\sigma})$ $\quad t_3\begin{pmatrix}1\\0\end{pmatrix} = \frac{1}{2}\begin{pmatrix}1\\0\end{pmatrix}$

proton: $\begin{pmatrix}0\\1\end{pmatrix}$ $g(\vec{r},\vec{\sigma})$ $\quad t_3\begin{pmatrix}0\\1\end{pmatrix} = -\frac{1}{2}\begin{pmatrix}0\\1\end{pmatrix}$

$$(1)$$

These are eigenfunctions of an operator t_3 corresponding to the eigenvalue (+ 1/2) for neutrons and (- 1/2) for protons. Two other operators are needed to express an exchange interaction between a neutron and a proton. Such an interaction effectively turns a neutron into a proton at one point, and a proton into a neutron at another point. Operators to express this are t_+ and t_-, satisfying

$$t_+\begin{pmatrix}0\\1\end{pmatrix} = \begin{pmatrix}1\\0\end{pmatrix} \qquad\quad t_-\begin{pmatrix}1\\0\end{pmatrix} = \begin{pmatrix}0\\1\end{pmatrix}$$

$$t_+\begin{pmatrix}1\\0\end{pmatrix} = 0 \qquad\quad t_-\begin{pmatrix}0\\1\end{pmatrix} = 0$$

$$(2)$$

The operators t_+, t_-, t_3 satisfy the commutation relations for the components of a spherical tensor operator of the first rank (vector).

Corresponding operators for an A nucleon system are

$$T_+ = \sum_{i=1}^{A} t_+(i) \qquad T_- = \sum_{i=1}^{A} t_-(i) \qquad T_3 = \sum_{i=1}^{A} t_3(i) \qquad (3)$$

A complete set of eigenfunctions for such a system can be taken as eigenfunctions of T_3 and T^2 where

$$T^2 = T_+ T_- + T_3^2 - T_3 \tag{4}$$

The eigenvalues of T^2 are $T'(T' + 1)$, and those of T_3 are $1/2(N - Z)$. Such functions would be eigenfunctions of a Hamiltonian in which the interaction, exchange and non-exchange, between both like and unlike nucleons are equal, i.e.

$$V(\vec{r}_1, \vec{r}_2) = f(\vec{r}_1\vec{\sigma}_1, \vec{r}_2\vec{\sigma}_2) + g(\vec{r}_1\vec{\sigma}_1, \vec{r}_2\vec{\sigma}_2)[2t_3(i)t_3(j)$$

$$+ t_+(i)\ t_-(j) + t_-(i)\ t_+(j)] \tag{5}$$

Isobaric Mass Formula

For a Hamiltonian with this interaction the states for a set of A nucleons form multiplets, characterized by a quantum number T, which appear in all the nuclei for which $-T \leqslant T_3 \leqslant T$. The first, and most striking, evidence for the usefulness of the isobaric spin quantum number is the existence of such corresponding states in nuclei. However, these states do not have the same energy, as should be the case for a charge independent Hamiltonian, but a shift is introduced by the Coulomb interaction.

This shift can be calculated in perturbation theory using eigenfunctions of isobaric spin. The resulting "isobaric mass formula" follows directly from the tensor decomposition of the Coulomb operator.

$$\Delta E_{Coulomb} = a + b\ T_3 + c\ T_3^2 \tag{6}$$

The accuracy of this formula for stable states of nuclei has been verified in a number of cases. Striking examples are furnished by the recently established isobaric spin quartets in the A = 9 and A = 13 nuclei.[6,7] From Li^7, Be^9, and B^9 the mass excess of C^9 is predicted as 29.00 $\pm$ .05 MeV. The measured value is 28.99 $\pm$ 0.07 MeV. In the A = 13 nuclei the mass of O^{13} can be calculated from N^{13}, C^{13}, and B^{13} to be 23.11 $\pm$ .018 MeV. The measured value is 23.11 $\pm$ .07 MeV.

The effect of the Coulomb distortion on the nuclear wave functions is, however, very difficult to assess from the application of the isobaric mass formula.

176

As is well known the energy shift produced by a perturbation is of second order with respect to the perturbation of the wave function. Furthermore, the effect of the Coulomb distortion is to introduce a dependence on T_3 of the coefficients which appear in the mass formula. The Coulomb distortion of the wave functions could therefore be detected only through the appearance of a T_3^3 dependence (or higher) of the Coulomb shifts. In addition this could only arise through the tensor component of the Coulomb interaction, as pointed out by E. P. Wigner.

Fermi Matrix Elements

Striking as the isobaric multiplets are, for more detailed information on the symmetries of the nuclear states we should obviously turn to selection rules or values for reaction amplitudes which are provided by isobaric spin. The first examples came from E. P. Wigner[8] who applied the concepts of isobaric spin to beta decay. The Fermi matrix elements are of greatest interest because both a selection rule and the absolute value of the matrix element are predicted.

The Fermi matrix element is simply

$$M_F = \int \Psi_f {}^* T_\pm \Psi_i \qquad (7)$$

from which immediately follows the selection rule

$$\Delta T = 0 \qquad (8)$$

and the value

$$M_F = \sqrt{(T \mp T_3^{\frac{1}{2}})(T \pm T_3^{\frac{1}{2}} + 1)} \qquad (9)$$

In order to insure that only the Fermi matrix element enters one need only look at beta decays of the type $J = 0^+ \to J = 0^+$. For such decays the Gamow-Teller nuclear matrix element is zero.

The prediction for the value of the Fermi matrix element assumed considerable importance several years ago when it was used to determine the vector coupling constant. The ft value selected for this purpose was that for the positron decay of O^{14} to the first excited state of N^{14} at 2.31 MeV. For this transition the matrix element has the value

$$M_F = \sqrt{2}.$$

It is easy to see that this value may be altered by the Coulomb interaction because of two effects between which it is worthwhile to distinguish. The first effect is the mixing of states of different isobaric spin to both the initial and final states. In the O^{14} wave function we may expect to have not only the dominant $T = 1$ component, but also a small amount of $T = 2$. In the N^{14} excited $T = 1$ state we can have some components of $T = 0$ states as well as $T = 2$ states. A second effect of the Coulomb force is properly called dynamic distortion because it is the mixing of other $T = 1$ states into the dominant $T = 1$ states of $N^{14*}(2.31)$ and O^{14}. At first sight one might not expect mixing to effect the value of M_F. On the further reflection it is clear that this will be true if, and only if, the amplitudes of such components are the same for $N^{14*}(2.31)$ and O^{14}.

Both effects on the Fermi matrix element are easily followed by looking at the simple case in which only $T = 0$ and $T = 1$ states are included in the wave function. The wave function for O^{14} will be

$$\Psi_i = \sum_\alpha c_\alpha \, \Psi_\alpha(1, -1) \tag{10}$$

while for $N^{14*}(2.31)$ we have

$$\Psi_f = \sum_\alpha a_\alpha \Psi_\alpha(1,0) + \sum_\alpha b_\alpha \Psi_\alpha(0,0). \tag{11}$$

The Fermi matrix element can be evaluated easily[9]

$$M_F = \sqrt{2} \left(1 - \frac{\delta}{2}\right)$$

$$\delta = \sum_{\alpha} (b_\alpha)^2 + \sum_{\alpha} (a_\alpha - c_\alpha)^2 \qquad (12)$$

The first term of this expression for δ shows that the Fermi matrix element is reduced by the $T = 0$ impurity in the dominantly $T = 1$ wave function for N^{14}. This is obvious because the $T = 0$ impurity does not contribute to M_F.

The second term of δ exhibits the less obvious effect of the mixing of $T = 1$ states belonging to other configurations. If the amplitudes of these added $T = 1$ components are the same in both N^{14*} and O^{14}, then the value of the Fermi matrix element is not affected. However, if these amplitudes are different, the matrix **element is reduced.** Thus the isobaric spin will not be a good quantum number <u>dynamically</u>, even though the isobaric spin impurity is small. This effect is called dynamic distortion.

The magnitude of the Coulomb correction to the matrix element was actually calculated before the advent of the V - A conserved vector current theory.[9] But the very small result, $\delta < 0.10\%$, became a burning theoretical issue when the experimentally determined value of the vector coupling constant was discovered to disagree with that found from mu-meson decay. In an attempt to obtain the correction of $\delta = 2\%$ necessary to resolve the discrepancy, the first theoretical calculations were repeated and small corrections were computed by R. Blin-Stoyle and J. Le Tourneaux,[10] by L. Lovitch,[11] and by H. Weidenmüller.[12]

179

The result of all these efforts was agreement on the value of δ given above for the effect of Coulomb forces. It should be noted that a much larger value was obtained by Weidenmüller[12] as the effect of a collective expansion produced by the addition of a single proton. However, the result is due to an unrealistic approximation, as pointed out in a note added in proof to that paper. When an improved calculation is made, the value of δ agrees very well with the detailed shell model calculations. The reason for this agreement will be discussed in the next main section.

In addition to Coulomb effects the contributions to δ arising from a charge dependent force have also been considered.[10,13] Although there is some uncertainty in the magnitude of the charge dependent (effective) potential as determined from experimental data on the A = 14 triad,[13,14] the conclusion is that neither Coulomb forces nor a charge dependent nuclear interaction can explain the discrepancy between the coupling constants G_μ and G_v. Fortunately in the interim between the first and final calculations the theory of Cabbibo[15] has appeared which requires a small difference between the coupling constants G_v and G_μ. It has therefore become undesirable to obtain a large value for δ. In addition, the ft values for a number of other $J = 0^+ \to J = 0^+$ have been very accurately measured.[16] All but one of these ft values are in agreement to within the quoted experimental error. This is additional evidence for a small Coulomb correction.

Calculations have also been carried out[17] to determine the extent of the violation of the $\Delta T = 0$ selection rule which is produced by Coulomb forces and a possible charge dependent force. The matrix elements for forbidden Fermi transitions have been obtained from measurements on the β-γ circular polarization symmetry parameter in the decay of Na^{24}, A^{41}, Sc^{44}, and Mn^{52}. The magnitudes of these matrix elements are all consistent with Coulomb induced impurities of order of 10^{-2} or less. A more detailed review of the present situation has been given by S. D. Bloom* at this conference.

Reduced Width Ratios

The same effects of isobaric spin mixing and dynamic distortion are to be seen in ratios of reduced widths predicted from charge independence. These relations were first pointed out by R. K. Adair[18] and follow simply from the vector coupling of target and projectile isobaric spins in the formation of compound resonances. A simple example is found in the analysis[19] of the T = 1 levels in B^{10} (8.89 MeV) and Be^{10} (7.37 MeV).

The isobaric wave function $\Psi_{\alpha\beta}(TT_3)$ will be written as a core described by $\Phi_\alpha(T',T_3')$ coupled to a single nucleon $\psi_\beta(t_3)$.

$$\Psi_{\alpha\beta}(1,0) = \frac{1}{\sqrt{2}} \ [\Phi_\alpha(\tfrac{1}{2},-\tfrac{1}{2}) \ \psi_\beta(\tfrac{1}{2}) + \Phi_\alpha(\tfrac{1}{2}\,\tfrac{1}{2}) \ \psi_\beta(-\tfrac{1}{2})]$$

$$\Psi_{\alpha\beta}(0,0) = \frac{1}{\sqrt{2}} \ [\Phi_\alpha(\tfrac{1}{2},-\tfrac{1}{2}) \ \psi_\beta(\tfrac{1}{2}) - \Phi_\alpha(\tfrac{1}{2}\,\tfrac{1}{2}) \ \psi_\beta(-\tfrac{1}{2})]$$

$$(13)$$

The physical wave functions for B^{10}(8.89 MeV) and Be^{10} (7.37 MeV) will contain both T = 0 and T = 1 components.

$$\Psi(\lambda, T_3 = 0) = \sum_{\alpha,\beta} a_{\alpha\beta}^\lambda \ \Psi_{\alpha\beta}(1,0) + \sum_{\alpha,\beta} b_{\alpha\beta}^\lambda \ \Psi_{\alpha\beta}(0,0)$$

$$\Psi(\lambda, T_3 = 1) = \sum_{\alpha,\beta} c_{\alpha\beta} \ \Psi_{\alpha\beta}(1,1) \qquad (14)$$

*Paper B1.

181

The ratio of neutron to proton reduced widths in B^{10}

$$R_1 = \frac{\gamma_n^2(\lambda,0)}{\gamma_p^2(\lambda,0)} = \frac{(\sum_{\alpha\beta} a_{\alpha\beta}^\lambda + \sum_{\alpha\beta} b_{\alpha\beta}^\lambda)^2}{(\sum_{\alpha\beta} a_{\alpha\beta}^\lambda - \sum_{\alpha\beta} b_{\alpha\beta}^\lambda)^2} = \frac{(A + B)^2}{(A - B)^2} \qquad (15)$$

For simplicity the single particle widths for all states have been taken to be equal. This relation was first derived by Barker and Mann[20] who pointed out the large effect of isobaric spin impurity.

Interestingly enough the ratio

$$R_2 = \frac{\gamma_n^2(\lambda,0) + \gamma_p^2(\lambda,0)}{\gamma_n^2(\lambda,1)} = \frac{A^2 + B^2}{C^2} \qquad (16)$$

does not display a sensitive dependence upon isobaric spin impurity, which enters only as the square.[19] On the other hand, writing

$$R_2 = 1 + \frac{(A - C)(A + C) + B^2}{C^2} \qquad (17)$$

one sees that R_2 is affected by the dynamic distortion. If the different $T = 1$ states which are admixed by the Coulomb interaction appear with equal amplitudes in Be^{10} and B^{10}, i.e. if $A = \pm C$, then the effect of the dynamic distortion is zero.

The requirement that R_1 and R_2 be nearly equal to unity, as expected from calculations of Coulomb effects, led to the discovery that the $T = 1$ levels were not $J^\pi = 3^+$, but $J^\pi = 3^-$. This is the only example known to me in which isobaric spin relations have been used to predict the parity of a nuclear level.

Electromagnetic Transitions

The data provided by electromagnetic transitions also provide additional information, when properly interpreted, on the validity of the isobaric spin as a quantum number for the excited states of nuclei. All of the isobaric spin selection rules and relations between electromagnetic transitions have been reviewed by E. K. Warburton* at this conference. I shall therefore not discuss this subject further.

NATURE OF COULOMB DISTORTIONS AND ANALOGUE SPIN

As a result of detailed theoretical calculations the way in which the Coulomb interaction distorts isobaric spin eigenfunctions is rather well understood. The nature of these distortions is characterized by the long range nature of the Coulomb force. Detailed calculations of Coulomb matrix elements reveal that largest by an order of magnitude are matrix elements between states differing only in the excitation of a proton from a state $(n\ell j)$ to a state $(n + 1\ell j)$. This is the characteristic of a control force whose principal effect is to expand proton orbitals.

In many calculations a very good approximation is simply to consider the effect of an average Coulomb field. A reasonable approximation is to use that for a sphere of uniform charge density.

$$C(r) = \frac{3\ Ze^2}{2R^3}\ (R^2 - \frac{1}{3}\ r^2) \qquad r \leqslant R$$
$$= \frac{Ze^2}{r} \qquad\qquad\qquad r \geqslant R$$

$$(18)$$

This idea has, in fact, been used by Iwao and French[22] to calculate the isobaric spin impurity in the ground states of a number of nuclei. The radial wave functions for a neutron and a proton are taken to be different due to the expansion of a proton wave function.

*Paper A4.

If harmonic oscillator wave functions are used, the effect of the Coulomb field inside the nucleus is simply to decrease the spring constant for protons,

$$\upsilon_p = \upsilon_n - \frac{2M}{\hbar^2} \frac{Ze^2}{2R^3}$$

Since $R^3 \propto A$ and Z/A decreases with A, the absolute change in υ_n due to Coulomb expansion decreases with A. Of course, υ_n decreases with increasing A, so the _fractional change_ in the spring constant slowly increases with A. The isobaric spin impurity is then found by calculating the expectation value of $\langle T(T + 1) \rangle$ and subtracting the unperturbed value $T_o(T_o + 1)$. The resulting values for isobaric spin impurity agree with the perturbation calculations in light nuclei and run from 3×10^{-3} for O^{16} to 10^{-2} for Zr^{90}.

Small as are these values for the isobaric spin impurity for the ground states of nuclei, the actual distortion of the nuclear wave function is considerably greater.[23] This effect shows up as the addition of amplitudes of excited states of the same isobaric spin into a given state. As I pointed out in the preceding section, this dynamic distortion destroys the usefulness of isobaric spin as effectively as does isobaric spin mixing. This distortion is, of course, much greater for weakly bound states. In the continuum, neutron and proton orbitals will have very different asymptotic behavior and their amplitudes over the nuclear volume will be very different.

The exchange property of nuclear forces and the fact that the np, pp, and nn interactions are (very nearly) equal means that the eigenfunctions of the nuclear Hamiltonian will have the _symmetry_ of isobaric

spin states even if the actual shape of the single proton and single neutron orbitals is different. I now
wish to present a generalization of isobaric spin which
is particularly adapted to including the effect of Coulomb distortion in shell model wave functions of a more
general symmetry than those of isobaric spin. These
wave functions are eigenfunctions of a quantum number
called the analogue spin.

I shall begin by specifying a complete set of
single particle wave functions for protons and another
complete set for neutrons. These will be eigenfunctions
of a single particle Hamiltonian with different finite
potentials.

$$(-\frac{\hbar^2}{2M} \nabla^2 + U_{p,n}) \, \phi_\alpha^{p,n} = \varepsilon_\alpha^{p,n} \, \phi_\alpha^{p,n} \tag{19}$$

The potentials U_p and U_n differ by a central Coulomb
field and if desired, by a symmetry energy.

The wave functions for a neutron and a proton are
then written as follows.

$$\text{neutron:} \begin{pmatrix} \phi_\alpha^n \\ 0 \end{pmatrix}$$

$$\text{proton:} \begin{pmatrix} 0 \\ \phi_\alpha^p \end{pmatrix} \tag{20}$$

Now define the operators for analogue spin by the
equations

$$w_3 \begin{pmatrix} \phi_\alpha^n \\ 0 \end{pmatrix} = \frac{1}{2} \begin{pmatrix} \phi_\alpha^n \\ 0 \end{pmatrix} \qquad w_3 \begin{pmatrix} 0 \\ \phi_\alpha^p \end{pmatrix} = -\frac{1}{2} \begin{pmatrix} 0 \\ \phi_\alpha^p \end{pmatrix}$$

$$w_+ \begin{pmatrix} 0 \\ \phi_\alpha^p \end{pmatrix} = \begin{pmatrix} \phi_\alpha^n \\ 0 \end{pmatrix} \qquad w_- \begin{pmatrix} \phi_\alpha^n \\ 0 \end{pmatrix} = \begin{pmatrix} 0 \\ \phi_\alpha^p \end{pmatrix}$$

$$w_+ \begin{pmatrix} \phi_\alpha^n \\ 0 \end{pmatrix} = 0 \qquad\qquad w_- \begin{pmatrix} 0 \\ \phi_\alpha^p \end{pmatrix} = 0 \qquad (21)$$

The operators for an A nucleon system will be

$$W_\pm = \sum_{i=1}^{A} w_\pm(i) \qquad\qquad W_3 = \sum_{i=1}^{A} w_3(i) \qquad (22)$$

It is easy to verify that the analogue spin operators satisfy the usual commutation relations for an angular momentum operator.

Eigenfunctions can be constructed of W^2 and W_3 which are related by the usual relations

$$W^2 |W'W_3'\rangle = W'(W' + 1) |W'W_3'\rangle$$

$$W_3 |W'W_3'\rangle = W_3' |W'W_3'\rangle \qquad (23)$$

$$W_\pm |W'W_3'\rangle = \sqrt{(W' \mp W_3')(W' \pm W_3' + 1)} \, |W'W_3' \pm 1\rangle$$

The eigenvalue of W_3 is $W_3' = \frac{1}{2} (N - Z)$, and this is the lowest eigenvalue W' of the states for a given nucleus.

As an example I shall give the antisymmetrized eigenfunctions for two nucleons in states characterized by single particle quantum numbers α and β.

$W = 1$

$$W_3 = 1 \quad \Psi(1,1) = \frac{1}{\sqrt{2}} \left[\begin{pmatrix} \phi_\alpha^n(1) \\ 0 \end{pmatrix} \begin{pmatrix} \phi_\beta^n(2) \\ 0 \end{pmatrix} - \begin{pmatrix} \phi_\beta^n(1) \\ 0 \end{pmatrix} \begin{pmatrix} \phi_\alpha^n(2) \\ 0 \end{pmatrix} \right]$$

$$W_3 = 0 \quad \Psi(1,0) = \frac{1}{2} \left[\begin{pmatrix} 0 \\ \phi_\alpha^p(1) \end{pmatrix} \begin{pmatrix} \phi_\beta^n(1) \\ 0 \end{pmatrix} + \begin{pmatrix} \phi_\alpha^n(1) \\ 0 \end{pmatrix} \begin{pmatrix} 0 \\ \phi_\beta^p(2) \end{pmatrix} \right.$$

$$\left. \begin{pmatrix} 0 \\ \phi_\beta^p(1) \end{pmatrix} \begin{pmatrix} \phi_\alpha^n(2) \\ 0 \end{pmatrix} - \begin{pmatrix} \phi_\beta^n(1) \\ 0 \end{pmatrix} \begin{pmatrix} 0 \\ \phi_\alpha^p(2) \end{pmatrix} \right]$$

186

$$W_3 = -1$$

$$\Psi(1,-1) = \frac{1}{\sqrt{2}}\left[\begin{pmatrix} 0 \\ \phi_\alpha^p(1) \end{pmatrix}\begin{pmatrix} 0 \\ \phi_\beta^p(2) \end{pmatrix} - \begin{pmatrix} 0 \\ \phi_\beta^p(1) \end{pmatrix}\begin{pmatrix} 0 \\ \phi_\alpha^p(2) \end{pmatrix}\right]$$

$$W = 0 \quad W_3 = 0$$

$$\Psi(0,0) = \frac{1}{2}\left[\begin{pmatrix} 0 \\ \phi_\alpha^p(1) \end{pmatrix}\begin{pmatrix} \phi_\beta^n(2) \\ 0 \end{pmatrix} - \begin{pmatrix} \phi_\alpha^n(1) \\ 0 \end{pmatrix}\begin{pmatrix} 0 \\ \phi_\beta^p(2) \end{pmatrix}\right.$$

$$\left. + \begin{pmatrix} 0 \\ \phi_\beta^p(1) \end{pmatrix}\begin{pmatrix} \phi_\alpha^n(2) \\ 0 \end{pmatrix} - \begin{pmatrix} \phi_\alpha^n(1) \\ 0 \end{pmatrix}\begin{pmatrix} 0 \\ \phi_\alpha^p(2) \end{pmatrix}\right]$$

$$W_- \Psi(1,1) = \sqrt{2}\,\Psi(1,0)$$

$$W_- \Psi(1,0) = \sqrt{2}\,\Psi(1,-1)$$

$$W_3 \Psi(1,W_3') = W_3'\,\Psi(1,W_3') \tag{24}$$

In the construction and use of many-particle wave functions the formalism of second quantization is useful. In a basis provided by the single particle states ϕ_α^p and ϕ_α^n the analogue spin operators are easily given,

$$W_+ = \sum_\alpha (a_\alpha^n)^+ a_\alpha^p$$

$$W_- = \sum_\alpha (a_\alpha^p)^+ a_\alpha^n$$

$$W_3 = \frac{1}{2} \sum (N_\alpha^n - N_\alpha^p) \tag{25}$$

In the pictorial representation which is currently fashionable the effect of the analogue spin operators is easily shown

187

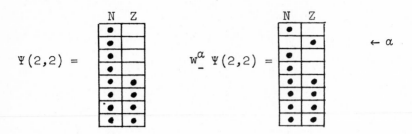

ground state of
N,Z nucleus

Particle-hole state
N - 1, Z + 1 nucleus

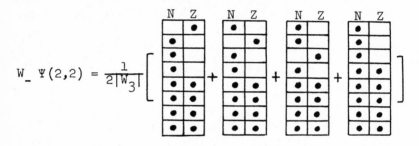

analogue state of $(N - 1,\ Z + 1)$ nucleus

In this pictorial representation the eigenfunction of
analogue spin and of isobaric spin appear to be identical. However, the corresponding isobaric spin equations
are valid only if the neutron and proton wave functions
are identical, i.e., if the entire Coulomb field is
treated as a perturbation.

It is important to realize, in fact, the analogue
spin is not merely an example of the introduction of
colorful nomenclature for a familiar concept. The differences between analogue spin and isobaric spin are
very real, and not all in favor of analogue spin. For
example, calculations with analogue spin will certainly
be more difficult than with isobaric spin because of the
lack of commutativity between spin and scalar functions.

188

Of course, the simplicity of calculations with isobaric spin is gained at the expense of using unrealistic wave functions, particularly in the asymptotic region and particularly for continuum states. In the shell model approach to reaction theory,[24] or in coupled channel equations, this compromise appears to be unacceptable. In these approaches analogue spin is a most natural and useful concept.

REFERENCES

1) W. Heisenberg, Zeitschrift f. Physik 77 (1932) 1.

2) G. Breit, E. Condon, and R. D. Present, Phys. Rev. 50 (1936) 825; G. Breit and E. Feenberg, Phys. Rev. 50 (1936) 850.

3) E. P. Wigner, Phys. Rev. 51 (1937) 106.

4) Reviews of isobaric spin in nuclei have been given by W. E. Burcham, Progress in Nuclear Physics 4 (1955) 171; W. MacDonald, Nuclear Spectroscopy, ed. F. Ajzenberg-Selove, Academic Press (1960); E. P. Wigner, Proc. of Robert A. Welch Foundation Conf. on Chemical Research, Vol. I, Chapt. IV, p. 67(1957)

5) W. M. MacDonald, Phys. Rev. 100 (1955) 51.

6) J. Cerny, R. H. Pehl, F. S. Goulding, and D. A. Landis, Phys. Rev. Letts. 13 (1964) 726; J. Cerny, R. H. Pehl, G. Butler, D. G. Fleming, C. Maples, and C. Detraz, Phys. Letts. 20 (1966) 35.

7) W. L. Imhof, L. F. Chase, Jr., D. B. Fossan, Phys. Rev. 139 (1965) B904.

8) E. P. Wigner, Phys. Rev. 56 (1939) 519.

9) W. MacDonald, Phys. Rev. 110 (1958) 1420.

10) R. J. Blin-Stoyle and J. Le Tourneaux, Phys. Rev. 123 (1961) 627; Ann. Phys. (N.Y.) 18 (1961) 12.

11) L. Lovitch, Nucl. Phys. $\underline{46}$ (1963) 353.

12) H. Weidenmüller, Phys. Rev. $\underline{128}$ (1962) 841.

13) A. Altman and W. M. MacDonald, Nucl. Phys. $\underline{35}$ (1962) 593.

14) R. J. Blin-Stoyle, S. C. K. Nair, and S. Papageorgion, Proc. Phys. Soc. (London) $\underline{85}$(1965)477; R. J. Blin-Stoyle and S. C. K. Nair, Phys. Letts. $\underline{7}$ (1963) 161.

15) N. Cabbibo, Phys. Rev. Letts. $\underline{10}$ (1963) 531.

16) J. M. Freeman, J. H. Montague, G. Murray, and R. E. White, Phys. Letts. $\underline{8}$ (1964) 115.

17) P. S. Kelly and S. A. Moskowski, Z. f. Phys. $\underline{158}$ (1960) 304; C. C. Bouchiat, Phys. Rev. $\underline{118}$ (1960) 540; R. J. Blin-Stoyle and L. Novakovic, Nucl. Phys. $\underline{51}$ (1964) 133.

18) R. K. Adair, Phys. Rev. $\underline{92}$ (1952) 1491.

19) A. Altman, W. M. MacDonald, J. B. Marion, Nucl. Phys. $\underline{35}$ (1962) 85.

20) F. C. Barker and A. K. Mann, Phil. Mag. $\underline{2}$ (1957)5.

21) W. M. MacDonald, Phys. Rev. $\underline{101}$ (1956) 271.

22) S. Iwao, Thesis, University of Rochester, 1960 (unpublished).

23) A. M. Lane and J. M. Soper, Nucl. Phys. $\underline{37}$ (1962) 663.

24) W. M. MacDonald, Nucl. Phys. $\underline{54}$ (1964) 393.

DISCUSSION

BAYMAN, University of Minnesota: In Minnesota, we have worked a bit with this analogue spin formalism. However, we worry about the following point: What do you do in a situation in which a neutron single particle state is bound in the neutron well, but the corresponding proton single particle state is not bound in the proton well?

How do you then define the correspondence between the proton and neutron states?

MacDONALD: Well, there was a paper by myself and Leonard Garside in the "Physical Review". You can, in fact, treat the Coulomb interaction on the state as a perturbation on the proton wave function.

There are other tricks one can use even if the proton wave function is unbound. However, the difference between it and a bound neutron wave function over the interior of the nucleus is small.

Therefore, a wave function which approximately diagonalizes the nuclear Hamiltonian will possess the symmetry of isobaric spin functions. I'm sure you will agree that it is more sensible to begin a calculation with functions for which the nuclear Hamiltonian is at least approximately diagonal.

This is the main reason for my introducing these analogue spin functions. But as I say, you do lose certain advantages of ordinary isobaric spin. What you gain is the possibility of allowing the neutron-proton wave function to be quite different.

BAYMAN: Your T^+ operator and the T^- operator are still well defined in this case?

191

MacDONALD: W.

BAYMAN: Yes W.

MacDONALD: Yes, the W are well defined.

WIGNER, Princeton: I am wondering if you dis-
regard the problem brought out by Bayman and assume
that the effect of the Coulomb force is only a flatten-
ing of the potential, could you give the order of magnitude of the impurity, let us say in Ca or in some
elements which you can think of?

MacDONALD: Oh, the impurity of isobaric spin
would be the same as one would calculate it in the
usual way.

WIGNER: Yes, but how much is it?

MacDONALD: These are now unbound single particle states?

WIGNER: No, they are bound states and just take
into account the Coulomb effect.

MacDONALD: Well, the impurities which have been
calculated on single particle wave functions are of
the order of one percent for the total isobaric spin
impurity in the wave functions.

WIGNER: In what element?

MacDONALD: They have been done in a whole range
of elements by Iwao and French, essentially starting
with very light nuclei and going up to quite heavy ones.

WIGNER: But, for example, I don't think that
the 3S wave functions for a neutron and a proton in
that heavy nucleus would overlap so well.

MacDONALD: The overlap of neutron wave functions with proton wave functions?

WIGNER: In order to calculate the isobaric spin
impurity, you have to take the product of the overlaps
of the somewhat expanded proton wave functions with the

192

neutron wave functions. Now, as you point out, in
the 1S state, 1P state, 1D state, etc., it's very good.

MacDONALD: Yes.

WIGNER: But if you go to 2S, 3S, then it's
much poorer, and if you have a lot of them, the total
overlap could be very poor.

MacDONALD: That is not the case, but I should
make a qualification which has to do with almost all
the calculations, particularly those in heavy nuclei.
These calculations have not properly treated the
asymptotic aspect of the single particle wave functions.
Now, how large these effects are, I really don't know.
They have always taken something like harmonic oscillator wave functions or infinite square well wave
functions and calculated with those.

In light nuclei on the O^{14} case where the chips
were really down, Weidenmüller did the calculation
very carefully, and there the effect of the finite
well was not an important one. But as you say, one
really doesn't have the range of S states, for example,
that one has in heavier nuclei.

B5. ISOBARIC-SPIN PURITY IN THE GIANT RESONANCE[*]

R. E. Segel

Argonne National Laboratory
Argonne, Illinois

The term giant resonance in the title refers to
the giant dipole resonance which is the well-known phenomenon that the absorption of gamma rays by almost any
nucleus is dominated by what looks like, at least in
a poor resolution, a single resonance several MeV wide.
The peak of the giant resonance is at about 20 MeV in
the light nuclei and gradually decreases with increasing atomic number to about half that value for the
heaviest nuclei. The main features of the giant resonance can be explained in terms of the shell model
with the giant resonance representing transitions of
single nucleons from one major nuclear shell to another.
The energy of the giant resonance is somewhat greater
than the spacing between the nuclear shells, but this
difference has been shown to be due to the residual
interaction between the particle and the hole that it
has vacated. In this picture the isobaric-spin question stands out clearly. Since either a neutron or a
proton can be excited and since neutrons can be dif-
ferentiated from protons, it follows that even for a
self-conjugate nucleus the state formed will be different depending on whether a neutron or a proton

---

[*]Work performed under the auspices of the U. S. Atomic
Energy Commission

particle-hole pair is created. On the other hand, if charge-symmetry holds one speaks about exciting a nucleon, and the two states that are formed are characterized by the nucleon particle and hole combining in an isobaric spin 0 or an isobaric spin 1 state. The question to be considered is then which of the two descriptions (neutron excitation and proton excitation or different isobaric spins) best describes the states of the giant resonance. Actually, it is to be expected that, to some approximation, isobaric spin will be a good quantum number. The approach therefore is to describe the giant resonance in terms of pure isobaric spin states and then see how much, if any, modification is required by the experimental data. The present work constitutes a brief review of the situation in this light.

The most direct thing that can be done along these lines is to compare the giant resonance in a self-conjugate nucleus as observed with neutrons with that observed with protons. However, the situation is not really as straightforward as it sounds, as can be seen by Fig. 1 which shows the giant resonance in C^{12} for various channels. Here, good resolution data demonstrates that the giant resonance is not really a single resonance but rather has a good deal of structure. Actually, because C^{12} is such a light nucleus, the structure here is much less than is seen in other cases; in heavier nuclei there is much more dramatic and violent structure. The structure arises because a good number of levels contribute to the giant resonance and the interference between these levels can be shown to be mainly responsible for the structure. These interferences are very sensitive to the detailed properties of the various levels so that even slight differences between neutrons and protons could make very significant differences in the fine structure. Therefore, the interest is not in the fine structure but rather in the giant resonance as a whole, and the isobaric spin purity can be determined from the degree to which the properties of the giant resonance depend on whether the giant resonance is observed with neutrons or with protons.

In a self-conjugate nucleus there is the added simplicity that E1 transitions can only take place between states differing by one unit of isobaric spin and, since the ground state is almost invariably $T = 0$, it follows that the giant resonance will be $T = 1$. Barker and Mann[4] have shown how the ratio of the emission rates for neutrons and protons is related to the isobaric spin impurity (Fig. 2). The point here is that the amplitudes for neutron or proton emission from the two different isobaric spin parts of a state are coherent and Barker and Mann have shown that if for the giant-resonance state the interference is constructive for neutrons it will be destructive for protons and vice-versa. This situation comes about because of a change in sign of a Clebsch-Gordan coefficient. The $T = 0$ impurity can be obtained directly from the observed ratio of proton to neutron emission by use of the Barker and Mann formula; and it is clear from the formula that this ratio is very sensitive to small impurities.

A number of proton-to-neutron ratios have been measured for self-conjugate nuclei, and the results are summarized in Table I. The ratio of proton-to-neutron emission increases with increasing atomic

number reaching the value of about 5 for Ca^{40}. From
these data it can be seen that the intensity of the
$T = 0$ impurity, α^2, is very small for the lightest nuclei and rises to about 15% for Ca^{40}. It would be
desirable to go higher but Ca^{40} is the heaviest stable
self-conjugate nucleus. Some non-self-conjugate nuclei
are included in Table I, and for these the ratio of
proton-to-neutron emission is much less. Thus, the
effectiveness of the special coherence that is present
in self-conjugate nuclei in enhancing the effect of the
isobaric-spin impurity is demonstrated. The fact that
the ratio tends to drop below unity for the non-self-
conjugate nuclei is probably attributable to the fact
that such nuclei have an excess of neutrons, and these
valence neutrons can come off quite easily.

The behavior of the self-conjugate nuclei demonstrates the importance of the neutron excess in establishing the isobaric-spin purity of states in the
heavier nuclei. The rise of the impurity with atomic
number up to Ca^{40} implies that for much heavier self-
conjugate nuclei isobaric spin for highly excited
states would be a poor quantum number indeed. It is
thus corroborated[15] that the rather strict obedience
to isobaric-spin selection rules by states of heavier,
but high T, nuclei is due to the neutron excess in
these nuclei.

In the non-self-conjugate nuclei the giant resonance is expected to consist of two isobaric-spin
states. The giant resonance has a great deal of structure of which only a small part can be attributed to
isobaric-spin splitting. Therefore, the relevant question is how well the giant resonance can be described
as consisting of two different groups of states, each

group having a well-defined isobaric spin. Some experimental evidence exists on this point. The case that has been the most studied is the mass 13 giant resonance (Fig.3). C^{13} and N^{13} both have isobaric spin 1/2 and, therefore, the giant resonance will have isobaric spin 1/2 and isobaric spin 3/2 components (see Fig. 3). The $T = 1/2$ components of the C^{13} giant resonance can decay to either $T = 0$ or $T = 1$ states of C^{12}, but the $T = 3/2$ components' decay to the $T = 0$ states of C^{12} is isobaric spin forbidden. The ground state of C^{12} is, of course, $T = 0$ and therefore if we try to make the giant resonance in the mass 13 nuclei by bombarding C^{12} with a nucleon, we should only form $T = 1/2$ components.

Figure 4 shows some of the data for the (γ,n) reaction in C^{13}. This includes all the neutrons - those reaching the higher, $T = 1$, states as well as those reaching the lower, $T = 0$, states. The yield curve for the $C^{12}(p,\gamma)$ reaction, which goes through the giant resonance in N^{13}, is also shown and it can be seen that some, but not all, of the structure in $C^{13}(\gamma,n)$ is present in $C^{12}(p,\gamma)$. The two lower peaks of $C^{13}(\gamma,n)$ are very prominent in $C^{12}(p,\gamma)$, but the big peak at about 26 MeV in $C^{13}(\gamma,n)$ is missing entirely in $C^{12}(p,\gamma)$. The giant resonance, therefore, seems to divide into states having one or the other of the two isobaric spins with the lower energy states usually having isobaric spin 1/2 and the higher states being isobaric spin 3/2. A complete shell-model analysis of these data have been made by Measday, Clegg, and Fisher[17], who have shown that while a fairly good description is possible in terms of pure isobaric-spin states, some small amount of mixing is necessary in

order to quantitatively fit the data. The similar
energy level diagram for heavier nuclei is shown schematically in Fig. 5. In a heavy nucleus there is an
excess of neutrons, and the ground-state isobaric spin
is just equal to half the number of excess neutrons.
The isobaric-spin splitting is roughly proportional to
$(2T + 1)$ and where the neutron excess is great enough,
the two groups of states with different isobaric spin
will be well separated. The lower state can decay by
either neutron or proton emission to the low-lying
states in the respective daughter nucleus, while the
upper state can only decay by proton emission to low-
lying states. If isobaric spin is conserved, neutron
emission must be to a state with higher isobaric spin
(and, therefore higher energy) in the daughter nucleus.
In a heavy enough nucleus the higher isobaric-spin
states are unbound and consequently decays through
them can be distinguished in an activation measurement.
In brief, then, isobaric-spin conservation allows both
isobaric-spin components of the giant resonance to contribute to the (γ,p) reaction, but only the T_{lower}
component can contribute to the (γ,n) reaction.

　　　Unfortunately, there is a complication: by the
time the nucleus is heavy enough for Fig. 5 to hold,
the Coulomb barrier on the outgoing protons has become
great enough to inhibit proton emission from components
having the lower isobaric spin. Therefore one expects
neutrons coming from the lower isobaric-spin states and
protons from the higher isobaric spin states and the
most significant point is the intensity of neutron emission from the higher state. One of the few such cases
that have been studied experimentally is the giant resonance in Cu^{65} which is shown in Fig. 6. It can

be seen that the neutrons do indeed peak at a lower excitation energy than the protons. The absence of a proton peak at the neutron peak can, to a great degree, be ascribed to the Coulomb barrier. More importantly, there does not seem to be much neutron emission at the proton peak although there is an indication of a small anomaly. The conclusion from the non-self-conjugate nuclei then is that the giant resonance can be described as being split into two groups of states with different isobaric spins, but some mixing is required. It is, however, difficult to extract quantitative information.

In addition to the forbidden neutron transition from the higher isobaric-spin component in the non-self-conjugate nuclei, there are other T forbidden transitions from the giant resonance which can be examined. In particular, the question of α emission from the giant resonance in self-conjugate nuclei has been investigated, the most thoroughly studied case being Si^{28} whose energy level diagram is shown in Fig. 7. The Si^{28} nucleus is self-conjugate; it has 14 neutrons and 14 protons, and therefore has a ground-state isobaric spin of 0. The giant resonance therefore has isobaric spin 1. It is possible for the Si^{28} giant resonance to decay into Mg^{24} plus an α particle; but since both Mg^{24} and the α particle are $T = 0$, this decay is isobaric-spin forbidden. E1 radiation to the Si^{28} ground state has been found in the radiative capture of α particles by Mg^{24}. This in itself is a violation of isobaric-spin conservation.

Of course, radiative capture is not identical to the entire (γ, α) reaction, as in radiative capture only the α transition to the ground state participates.

However, proton-capture studies both on this nucleus
and on a number of other nuclei have shown that all of
the main features of the giant resonance can be observed in the inverse reaction. The yield curve obtained from the (α,γ_o) reaction on Mg^{24} is shown in
Fig. 8, along with the yield curve for the (p,γ_o) reaction on Al^{27}. The actual quantities plotted are the
cross sections for the (γ,p_o) and (γ,α_o) reactions,
which can be computed from the radiative-capture cross
sections by use of detailed balancing. Irrelevant
phase space factors are eliminated in this way, and the
two reactions can be compared directly. The (γ,p_o)
curve can be taken as mirroring the giant resonance in
Si^{28}. In this case it can be seen that the giant resonance as observed in the (γ,α_o) reaction is somewhat
distorted but nevertheless the main features are there.
Angular distribution measurements have verified that
the alpha-capture radiation is mainly electric dipole[22].
While the two yield curves are similar in that they
both show the overall giant-resonance shape, they differ in two very important ways. First, the cross section for the (γ,α_o) is smaller by about a factor of 10.
Second, differences are present in the character of the
structure in the two reactions. The structure in the
(γ,p_o) reaction can be described as fluctuations about
the giant resonance envelope. There is also indication
of an intermediate structure which for present purposes
need not be considered. The fluctuations in the (γ,α_o)
yield curve are relatively much greater; the yield
curve can be described as fluctuations contained within
the giant resonance envelope, i.e. there does not appear to be a broad component under the fine structure.
A statistical analysis along the lines laid down by

Ericson[23] has shown[21] that most of the yield from the
(γ, p_o) reaction is due to the broad state, with the
fine structure accounting for only a few percent of the
cross section. The fluctuations in the yield curve are
mainly the result of the interference between the fine
structure and the broad giant-resonance envelope; the
intensity of the fine structure component is only a
few percent. For the (γ, α_o) data, on the other hand,
the analysis indicates that the broad component is by
and large suppressed, and that most of the intensity
is in the fine structure. It thus appears that the
isobaric-spin impurity gets into the giant resonance
mainly through the fine structure; the broad state,
which contains most of the giant-resonance strength, is
quite well suppressed in the isobaric-spin forbidden
reaction. In fact, when one goes through the numbers
it is questionable whether the fine structure is of
well-defined isobaric spin at all because the cross
section for the fine-structure component in the (γ, p_o)
reaction is about the same as in the (γ, α_o).

An added piece of evidence supporting this point
of view is shown in Fig. 8 which shows the $Si^{30}(\gamma, \alpha_o)$
yield curve. Again, these are from (α, γ) data that
have been converted by detailed balancing. The Si^{30}
nucleus is not self-conjugate because it has two more
neutrons than protons. The Si^{30} ground state is therefore isobaric spin 1 and the giant resonance can be
expected to have isobaric spin 1 and isobaric spin 2
components with both making a major contribution. Since
Mg^{26} has also isobaric spin 1 and therefore Mg^{26} + an α
particle can form the isobaric spin 1 component of the
Si^{30} giant resonance. However, it can be seen from
Figs. 8 and 9 that the integrated cross section is no

greater for the isobaric-spin-allowed $Si^{30}(\gamma,\alpha_0)$ reaction than it is for the isobaric-spin-forbidden Si^{28} (γ,α_0) reaction. In fact, the cross section is somewhat lower for the $Si^{30}(\gamma,\alpha)$ reaction. Both reactions appear to proceed mainly through the fine structure, and this fine structure appears to be ineffective in inhibiting an isobaric-spin-forbidden formation of the giant resonance.

In summary, it appears that the giant resonance can, to a first approximation, be described as one or two states with well-defined isobaric spin. Most of the data is for nuclei up to about Ca^{40} and in this region there is very definite evidence that isobaric-spin impurities are present. The ratio of proton-to-neutron emission indicates the presence of an isobaric-spin impurity in the giant resonance of the self-conjugate nuclei that rises with atomic number and reaches a value of about 15% at Ca^{40}, the highest stable self-conjugate nucleus. The radiative capture work helps to better pinpoint how the isobaric-spin impurity enters the giant resonance. The picture that emerges[25] from these studies is that most of the radiation is from a single (in a self-conjugate nucleus) broad state which can be called the giant-resonance state. This state is well described by the particle-hole model and has a well-defined isobaric spin. However, this is not the whole story. The rather simple giant-resonance state interacts with the rest of the nucleus, and to some degree the giant resonance configuration gets spread among the many complicated (and therefore long-lived) states that represent the actual compound nucleus at high excitation energies. The fine structure that results from this mixing does not seem to have a

pure isobaric spin and it is through this fine structure that the isobaric-spin impurity in the giant resonance appears to come about.

The author acknowledges with pleasure the many
fruitful discussions with his colleagues, L. Meyer-
Schützmeister and Z. Vager.

REFERENCES

1) R. G. Allas, S. S. Hanna, L. Meyer-Schützmeister,
   and R. E. Segel, Nucl. Phys. 58 (1964) 122.

2) W. R. Dodge and W. C. Barber, Phys. Rev. 127
   (1962) 1746.

3) F. W. Firk, K. H. Lokan, and E. M. Bowey, Proc.
   Int. Con. on Direct Interactions and Nuclear Reac-
   tion Mechanisms, Padua (Gordon and Breach, New
   York, 1963), p. 804.

4) F. C. Barker and A. K. Mann, Phil. Mag. 2 (1957)
   5.

5) K. Min and W. D. Whitehead, Phys. Rev. B137 (1965)
   301.

6) H. Fuchs and C. Salander, Contributions to the
   Karlsruhe Conference, 1960 (Erstes Physikalisches
   Institut der Universität Heidelberg, Heidelberg,
   1961), p. All.

7) J. T. Caldwell, R. L. Bramblett, B. L. Berman,
   R. R. Harvey, and S. C. Fultz, Phys. Rev. Letts. 15
   (1965) 976.

8) G. A. Ferguson, J. Halpern, R. Nathans, and P. F.
   Yergen, Phys. Rev. 95 (1954) 776.

9) B. S. Ishkanov, I. M. Kapitoniv, V. G. Shevchenko

and B. A. Yur'ev, Phys. Letters 9 (1964) 162.

10) S. A. E. Johanssen, Phys. Rev. 97 (1955) 1186.

11) J. T. Caldwell, R. R. Harvey, R. L. Bramblett and S. C. Fultz, Phys. Letters 6 (1963) 213.

12) L. N. Bolen and W. D. Whitehead, Phys. Rev. 132 (1963) 2251.

13) H. G. Dosch, K. H. Lindenberger, and P. Brix, Nucl. Phys. 18 (1960) 615.

14) S. C. Fultz, R. L. Bramblett, J. T. Caldwell, N. E. Hansen and C. P. Jupiter, Phys. Rev. 128 (1962) 2345.

15) A. M. Lane and J. M. Soper, Nucl. Phys. 37 (1962) 663.

16) B. C. Cook, Phys. Rev. 106 (1957) 300.

17) D. F. Measday, A. B. Clegg, and P. S. Fisher, Nucl. Phys. 61 (1965) 269.

18) P. S. Fisher, D. F. Measday, F. A. Nikolaev, A. Kalmykov and A. B. Clegg, Nucl. Phys. 45 (1963) 113.

19) S. C. Fultz, R. L. Bramblett, J. T. Caldwell, and R. R. Harvey, Phys. Rev. 133 (1964) B1149.

20) N. V. Lin'kova, R. M. Osvkina, B. S. Ratner, R. Sh. Amerov and V. V. Akindinov, Soviet Physics, JETP, 11 (1960) 566.

21) P. P. Singh, R. E. Segel, L. Meyer-Schützmeister, S. S. Hanna, and R. G. Allas, Nucl. Phys. 65 (1965) 577.

22) L. Meyer-Schützmeister, Z. Vager, and R. E. Segel, Bull. Am. Phys. Soc. 10 (1965) 463, and (to be published).

23) T. Ericson, Ann. Phys. 23 (1963) 390.

24) Z. Vager, L. Meyer-Schützmeister, R. E. Segel, and P. P. Singh, Bull. Am. Phys. Soc. 10 (1965) 1084,

and (to be published).

25) R. G. Allas, S. S. Hanna, L. Meyer-Schützmeister,
     R. E. Segel, P. P. Singh and Z. Vager, Phys. Rev.
     Letters 13 (1964) 628.

TABLE I. Integrated (γ,p) and (γ,n) cross sections in units of the electric dipole sum ($= 2\pi^2 e^2 \hbar/Mc)(NZ/A)$ for a number of lighter nuclei. Most of the nuclei are self-conjugate although a few non-self-conjugate nuclei are included for comparison. The intensity of the $T = 0$ impurity in the giant resonance in the self-conjugate nuclei, α^2, is obtained from the formula $^{4)} \int \sigma(\gamma,n)dE / \int \sigma(\gamma,p)dE = (1 + \alpha)^2/(1 - \alpha)^2$

Nucleus	T	$\int^{\sim 30} \sigma(\gamma,n)dE$ / Dipole Sum	$\int^{\sim 30} \sigma(\gamma,p)dE$ / Dipole Sum	$\dfrac{(\gamma,p)}{(\gamma,n)}$	α^2	Reference
C^{12}	0	0.22	0.28	1.27	0.0038	2,5
O^{16}	0	0.22	0.23	1.05	0.00012	2,6,7
Ne^{20}	0	0.17	0.22	1.29	0.0041	2,8
Mg^{24}	0	0.25	0.50	2.00	0.029	4,9,10
Si^{28}	0	0.16	0.64	4.00	0.11	10,11,12
P^{31}	1/2	0.27	0.75	2.76		9,12
S^{32}	0	0.17	0.72	4.31	0.12	9,10
Ar^{40}	2	0.40	0.17	0.42		8,13
Ca^{40}	0	0.14	0.73	5.21	0.15	9,12
Ca^{44}	2		0.19			13
V^{51}	5/2	0.60				14

DISCUSSION

BLOOM, <u>Livermore</u>: In that case, if we use the value of alpha implied by what you gave in the table, we arrive at an estimate for the charge dependent matrix element which I will assume is mainly a Coulomb matrix element mixing the T and the T - 1 states of about 1 MeV. I emphasize, of course, that we are taking the square root of $(alpha)^2$ in order to get alpha.

SEGEL: Well, I would think that once we have as much as 15% mixing. . .

BLOOM: No, it's much worse than this. The square root of .15 is more like .4.

SEGEL: No, I gave $(alpha)^2$.

BLOOM: Yes, you take the square root of that.

SEGEL: Oh, all right.

BLOOM: And that converts into the Coulomb energy and gives a value of 1 MeV. Is this a reasonable characterization of those states?

SEGEL: Well, what I am trying to point out is that I don't think it's a denial. I think it is the only time that such highly excited states have been studied in self-conjugate nuclei.

MORINAGA, <u>Max Planck Institut</u>: I don't think this comparison of (γ,p) to (γ,n) can be used to get the value of alpha. There are many levels in the residual nuclei which could be reached by protons but not by neutrons. Therefore, (γ,p) and (γ,n) are not symmetric to each other, especially if you go up as far as Ca^{40}. So this means the level density becomes an important parameter. It is different from comparing

(γ, p_o) and (γ, n_o).

SEGEL: Well, let me answer the first part of this, and that is that the spectrum of neutrons and protons that you get from the giant resonance is not an evaporation spectrum. Particularly in the light nuclei there is a large direct interaction component. As a matter of fact, on the basis of the particle-hole model, you would expect the removal of a single nucleon to represent mainly ground state to ground state transitions.

Now, I certainly won't argue about the part that's going through the compound nucleus. That is really the fine structure I was talking about, and I think that does represent the isobaric spin impurity, but I think that this broad single level is not only seen in poor resolution, but also in good resolution experiments.

MORINAGA: But how much is direct and how much is compound?

SEGEL: Well, that is what the statistical analysis tells you.

MORINAGA: But I don't think you have got the number unless you can specify how much is direct and how much is compound.

SEGEL: Yes, well that is what the analysis of the good resolution data tells you, and I agree that one has to decide how much you want to believe the numbers, but I think that qualitatively we can say that most of the giant resonance strength is in the single broad state which corresponds to the direct interaction component.

MORINAGA: Yes, maybe the strength is there, but the proton spectrum is not completely out of the spec-

209

trum for ground state transitions. Partly it could
be so, but I don't think the main part is in the
ground state transitions. You cannot say anything
about that number.

SEGEL: You can get numbers, and it's up to
you to decide how much to believe.

JONES, Harwell: Is there any correlation in
the fluctuations of (γ, p) and (γ, α)?

SEGEL: We have found no statistically signi-
ficant correlation between the (γ, p) and the (γ, α)
fine structure.

BONDORF, Copenhagen: I would like to ask was
there any calculation in the statistical analysis or
was it your Ericson fluctuation analysis?

SEGEL: We have only done a statistical analysis within the framework outlined by Ericson. The
difficulty is that the Ericson calculation assumes
that the direct interaction component does not vary
with energy. This is, of course, not applicable here,
as what corresponds to the direct interaction in the
Ericson analysis is the giant resonance envelope in
the present case.

We have therefore had to modify the Ericson formula in order to allow for the energy variation of the
direct interaction component. Furthermore, we have
the additional complication of the intermediate structure.

We have tried to handle this as best we can, but
we certainly end up with some uncertainty in the result,
and I wouldn't quibble between something like 75 percent rather than 95 percent direct interaction if we
include the intermediate structure as part of the
broad or direct interaction component.

STEIN, University of Washington, Seattle: In
cases where you deduce the (γ,α_o) from the (α,γ)
reaction, is it energetically possible to reach states
such as (γ,α_1), (γ,α_2), etc.?

SEGEL: ·Oh, sure, yes.

STEIN: So how can you draw conclusions about
the alpha decay of the giant resonance based on that?

SEGEL: It is certainly true that we only study
the ground state alpha transition. We do rely on the
fact that in the (p,γ) studies we only look at one of
the possible channels and it has been shown that the
radiative capture yield curve mirrors the giant resonance very well. Therefore, I think it reasonable to
expect that the alpha radiative capture yield curve
would be a fair representation of what the entire
(γ,α) reaction looks like.

One might expect the intensity of the different
alpha groups to vary, but I would think that the character of the structure would be primarily the same for
all of the alpha transitions. It is certainly true
that the character of the structure varies very little
between the three ground state alpha transitions that
we have studied.

WIGNER, Princeton: I also would like to ask a
question of something I did not understand, and it's
also related to this (γ,p) - (γ,n) comparison. How is
the Coulomb barrier taken into account, or is it
taken into account, for the emission of the proton?

SEGEL: Well, what was written down was just the
integrated (γ,p) cross-sections as quoted from the
literature after trying to decide what is the most valid
data. Actually, in these light nuclei, the giant resonance tends to be at about 20 MeV excitation, so that

there is some 12 MeV available for proton emission.
Consequently the Coulomb barrier will only be important
for states that are fairly high up in the daughter nucleus. Since the giant resonance favors the emission
of high-energy protons, the Coulomb barrier might not
be too important. At any rate, non-self-conjugate
nuclei were also shown in the table, and, for these,
the ratio of proton to neutron emission was much less.
I do not think that the Coulomb barrier effects would
be very different for adjacent nuclei differing only
by a small number of units of isobaric spin. For instance, the ratio for Ar^{40} is only about a tenth of
what it is for Ca^{40}. I therefore think that the
Barker and Mann formula is, to a considerable degree,
applicable to the giant resonance in these nuclei.

MacDONALD, University of Maryland: In the case
of O^{16} the remark which you just made happens not to
be the case. In fact, the ratio (γ,p) over (γ,n),
which was formerly quoted, was that protons actually
do not go to the ground state with the same probability
as to the excited states. The branching ratios are
such that this two-to-one ratio one gets for (γ,p) over
(γ,n) is strictly due to the effect of penetrability
factors.

SEGEL: Yes, but I believe that the main question in the O^{16} resonance decay is for the decay to the
excited state of N^{15}. This state is quite high in
energy, and I believe that it is a special situation.

MacDONALD: Yes, and the protons do go to that
state as soon as it becomes possible. But this does
not happen accidentally in these other cases, does it?
In other words, it may not be an accident. The configuration of the giant dipole states in O^{16} may be such

that protons or neutrons are generally emitted with preference to the excited states.

SEGEL: Well, I must admit that I have not looked into the oxygen situation in detail, but I would think that the difference between Ar^{40} and Ca^{40} would not be an accident, in fact, that the ratio is one half in Ar^{40} and something like five in Ca^{40}. I do not think that this could come about mainly through barrier penetrabilities.

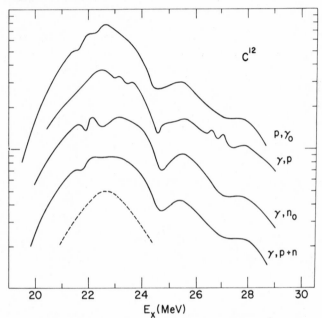

Fig. 1. The giant resonance in C^{12} as observed in different reactions. The curves are arbitrarily displaced in the vertical direction. The (p,γ_o) curve is from Allas et al.[1], (γ,p) from Dodge and Barber[2], (γ,n_o) from Firk et al.[3], and $(\gamma,p+n)$ is obtained by summing (with equal weights) the (p,γ_o) and the (γ,n_o) curves. The dotted line is a Lorentzian that is included for comparison.

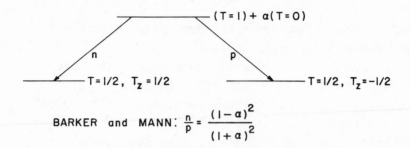

$$\text{BARKER and MANN:} \quad \frac{n}{p} = \frac{(1-\alpha)^2}{(1+\alpha)^2}$$

Fig. 2. Schematic diagram of the decay of the giant-resonance state of a self-conjugate nucleus. Here α is the amplitude of the $T = 0$ component in the pre-dominantly $T = 1$ giant resonance. The formula of Barker and Mann is from Ref. 4.

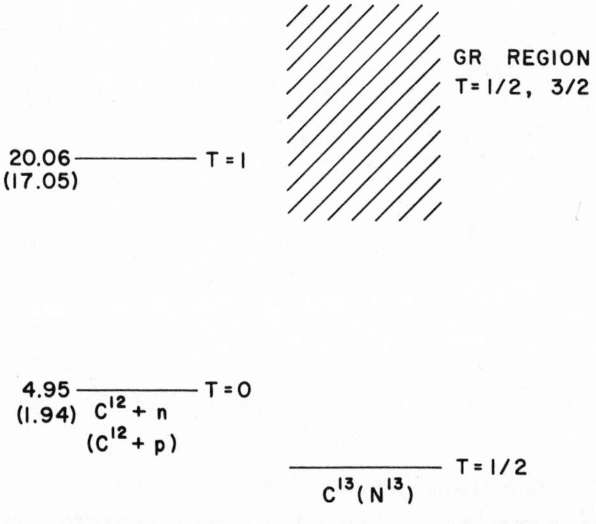

GR REGION
$T = 1/2, \ 3/2$

$20.06 \ \underline{\hspace{2cm}} \ T = 1$
(17.05)

$4.95 \ \underline{\hspace{2cm}} \ T = 0$
$(1.94) \ \ C^{12} + n$
$(C^{12} + p)$

$\underline{\hspace{2cm}} \ T = 1/2$
$C^{13} (N^{13})$

Fig. 3. Energy level diagram for the $C^{13}(\gamma,n)$ reaction. The quantities in parentheses are for the $N^{13}(\gamma,p)$ reaction. The two levels shown in the $(C^{12} + \text{nucleon})$ system represent the system with C^{12} in its lowest $T = 0$ and lowest $T = 1$ state, respectively.

214

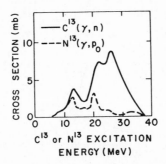

Fig. 4. Two different reactions through the mass-13 giant resonance. The $C^{13}(\gamma,n)$ curve is from the work of Cook[16] while the $N^{13}(\gamma,p_0)$ curve was computed by Measday, Clegg and Fisher[17] from the $C^{12}(p,\gamma)$ data of Fisher et al.[18].

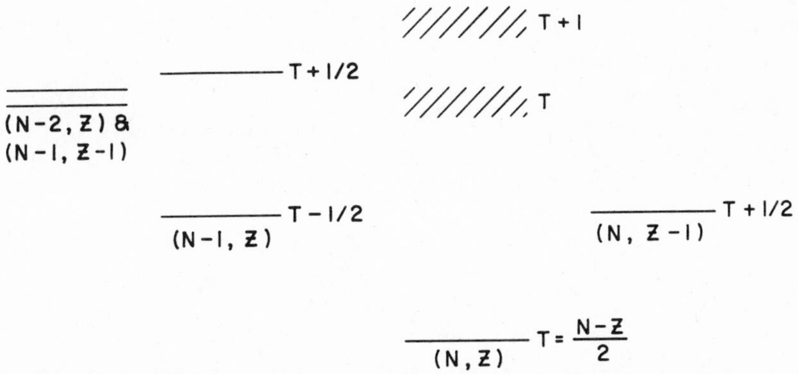

Fig. 5. Energy level diagram illustrating the various isobaric-spin states that play a role in the decay of the giant resonance of a nucleus with a significant neutron excess.

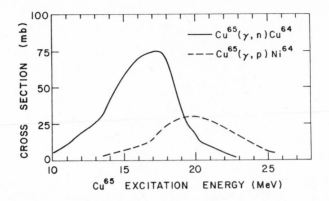

Fig. 6. The (γ,n) and (γ,p) reactions on Cu^{65} (T=3). The (γ,n) curve is from Fultz et al.[19] and the (γ,p) curve from Lin'kova et al.[20].

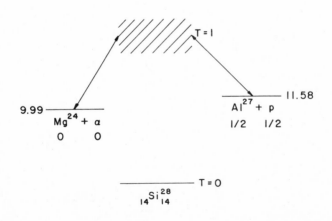

Fig. 7. Energy level diagram from the $Si^{28}(\gamma,p_o)$ and (γ,α_o) reactions through the Si^{28} giant resonance. The numbers under the various reaction products refer to their isobaric spins.

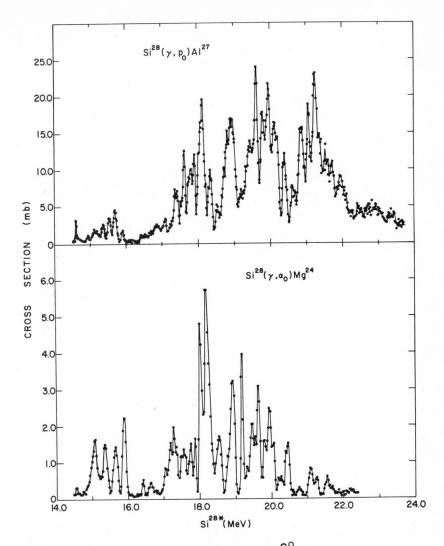

Fig. 8. Yield curves for the $Si^{28}(\gamma, p_0)$ and $Si^{28}(\gamma, \alpha_0)$ reactions in the giant-resonance region. The (γ, p_0) curve is computed from the $Al^{27}(p, \gamma_0)$ data of Singh <u>et</u> <u>al</u>.[21]; the (γ, α_0) data are from Meyer-Schützmeister, Vager, and Segel[22].

217

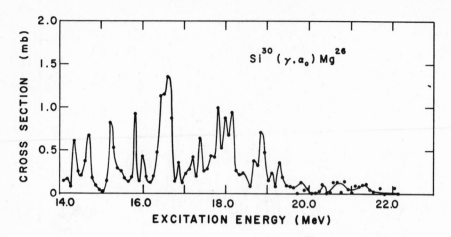

Fig. 9. Yield curve for $Si^{30}(\gamma,\alpha_0)$. It was obtained from the $Mg^{26}(\alpha,\gamma)$ data of Vager et al.[24]

B6. GAMMA DECAY OF T-SPIN ANALOGUE RESONANCES IN Tc^{93} AND Y^{89}*

S. M. Shafroth
Bartol Research Foundation of the Franklin Institute
Swarthmore, Pennsylvania

and

G. J. F. Legge
University of Pennsylvania, Philadelphia, Pennsylvania

INTRODUCTION

Very little work has yet been done concerning the gamma-decay of T-spin analogue levels in medium weight nuclei with a significant neutron excess. Such studies offer interesting possibilities since the structure of a "daughter" analogue state is simply related to the structure of a low-lying "parent" analogue state. An example of a case where the gamma-decay of analogue resonances has been studied is the $Y^{89}(p,\gamma)$ reaction.[1] The proton bombarding energies were such as to give rise to excitation energies in Zr^{90} in the giant dipole region. However, detailed balance considerations indicate that the effect of the giant dipole resonance on the (p,γ) cross section will be much smaller than the effect of analogue state resonances. A problem in the $Y^{89}(p,\gamma)$ study arose in relating γ-ray resonances with bound levels in Y^{90} because of the high level density in that odd-odd nucleus. The Sr^{88} + p system

*Research supported by the National Science Foundation

has the advantage that the parent analogue nucleus, Sr^{89}, has a much lower level density (Fig. 1). Although there is some lack of agreement in the literature concerning higher excited levels in Sr^{89} populated in the $Sr^{88}(d,p)$ reaction,[2,3] it has not affected the interpretation of the present results, and, in fact, a study of the analogues of these levels should clear up this matter.

Thus, the objects of the present investigation are: (a) to compare the present $Sr^{88}(p,\gamma)$ results with the $Y^{89}(p,\gamma)$ results,[1] since these nuclei are neighboring and therefore closely related, (b) to study several exit channels at the same time since analogue resonances are excellent examples of intermediate resonances,[4] and (c) to show how the structure of a parent analogue state can render a potential E1 resonance unobservable as in the $Mo^{92}(p,\gamma)$ case.

EXPERIMENT

The University of Pennsylvania tandem Van de Graaff was used to accelerate microampere beams of protons which were incident on targets of Mo^{92} and Sr of various thicknesses. Gamma rays were detected with a 5 in x 4 in NaI crystal at the lower bombarding energies (<7 MeV), and a 9 in x 9 in NaI crystal gated by annihilation radiation[5] for E > 7.0 MeV. Elastically and inelastically scattered protons were detected with solid state counters. Figure 2 shows typical spectra for each type of counter. At the higher bombarding energies the major portion of the beam was stopped outside of the target room, 20 feet behind the self-supporting target. Any scattered beam was stopped by a carbon lining of the shielded exit tube.

RESULTS AND CONCLUSIONS

The $Mo^{92}(p,\gamma)$ reaction was studied in the neighborhood of the 5.3 MeV s-wave analogue state resonance. A 13 keV enriched Mo^{92} target evaporated onto a thin carbon backing was used. This resonance, where fine structure was first reported,[6] was selected for study partly because it occurs at a proton bombarding energy below the (p,n) threshold. No resonance in El radiation to the 0.39 MeV $p_{1/2}$ proton-hole level in Tc^{93} was found. An explanation for this negative result is that the parent $1/2^{+}$ analogue state in Mo^{93} has the $2p_{1/2}$ proton shell occupied with high probability, in which case no $s_{1/2} \rightarrow p_{1/2}$ transition can occur.

The $Sr^{88}(p,p_{o})$ reaction was first studied by Fox, Moore and Robson.[7] The present Sr^{88} + p data for the resonance at 6.1 MeV is shown in Fig. 3. It can be seen that the (p,γ_{o}) resonance is quite sharp and a weak effect is seen in the (p,p') channel. The radiative strength for this resonance is $\Gamma_{\gamma} = \Gamma/\Gamma_{p}$ (20 ± 10)eV, and for the corresponding s-wave resonance in $Y^{89}(p,\gamma_{o})$ at E_{p} = 6.15 MeV is $\Gamma_{\gamma} = (\Gamma/\Gamma_{p})$ (17 ± 8) eV according to our measurements. The present value for Γ_{γ} for $Y^{89}(p,\gamma)$ differs from the estimate in Ref. 2 by a factor of two and this discrepancy is being investigated. In any case, the El radiative strength of these resonances is much weaker than single particle $(\Gamma_{\gamma s.p.}$ = 4 keV) which is evidence that the analogue state has a complex structure.

Shell model calculations of the odd-parity excited-state spectrum of Y^{90} taking into account proton-hole and neutron-particle configurations[8] give quite a good representation of these levels. However, each level involves several different configurations and hence its

analogue is quite complicated. Since many components
are inert for El decay, or have phases which cancel with
other components in the matrix element, the El decay is
much weaker than single particle as observed.

The s-wave resonance at 7.51 MeV was studied as
indicated in Fig. 3 and of particular interest is the
strong resonance in the p' channel. A highly oversimplified model[9] for understanding the two observed
s-wave resonances in Sr^{88} + p can be given. It involves
coupling a 2^+ two quasi-particle state to a $d_{5/2}$
particle to obtain a component of the s-wave function in
addition to the single particle component. The presence
of a strong resonance in the p' channel is associated
with d-wave proton escape leaving the residual nucleus
in the first excited state. One can then relate the
strengths of the 7.51 MeV and 6.10 MeV resonances in
the p' channel and the γ-decay channel.

We wish to acknowledge stimulating discussions
with Dr. S. Fallieros and to thank Dr. R. H. Venter for
encouraging us to study the $Sr^{88}(p,\gamma)$ reaction. We are
grateful to Dr. D. M. Van Patter for experimental
assistance.

REFERENCES

1) J. L. Black and N. W. Tanner, Phys. Letts. $\underline{11}$ (1964) 135.

2) R. L. Preston, M. B. Sampson and H. J. Martin, Can. J. Phys. $\underline{42}$ (1964) 321.

3) B. L. Cohen, Phys. Rev. $\underline{125}$ (1962) 1358.

4) S. Fallieros, Proc. Conf. on Nuclear Spectroscopy with Direct Reactions 143 (1964), F. E. Throw, ed.

5) B. Ziegler, J. M. Wyckoff, H. W. Koch, Nucl. Instr. Methods $\underline{24}$ (1963) 301.

6) P. Richard, C. F. Moore, D. Robson and J. D. Fox, Phys. Rev. Letts. $\underline{13}$ (1964) 343.

7) J. D. Fox, C. F. Moore and D. Robson, Phys. Rev. Letts. $\underline{12}$ (1964) 198; C. F. Moore, Ph.D. Dissertation Florida State University, 1964, (unpublished).

8) T. A. Hughes and S. Fallieros, Bull. Am. Phys. Soc. $\underline{11}$ (1966) 84.

9) S. Fallieros, private communication, 1966.

DISCUSSION

YAVIN, University of Illinois: I thought that it might be worthwhile pointing out that we have conducted an experiment which somewhat ties up with the experiment reported here now, as well as with a previous paper.

We have heard a talk about gamma transitions between giant dipole resonances and ground states. We also heard a talk about gamma transitions between analogue (to ground) states and the corresponding ground states.

In our experiment we studied gamma transitions "upward" from the analogue states, namely, transitions from the analogue state to its own (assumed dipole giant resonance). We observed the proton decay of the analogue state, which follows a (p, γ) process. The purpose of the experiment was to investigate whether analogue states can have their own giant dipole resonance.[*]

HAMBURGER, University of Pittsburgh: You mentioned a discrepancy between the widths in the elastic channel and the inelastic channel. Is this just looking at the data or did you actually fit the elastic data?

SHAFROTH: Just looking. We haven't done any fitting yet. In fact, we are not sure how to treat the inelastic data yet.

HAMBURGER: The elastic resonance at 7.51 MeV looks broader than the inelastic resonance.

SHAFROTH: Yes.

---

[*]See paper S9 for further discussion of this experiment.

HAMBURGER: And the other question: Would you explain the discrepancy of the factor of 100 in the transition strength which you found?

SHAFROTH: First, let me say that Γ_{γ_0} for the 6.10 MeV resonance can now be evaluated by taking the result of Cosman et al., who in a contribution to this conference reported on the $Sr^{88}(p,p)$ and $Sr^{88}(p,p')$ reactions and found $T/T_p = 1.5$. Thus, we obtain $\Gamma_{\gamma_0} = 26$ eV.

This is $1/150$ $\Gamma(s.p.)$. We expect the E1 strength to be weakened by a factor $(2T + 1)$, i.e. 13. The fact that there is an additional hinderance by a factor of 10 indicates that the parent analogue state is more complex than a single neutron in the $3S_{1/2}$ orbit.

I already mentioned one additional configuration. Studies of $Sr^{88}(d,p)Sr^{89}$ lead to spectroscopic factors which are just squared amplitudes of the single particle components of the wave functions for various excited states. Knowledge of the radiative strength for E1 decay gives information about the amplitude, including the sign of the various components of the wave function.

The present result indicates that a cancellation occurs between the various components of the Sr^{89} parent-state wave function. A similar hindrance has been observed for Zr^{90}. This is presumably for reasons similar to those just mentioned. A general explanation for this weakening of E1 strength is that wave functions with coherently adding amplitudes lie about 5 MeV above the giant dipole resonance according to Fallieros, Goulard, Venter and Hughes.

Admittedly, the coupling of the initial state wave functions to the continuum is neglected, but this is not expected to affect the qualitative conclusions.

HAMBURGER: Is this mixing of configurations due to the isobaric resonance or just an ordinary mixing?

SHAFROTH: The mixing of different configurations in the analogue resonances just reflects the mixing in the low-lying parent states, which manifests itself as fragmentation of single particle levels, for reasons unrelated to isobaric spin.

AXEL, University of Illinois: I would like to answer that question in a slightly different way which is not at all that detailed. I think it's very clear that the things you would estimate as single particle strengths can't be where you thought they were.

The giant resonance is taking the dipole sum of all the single particle transitions. Now, to get a theory which includes the analogue state and its mixing with the giant resonance to see how much the giant resonance has taken out of it is many years off, but I don't think that one has to be concerned with the depression of the single particle transition rate until that problem is solved.

STEIN, University of Washington, Seattle: Can you understand the large cross-section of the (p,p') to the 2^+ in terms of the particular configuration of the analogue state? In other words, how do you understand the very strong transition of the analogue state to the 2^+ state?

SHAFROTH: I tried to explain that in my talk, where a very oversimplified model for understanding the two s-wave resonances was given. According to this model, the ratio of the squared amplitudes of the single $3S_{1/2}$ particle components for the two $S_{1/2}$

resonances should be the same as the inverse ratio of the reduced widths for the (p,p') channel and this should be the same as the ratio of the spectroscopic factors from the $Sr^{88}(d,p)Sr^{89}$ reaction.

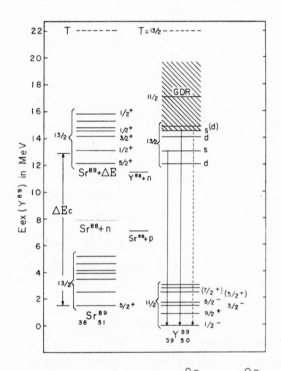

Fig. 1. Level diagrams for Sr^{89} and Y^{89}. The Sr^{89} level scheme is shown at the true energy with respect to Y^{89}. It is also shown shifted up by the Coulomb energy difference minus the n-H mass difference. Analogue states in Y^{89} having ground state γ-ray resonances are indicated.

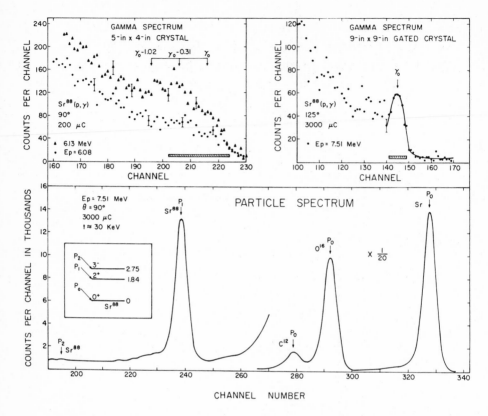

Fig. 2. Spectra. Upper left: 5 in x 4 in. Crystal γ-ray spectrum at resonance and at 75 keV above the 6.10 MeV resonance. Upper right: 9 in x 9 in gated crystal γ-ray spectrum taken at the 7.51 MeV resonance. The background below the ground state peak is mostly due to lower energy gamma rays. Bottom: Solid state counter spectrum taken at 90° at the 7.51 MeV resonance, showing the p_1 proton group.

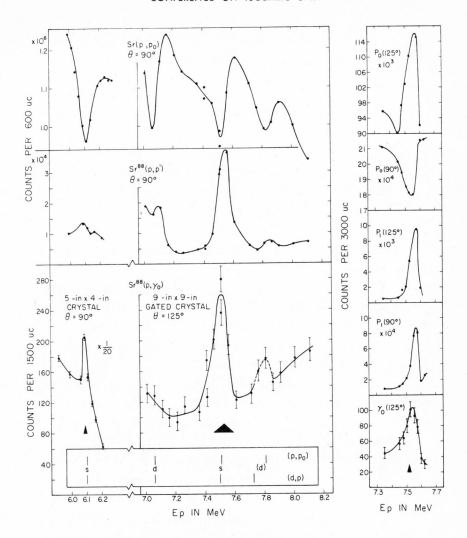

Fig. 3. Yield curve data for the various observed outgoing channels. The resolution is indicated by the solid triangles. At the far right is shown a more detailed study of the resonances at E_p = 7.51 MeV.

B7. COULOMB DISPLACEMENT ENERGY SYSTEMATICS FROM CALCIUM TO SAMARIUM

A. A. Jaffe and M. Harchol
Physics Department, The Hebrew University,
Jerusalem, Israel

The figure shows the available data on Coulomb displacement energies (ΔE_c) for cases where the values of ΔE_c are known to an accuracy of better than 50 keV for values of $19 < Z < 63$. The data includes some of our own measurements and also that of many other workers and has been obtained in a variety of ways including the study of analogue resonances, (p,d) reactions and (He^3,t) reactions. A table of the Coulomb displacement energies and details of the sources of the data used will shortly be published elsewhere.

Anderson[1] found a good fit to the Coulomb displacement energies using the empirical relation $\Delta E_c = 1.444$ Z $/A^{1/3} - 1.13$ MeV (where Z is the mean value of the atomic number for a pair of analogue states of mass A, differing by one unit in Z). The values of ΔE_c fitted by Anderson were less accurate, on the average, by almost one order of magnitude than those used here. In order to display the variations in ΔE_c on an expanded scale the difference between the measured values and those predicted by the above relation are plotted as ordinates. The value of the neutron number and of Z refer to the member of the analogue pair having the

230

lower value of Z.

Considering the variation of ΔE_c with atomic number it may be seen (for example for both N = 28, N = 30 where there are five different values of Z represented, and also for many other values of N) that there are virtually no significant deviations from the $Z/A^{1/3}$ dependence since the points for different values of Z almost coincide. In particular there is no evidence for Coulomb pairing energy effects which would appear as a difference in ordinate for odd and even values of Z. The absence of such effects (well known in light nuclei) is expected since most of the nuclei have quite large values of T. The points representing Sm^{145} and Nd^{143} which are somewhat low (though not clearly so) may exhibit the effect of the onset of deformation.

The variation of ΔE_c with neutron number shows some systematic effects. In the region of the $f_{7/2}$ shell (N = 21 → 28) the initial rise in the position of the points with increasing N corresponds to the fact that the Coulomb radius changes more slowly than $A^{1/3}$. Following the completion of the $g_{9/2}$ shell at N = 50 there is a systematic fall in the points as more and more neutrons are added (and hence the added proton in the analogue state spends correspondingly more time outside the closed shell).

REFERENCES

1. J. D. Anderson, C. Wong and J. W. McClure, Phys. Rev. 138 (1965) B615.

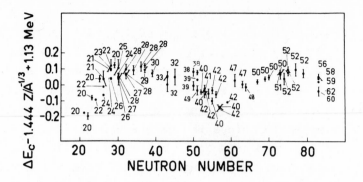

Fig. 1.   Variation of E_c with neutron number.

SESSION C

D. Inglis, Chairman

C1. HIGH RESOLUTION STUDIES
OF SOME ISOBARIC LEVELS

E. G. Bilpuch

Duke University
Durham, North Carolina

At neutron physics meetings there is a game called "Resolutionsmanship" and two of the most skilled participants are H. W. Newson of Duke University and W. W. Havens of Columbia University. The object of this game is to outdo your opponent in the art of high resolution or at least to make it appear so. This game is very similar to one called "Slidesmanship" which was discussed by Wilkinson at the Nuclear Structure Conference in Kingston[1]. Interested persons can learn more about the ground rules of this game if they read the papers by Newson and Havens which were given at the Fast Neutron Physics Conference at Houston, Texas[2]. I mention this point because I've worked with Henry Newson for the past 12 years, first as a student and then as an associate. I've been personally associated with our high resolution developments so I know first hand that our main purpose was to learn more about the nucleus and not simply to claim the best resolution in the country.

In the charged particle experiment I want to discuss today, we have simply used the resolution techniques which we developed in our neutron physics program. The homogenizer is a device which has already

been described in the literature[3]. Briefly, it is a
device which removes the time dependent energy fluctuations which are present in a Van de Graaff beam and
can be as large as $\pm$ 1 keV. The incoherent energy
spread from an RF source is reported to be about 70 eV
(full width at half maximum) so that if this beam were
accelerated to 2.1 MeV then a beam resolution of 1 part
in 30,000 should be possible. One can improve this
by a factor of 3 if a duoplasmatron source is used
since the energy spread of a duoplasmatron is reported
to be about 25 eV.

Normally this resolution is unobservable because of the target Doppler effect and the target
thickness effect. We circumvented these effects by
developing a windowless gas target chamber which normally runs at very low temperatures and we called this
device "The Cryogenic Target Chamber"[4]. We can operate the target chamber from room temperature to 4° K;
the operating temperature is determined by the liquification point of the target gas. Normally our target
gas is less than 100 eV thick and the low yield from
so thin a target is compensated for by increasing the
beam to 20 or 30 µ amp. We can increase the beam to
large values because we do not have a target backing
and very little energy is lost in our vapor target. A
high resolution 20 or 30 µ amp beam is possible since
we corona control and derive our energy correction signal from the HH$^+$ beam. The floor plan for our work on
A^{40} is shown in Fig. 1. In this figure you can see
that we put the HH$^+$ beam through our electrostatic analyzer and derive the energy correction signal from the
analyzer image slits. Normally our target chamber is
at a potential of 3500 volts and is modulated with the

236

homogenizer correction signal. From this figure we can see why a proton beam of 30 μ amps is possible since the H^+ port has no slits except for a collimator just before the target chamber. For our high resolution work we use quadrupole lens and deflectors on the H^+ port and have been able to focus 30 μ amps through an .065 inch hole. We can probably get higher usable beams with our 3 MeV Van de Graaff but have not found it necessary to do so up to the present time. For example, with a 30 μ amp beam and counting for 300 μ coulombs we require a counting time of only 10 secs.

In Fig. 2 we show an isometric drawing of our charged particle target chamber which is appended to the bottom of our cryostat. For the $Ar^{40}(p,p)$ reaction liquid helium was the primary refrigerant and liquid air was the secondary refrigerant which was used as a radiation shield and also served to precool the target gas. The target chamber is essentially four concentric cylinders: the outermost is the radiation shield and was run at 77° K, the next two surfaces were run at 4° K and served as very efficient pumps for the target gas which escaped from the cooling cavity which is the innermost surface. For argon the cooling cavity was run at 60° K and the gas input rate was 20 cc/min. The gas was bled into the cooling cavity via a capillary tube which is controlled by a flow gauge located at the console. The temperature gradient rods governs the amount of heat transferred to the liquid helium reservoir and the heater allows a precise adjustment of the cooling cavity temperature. The openings through the target chamber are 1/8 inch and the beam is collimated to a diameter of 0.065 inch. This allows the beam to traverse the target chamber without touching

any of the surfaces. This is important since our temperatures must be held constant if we are to expect a
constant gas density. The deicers are shown more
clearly in Fig. 3. Gas escaping from the reaction
chamber would normally freeze out on the 4° surfaces
along the beam line. In the case of a (p,n) reaction
we would get a thick target yield and in the case of
an elastic scattering reaction the opening for the
scattered particle would close up. In order to keep
the beam line and the opening for the scattered particle detector clear we have installed deicers. The
deicers (like the cooling cavity) are maintained at a
temperature just a few degrees above the liquification
point of the target gas.

A typical detector spectrum taken with a 100
channel pulse height analyzer is shown in Fig. 4. The
nearly total lack of background counts results from
the pure gas target and the well defined detector
acceptance angle which is 5 milli-steradians. The
major peak is the proton elastic peak and the small
peak around channel 70 is due to the $A^{40}(p,\alpha)Cl^{37}$ reaction. The inset shows the α peak expanded by a factor
of 100. From this spectrum it is clear that the excitation function for protons and α's can be obtained
simultaneously be setting wide gates on each peak.
Our total energy spread is about 200 eV for this reaction and the energy resolution of the detector is not
important since its only function is to detect the
particles.

In Fig. 5 we show the level diagram for A^{40} + p
and the five possible reactions which are (p,p), (p,α),
(p,n), (p,p') and (p,γ). From this level scheme we
expect that inelastic proton scattering will be very

small since our proton energies only go up to 2.7 MeV
and the first excited state of A^{40} is at 1.462 MeV.
We also can assume that the partial width of the (p,γ)
reaction will be small in comparison to the other exit
channels. Also, below the (p,n) threshold (2.344 MeV)
the neutron channel will be closed. Above the neutron
threshold the spin change from A^{40} to K^{40} is 0^+ to 4^-.
This means that neutron penetration factors will play
an important role as to which compound nucleus state
we can observe through the (p,n) reaction. For example, an $\ell = 0$ proton forming a $1/2^+$ state would require an f-wave neutron out to form the nucleus K^{40}.
For the first several hundred keV of neutron energy
this would certainly be unobservable. For the α particle reaction the change of spin is 0^+ to $3/2^+$. Probably the most likely reaction here is an $\ell = 2$ proton
in to form a $3/2^+$ state and an $\ell = 0$ α out to the ground
state of Cl^{37}.

Figure 6 shows the excitation function for the
$A^{40}(p,n)K^{40}$ reaction about 100 keV above threshold.
The energy range is 32 keV and the inset shows two resonances which are separated by only 360 eV. The resonance at 2.4425 MeV has a total width of 140 eV.
This number includes the target thickness, the beam
spread, the target Doppler and the natural width of the
level. One should notice that there is nothing unusual
in this energy region. This energy region is where
one would expect to find the isobaric analogue of the
6th excited state of A^{41}. I will come back to this
point in a few minutes.

In Fig. 7 we show the effect of the homogenizer
on our resolution. The triangles are data taken with
our gas target but without the homogenizer. The closed

circles represent the same data except that the homogenizer is on the target. The improvement in resolution is quite dramatic showing an increased resolution
greater than a factor of 4.

Figure 8 shows the level scheme for A^{41} and K^{41}.
When we form the compound state of K^{41} by A^{40} + p we
are 10 to 11 MeV up in excitation. By correcting for
the Coulomb energy difference and the neutron proton
mass difference we can compare these two nuclei. The
proton energy is measured from the ground state of A^{41}
for ease of comparing levels. 0.497 MeV should be
added to each energy level in K^{41} to get the kinetic
energy of the proton in the CM system. For example,
the $3/2^-$ level in K^{41} is at a proton energy of 1.825
MeV and the $1/2^+$ level is at a proton energy of 2.390
in the CM system. These energies would be 1.87 MeV
and 2.45 MeV in the laboratory system. The energy
levels of A^{41} are from Kashy et al.[5] The 6th excited state has $\ell_n = 0$ and therefore $J^\pi = 1/2^+$. The
4th excited state has $\ell_n = 1$ and $J^\pi = 3/2^-$ or $1/2^-$.
Recently, Allen et al.[6] through a $A^{40}(d,p\gamma)A^{41}$ experiment have assigned a $J^\pi = 3/2^-$ to this level and
to the 2nd excited state. The spectroscopic factors
which we derived from Kashy's data for the 2nd, 4th
and 6th excited states are roughly 0.13, 0.54 and 0.027,
respectively. The other excited states have a high
angular momentum or are very weak and we saw no signs
of them in the analogue region in K^{41}. The regions
which we studied in detail in the K^{41} nucleus are isobaric analogues of the 2nd, 4th and 6th excited states
of A^{41}.

In Fig. 9 we show a single-level phase shift
calculation for an energy of 1.813 MeV and for various

values of the angular momentum of the proton. All our
elastic scattering data from argon were taken at an
angle of 135° with respect to the proton beam. The
calculations shown in this figure are for that angle.
It is quite clear that if one can resolve the levels
one can assign the spin and parity of each level almost by inspection. In the upper portion of this figure we show an observed level fitted with $J^{\pi} = 1/2^{-}$
and $3/2^{-}$. To get the fits shown we used the indicated
parameters. Since our resolution is about 200 eV we
would prefer a J^{π} of $3/2^{-}$ and a level width of 70 eV.

　　　In Fig. 10 (upper curve) we show the data of
Barnard and Kim[7] for A^{40} + p from 1.77 MeV to 2.6 MeV.
I would like to draw your attention to two regions of
the upper curve which are the resonance anomalies at
1.87 MeV and 2.45 MeV. These two regions correspond
to the analogue regions of the 4th and 6th excited
states of A^{41}. Barnard and Kim have taken angular distributions and assign a $J^{\pi} = 3/2^{-}$ to the level at
1.87 MeV and $J^{\pi} = 1/2^{+}$ to the level at 2.45 MeV.

　　　The middle curve in this figure shows our recent high resolution data for the first 280 keV of
the upper curve (data from 1.77 MeV to 2.05 MeV). We
see many levels in the region of 1.87 MeV $\pm$ 50 keV.
Outside this region we see very few levels. In order
to show this region of activity in greater detail we
have expanded 60 keV of the middle curve and show it
in the bottom portion of this figure. All of the resonances in the bottom curve have been fitted with
$J^{\pi} = 3/2^{-}$. The points over the resonances were taken
in steps of 100 eV and the solid line is simply a line
through the points but our fit to these data is almost
as good. This point is illustrated by a fit to the

241

data in the complex region between 1.855 and 1.88 MeV
which is shown in Fig. 11. These data were fitted with
the indicated J^{π}'s and the Γ's with the assumption that
$\Gamma = \Gamma_p$.

In Fig. 12 we show our data in the region above
2 MeV up to 2.6 MeV (the upper and middle curves). The
upper curve represents the excitation curve from 2 MeV
to 2.30 MeV and level structure is evident. In the
middle curve of Fig. 12 we show the data from 2.3 to
2.6 MeV and once again we see a band of strong levels
around 2.45 MeV. This is exactly the energy region
where one would expect the isobaric analogue of the 6th
excited state of A^{41} to occur. The 6th excited state
has been assigned $\ell_n=0$ from (d,p) work. Again we expand 50 keV about the energy 2.45 MeV and show these
data in the lower curve. The line through the data is
now a calculated fit and we see that the large levels
have a $J^{\pi}=1/2^+$. It is interesting to note that the
level spacings for the $1/2^+$ states around 2.45 MeV is
about 10 keV and the spacing for $3/2^-$ states around
1.87 MeV is about 5 keV. This is what one would expect
for a 2J+1 dependence for the level spacing.

From the analysis of these data we have extracted
the reduced widths of all the levels that we observed.
In Fig. 13 we have plotted the sum of the reduced widths
as a function of the proton energy for states of $J^{\pi}=1/2^+$,
$1/2^-$ and $3/2^-$. The isobaric analogue positions in the
compound nucleus K^{41} are located by the sudden increase
in the sum of the reduced widths for the $3/2^-$ case and
for the $1/2^+$ case. For the $1/2^-$ case we see that the sum
of the reduced widths have a constant slope. It should
be pointed out here that the slope of each curve is a
measure of the local value of the strength function.

From these data we are convinced that the analogue
state has lost its identity as a single state and is
represented by the enhancement of the normal T states
of the compound nucleus. At least for this nucleus it
appears that we have strong mixing.

Robson has recently published[8] calculations of
the enhancement of the fine structure in the neighborhood of an isobaric analogue resonance. A characteristic result of these calculations is an asymmetry of
the enhancement; that is, the fine structure is expected to be strongly enhanced over a considerable
energy range below the position of the analogue resonance but much less so immediately above. In Fig. 13
we see that the qualitative behavior of the s-wave plot
seems to confirm this prediction. The slope of the
curve increases slowly in the region just below the
analogue resonance but cuts off sharply above it. However, there is little indication of a similar behavior
in the $3/2^-$ plot. Recent unpublished results of Robson
now indicate asymmetry for the $1/2^+$ case and no asymmetry for the $3/2^-$ case in agreement with the data
shown in Fig. 13.

We have averaged our data with a 6 keV running
average and Fig. 14 shows that the fine structure is
now unobservable but the two analogue regions still
show anomalous behavior. A wider resolution function
can make these regions look like single levels. This
leads one to think that perhaps if levels were very
close one still gets enhancement but through resonance-
resonance interference and the addition of tails of
resonances the analogue state could appear as a single
state. Preliminary calculations by Dr. Kyker of our
group indicate that many closely spaced levels can

appear as a single level.

In Fig. 15 we show some data between the analogue regions. These data (the (p,n), (p,α) and (p,p))
were taken simultaneously and slight differences in
energy have some meaning. It should be pointed out at
this point that the (p,α) resonances and (p,n) resonance did not show an enhancement of levels at the
analogue regions. The data in Fig.15 shows the importance of exit channel spins for the various decay
modes. At several energies we see neutron and α resonances but very little sign of a resonance for the
proton. This probably means that these states are
formed by $\ell = 2$ or $\ell = 3$ protons and that the partial
widths for neutron and α decay are much larger than
the proton partial width.

Recently Winkler et al. at the University of
Zurich reported[9] two narrow elastic resonances at a
proton energy of 1.086 and 1.1018 MeV. This is the
excitation region where one would expect to see the
analogue of the 2nd excited state of A^{41}. From (d,p)
work the 2nd excited state has $\ell_n = 1$ and therefore
$J^{\pi} = 1/2^-$ or $3/2^-$. The Zurich group reported the level
at 1.086 MeV to be either $1/2^-$ and $\Gamma = 10 \pm 5$ eV or
$3/2^-$ and $\Gamma = 5 \pm 3$ eV. The level at 1.1018 MeV is reported to be $\ell = 1$, $J^{\pi} = 3/2^-$ and $\Gamma = 20 \pm 7$ eV. We
have also looked at this region and the data is shown
in Fig. 16. We have drawn a line through the data and
the two levels shown are the ones observed by the
Zurich group. Our energy scale should be shifted down
by 2 keV to make the energy scales for the two experiments agree. There are probably smaller levels in
this region but we would have to have better statistics
in order to observe them. The Zurich group reports

resonance anomalies ranging from .5% to 5%. The larger
resonance in our data goes through a change of 12% and
our preliminary assignment for this resonance is $J^{\pi} =$
$3/2^{-}$.

The second excited state of A^{41} has only 1/4
the strength of the 4th excited state. This fact
coupled with the lower energy probably is the reason
we see only two weak resonances in this analogue region.

In conclusion I would like to acknowledge several people who deserve a lot of the credit for this
experiment. My graduate student, G. A. Keyworth, II,
designed the charged particle scattering chamber and
spent many hours taking and fitting the data. He was
assisted throughout by Mr. D. L. Sellin. My associate,
Dr. G. C. Kyker, Jr., also assisted in the experiment
and spent many hours performing calculations and writing the program for the single level and multi-level
fits. I would also like to acknowledge valuable discussions with Dr. D. Robson of Florida State University
and Dr. L. C. Biedenharn and Dr. N. R. Roberson of
Duke University.

REFERENCES

1) D. H. Wilkinson, Proc. of Inter. Conf. on Nucl. Struc., Edited by D. A. Bromley and E. W. Vogt (University of Toronto Press, Toronto, 1960), p. 906.

2) H. W. Newson, Progress in Fast Neutron Physics, Edited by G. C. Phillips, J. B. Marion, and J. R. Risser (The University of Chicago Press, Chicago, 1963), p. 235.

3) P. B. Parks, H. W. Newson and R. M. Williamson, Rev. Sci. Instr. 29 (1958) 834.

4) P. B. Parks, P. M. Beard, E. G. Bilpuch and H. W. Newson, Rev. of Sci. Instr. 35 (1964) 549.

5) E. Kashy, A. M. Hoogenboom and W. W. Buechner, Phys. Rev. 124 (1961) 1917.

6) J. P. Allen, A. J. Howard and D. A. Bromley, Bull. Am. Phys. Soc., Series II, Vol. 11 (1966) 81.

7) A. C. L. Barnard and C. C. Kim, Nucl. Phys. 28 (1961) 428.

8) D. Robson, Phys. Rev. 137 (1965) B535.

9) H. Winkler, R. E. Pixley and R. Bloch, Bull. Am. Phys. Soc., Series II, Vol. 10 (1966) 1204.

DISCUSSION

ROBSON, Florida State: The asymmetries in strength functions or fluctuations appear to arise from the coherent nature of isobaric spin mixing between fine structure states and a particular analogue state. Each fine structure state observed will, from first order perturbation theory, have two contributions of interest i.e.

$$|\bar{\mu}\rangle \approx |\mu\rangle - \frac{h_{\lambda\mu}}{\mathcal{E}_\lambda - \mathcal{E}_\mu} |\lambda\rangle \qquad \text{(h = Coulomb operator)}$$

wherein $|\mu\rangle$ is the original unmixed fine structure $(T_<)$ state and $|\lambda\rangle$ is the unmixed analogue state $(T_>)$ of interest. The corresponding reduced width relation for the proton channel is

$$\gamma_{p\bar{\mu}} \approx \gamma_{p\mu} - \frac{h_{\lambda\mu}}{\mathcal{E}_\lambda - \mathcal{E}_\mu} \gamma_{p\lambda}$$

and we see that interference will take place between the two contributions.

The important factor however is the energy denominator which is opposite sign depending on whether the fine structure energy $\mathcal{E}_\mu$ is below or above the analogue state energy. Provided $h_{\lambda\mu}\gamma_{p\lambda}$ and $\gamma_{p\mu}$ have roughly the same phase for all fine structure states then we get constructive interference on one side and destructive on the other. For the single channel case it is easy to show that $h_{\lambda\mu}\gamma_{p\lambda}$ and $\gamma_{p\mu}$ have the same phase so that asymmetries in the strength function are to be expected. However the degree of asymmetry depends on the presence of $T_<$ proton strength since otherwise no interference occurs in squaring the reduced width amplitude $\gamma_{p\bar{\mu}}$.

Putting in numbers one find that asymmetries are more likely for s-waves than higher partial waves and this appears to be the case experimentally.

WIGNER, <u>Princeton</u>: Could I ask Robson, why are the phases of the $\gamma_{\mu p}$ all the same sign? Mostly, I would have thought that the $\gamma_{\mu p}$ would fluctuate in sign.

ROBSON: If we go back to this phase requirement, we see that the state $|\mu\rangle$ appears in the matrix element $h_{\lambda\mu}$, and if you evaluate that, assuming the R-matrix-type approach, you come out with a constant L_p times $\gamma_{\lambda p}\,\gamma_{\mu p}$, and so the $\gamma_{\mu p}$ part is the same in both contributions; consequently, the phase is the same in both cases.

That's why it only works in such cases. Of course, if you have contributions other than this proton channel, then you will not get a simple phase relationship.

WIGNER: What is the origin of this formula, the $h_{\lambda\mu}$. I believe it is the interaction matrix which connects the state λ and the state μ.

The $\gamma_{\mu p}$ is the phase of the proton wave function at the nuclear surface. I would have expected that both $h_{\lambda\mu}$ and $\gamma_{\mu p}$ fluctuate in sign.

ROBSON: Correct. The approximation I have mentioned is that most of the mixing comes from the surface region.

WIGNER: Thank you very much.

SEGEL, <u>Argonne</u>: Do you feel that in the nuclei about mass 100 that with good enough resolution you would also see the same pattern of isolated levels with no effect of the analogue state between these?

BILPUCH: That is what this data seems to indicate.

SEGEL: But did you take data at mass 100?

BILPUCH: No, we haven't taken data, but we have

done some preliminary calculations with some levels very
close to each other and see what happens, and it looks
like we do get sort of an envelope for these levels
which represent the analogue state.

I don't know, I am just guessing, but it seems
that when you take our data and you average it by wide
enough resolution, you do indeed get an envelope, and
if you measure angular distributions of these envelopes,
you do indeed see that it's a $3/2^-$ state.

SEGEL: Yes, I understand, but I am not clear on
how good was the resolution for the data--I believe it
was taken here at Florida State-- which showed this fine
structure.

BILPUCH: I think that was the order of a kilovolt,
and when you get up to A = 100, you are getting up to
where you have spacings of the order of 10 eV, and I
don't think anybody could resolve these levels. I
think the thing to do is to work through this level
density region maybe from a case where the level density
is very small to a nucleus where the level density is
large and see what happens.

I think that maybe what you are getting is indeed
enhancement of normal T levels. Then if you looked at
a nucleus with a spacing of two or three levels within
the region of the analogue, that you might see these two
or three levels suddenly take the strength of the analogue level. This I'd like to do and I am planning to
do.

MOORE, Texas: Your fit to the data was rather
impressive and I was just wondering when you stated in
your talk whether you used a multi-level multi-channel
formula to fit all the levels or whether you used a
series of single-channel formulas.

BILPUCH: We used a multi-level formula.

MOORE: The formula is rather complicated compared to a series of single-level formulas, and when you have not only two levels, but seven levels like you are fitting, it really is a very impressive formula, is it not?

KYKER, Duke: I just wanted to respond to the last question. I have a copy in detail of the multi-level approximation that we used to fit this data. I'd be happy to discuss it with you.

MOORE: Thank you.

WEIL, Kentucky: I have two questions. First, you had a dashed line on the chlorine 37 level that somebody reported once, but that nobody has seen since, and I wondered if you ever saw any alpha particle group to that level.

BILPUCH: At about 1 MeV.

WEIL: Yes. 0.85 MeV.

BILPUCH: No, we will have data that high up, but that has not yet been taken. We are in the process of taking it.

WEIL: The other question was concerning your (p,n) data. There were high energy tails on your high resolution data. I wonder if that was instrumental or if there was significance to it.

BILPUCH: We have worried about the tails on the (p,n) data. We have worried about this for some time, and we reflect the first half of the resonances onto the second half and take the difference. We see something that rises in about 8 eV, and then it tails off to about two kilovolts.

Now, at first, we thought that was an electronic effect like the KLM-shell electrons, because in the

(p,n) data, every neutron that you see must have been
formed by a proton penetrating an electron shell since
the K-shell electron is bound by about 2.3 keV it could
explain this.

Merzbacher has made some preliminary calculations
on this, and he can't explain all of the tail in the
cross-section with the K or L shell.

KYKER: I would just say, in answer to Weil's
questions that I have seen the same sort of asymmetry
on the upper side of the resonance in high resolution
inelastic proton scattering. The data was on somewhat
thicker targets where it's possible to be more classical
about it, and in that case, the usual (Landau) energy-
loss formulas fit the shape of the tail rather well. I
think it's just a function of the manner of the energy
loss.

GARVEY, Princeton: I am just wondering if mistakes
can be made by taking a width as measured in poor resolution, and from this width extract a reduced width
for the proton, rather than doing very high resolution
work and adding up all the pieces to get the width.

WIGNER: May I ask one more question? In your
graph, in which you plot the sum of the reduced widths,
those sums of reduced widths increase suddenly at the
analogue state.

Now, according to the explanation which Robson just
gave, and with which I think we are all very much in
agreement, the density of the resonance levels, that is,
the number of the steps per unit energy interval on your
curve, should be the same all through the graph. This
does not appear to be the case. In fact, the number of
levels appeared to be much greater near the analogue
states than far from the analogue states. Could this be

instrumental or can you see some reason for the levels
to congregate near the analogue states?

BILPUCH: I think these levels in this nucleus,
are just at the point of being observable, and what we
see out of the distribution of all levels are the levels
of big widths. These levels, if they were not enhanced,
and if the analogue state did not exist, would not be
observable. In that case I don't think you would see
two-thirds of the levels we saw.

WIGNER: I see.

BILPUCH: I'd like to say one more thing. If we
take the spacing over the analogue region for the s-waves,
say, then we get a spacing of about 10 kilovolts, and if
we take the spacing for the 3/2⁻ case, we get a spacing
of about 5 kilovolts, and this is what you would expect
from a (2J+1) dependence. I think there are thousands
of levels here, and if the analogue is selectively enhancing certain spins and parities and bringing them out
of the background then it makes them observable; I think
if one had an infinitely good resolution, then you'd
see all of them.

WIGNER: These giant resonances and their fine
structure, can be calculated in all their details, and
they can be observed much more beautifully than the
original giant resonances could be seen. Isn't that so?

ROBSON: Yes, I agree completely. These are
marvelous places for an experimentalist to really look
at a giant resonance. To my knowledge, these are the
only situations we have in nuclear physics (except perhaps the giant dipole resonance) where we can actually
look at one spin and parity at a time.

FLOOR PLAN

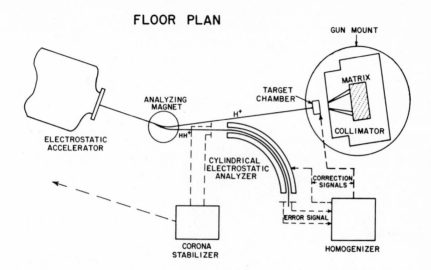

Fig. 1. Floor plan of the 3 MeV Van de Graaff accelerator laboratory. The electrostatic analyzer is used to generate a correction signal from the HH$^+$ beam.

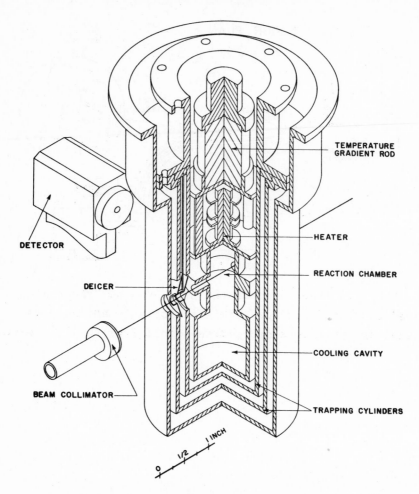

TEMPERATURE
GRADIENT ROD

HEATER

REACTION CHAMBER

DETECTOR

DEICER

COOLING CAVITY

BEAM COLLIMATOR

TRAPPING CYLINDERS

0   1/2   1 INCH

CHARGED PARTICLE CRYOGENIC TARGET CHAMBER

Fig. 2.   Charged particle target chamber.   The reaction chamber assembly and trapping cylinders are attached to a primary refrigerant reservoir containing, in this experiment, liquid helium.   Proper choice of temperature gradient rod and primary refrigerant allows the use of a wide variety of gases.

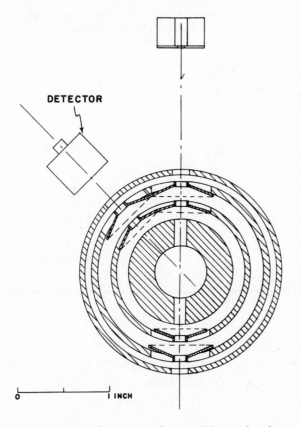

Fig. 3. Sectional view of reaction chamber and trapping cylinders showing the deicer assemblies. These deicers are heated and prevent the target gas from freezing into the beam path.

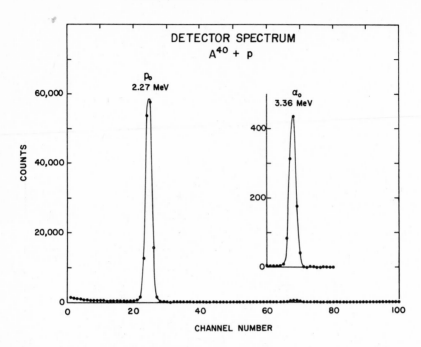

Fig. 4. Typical detector spectrum as measured by a multichannel pulse height analyzer. The near total lack of background is demonstrated. The α-particle, barely discernable, is expanded in the inset.

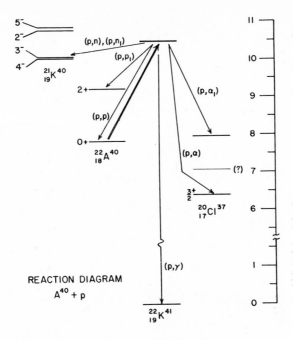

Fig. 5.   Reaction diagram for A^{40} + p.   The (p,p), (p,α) and (p,n) yields were measured.   The cross sections for (p,p') and (p,γ) are much smaller and were not measured.

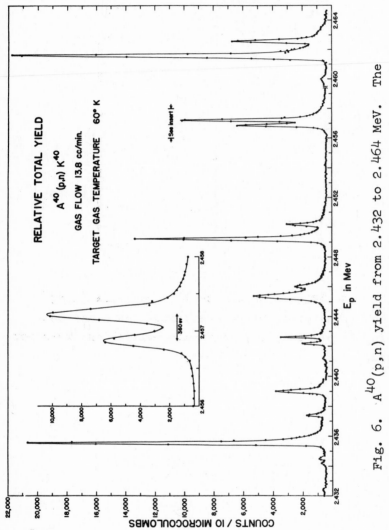

Fig. 6. $A^{40}(p,n)$ yield from 2.432 to 2.464 MeV. The expanded inset illustrates our ability to separate closely spaced levels. Points over the resonances were taken in 50 eV steps

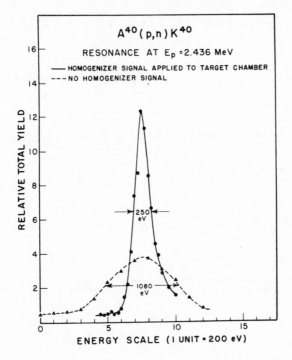

Fig. 7. The effect of the homogenizer on our re-solution.

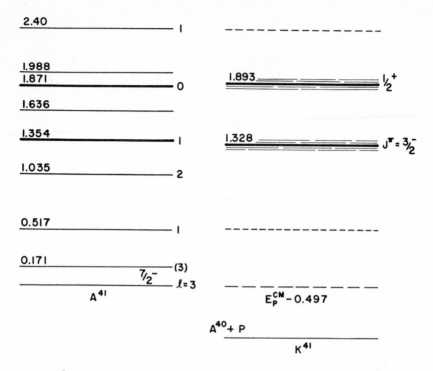

Fig. 8. Energy level diagram for the isobaric doublet A^{41} and K^{41}. The regions of enhanced structure in K^{41} due to the fourth and sixth excited states of A^{41} which are shaded where measured in this experiment. The dashed line in K^{41} corresponding to the second excited state in A^{41} represents the recently measured possible analogue state at 1.1 MeV incident proton energy and the upper dashed line represents another possible analogue state at $E_p = 3.4$ MeV corresponding to the eighth excited state in A^{41}.

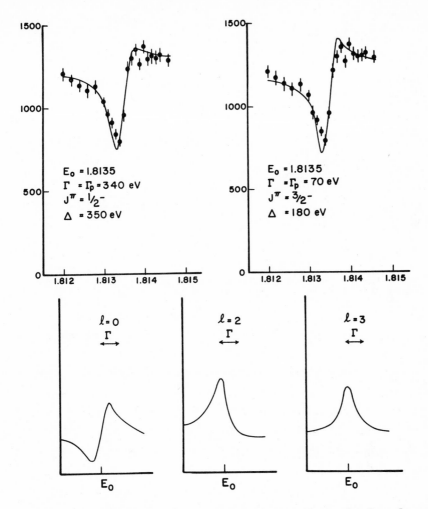

Fig. 9. The upper plots show computed single level fits to the data at 1.813 MeV for two values of J^π. The fit for $J^\pi = 1/2^-$ requires the unusually poor resolution of 350 eV. The lower curves show computed shapes for other values of angular momentum at the same energy.

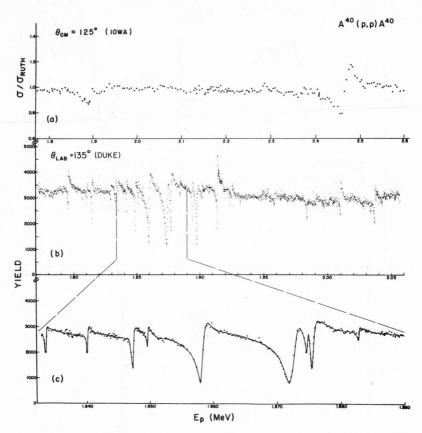

Fig. 10. Elastic proton yield from $A^{40}(p,p)A^{40}$.
(a) Data of Ref. 7 taken with a 6 keV target, for comparison. (b) Duke data from 1.77 MeV to 2.05 MeV.
(c) Expansion of present data near the 1.87 MeV analogue resonance.

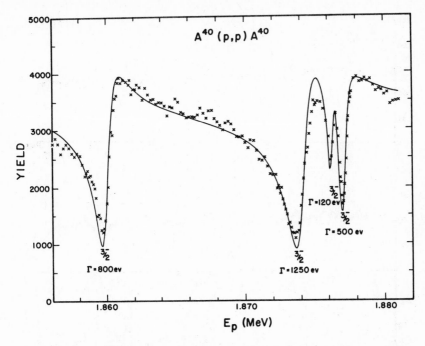

Fig. 11. Sample multilevel fit to the proton scattering data near 1.87 MeV. The solid curve is a theoretical fit. Resonance parameters (as indicated) are determined by trial and error comparison with the data.

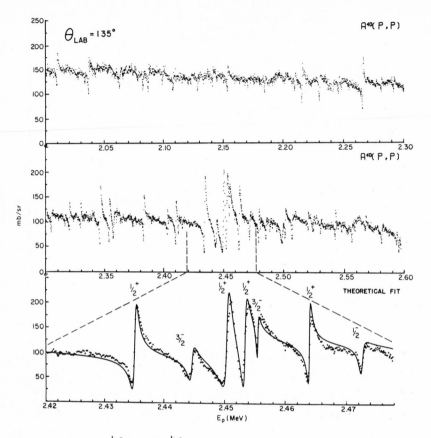

Fig. 12. $A^{40}(p,p)A^{40}$ data at 135° from 2.05 to 2.60 MeV. In the middle curve we again see a strong band of levels around 2.45 MeV which is the analogue region for the 6th excited state of A^{41}. The lower curve is a theoretical fit to the data around the energy 2.45 MeV.

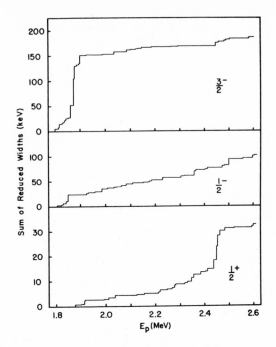

Fig. 13. Integral histogram of reduced widths of resonances in $A^{40}(p,p)A^{40}$ for which spin assignments have been made. The effects of the two analogue resonances are visible in the anomalous behavior of the $3/2^-$ plot near 1.87 MeV and the $1/2^+$ plot near 2.45 MeV.

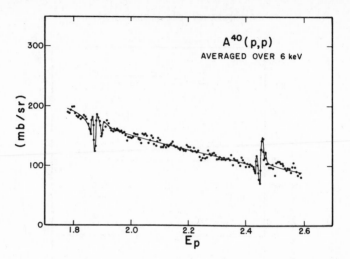

Fig. 14. Our high resolution data averaged with a
6 keV running average. This illustrates again the
particular activity in the analogue level regions.

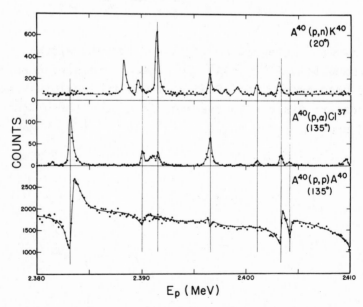

Fig. 15. $A^{40}(p,n)K^{40}$, $A^{40}(p,\alpha)$, $A^{40}(p,p)A^{40}$ data
taken simultaneously.

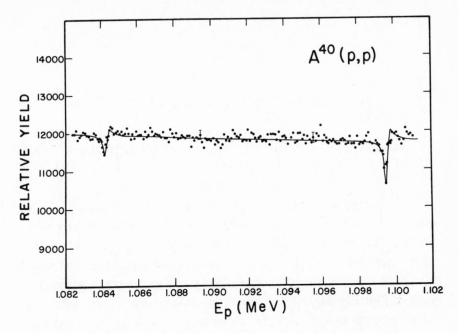

Fig. 16. Recently measured data showing two very narrow levels also reported in Ref. 9. This is the analogue region of the second excited state of A^{41}.

C2. RESONANCE REACTIONS AND SPECTROSCOPY

P. von Brentano

Max-Planck-Institut für Kernphysik, Heidelberg

INTRODUCTION

After the discovery of excitation of isobaric analogue states as resonances in 1964 by Fox, Moore and Robson[2] very many analogue states have been studied in this fashion. These studies served to identify and locate many isobaric analogues of excited states in heavy nuclei, which cannot be studied easily by other means. They have given us a very thorough knowledge of Coulomb energies, throughout the periodic system. They have led and will lead to a deeper understanding of the optical model, especially its isobaric spin part, its imaginary part and also the strength function. Furthermore with reaction mechanism of the resonance reaction being cleared up, we can extract very reliable nucleon widths from analogue states. In the case of elastic resonant scattering one can obtain reduced nucleon widths which can in principle also be measured by a (d,p) reaction on the same target. There is no reason why the widths measured from analogue states should not become as reliable, if not more reliable as widths from (d,p) studies since there are not the difficulties of DWBA approximations in resonance theory. In resonant inelastic scattering we are able to measure nucleon widths between a pair of excited states, information which could otherwise only be obtained by doing stripping and pickup reactions on a target nucleus in an excited state. The knowledge of these widths will obviously increase our knowledge of excited states very much, since it is possible to measure complete wave functions of excited states by this method. We therefore expect that many more of these experiments will be performed in the near future. In this talk, we will give a survey of reactions which do excite analogue states; we give a collision matrix and discuss resonance analysis; we discuss the spectroscopy with analogue states; and we present the results of some recent experiments.

SURVEY OF REACTIONS

One of the most widely used reactions for the study of analogue states as resonances is elastic proton scattering. Figure 1 shows an example of this work in an experiment done by the Florida State group. In the excitation curve of the differential cross section on Zr^{92} targets, one sees strong anomalies and these anomalies are interpreted as being due to isobaric analogue states. In Fig. 2 we show analogue resonances in Sb^{119} observed by the Harwell group, which decay predominantly to an excited 2^+ state in Sn^{118}. It is very interesting to see that these resonances show up much more clearly and pronounced in the inelastic channel than in the elastic channel. The reason is that the ratio of resonance to direct amplitude is larger for inelastic channels. These measurements of inelastic scattering are very important for spectroscopy and one would like to have more of them. Unfortunately they are also rather difficult experiments.

The general method and explanation of these experiments is illustrated in Fig. 3. It consists of

bombarding a nucleus C (for core) with protons forming
thereby compound states in the nucleus (C + p). Subsequently one observes the decay of these resonances
into various exit channels. The compound states of interest here are due to isobaric analogues of low-lying
states of the nucleus (C + n). We will call them
shortly "analogue states" and following a suggestion by
G. M. Temmer we will call the corresponding low-lying
states "parent analogue states". We will now indicate
a connection between these resonances and the bound isobaric analogue states found in light nuclei. We get
this connection by decomposing the total Hamiltonian H
of the system having the resonances into a part H_M which
has bound states and a part V_{res} which couples the bound
states to the continuum. So we have $H = H_M + V_{res}$.
Such a decomposition will be meaningful, if the resonances are sharp because then we can expect V_{res} to have
a small influence on the interior wavefunction of the
resonance. In our case we take for H_M the mass formula
(see e.g. Ref. 25)

$$H_M = H_o + [1/2 \; A - T_z]^2 \cdot \frac{e^2}{2R_M}$$

In this formula H_o stands for the nuclear forces and the
kinetic energy. From charge independence it will obey
the relation $[H_o, T_+] = 0$. The second part of H_M is
obtained from the scalar Coulomb force by neglecting
its radial dependence. By making these simplifications
we have got a Hamiltonian, which has the analogue states
as eigenstates. We find that the following two equations
imply each other.

$$H_M \; \psi_\lambda = E_\lambda \; \psi_\lambda$$
$$H_M(T_- \; \psi_\lambda) = (E_\lambda + \Delta) \cdot T_- \; \psi_\lambda$$

This model predicts that the energy of an analogue state and its parent analogue state differ by a constant, which is essentially the single particle Coulomb energy. While we do not find such a constant Coulomb shift in light nuclei, which have an isobaric spin $T \approx 0$, we find that this prediction is in excellent agreement with data in heavy elements, which have $T \gg 0$. This fact can be used to make a unique identification of the resonances. This correspondence has now been demonstrated by many experiments, so we do not want to discuss it here. The crude model given above is a considerable over simplification. It leads us to expect that the resonances have good isobaric spin and emit no neutrons. The contrary is true as seen in Fig. 4, where we see strong resonances in the (p,n) cross section on Sm^{144}. Of special interest is the magnitude of the absolute resonant cross section, which was measured with the activation method by Messlinger and Morinaga. This cross section is quite big and comparable with the elastic cross section. One has to consider however, that the measured yield is a cross section to all neutron exit channels. If we assume an equal population of the exit levels, each exit channel gets only a very small cross section and in this sense a selection rule seems still to be valid. We will call these reaction forbidden. The occurence of the neutrons shows clearly that the analogue states mix strongly with the surrounding $T_<$ states, and that it is a giant resonance rather than a single state. A direct verification of this behavior has been given by the fine structure measurements by the Florida State and Duke groups.

COLLISION MATRIX

Before we give an interpretation of experiments in terms of Breit-Wigner fits and R-matrix-theory, we want to mention a different approach in terms of a generalized optical model theory. A simplified version of such an approach is the study of the Lane equations, as interpreted by Robson. By using these differential equations, a fit of excitation curves seems possible just as an extension of the usual optical model. Such an approach may prove to be more satisfactory from the point of data analysis but too little has been done until recently to include it in a discussion. See, however, Refs. 17, 18 and 19. In order to discuss these resonances in a unified and quantitative way, we will write down a collision matrix. Our formulation will be only approximately valid, but most analyses made up to now have been made with this formulation. A rigorous form is given by Robson[7]. As we do not want to discuss fluctuations we have to remove the fluctuations by averaging the cross section over an energy interval ΔE. This can only be done for heavy elements, when the condition $\Gamma_< << \Delta E << \Gamma_>$ can be met. Here $\Gamma_<$, $\Gamma_>$ are the total widths of the $T_<$ or $T_>$ states respectively.

The matrix is given for an isolated resonance by

$$U_{a,b,\lambda(J)} = U^D_{ab,J,M} \tag{I}$$

$$+ U^{fl}_{ab,\lambda(J)} \tag{II}$$

$$+ (-i)e^{i(\delta_a+\delta_b)} \cdot \frac{\Gamma^{1/2}_{a\lambda} \Gamma^{1/2}_{\lambda b}}{E-E_\lambda + i/2 \ \Gamma_\lambda} \tag{III}$$

$$+ \frac{\Gamma_{a\lambda}^{1/2}}{\Gamma_{a\ S.P.}^{1/2}} \cdot U_{ab,\lambda}^{fl} \cdot \frac{E-E_\lambda - \Delta_\lambda}{E-E_\lambda + 1/2\ \Gamma_\lambda} \tag{IV}$$

$$+ \frac{\Gamma_{\lambda b}^{1/2}}{\Gamma_{b\ S.P.}} \cdot U_{ab,\lambda}^{fl} \cdot \frac{E-E_\lambda - \Delta_\lambda}{E-E_\lambda + 1/2\ \Gamma_\lambda} \tag{V}$$

$$\tag{1}$$

In this formula a and b denote reaction channels and $\lambda(J)$ stands for the qunatum numbers of the level.

$$\Gamma_\lambda, \ \Gamma_{a\lambda}, \ \Gamma_{\lambda b}, \ \delta_a, \ \delta_b,$$

denote the total and partial width and a phase of the level. The width $\Gamma_{\lambda,S.P.}$ will be explained later.

We now want to discuss the various terms: (I) is the direct amplitude, (II) the compound amplitude, (III) the resonance term, (IV) is a term, which represents a process in which the particle enters the resonant state by an allowed process, but decays through a mixing of the analogue state with the background T< states. In (V) the roles of entrance and exit channels are just reversed. Comparing (III) with (IV) and (V), we can see that (III) is an allowed process in both entrance and exit channels, whereas (IV) and (V) are forbidden in one of them. In the discussion of allowed processes we will forget about contributions of the forbidden processes, because the cross sections of these to a definite channel are normally much smaller. However, we do get appreciable cross sections also for the forbidden reactions, if we sum over all available exit channels as we do for instance in the measurement of a (p,n) cross section, or if there are only a few open channels.

The above form of the collision matrix has been used by the Florida State group to make a number of remarkable predictions. First, the terms (IV) and (V) show that the ratio of cross sections to various forbidden exit channels should not change as we vary the energy over the resonance. This prediction can now be checked, as time of flight measurements of neutron spectra coming from analogue states become available. Such a measurement was done by the Berlin group and is presented in a contributed paper[21] and Fig. 5. Another astonishing prediction is that the shape of the (p,n) resonances should be asymmetric. This asymmetry is different from the asymmetries observed in (p,p) and (p,p') resonances. In these cases the asymmetry is due to an interference of the resonance amplitude with a direct background amplitude U^D. In the case of (p,n) resonances we have reason to assume that the background comes from the compound reaction amplitude U^{fl} and should not show an interference pattern with the resonances after we have averaged out the fluctuations (see Ref. 26). An example of this interference is shown in Fig. 6. This asymmetry is thus another indication of the giant resonance character of the analogue states. From the above form of the collision matrix, we can easily work out fitting formulas for the differential cross section. In the case of elastic scattering on spin 0 targets we get a particularly simple formula[4].

$$\frac{d\sigma}{d\Omega} = \left| \rho_A e^{i\psi_A} + \frac{\lambdabar}{2i} \sum_\lambda e^{2i\delta(\ell,\lambda)} \cdot \frac{\Gamma_{p\lambda} \cdot (J+1/2)P_\ell(\cos\theta)}{E-E_\lambda + i/2\,\Gamma_\lambda} \right|^2$$

$$+ \left| \rho_B e^{i\psi_B} - \frac{\lambdabar}{2} \sum_\lambda e^{2i\delta(\ell,\lambda)} \cdot \frac{\Gamma_{p\lambda} \cdot P_\ell^1(\cos\theta)}{E-E_\lambda + i/2\,\Gamma_\lambda} \right|^2 \qquad (2)$$

We have to specify the following set of parameters for each resonance.

a) ℓ_λ, $(2J + 1)\, \Gamma_{p\lambda} \cdot \Gamma_\lambda^{-1}$, E_λ

b) Γ_λ, $\left(\psi_A - 2\, \delta(\ell,\lambda)\right)$, ρ_A

c) J_λ, ρ_B, $\left(\psi_B - 2\, \delta(\ell,\lambda)\right)$

A very important simplification occurs in the above formulas if we are at sufficiently low energy, so that we can neglect the direct spin-flip amplitude. In this case we usually can find unique parameters for the resonances even from one angle. In order to make the above formula unique, we have yet to specify the energy dependence of ρ_A and ψ_A. These have to be taken as constants for fits over a small energy interval and as slowly varying over larger intervals. This slow energy variation can be obtained by expanding ρ_A and ψ_A in a power series of $1/E$ and keeping only the first few terms. We show two examples of such fits made by the Florida State and Heidelberg groups in Fig. 7 and Fig. 8. We have arranged the above parameters in 3 sets in order to indicate the degree of accuracy with which an analysis will give the parameters. As we need it for our later discussion we will quickly discuss the accuracy with which these parameters are determined separately. The transfered orbital angular momentum quantum number ℓ is uniquely obtained from the behavior of the cross section at the zeroes of the Legendre Polynomials. This behavior of the cross section can be seen in Fig. 7 for the second resonance, which has $\ell = 2$ and therefore does not show up at $\theta = 125°$. The error of $(2J+1)\Gamma_{p\lambda} \cdot \Gamma_\lambda^{-1}$ can be found from Haeberli's rule to be essentially proportional to the error of the absolute cross section.

The resonance energy E_λ can be found rather accurately. The extraction of the true total width Γ_λ from an excitation curve, seems to be a little bit more difficult, because of the influence of the background matrix. The error on the quantity $(2\ J+1)\ \Gamma_{p\lambda}$ is therefore essentially given by the error of Γ_λ. Similar remarks can be made for the other parameters. The determination of J seems in general to require data of a great accuracy. So it is very nice that in a contributed paper by the Texas group to this conference[20] polarization measurements have been used to fix J uniquely. The connection between the fit parameters and nuclear structure is established by deriving the collision matrix from a theory of analogue states as done by Robson. We will discuss this connection below. Here we want to mention only some consequences of this derivation relevant to data fitting. First the above collision matrix has to be modified, if we have two nearby resonances, with same spin and parity. Secondly the splitting of the reaction amplitude into a weakly energy dependent part and a resonance amplitude, will in general determine a radius R, which can be obtained from the fit. We will later introduce another radius R, which is introduced from nuclear structure considerations, and it will be an important consistency check that the two radii are equal. The data analysis becomes much more complicated for inelastic scattering or for elastic scattering on targets with spin $J \neq 0$. In such cases, for each resonance there will be in general several partial widths for a definite reaction channel. In order to determine these widths uniquely one has to combine excitation functions at different angles. Similarly there will be in general several independent direct amplitudes in the various spin channels. It is very useful therefore to introduce some model for the direct amplitudes. A fit formula can again be derived from the collision matrix (Eq. 1), a practical form using a simple model for the direct amplitude has been given in a contributed paper by Heidelberg , see Ref. 22.

SPECTROSCOPY WITH ANALOGUE STATES

We have shown how one gets from a fit to the resonances the partial widths Γ_p. The next question is, what do we learn from these widths, or what is the connection between appropriate reduced widths and nuclear structure. In the following we will answer this by giving relations between proton widths of the analogue state and neutron widths of the corresponding parent analogue state. For a definition of these widths, see e.g. Ref. 5. We denote the reduced partial width of the analogue state $\Phi_{\lambda A}$, which has a spin J for decay into the state C' which has a spin I by emission of a proton with spin j by $\gamma_{\lambda, C'p'}$ or, if explicit reference to angular momenta is required, by $\gamma_{J, Ij}$.

Similarly we denote the decay width of the parent analogue state into the state C' and a neutron by $\gamma_{\lambda, C'n'}$. We then have the relations (see Refs. 7, 17, 23)

$$\gamma_{\lambda(A), C'p'} (R, E_p) = \frac{1}{\sqrt{2T+1}} \cdot \gamma_{\lambda, C'n'} (R, E_n) \qquad (3)$$

isobaric spin forbidden,

$$\gamma_{\lambda(A), C'n'} = 0 \qquad (4)$$

$$\gamma_{\lambda(A), (\vec{T}_- C')n'} \neq 0 \qquad (5)$$

but usually energetically forbidden.

The choice of radius in these equations is not free, but it is the Robson radius R, fixed essentially by requiring

that there should be no mixing between the $T_>$ state and
the corresponding $T_<$ in the region defined by R, see
Ref. 23. These relations are the basis of nuclear spectroscopy with analogue states. They allow us to obtain
spectroscopic information on low lying levels from
measurements made on their isobaric analogue states. In
the Eqs. 3 and 4 we find the basis for the distinction
made above between allowed and forbidden processes,
depending on whether $\gamma \neq 0$ or $\gamma = 0$.

An intuitive explanation of these relations can be
obtained by approximating the wave function of the analogue state by

$$\sqrt{2T + 1} \quad \Phi_\lambda(A) = (\sum_i \vec{t}_-^{\ i}) \ \psi_\lambda =$$

$$\sum_i \left(p_i \otimes (n_i^{-1} \otimes \psi_\lambda) \right)_J$$

The last formula is written in a symbolic notation, in
which p_i denotes a proton and n_i^{-1} a neutron hole. The
wave function ψ_λ is assumed to be antisymmetrized. The
allowed decay width of the analogue state is thus seen
to come just from the protons p_i, which can tunnel
through the Coulomb barrier and leave the nucleus.

We have to mention however, that the relations
Eqs. 3 and 4 given previously are only approximately
valid according to Refs. 7 and 17. For a simple case,
Weidenmüller has given formulas which replace Eq. 3.
These formulas contain additonal terms, which are probably not connected with the single particle character
of the analogue state but which seem to come from the
isobaric spin forbidden decay. These terms seem to arise
naturally from a doorway interpretation of the analogue
state. Unfortunately, there seem to be no available

numerical estimates of the relative importance of these terms. These terms may put a limit to the accuracy of spectroscopy possible with analogue states. In the following we will neglect them.

Finally we want to mention that the neutron widths $\gamma^2_{\lambda,C'n'}$ are usually measured by stripping or pickup reactions. In these experiments one is limited however, by the fact that the target nucleus will be in its ground state. No such limitation occurs in the measurement of these widths made by analogue studies, because in this case both the analogue state $\Phi_{\lambda(A)}$ and the final state C' can be excited states. For an illustration we refer to Fig. 3. We are therefore able to measure by this method neutron widths between a pair of excited states.

Since it is more convenient to work with spectroscopic factors than widths, we will now introduce spectroscopic factors. To do so we have to define single particle widths $\gamma^2_{\lambda,S.P.}$

$$\gamma^2_{IjJ} = \frac{\hbar^2}{2M_C R} \cdot |\phi_j(R,E_n)|^2 \qquad (6)$$

$$\int_0^R |\phi_j(r)|^2 \, dr = 1$$

Here $r^{-1}\phi_j(r)$ is the radial part of the appropriate neutron single particle wave function, which has a special normalization given above. The choice of the radius R in these equations has been discussed above, it is nice however, that the corresponding partial widths Γ_p are only weakly dependent on this radius

$$\Gamma_p(R,E_p) = 2 P_\ell(R,E_p) \cdot \gamma^2_n(R,E_n) \qquad (7)$$

We show this radius dependence of $\Gamma_{p,S.P.}$ in
Fig. 11. The widths shown are calculated for single
particle states in Ba^{139}. These curves show plateaus,
which are broader for the more narrow $\ell = 3$ states than
for the broad $\ell = 1$ states. Another method to obtain
$\Gamma_{p,S.P.}$ has been used by Schiffer. This method consists
in calculating single particle resonances in a real
potential $V = V_{neutron} + V_{Coulomb}$. Here $V_{neutron}$ is the
potential giving the proper binding to the bound parent
analogue state in the (C+n) nucleus and $V_{Coulomb}$ is the
single particle Coulomb energy. If we calculate an
excitation function for proton scattering with this
potential, we find single particle resonances, which can
be analyzed for their width. The two methods give
similar results. A third method would be to solve the
Lane equation[7,18,19]. With these single particle
widths we define spectroscopic factors S_p for analogue
states by

$$S_p = (2T + 1) \cdot \Gamma_{IjJ} \cdot \Gamma^{-1}_{IjJ,S.P.} \qquad (8)$$

Similar spectroscopic factors can be defined for the
parent analogue states,

$$S_n = \gamma^2_{IjJ,n} \cdot \gamma^{-2}_{IjJ,nS.P.} \qquad (9)$$

and we expect these two spectroscopic factors to be
equal according to Eq. 3.

DISCUSSION OF RECENT EXPERIMENTS

The connection between proton widths of the analogue states and neutron widths of the parent analogue
states, can easily be checked for the case of elastic
proton scattering. In this case, we can measure the
widths of the parent analogue state by a (d,p) experiment on the same target nucleus. In Table I we show a

comparison made with Ca^{48} as target nucleus, see Ref. 15
The spectroscopic factors were calculated with the
method mentioned above of Schiffer. The agreement seems
to be reasonable. A similar comparison for Ba^{138} (Ref.10)
is shown in Fig. 13 and gives poor agreement. The spectroscopic factors being off by factors 2-3 for $\ell = 1$
states. Such an effect is expected from the giant resonance theory of the analogue states.[7,23] According to
this theory Eq. 7 is not valid, but has to be modified
by introducing an absorption correction. The correct
formula for the partial width being

$$\Gamma_p = |1 - R_\ell \, L_\ell|^{-2} \cdot 2P_\ell \cdot \gamma^2_n . \tag{10}$$

In these equations R_ℓ is the background matrix and L_ℓ a
generalized shift function. We can calculate this correction, if we assume that the background R-matrix is
given by the optical model for the $T_<$ states and
obtain[23]

$$|1 - R_\ell \, L_\ell|^{-2} = \left| \frac{f_\ell - S_{n\ell}}{f_\ell - S_\ell - iP_\ell} \right|^2 \tag{11}$$

Here f_ℓ is the logarithmic derivative of the optical
model proton wave function at the radius R. S_ℓ, P_ℓ,
$S_{n\ell}$, are shift functions for the proton channel of the
analogue state and the neutron channel of the parent
analogue state respectively.

In Table II we have made an approximate calculation of these correction terms by using the approximation
$|1-R_\ell L_\ell|^{-2} \sim \sqrt{1-T_\ell}$. Here T_ℓ is the optical model transmission coefficient for the $T_<$ states. This approxi-
mation comes from using complex optical model phases in
the collision matrix (Eq. 1). The results seem to be in
good agreement. An intuitive explanation of this
absorption correction is, that the mixing of the

$T_>$ state with the surrounding $T_<$ states diverts some of the flux, into the forbidden channels. Thus the mechanism which decreases the cross section in the allowed channels, gives rise to a cross section in the forbidden channels. Another method to calculate spectroscopic factors has been used by the Florida State group; they use the expression

$$S_p = \frac{\Gamma_p}{\Gamma - \Gamma_p} \cdot I_m(R_\ell) \cdot P_\ell^{-1} \cdot |L_\ell|^2 . \qquad (12)$$

This expression is an approximation following from giant resonance theory[7,9)]. In Table III we give a comparison of data for the target nucleus Sn^{116}. The agreement is again rather good, and this method seems to be successful. For the calculations leading to Fig. 14 the matrix Im R_ℓ was approximated by a value derived from the black nucleus model Im $R_\ell = \frac{1}{kR}$ where k is the wave number of the proton in the nucleus.

Finally, we want to discuss the information which can be obtained from inelastic scattering. From these experiments (e.g. Ref. 16) we get a set of widths or spectroscopic factors $S_{IjJ}^{1/2}$. What can we learn from them? As well known the spectroscopic factors can be written (e.g. Ref. 5)

$$S_{IjJ}^{1/2} = n(A) \cdot <(C(I) \otimes j_n)_J | \psi (J) > \qquad (13)$$

In this formula C(I) is the wave function of the final state and it is vector coupled with a neutron single particle wave function with spin j to the total spin J. $\psi(J)$ is the wave function of the parent analogue state which has spin J. A normalization factor n(A) comes from antisymmetrization. This matrix element can easily be evaluated in two cases which will be discussed now.

a) The state $C(I)$ has a closed neutron shell and is a pure proton configuration. In this case the antisymmetrized wave functions $(C(I) \otimes j_n)_J$ are orthogonal and the $S_{IjJ}^{1/2}$ are just expansion coefficients of the state $\psi(J)$.

$$\psi(J) = \sum_{j,I} S_{IjJ}^{1/2} \cdot (C(I) \otimes j_n)_J \qquad (14)$$

b) The state $\psi(J)$ is the single particle state $\psi(J) = C(0) \otimes j_n$ and $C(0)$ has a closed neutron shell. In this case either $S = 0$ or $C(I)$ is a neutron-neutron hole configuration $C(I) = (j_n \otimes j_n^{-1})_I \otimes C(0)$

In this case we get information on the structure of the state $C(I)$. Both of these pure cases seem to be realized in two experiments reported in contributed papers to this conference. Case a in an experiment on inelastic scattering on Ce^{140} and Nd^{142} (Ref. 22) and Case b in a similar experiment on Pb^{208} (Ref. 24).

I wish to thank Prof. W. Gentner, Dr. C. Mahaux, Prof. H. Morinaga, Prof. H. Weidenmuller and Dr. S. A. A. Zaidi for their continuous interest and for valuable discussions.

REFERENCES

1) J. D. Anderson and C. Wong, Phys. Rev. Letts. 7 (1961) 250.

2) J. D. Fox, C. F. Moore and D. Robson, Phys. Rev. Letts. 12 (1964) 198.

3) J. D. Fox, Nuclear Spectroscopy with Direct Reactions, Argonne (1964) ANL, 6878.

4) H. Feshbach, Nuclear Spectroscopy, ed. by Fay Ajzenberg-Selove, Part B, 1, 625.

5) A. M. Lane, Rev. Mod. Phys. 32 (1960) 519

6) D. L. Allan, G. A. Jones, G. C. Morrison, R. B. Taylor, and R. O. Weinberg, Phys. Letts. 17 (1965) 56.

7) D. Robson, Phys. Rev. 137 (1965) B535.

8) D. Robson, J. D. Fox, P. Richard, and C. F. Moore, Phys. Letts. 18 (1965) 86.

9) P. Richard, C. F. Moore, J. A. Becker, and J. D. Fox, to be published.

10) C. A. Wiedner, H. L. Harney, et al., to be published

11) P. von Brentano, N. Marquardt, J. P. Wurm and S. A. A. Zaidi, Phys. Letts. 17 (1965) 124.

12) R. Messlinger and H. Morinaga, Paper S19.

13) C. F. Moore and R. K. Jolly, Phys. Letts. 19 (1965) 138.

14) G. A. Jones, A. M. Lane and G. C. Morrison, Phys. Letts. 11 (1964) 329.

15) K. W. Jones, J. P. Schiffer, C. L. Leo, Jr., A. Marinov, and J. L. Lerner, to be published.

16) S. A. A. Zaidi, P. von Brentano, D. Riek, and J. P. Wurm, Phys. Letts 19 (1965) 46.

17) H. A. Weidenmüller, to be published.

18) J. P. Bondorf, S. Jägare, H. Lütken, Paper E5.

19) T. Tamura, Paper D4.

20) G. E. Terrell, C. F. Moore, J.L. Adams and D. Robson, Paper C6.

21) E. Finckh, U. Jahnke, J. Wirsich, Paper S8.

22) S. A. A. Zaidi, P. von Brentano, K. Melchior, P. Rauser, and J. P. Wurm, Paper S18.

23) D. Robson, Paper D2.

24) N. Stein, C. D. Kavaloski, J. S. Lilley, and P. Richard, Paper C4.

25) D. H. Wilkinson, Paper A2.

26) H. J. Kim and R. L. Robinson, Paper D8.

DISCUSSION

MacDONALD, Maryland: The H_o that you used to construct your parent nucleus-for that Hamiltonian, your parent nucleus has stable states, is that correct?

BRENTANO: Yes.

MacDONALD: And the perturbation which you use is a constant?

BRENTANO: Yes.

MacDONALD: Is that the energy shift?

BRENTANO: Yes.

MacDONALD: If the perturbation is a constant, I don't understand how it can give rise to unstable states.

BRENTANO: Oh, the point was this: I wrote it as $H_{model} + V_{res.}$ and $V_{res.}$ couples my state to the continuum. Therefore, only if I bring in the residual force, and this is in this case what we are doing, it is just $\Sigma[\Delta-v_c(r)]$, and this couples it to the continuum. This was only a naive picture.

STEIN, Washington: I want to ask about the possibility of inelastic scattering via the analogue state. Part of the decay to the inelastic state could go via mixing with the T - lower states and not via the spectroscopic factor usually associated with the decay.

BRENTANO: Well, I have written especially the collision matrix in the beginning in order to include this term. There is certainly a cross section which goes this way, but this cross section comes from the T-lower states and thus it is rather uniformly distributed and it goes via a Hauser-Feshbach mechanism.

So, if you have a thousand neutron levels, you can expect that only 10^{-3} of our total cross section will go

to the particular level you are looking for. Therefore,
I don't think this will be an important contribution.
But it can be that this picture is not true, but I think
the measurement of this can give us some kind of knowledge.

STEIN: Well, we have some data which will be presented shortly which provides some tentative evidence
that there is decay to an inelastic channel, even when
there is reason to believe that the matrix element is
very small.

BRENTANO: I'd be happy to see that.

BASSANI, Saclay: If you do have a good experiment,
what can you learn from an analogue state elastic scattering experiment?

BRENTANO: Well, the point is that elastic scattering was a very interesting phenomenon, because you
have seen this kind of absorption correction, and this
giant resonance picture can only be studied in detail by
elastic scattering.

We never can hope to reliably understand inelastic
scattering if you have not done enough of the elastic
studies, but in principle, there is no new spectroscopic
information. There is however, very much information
about reaction mechanism and the Coulomb energies and
things like that.

Later, Moore will give a wonderful method to determine the spin of the resonance by polarization measurements. This is certainly a step further, but with
just the angular distribution I cannot determine the
spin to any reliability, because contrary to Bilpuch's
case, Γ_p is not Γ, and therefore, this method doesn't
work.

HAMBURGER, Pittsburgh: In regard to the possibility of getting quantitative spectroscopic information from the spectroscopic factors, I want to raise a
little doubt. If one compares, for instance, the very
nice and complete data on the tin isotopes, which were
taken here in Tallahassee by Fox and collaborators, with
the data from (d,p) stripping reactions on the same
isotopes, you find the following: The spectroscopic
factor for a given level, say $S_{1/2}$, extracted from
stripping data, decreases monotonically as you go from
the lighter isotopes to the heavier ones, i.e., as the
level is filled.

On the other hand, the spectroscopic factor extracted from the proton scattering to the analogue state
jumps up and down in a very disturbing manner, by factors
up to 2, as you go from isotope to isotope. So I think
one must be a little careful when one wants to extract
quantitative information from the analogue spectroscopic
factors.

BRENTANO: Well, if I might answer, the point is
that the absorption corrections, which I mentioned, are
not yet done. Normally, they are neglected, or done in
a very rough way. We have to really follow closely the
R-matrix prescription of this, and this nobody seems to
have done. Only if we have done this can we really say
that that is not true, but I think then also you must
be a little bit careful because some of this data, for
instance, may have doublets and may not easily be resolved. So if you take good data, I think it will agree
nicely.

SCHIFFER, Argonne: I would just like to comment
on that. I think that the method that he referred to
for extracting spectroscopic factors for analogue states

uses some approximations. This is the method described in Robson's paper where penetrabilities are never introduced. I believe that the Florida State people would agree that these spectroscopic factors are not better than a factor two; one does expect fluctuations of that order.

If the same data were analyzed by some such methods as were suggested here, where the penetrabilities are explicitly introduced and absorption corrections made, I should hope that the numbers would be in much better agreement with spectroscopic factors from (d,p) experiments.

AXEL, Illinois: I have a comment and a question. Some of the remarks which have been made indicate confusion about our current ability to exploit the information available from analogue states. Our position with respect to the analogue states is not very different from from the one nuclear physicists were in with regard to stripping reactions soon after Butler's earliest contributions. It could have been argued then that stripping reactions were not worth doing because the gamma ray transitions, which were better understood, could give more reliable information about nuclear wave functions.

I think that once we learn about the reaction mechanics which describe the excitation and decay of analogue states, the nuclear information that can be extracted may be more reliable than that now obtainable from DWBA analyses.

This leads to my question, which Schiffer may have answered. While you were talking about spectroscopic factors and comparisons with (d,p) experiments, I was wondering whether you were using the same nuclear model that is used in the (d,p) analyses. The spectroscopic

factor is an indication of the degree to which the state
under study appears to be describable as the residual
state coupled to a single particle. In order to decide
this, one must use a particular single particle potential.

BRENTANO: The neutron width was calculated from
the same wave function, namely, the one which we used
for the (d,p) analysis. It's quite obvious here that
you use the the same wave function for the neutron and
the proton.

AXEL: Does this mean that you do an optical model
calculation?

BRENTANO: Well, what we are doing is to solve for
the bound state of a Woods-Saxon well. Would you call
that optical model?

AXEL: All right, that would be one part of it,
and then what about the probability that the particle
would come out? What would be the width of a single
particle state according to the optical model you use?

BRENTANO: Well, this is the penetrability and
that is good, but then there comes this correction
$|1-RL|^{-2}$, and the bad thing about this is that it is an
absorption, and we need -- in order to calculate it --
to have very good data on the optical model for the
T-lower states. I must say, however, it's not so long
since we realize this correction is really large.

I think the optical model for protons is not so
bad, and therefore, I expect that we can make this correction very reliably. However, I should remind you
that the formula is approximate. Another problem which
seems to me much more serious is a question as to whether
the formula giving the relationship between proton and
neutron reduced widths is exact, because, for example,

in the paper by Weidenmüller he gives additional terms.
I think this will be discussed this evening.

MacFARLANE, <u>Argonne</u>: Peter Axel made a rather
elegant comparison between the state of isobaric analogues and knowledge today with regard to stripping
reactions. Now this, in fact, may be in some sense true.
If so, then perhaps when enough industry has been in-
vested into the extraction of spectroscopic factors from
analogue reactions perhaps one will get a lot of information in favorable situations.

The second point I wanted to make is in reference
to Bassani's remark. I think it's important to remember
that inelastic scattering to analogue states gets you
information for which you have to do stripping on excited
states; an experiment which would be quite difficult to
carry out!

BASSANI: I asked for elastic scattering.

MacFARLANE: I know that, but then I don't think
you would be able to analyze the inelastic scattering
before you did a good job on the elastic scattering.

BASSANI: Well, if you do an experiment on the
analogue state, you must do the inelastic scattering.
If you do just elastic, you don't get any more information than stripping.

HAMBURGER: I just wanted to answer Axel. I believe in isobaric reactions also. I am doing them, as
a matter of fact, but Robson privately gave me a different answer than Schiffer, and I think it would be
very interesting if he could elaborate on that.

ROBSON: There is a problem with antisymmetrization but I will leave it until the evening session.

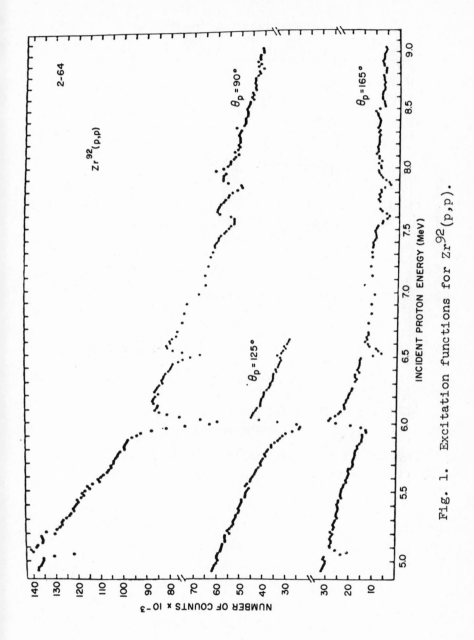

Fig. 1. Excitation functions for $Zr^{92}(p,p)$.

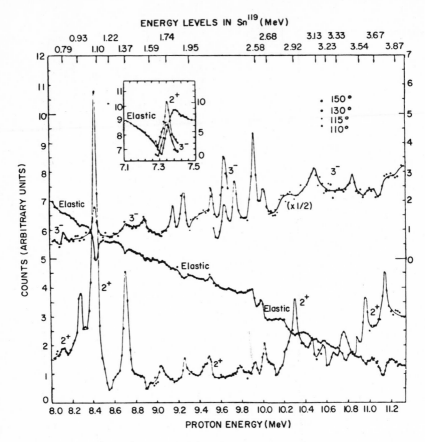

Fig. 2. Excitation functions for elastic and inelastic scattering of protons on Sn[118]. (Ref. 6)

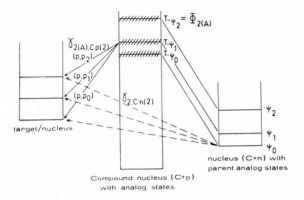

Fig. 3. Schematic diagram showing the position of isobaric analogue states formed by proton scattering on the target C and the corresponding parent analogue states in the nucleus (C + n).

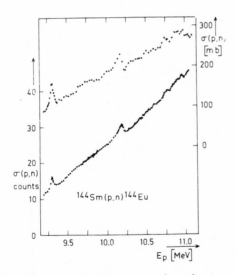

Fig. 4. Excitation function of (p,n) cross section on Sm[144] targets. The upper curve is measured by activation method (see Ref. 12) and the lower curve is measured with a long counter (see Ref. 13).

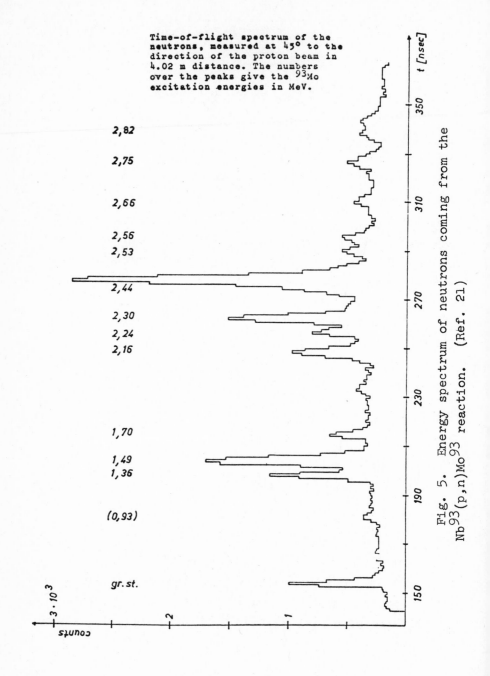

Time-of-flight spectrum of the neutrons, measured at 45° to the direction of the proton beam in 4.02 m distance. The numbers over the peaks give the ^{93}Mo excitation energies in MeV.

Fig. 5. Energy spectrum of neutrons coming from the Nb^{93}(p,n)Mo^{93} reaction. (Réf. 21)

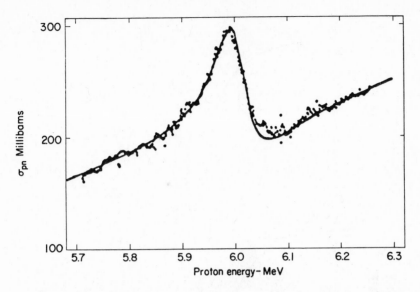

Fig. 6. Excitation function of (p,n) cross section on Zr^{92}. (Ref. 8)

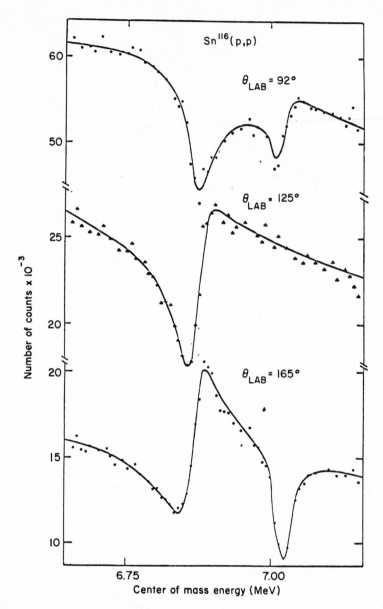

Fig. 7. Excitation function and fit of elastic proton scattering on Sn^{116}. (Ref. 9)

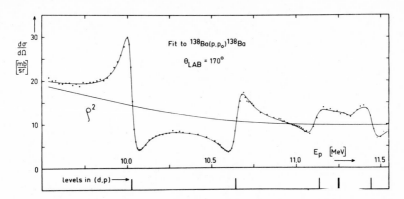

Fig. 8. Excitation function and fit of elastic proton scattering on Ba^{138}. (Refs. 10 and 11)

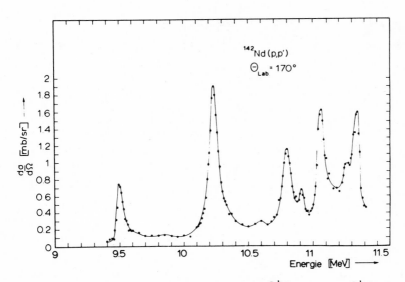

Fig. 9. Excitation function of Nd^{142}(p,p')Nd^{142}(2$^+$). (Ref. 22)

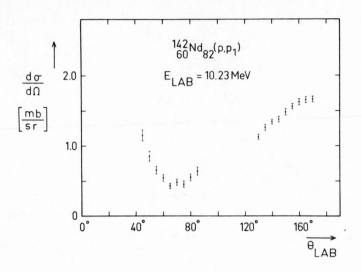

Fig. 10. Angular distribution of $Nd^{142}(p,p')Nd^{142}(2^+)$ measured at the energy of the second analogue resonance. (Ref. 22)

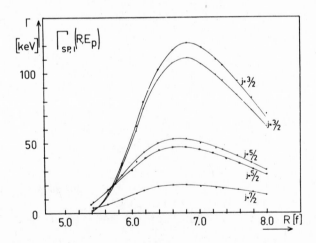

Fig. 11. Single particle width for isobaric analogues of states in Ba^{139}. The quantity plotted is $(2T + 1)^{-1} \cdot \Gamma_{p,S.P.}$. (Ref. 10)

^{48}Ca				
J^π	Γ_{tot} [keV]	Γ_p [keV]	S_{pp}	S_{dp}
$3/2^-$	8.2	2	0.64 ± 0.07	1.03
$1/2^-$	200	136	1.24 ± 0.27	1.33
$5/2^-$	40	24	0.91 ± 0.19	0.72
$9/2^+$	25	2.7	0.31 ± 0.09	0.31

Fig. 12. Comparison of spectroscopic factors S_p obtained from analysis of analogue states seen in elastic proton scattering on Ca^{48} and of spectroscopic factors S_{dp} obtained from a (d,p) reaction on Ca^{48}. The method of analysis of S_p is outlined in the text. (Ref.15)

^{138}Ba					
J^{π}	Γ_{tot} [keV]	Γ_p [keV]	S_{pp}	S_{dp}	S_{pp}^{Corr}
$7/2^-$	71	14	0.635	0.76	0.74
$3/2^-$	84	21	0.18	0.49	0.435
$(3/2^-)$	96	11	0.092	0.21	0.205
$(5/2^-)$	80	8	0.19	0.24	0.275
$(5/2^-)$	80	8	0.16	0.24	0.225

Fig. 13. Comparison of S_p and S_{dp} for Ba^{138} as target nucleus. The factor S_p is corrected for absorption as explained in the text. (Ref. 10)

^{116}Sn				
J^{π}	Γ_{tot} [keV]	Γ_p [keV]	S_{pp}	S_{dp}
$1/2^+$	42	16.5	0.58	0.647
$3/2^+$	37	8.3	0.43	0.549
$5/2^+$	42	1.8	0.040	0.061
$5/2^+$	35	1.4	0.035	0.033
$7/2^-$	—	—	—	0.029

Fig. 14. Comparison of S_p and S_{dp} for Sn^{116} as target nucleus. (Ref. 9)

300

C3. ISOBARIC SPIN AND
PARTICLE-HOLE EXCITATIONS*

Larry Zamick

Princeton University
Princeton, New Jersey

I shall discuss excited states of nuclei, whose
configurations consist of n holes and m + n particles;
for example, holes in the $1d^{3/2}$ shell and particles in
the $1f^{7/2}$ shell. Consider basis states (as opposed to
eigenstates) of the system in which the particles have
a definite isobaric spin T_p, the holes a definite isobaric spin T_H, and the total system has an isobaric
spin T. For brevity we write $[T_p, T_H]T$. We all know
that T is a very good quantum number. I would like to
discuss the possibility that in some cases the quantum
numbers T_p and T_H are fairly good i.e. that the above
basis states $[T_p, T_H]T$ are fairly good approximations to
the eignestates of the system.

If one examines the negative parity states of a
doubly magic nucleus such as O^{16} or Ca^{40} one finds that
the T = 1 states have a much higher energy than the
T = 0 states. This leads to the somewhat idealized picture that the energy difference of the center of gravity
of the T = 1 states and of the T = 0 states is much
larger than the splitting of different negative parity
states with the same T. If we accept this, we can then

*Work supported by the U. S. Atomic Energy Commission
and the Higgins Scientific Trust Fund.

pretend that all the $T = 1$ states are degenerate and all the $T = 0$ states are also degenerate. We assume that the negative parity states are particle-hole excitations i.e., $d^{3/2}f^{7/2}$. Only 2 parameters are required to describe our idealized, highly degenerate spectrum. The first parameter, b, is the difference in center of gravity of the $T = 1$ and $T = 0$ states. The other parameter gives the energy of the $T = 0$ state relative to the ground state. The over simplified spectrum can be obtained from a monopole interaction involving only two parameters

$$H (1,2) = -a + b\; t_1 \cdot t_2 \qquad\qquad (1)$$

where, given the matrix elements $E^{IT} = \langle [d^{3/2}f^{7/2}]^{IT} | v\; [d^{3/2}f^{7/2}]^{IT} \rangle$ we have

$$a = \frac{\Sigma(2J+1)(2T+1)E^{IT}}{\Sigma(2J+1)(2T+1)} \qquad b = \frac{\Sigma(2J+1)(E^{IT=1}-E^{IT=0})}{\Sigma(2J+1)}$$

$$(1)$$

The above monopole interaction was invented by French and Bansal[1] and has yielded many fruitful results. One can very easily obtain the excitation energy of a state of n holes in the $d^{3/2}$ shell and (n+m) particles in the $f^{7/2}$ shell with quantum numbers $[T_p,T_H]T$[5]

$$E^* = E(\; (f^{7/2})^{m+n}\;) - E(\; (f^{7/2})^m\;)$$

$$+ E(\; (d^{-3/2})^n\;) - E(Ca^{40}) \qquad (2)$$

$$- n(m+n)a + b/2\; [T(T+1) - T_p(T_p+1) - T_H(T_H+1)]$$

$$+ \text{Coulomb correction}$$

It should be remembered that what makes the above formula interesting is that b is a large positive number.

A remarkable difference between the interaction
of particles and holes and the interaction of particles
amongst themselves (or holes amongst themselves) is
that in the former case one gets the lowest energy by
coupling the holes and particles separately to the
highest isobaric spin possible. This fact has been
pointed out by George Ripka[4] in his talk at the Paris
Conference in 1964. It is also evident from Eq. 2.

A very dramatic manifestation of this effect of
the particle-hole interaction favoring a maximum isobaric spin for the particles and holes, has been demonstrated by Conlon, Bayman and Kashy who find that
the neutron hole state with $J = 3/2^+$ in Ca^{43} lies at a
lower energy than the proton hole state. They did the
experiment $Ca^{44}(p,d)Ca^{43}$ (i.e. they pulled out a neutron from Ca^{44}). The lowest $J = 3/2^+$ state in Ca^{43} at
0.993 MeV was strongly excited but the next state at
1.4 MeV was not excited at all. The latter state
therefore has no neutron hole component. Now, for a
state in which the 4 $f^{7/2}$ particles have isobaric spin
$T_p = 1$, the $d^{3/2}$ hole is always a proton hole whereas
the state $[d^{3/2-1}(f^{7/2})^4 T_p = 2]^T = 3/2$ is 4/5 neutron
hole and 1/5 proton hole. The reason that it is a
surprise that the latter state should lie lower than
the $T_p = 1$ state, can best be illustrated by using the
Nilsson diagram, Fig. 1. We see that for a $T_p = 2$
state one of the neutrons is in a higher Nilsson orbital than is the proton in the $T_p = 1$ state. Nevertheless, as a result of the strong particle-hole interaction, the $T_p = 2$ state lies lower in energy. This
result, which was obtained by French and Bansal,[1]

simply shows that the Nilsson model is not too good for predicting the energies of states involving particles and holes, despite its great success for configurations involving only particles.

To confirm that the second $J = 3/2^+$ state is indeed a proton hole state, Sherr[3] has proposed a very interesting experiment -

1.40	$3/2^+$	$Sc^{45}(p,He^3)Ca^{43}$
0.993	$3/2^+$	

We consider the diagram, Fig. 2, which represents Sc^{45}. In order to reach a neutron hole state we must take the proton from the $f^{7/2}$ shell; to reach a proton hole state one must remove a proton from the $d^{3/2}$ shell. Since there are initially 4 protons in the $d^{3/2}$ shell and only one in the $f^{7/2}$ shell, one should reach the proton hole state 4 times as often as one reaches the neutron hole state. What amounts to the same thing, the $T_o = 1$ state will be reached 3.4 times as often as the $T_o = 2$ state. This completes Sherr's argument.

Let me mention an interesting possibility which results from examining Eq. 2. We consider the nucleus Ca^{42} and the various $T = 1$ states which have configurations consisting of 2 holes in the $d^{3/2}$ shell and 4 particles in the $f^{7/2}$ shell. The possible isobaric spin combinations $[T_p, T_H]T = 1$ are $[0,1]1$, $[1,0]1$, $[1,1]1$, and $[2,1]1$. The state $[0,1]1$ is predicted to have the lowest energy using Eq. 2 with the parameters $a = -0.3$, and $b = 2.9$ MeV. This state can be identified with the 1.84 MeV state in Ca^{42}. What is interesting is that the $[2,1]1$ state is also predicted to lie at a low energy - around 3 or 4 MeV. Although the four $f^{7/2}$ particles have $T_p = 2$, the particle-hole interaction is

304

sufficiently attractive to overcome this. Such a state
has not yet been seen. I think that it would be worthwhile to look for it and to see if indeed the isobaric
spin of the particles is T_p = 2. Since there are fewer
states which have high isobaric spin than low isobaric
spin the strength of the above basic state should not
be spread over too many states of the system. This
should make it easier to find.

REFERENCES

1. J. B. French, Proceedings Nuclear Spectroscopy with
   Direct Interactions, Argonne Report, 1964, 181;
   R. K. Bansal and J. B. French, Phys. Letts. 11
   (1964) 145.
2. T. W. Conlon, B. F. Bayman and E. Kashy, to be
   published.
3. R. Sherr, private communication.
4. G. Ripka, Int. Conf. of Nuclear Phys., Paris 2
   (1964) 390.
5. L. Zamick, Phys. Letts. 19 (1965) 580.

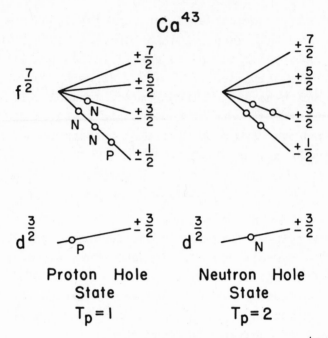

Fig. 1.   Nilssen diagram for levels in Ca^{43}.

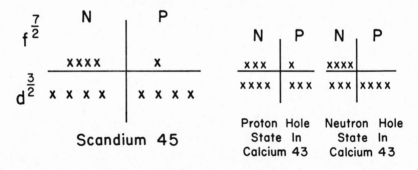

Fig. 2.   Schematic diagram of nucleon configurations for valence orbits in Sc^{45} and Ca^{43}.

C4. DECAY OF ISOBARIC ANALOGUE STATES
IN THE LEAD REGION

P. Richard, C. D. Kavaloski,
J. S. Lilley, and N. Stein

University of Washington
Seattle, Washington

Isobaric analogues of low-lying states of Pb^{207}, Pb^{208}, and Pb^{209} have been observed in proton elastic and inelastic scattering excitation functions. An important new feature is observed in these data; namely, many of the (p,p') analogue resonances have shapes quite different from the symmetric Breit-Wigner shapes observed in previous experiments with lighter nuclei at lower incident energies. This indicates the possible importance of another reaction mechanism which is competing with simple compound inelastic scattering via the analogue state, so that the analysis of such data may be considerably more complicated than the Breit-Wigner single-level analysis which has been used up to now.

The University of Washington tandem accelerator was used in obtaining the proton excitation functions. Solid state detectors were used to detect the protons scattered from thin self-supporting Pb targets. The overall spectrum resolution was usually about 60 keV. Figure 1 shows the results for Pb^{206} between 11.5 and 14.0 MeV. A p-wave resonance (see Table I) is observed in the elastic scattering at 12.2 MeV, which is

307

the incident energy corresponding to the isobaric
analogue of the $(3p_{1/2})^{-1}$ ground state of Pb^{207}. Except for a hint of the 0.894 MeV $(3p_{3/2})^{-1}$ state at
13.1 MeV none of the other neutron-hole states of Pb^{207}
shows an observable effect in elastic scattering. When
the penetrabilities for the $\ell = 3$, 5 and 6 protons are
taken into account these observations are consistent
with $Pb^{206}(d,p)Pb^{207}$ measurements[1].

Resonances in (p,p') to three excited states
of Pb^{206} were also observed at 12.2 MeV (see Fig. 1).
All three resonances display a symmetric shape and
were analyzed using a Breit-Wigner single-level formula.
These results (see Table I) are qualitatively consistent with the relative $(p_{1/2}^{-1}j^{-1})$ mixtures calculated
for these states[2] and with the $Pb^{207}(d,t)Pb^{206}$ measurements[1], in which the states excited most strongly
are the three measured here. According to calculations
of True and Ford[2] the ratio of the squares of the
coefficients of the $(p_{1/2}^{-1}, p_{3/2}^{-1})$ configuration in
the 0.804 MeV 2^+ to that in the 1.48 MeV 2^+ is 0.5,
and according to Guman[2], et al. it is 0.31. If we
assume this ratio is proportional to the ratio of reduced widths for the observed transitions, we obtain
0.18. In this estimate it has been assumed that most
of the observed width is from the $\ell = 1$ contribution.

At 13.1 MeV near the position of the $p_{3/2}^{-1}$
state of Pb^{207} an anomaly is seen in the 2^+ excitation
function which is quite different in shape from the
anomalies at 12.2 MeV and thus was not analyzed with
only a Breit-Wigner formula.

Above 12.5 MeV, light element contaminants in
the Pb^{206} target prevented observation of inelastic

scattering to states other than the 0.804 MeV state
and the 2.6 MeV (3^-) state mentioned below (see Figs.
1 and 2a).

In Figs. 2b and 2c, Pb^{207} and Pb^{208} data are
displayed for comparison with the Pb^{206} results. The
resonances at 14.9 MeV in the elastic scattering from
Pb^{206} and Pb^{208} are almost identical and correspond to
analogues of the $2g_{9/2}$ neutron states in Pb^{207} (2.74
MeV) and Pb^{209} (g.s.) $^{2}1$). This designation is supported by a resonance analysis consistent with $\ell = 4$
(see Table I). The double peak near 14.9 MeV in Pb^{207}
(p,p) is also related to the $g_{9/2}$ neutron state and
corresponds to analogues of the 3.198 MeV (5^-) and
3.46 MeV (4^-) states in Pb^{208}, which have the dominant
neutron configuration ($2g_{9/2}, 3p_{1/2}^{-1}$). The analogue
of the $1i_{11/2}$ neutron state occurs at 15.8 MeV in
Pb^{206}(p,p). Only a hint of this state appears in the
elastic scattering from the other targets, although
anomalies at the expected energy are seen in the inelastic scattering. Analogues of states in Pb^{207}
formed by coupling a $g_{9/2}$ neutron to the first excited
state (2^+) of the Pb^{206} core are also expected to lie
near this energy. These would enhance the resonance in
the exit channel to the 2^+ state and may account for
a large fraction of the strong yield seen in the 2^+
excitation function near 15.8 MeV.

The most striking examples of departure from a
symmetric resonance shape are the anomalies in the inelastic scattering from Pb^{206} and Pb^{208} at 14.9 MeV.
Other examples are seen in the inelastic scattering
from Pb^{206} at 13.1 MeV, Pb^{208} at 15.7 MeV, and possibly
Pb^{206} at 15.8 MeV. These shapes are in sharp contrast
to those observed at 12.2 MeV in Pb^{206}(p,p') and to

those seen in previous (p,p') studies[3,4], and indicate
that an analysis based on a Breit-Wigner single-level
formula will not be adequate.

Among the possible explanations for asymmetric
(p,p') resonance shapes are interference between neighboring analogue resonances and interference between a
resonance and a direct reaction amplitude. However, if
either of these mechanisms is adequate to explain the
anomalous shapes, it may be difficult to understand why
in previous experiments the deviations (if any) from
simple Breit-Wigner resonances are much smaller than
observed here. For example, in a Ba^{138}(p,p') experiment[4], one might have expected substantial interference
effects because both the between-resonance background
(assumed to be direct reaction plus level-level interference) and the density of analogue states are at
least as great as in the present case.

Another possible explanation for the asymmetries
is suggested by an examination of the entrance and exit
channels for the $g_{9/2}$ analogue resonance at 14.9 MeV
in Pb^{206}(p,p') to the 2^+ state. The strong effect in
the (p,p) excitation function indicates an entrance
channel resonance. However, the $1i_{13/2}$ neutron hole
state is the only state reasonably consistent with the
shell model that is available for coupling with a pure
$g_{9/2}$ single particle state to form 2^+. Direct decay
from the $g_{9/2}$ analogue to the 2^+ state therefore would
require an admixture of the $(1i_{13/2}^{-1}, 2g_{9/2})$ particle-
hole configuration in that state. In existing theoretical calculations[2] which agree in many details with
experimental data, it was not found necessary to include explicitly such configurations in the 2^+ state
(these involve promoting a particle across a major

shell). Pending further theoretical investigation, one may assume that the channel for direct decay from the analogue to the 2^+ state is either closed, or very weak. An overlap could also exist if the $9/2^+$ analogue state were not pure single particle, but, for example, contained some 2^+-phonon-admixtures[5]. However, examinations of Pb^{206} and $Pb^{208}(p,p)$ resonances and the (d,p) cross sections[1] show no evidence for any strong admixtures. To understand how a strong transition can occur with a closed exit channel, one may consider the (p,n) reaction via isobaric resonances where the exit channel is also closed. In this case, neutron emission is isobaric spin forbidden, but the decay is explained as proceeding via isobaric spin mixing[6-8] through the many states of lower $T(T_<)$ in the vicinity of the analogue state. If this is correct, the same mixing process may account for the observation of resonances in (p,p'), when the proton exit channel is closed. In addition, the mechanism may explain the interference shape of such resonances, since interference patterns have been shown to be a direct consequence of mixing, and have been observed in the (p,n) reaction[7].

The above process may be contrasted with the situation in which a (p,p') resonance is observed, with no resonance in the elastic channel[3]. In this case, the entrance channel is closed but the exit channel is probably strong. It has been suggested that mixing with $T_<$ states may account for the <u>formation</u>[3] of the analogue state and that asymmetric resonance shapes[7] might be expected. However, no clear evidence for these asymmetries has been reported.

The asymmetric resonances in the inelastic scattering to the 3^- states in Pb^{206} and Pb^{208} may be due to interference with a direct process or to mixing with $T_<$ states, even though in this case the entrance and exit channels are probably both open. It is evident that effects such as these will have to be considered carefully in a detailed analysis of all (p,p') analogue resonance data, even when the shapes are apparently symmetric.

REFERENCES

1) P. Mukherjee and B. L. Cohen, Phys. Rev. 127 (1962) 1284.

2) W. W. True and K. W. Ford, Phys. Rev. 109 (1958) 1675; V. N. Guman, et al., Nucl. Phys. 28 (1961) 192.

3) G. A. Jones, A. M. Lane and G. C. Morrison, Phys. Letters 11 (1964) 329.

4) S. A. A. Zaidi, P. von Brentano, D. Rieck and J. P. Wurm, Phys. Letters 19 (1965) 45.

5) I. Mukherjee and P. Mukherjee, Nucl. Phys. 57 (1964) 683.

6) D. Robson, Phys. Rev. 137 (1965) B535.

7) D. Robson, J. D. Fox, P. Richard, and C. F. Moore, Phys. Letters 18 (1965) 86.

8) C. Bloch and J. P. Schiffer, Phys. Letters 12 (1964) 22.

TABLE I. Resonance Analysis for Elastic[a] and Inelastic[b] Scattering[c].

Target Nucleus	E^{Lab}_{Res} (MeV)	ℓ	Γ_p (d) (keV)	$\Gamma_{p},^{2+}(.804)$(e) (keV)	$\Gamma_{p},^{2+}(1.48)$ (keV)	$\Gamma_{p},^{1+}(1.71)$ (keV)	$\Gamma^{(f)}$ keV	J^{π}
Pb^{206}	12.22	1	12	12.5	38.5	21	170	$1/2^-$
	14.90	4	23				230	$9/2^+$
Pb^{208}	14.90	4	17				215	$9/2^+$

(a) C. F. Moore and P. Richard, Florida State University, 1965 Technical Report, No. 8 (unpublished).

(b) Single-level Breit-Wigner resonance equation.

(c) Errors in resonance parameter are estimated to be less than 20%.

(d) Γ_p is proton partial width for elastic scattering.

(e) $\Gamma_{p},^{2+}$ (.804) is proton partial width for inelastic to 2^+ state at .804 MeV.

(f) Γ is the total width of the resonance.

DISCUSSION

ZAIDI, Max Planck, Heidelberg: Can I question you regarding the reason for this asymmetry. The question is whether it is due to resonance-resonance interference or whether it is due to interference with the background scattering.

Do you have this if you look at the angular distribution? You have got some inelastic scattering, and all the levels that are contributing have the same parity. Have you checked to see if the angular distribution from it is symmetric about 90°? Have you angular distribution measurements on the peak of the resonance?

RICHARD: No, we haven't, but we plan to do on and off resonance angular distributions in order to get some feeling of what the background cross section is also.

ZAIDI: You gave us the inelastic widths. Could you tell me how you obtain them?

RICHARD: It's from a simple Breit-Wigner analysis of (Γ_p, Γ_p). There are actually two inelastic widths involved. There is a gamma for an $f_{5/2}$ proton and one for a $p_{3/2}$ proton, but it turns out that this enters into the equation as a sum, so that Γ_p' is the sum of the widths for both $f_{5/2}$ and $p_{3/2}$ emission.

ZAIDI: Is this from the integrated cross section or the differential cross section?

RICHARD: Differential cross section.

MORINAGA, Max Planck, Heidelberg: I don't understand the last part of your discussion. The asymmetry may be due to the T-lower states. However, the T-lower states can emit neutrons, so protons cannot compete in the emission from T-lower states. If you use the

314

ordinary statistical model, you will get less than one percent by proton emission, so the proton doesn't come out from the T-lower state,, and I don't think that last item is important.

STEIN, University of Washington, Seattle: I'd like to comment that if you have isobaric spin mixing and you get into the T-lower states, then the ordinary compound nucleus follows. In other words, if this is due to mixing, then it will obey the ordinary Γ_p over Γ_n width relations. In other words, the point is that the cross section is very low here, and it is very important to know what the off-resonance (p,p') to the 2^+ state is due to. It's not very obvious that this is a direct reaction. It could be compound inelastic just by the ordinary rules of compound nucleus theory.

MORINAGA: But the emission is mainly by neutrons, and so (p,p') cannot compete.

STEIN: Right, so we expect the (p,n) cross section might be very strong. We intend to measure that. That is, the neutron decay will also be very strong, but this doesn't say there can't be any proton decay. We are way above the Coulomb barrier and you can have a $\Gamma_{p'}$. It would be small.

MORINAGA: There is an analogue width for the protons, and this could be strong.

STEIN: Yes, but the point is that we think we have a case in the lead region where there may be a very small overlap between the particular analogue states involved since the data both that we have and the (d,p) is consistent with this being a rather pure $g_{9/2}$ single particle state.

The point was that it would be very difficult for the known wave function belonging to the 2^+ state

315

to find an overlap with this single particle state, so
we suspect that there could be a possibility of decay
via the T-lower states. This is exactly the same
thing that other people have said concerning the formation of the analogue state when the entrance channels
are closed. It's well known that you see (p,p') when
you don't see any (p,p) effect. There it has been suggested that you form the analogue state by mixing.
Here we are suggesting that you form the analogue state
because it's a very strong entrance channel, but that
it decays via mixing.

BRENTANO, Max Planck, Heidelberg: I just want
to ask how big is your cross section? You make an
estimate of the proton cross section as 1mb. One has
probably a thousand neutron channels and expects a
cross section of maybe a barn. It is possible to calculate (p,p') via compound nucleus formation.

STEIN: Well, the whole question depends on what
the (p,p') cross section is due to, and this has to be
determined. It's not obvious that it's not a direct
reaction.

BRENTANO: No, but you can calculate it. If it
is compound nucleus via the ordinary T-lower states, as
I think Morinaga has already mentioned, then if you
do calculate it, you will find it's very small.

LEGG, Rice: I would first like to say that we
have seen asymmetries with light nuclei such as zirconium. Secondly, I would like to say that asymmetries
point out very nicely the problem in extracting numerical widths from the inelastic scattering. I think the
spectroscopic factors that we could get are very worthwhile as Brentano said. However, I think your data
illustrates very nicely the problems involved in getting

it.

RICHARD: I agree.

COSMAN, <u>Massachusetts Institute of Technology</u>:
I would like to remark that in the $Sr^{88}(p,p')$ reaction,
the angular distributions from the 2^+ transition show
strong deviations from symmetry around $90°$ when the
incident energy is on the analogue-state resonance.

This may be an interference effect with other
direct mechanisms, such as Coulomb excitation, and
should provide information on the background processes.

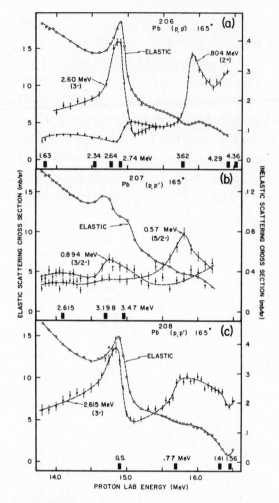

Fig. 1.   Pb^{206}(p,p) and (p,p') excitation functions
from 11.5 to 14 MeV.   The isobaric analogue resonance
of the $p_{1/2}^{-1}$ ground state of Pb^{207} at 12.2 MeV is seen
to resonate in the elastic scattering as well as in the
inelastic scattering to the 0.804 MeV (2$^+$), 1.48 MeV
(2$^+$) and 1.71 MeV (1$^+$) states of Pb^{206}.   The inelastic
scattering data shown is for θ_{Lab} = 165°.

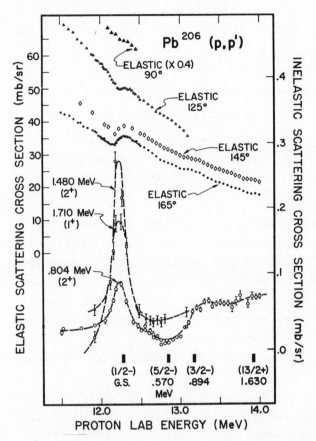

Fig. 2. Elastic and inelastic scattering from Pb^{206}, Pb^{207} and Pb^{208} over the energy region 14 to 16.5 MeV. Resonances are seen at the expected position of the $g_{9/2}$ and $i_{11/2}$ states of Pb^{207} and Pb^{209}. The 5$^-$ (3.198 MeV) and 4$^-$ (3.47 MeV) states of Pb^{208} are also seen near the same energy as the $g_{9/2}$ in Pb^{206} and Pb^{208}(p,p); whereas no effect is seen in either the elastic or inelastic at the position of the 3$^-$(2.615 MeV) state of Pb^{208}. Cross sections for the Pb^{207}(p,p') to the $p_{3/2}^{-1}$ (0.894 MeV) and $f_{5/2}^{-1}$ (0.57 MeV) are rather small and show broad effects near 14.9 and 15.8 MeV respectively.

C5. STUDY OF ISOBARIC-ANALOGUE STATES BY PROTON SCATTERING ON Ba ISOTOPES*

G. C. Morrison and Z. Vager[+]
Argonne National Laboratory
Argonne, Illinois

The isobaric analogues of some low-lying states in Ba isotopes have been observed as compound-nucleus resonances in elastic and inelastic proton scattering on Ba^{134}, Ba^{135}, Ba^{136}, Ba^{137}, and Ba^{138}. The neutron configurations of the even Ba isotopes are shown in Fig. 1. The states whose analogues have been studied are mainly odd-parity states above the $3s_{1/2}$, $2d_{3/2}$ shell closure at 82 neutrons. The experimental data for elastic proton scattering at 170° are shown in Fig. 2. The excitation functions are shown for the five Ba isotopes in the energy range from 9.0 to 11.4 MeV. The smooth lines are optical-model cross sections[1] which fit the data very well at lower energies.

The three resonances shown for Ba^{138} + p are those measured and identified by the Heidelberg group[2] and confirmed in our work as having spins of $7/2^-$, $3/2^-$, and $1/2^-$ or $3/2^-$. The cross sections for the other even-A isotopes show the same resonance shapes shifted to lower energies. A simple interpretation of this

*Work performed under the auspices of the U.S. Atomic Energy Commission.

[+]On leave of absence from the Weizman Institute of Science, Rehovoth, Israel.

phenomenon is that of the positions of single-particle
states relative to zero binding energy are about the
same for very slightly different well parameters. Thus
the (d,p) reaction to these states would have a similar
Q value and the analogues of these states should occur
at about the same proton energy.

It should be emphasized that only in the case of
Ba^{138} + p does the $f_{7/2}$ resonance correspond to the
ground state of the Ba^{139} analogue nucleus. For the
other Ba isotopes the ground-state analogue should be a
$d_{3/2}$ resonance. In the case of Ba^{136} and Ba^{134} targets,
the ground-state analogue resonances are predicted and
observed at energies of about 8.0 MeV. In the case of
Ba^{137} and Ba^{135} targets, the ground-state resonances are
predicted at about 6.0 MeV but should be very weak so
far below the Coulomb barrier. They have not been observed in either (p,p) or (p,n) reactions.

The odd-A isotopes are expected to show more complex structure in the energy region studied, because the
$3/2^+$ core should split the $f_{7/2}$ resonance into four
states of spin 2^-, 3^-, 4^-, and 5^-. In Ba^{137} the $3/2^+$
ground state is believed to be mainly a $d_{3/2}$ hole;
therefore, the splitting is due to $(d_{3/2}^{-1})f_{7/2}$ coupling
Two anomalies are seen clearly in the $Ba^{137}(p,p)$ cross
section at about the right energy. It is of interest
that a similar situation exists for the low-lying states
of K^{40}. There the four states arising from the
$(d_{3/2})^{-1}f_{7/2}$ coupling appear as two narrow doublets of
spin 4^-, 3^- and 2^-, 5^- well separated in energy. That
the total strength of the two anomalies observed on
Ba^{137} is similar to that in the neighboring even isotopes and about equally divided, as would follow from
the $2J + 1$ weighting factor, suggest that a situation

similar to that in K^{40} may exist in the analogue nucleus Ba^{138}. For Ba^{135} one can see the anomaly due to the splitting of the $f_{7/2}$ resonance but this anomaly is smaller than that on Ba^{137}. In Ba^{135} the splitting is in part due to $(d_{3/2})f_{7/2}$ coupling, and might be expected to be comparable with the situation existing for the low-lying states of Cl^{38}. However, the experimental situation is complicated by the possible interference of the $f_{7/2}$ resonances with those based on the $p_{3/2}$ resonances.

The results of a preliminary analysis of the elastic resonances in the even-A isotopes are shown in Table I. The spectroscopic factors are multiplied by $(2T + 1)$ so that they can be compared with those extracted from (d,p) reactions. The $f_{7/2}$ spectroscopic factor is almost constant. The $p_{3/2}$ spectroscopic factor is changing but not very significantly.

The relative position of the resonances in the different even-A isotopes are shown in Fig. 3. The two p-wave resonances seem to shift at the same rate and the f-wave resonances change somewhat more slowly. This difference is greater than one expects for Coulomb energy deviations and calculations show that it cannot be accounted for by inclusion of an isobaric-spin term in the optical-model potential. We associate it with the actual difference in the positions of the $7/2^-$ and $3/2^-$ states in the corresponding odd-A Ba isotopes, which have not yet been observed. The shift in energy of the $f_{7/2}$ single-particle states and the $p_{3/2}$ single-particle states may be related to the polarizability of the even-even cores, but only slightly as is indicated by the small change in the spectroscopic factors in the different isotopes. This shift is most probably due to

the character of the $([2d_{3/2}]^{2n}, f_{7/2})$ interaction and
the $([2d_{3/2}]^{2n}, p_{3/2})$ interaction and is dependent on the
number n of paired particles in the $2d_{3/2}$ subshell.

The inelastic cross sections for the reactions to
the 2^+ states in the even-even isotopes are shown in
Fig. 4. The intensity of the inelastic peaks increases
as A decreases from Ba^{138} through Ba^{136} to Ba^{134}. The
change is more pronounced for the decay of the $f_{7/2}$
resonance. A preliminary analysis, in which it was
assumed that the angular distributions for scattering
on Ba^{136} and Ba^{134} were similar to that observed at
Heidelberg[3] on Ba^{138}, gives the inelastic-scattering
results shown in Table II. The center-of-mass energies
of the inelastic protons are quoted. Since these energies are about the same for all the even-A isotopes,
it is meaningful to compare the partial inelastic widths
$\Gamma_{p'}$.

No detailed analysis of these results has yet been
attempted. The change of the decay rate to the 2^+ level
from isotope to isotope is probably due to changes in
the configuration of the 2^+ state. For this reason it
is clear that the inelastic widths contain important information on the changing constitution of the 2^+ state
as one moves away from the closed neutron shell of 82
neutrons. Angular-distribution measurements will be
useful in establishing these effects quantitatively.

No strong inelastic scattering was observed at the
resonances in the odd-A Ba isotopes. While inelastic
scattering to the low-lying $(3s_{1/2})^{-1}$ and $(h_{11/2})^{-1}$
states in Ba^{137} is expected to be small, inelastic
scattering to the $(d_{3/2})^2_{0^+} f_{7/2}$ state in Ba^{137} was expected to be favored for the $f_{7/2}$ resonances. (The
analogue of this state in Ba^{137} is the $f_{7/2}$ resonance

observed in Ba^{136} at a proton energy of 9.7 MeV, as shown in Fig. 2.) However, the emission of a $d_{3/2}$ proton leads not only to the state discussed above but also to those arising from $(d_{3/2})^2_{2+}$ $f_{7/2}$ configurations so that the expected inelastic strength is dissipated over many states and not observed. Situations similar to this may be expected to occur in most odd-A targets. Consequently, the observation of inelastic scattering will not be as useful a spectroscopic tool as was hoped in these cases.

REFERENCES

1) F. G. Perey, Phys. Rev. 131 (1963) 745.
2) P. von Brentano, N. Marquardt, J. P. Wurm, and S. A. A. Zaidi, Phys. Letts. 17 (1965) 124.
3) S. A. A. Zaidi, P. von Brentano, D. Rieck, and J. P. Wurm, Phys. Letts. 19 (1965) 45.

TABLE I. Parameters of the elastic-scattering resonances.

Nucleus	$(E_p)_{c.m.}$ (MeV)	Γ (keV)	Γ_p (keV)	S
		$f_{7/2}$		
Ba^{138}	9.93	65	16	0.50
Ba^{136}	9.63	70	11	0.45
Ba^{134}	9.25	70	8	0.45
		$p_{3/2}$		
Ba^{138}	10.56	80	22	0.24
Ba^{136}	10.01	75	15	0.20
Ba^{134}	9.37	70	8	0.15

TABLE II. Parameters of the inelastic-scattering resonances.

Nucleus	$(E_{p'})_{c.m.}$ (MeV)	Γ (keV)	$\Gamma_{p'}$ (keV)
$f_{7/2}$			
Ba^{138}	8.50	65	2
Ba^{136}	8.80	70	6
Ba^{134}	8.64	70	10
$p_{3/2}$			
Ba^{138}	9.13	80	9
Ba^{136}	9.18	75	12
Ba^{134}	8.76	70	23

DISCUSSION

BONDORF, Bohr Institute: The extracted proton width in an inelastic channel is very sensitive to the magnitude of the direct amplitude which interferes with the resonance amplitude. Did you look for this effect eventually by studying the inelastic cross section at several angles?

VAGER: The angular distribution for the Ba^{138} was measured by the Heidelberg group. We assumed the angular distribution for the inelastic process to be essentially the same for all the even Ba isotopes. The direct interaction background was simply subtracted and the angular distribution was then roughly integrated over the angles. It was assumed that effects of interference would be greatly reduced by such a procedure. Is this an answer?

BONDORF: Yes. That means that you have not taken into account the direct amplitude?

VAGER: That's right.

BRENTANO, Max Planck, Heidelberg: If the wave functions of the analogue states you discussed can mainly be described by two parts of which the first is a single particle coupled to the 0^+ ground state and the second as a single particle coupled to the 2^+ first excited state, then an increase in the inelastic process would imply a decrease in the elastic process. Did your experimental results show such a trend?

VAGER: Although the inelastic process increases when one goes from Ba^{138} through Ba^{136} to Ba^{134}, the spectroscopic factors for the 0^+ ground states seem to stay constant.

Therefore, the answer would be that the picture for the wave function of the analogue states must be more complex and include some other important contributions than those described by a single particle coupled to the 0^+ ground state and a single particle coupled to the 2^+ first excited state.

MORRISON, Argonne: Do you see any inelastic scattering in the case of the odd isotopes?

VAGER: Very slightly. The reason for this is because once you couple a particle to a hole, then you have a bunch of states which you can form in this way, and the strength for each inelastic group will go down by this multiplicity.

INGLIS: Any more planted questions?

AXEL, Illinois: I wonder if you could just tell me very briefly what the spectroscopic factor is. Does a value of 1/2 mean that you think that the width is a half of what would be expected for a single particle?

VAGER: Yes, within the framework of the existing theory of analogue states.

AXEL: But I don't know what that factor would be if the single particle shell model described the state perfectly. Would that number be one instead of 1/2?

VAGER: If the proton shell is also closed then I believe with the restrictions of Macfarlane it would increase.

MACFARLANE, Argonne: I think in the sense that Axel asked the question, the answer is yes.

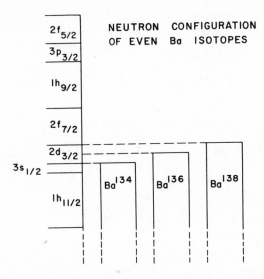

Fig. 1.   Neutron configuration of the even-A Ba isotopes.

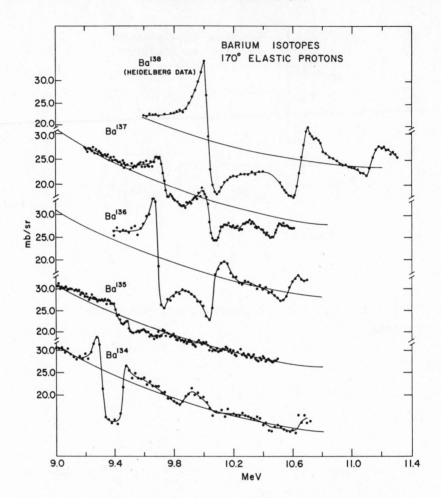

Fig. 2. Cross sections at 170° for elastic proton scattering from Ba isotopes. The smooth lines are calculated optical-model cross sections.

POSITION OF RESONANCES IN Ba ISOTOPES

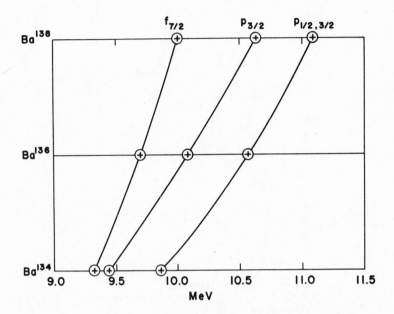

Fig. 3. Position of the resonances in the even-A Ba isotopes.

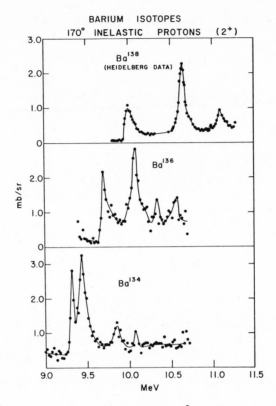

Fig. 4. Cross sections at 170° for inelastic proton scattering to the first 2+ excited state of the even-A Ba isotopes.

C6. SPIN AND PARITY MEASUREMENTS FOR ANALOGUE RESONANCES IN $Zr^{90}(p,p)$ [*]

G. Terrell and C. F. Moore
University of Texas
Austin, Texas
J. L. Adams and D. Robson
Florida State University
Tallahassee, Florida

INTRODUCTION

Double scattering techniques have been used to measure the polarization of protons elastically scattered by Zr^{90} for proton energies between 6.6 and 7.1 MeV. This region contains a resonance previously identified as an isobaric analogue state[1] in the compound nucleus Nb^{91}. The state in Zr^{91} which is a member of the same isobaric multiplet occurs at an excitation of 2.06 MeV and has been observed by Cohen and Chubinsky[2]. They reported this state to have a (d,p) angular distribution characteristic of an $\ell = 2$ orbital angular momentum transfer for the added neutron. A spin assignment of $d_{3/2}$ was made using this information and based in part on shell model predictions for locations of single particle states.

Recently the observation of j-dependent effects[3] in (d,p) stripping has revitalized interest in the study of $Zr^{90}(d,p)Zr^{91}$. Using this method the level at

*Supported in part by the United States Atomic Energy Commission and the United States Air Force Office of Scientific Research

2.06 MeV has been assigned as $d_{3/2}$ because its j-dependent behavior is consistent with assignments of states in other nuclei.

The polarization study of the analogue states serves to measure the spin in a direct fashion which can be analyzed using well-known model-independent techniques. Also, the magnitude and shape of the polarization excitation curve adds information to the measurements of resonance parameters made on the differential cross section.

EXPERIMENT

In this experiment the protons were first elastically scattered by Zr^{90} and then elastically scattered at a mean laboratory angle of 50° from a thick (~ 8.7 mg/cm^2) carbon analyzing target. In the proton energy region 5.4 - 6.4 MeV, the magnitude of the polarization produced in p-C^{12} elastic scattering at 50°(LAB) is high and a slowly varying function of both energy and angle. A polyethelene absorber was used to slow the protons down a half MeV. Since 0° scattering produces no polarization effects, this does not affect the measured asymmetries. Therefore, it is convenient, and in certain instances highly advantageous, to use a thick carbon target and rather poor geometry in the second scattering. The effective polarization of the polarimeter has been measured as a function of the energy of the protons incident on the second target. The results of this calibration are shown as full circles in Fig. 1. A more extensive calibration had been done previously for slightly different geometry and a somewhat thicker second target. The results of this initial calibration are shown as open circles in Fig. 1.

The thick second target could complicate corrections to the measured asymmetries due to the inherent finite geometry used in double scattering experiments. However, the lowest order geometry corrections are proportional to $(\Delta\theta_1)^2$ where $\Delta\theta_1$ is half the angular acceptance of the polarimeter about the first target[4]. For these measurements this half angle was less than 0.7°. With this angular resolution, the geometry corrections to this data are completely negligible.

The Zirconium target used in the polarization measurements was 0.67 mg/cm^2 (approximately 20 - 25 keV) and 98.6% Zr^{90}. If one assumes that the cross sections for p-contaminant and p- Zr^{90} scattering are equal, it can be shown that under the worst possible conditions the 1.4% contaminant would produce an error less than 0.02 in the calculated polarizations. Contaminants in the second target introduce no error in the measured asymmetries since in the calibration the measured effective polarizations are produced by the entire contents of the second target. Therefore, errors in the measured polarizations due to target contaminants were negligible. The target used for the differential cross section measurements was similar in content to the one described but was only 0.54 mg/cm^2 thick.

The laboratory and data processing techniques used to measure and analyze the data reduced all sources of instrumental error to zero or negligible proportions. An important feature in this respect is that measurements were taken on both sides of the beam, thus interchanging the roles of the two counters. The coincidence counting reduced the background to negligible proportions. In the forward angle region, calculations indicated that for $\ell = 2$ resonances polarization would be largest at 60°. Considerably larger polarizations were predicted in the back angle range from 130° - 160°. Thus the polarization was measured as a function of energy at laboratory angles of 60° and 140°. Polarization as a function of angle was also measured at proton laboratory energies of 6.775 and 6.825 MeV. These correspond to energies slightly below and above the resonance energy.

ANALYSIS

For elastic scattering of protons by spin zero nuclei the differential cross section and polarization can be expressed in terms of the coherent and incoherent scattering amplitudes, A and B respectively, in the following manner:

$$\frac{d\sigma}{d\Omega} = AA^* + BB^*$$

and

$$P = \frac{AB^* + A^*B}{AA^* + BB^*}$$

The amplitudes A and B can be expressed as

$$A = \frac{-\eta}{2k} \csc^2\left(\frac{\theta}{2}\right) \exp\left[-i\eta \log\left\{\sin^2\left(\frac{\theta}{2}\right)\right\}\right] +$$

$$\frac{+1}{2k} \sum_{L,J} (J + 1/2)\, iT_{L,J} \cdot P_L\,(\cos\theta) \text{ and}$$

$$B = \frac{1}{2k} \sum_{L,J} (-1)^{L + J + 1/2}\, T_{L,J} \cdot P_L^{\,1}\,(\cos\theta).$$

Here,

$$T_{L,J} = e^{2i\omega_L} - U_{L,J}$$

$$U_{L,J} = + e^{2i\omega_L} \left\{ e^{2i\zeta_L} + e^{2i\phi_L} \cdot \frac{i\ \Gamma_L^P}{E_J - E - 1/2\ i\ \Gamma_L} \right\}$$

$$\omega_L = \text{Coulomb phase} = \left\{ \begin{array}{l} 0 \text{ for } L = 0 \\ \sum\limits_{M=1}^{L} \tan^{-1}(\frac{\eta}{M})\ \text{ for } L > 0 \end{array} \right\}$$

$\zeta_L \equiv$ Optical phase, in general complex, (when Im $(\zeta_L) = 0$ then $(\zeta_L = \phi_L)$)

$\phi_L \equiv$ Resonance phase, real

$$\eta = 4.98 \cdot Z_I \cdot Z_T \cdot \left(\frac{M}{E}\right)^{1/2}$$

$$k^2 = .00478 \cdot M \cdot E\ (\text{barn}^{-1})$$

$$M = \frac{M_I \cdot M_T}{M_I + M_T}\ \text{a.m.u} \qquad E = \frac{M_I \cdot E_{lab}}{M_I + M_T}\ \text{keV}$$

The amplitudes can readily be calculated from the following expressions

Let:

$$a_L^{\pm} = \text{Re}\left\{ T_{L,J} \right\} = \cos(2\omega_L) - \cos(2\omega_L + 2\zeta_L^R) \cdot \exp(-2\zeta_L^I)$$

$$+ \frac{\Gamma_L^{P\pm}\left\{(E_L - E)\sin(2\omega_L + 2\phi_L) + 1/2\ \Gamma_L^{\pm}\cos(2\omega_L + 2\phi_L)\right\}}{(E_L - E)^2 + (1/2\ \Gamma_L)^2}$$

$$\beta^+_L = \text{Im}\left\{T_{L,J}\right\} = \frac{\sin(2\omega_L) - \sin(2\omega_L + 2\zeta^R_L) \cdot \exp(-2\zeta^I_L) +}{}$$

$$\frac{-\Gamma^{P\pm}_L\left\{(E_L - E)\cos(2\omega_L + 2\phi_L) - 1/2\ \Gamma^{\pm}_L \sin(2\omega_L + 2\phi_L)\right\}}{(E_L - E)^2 + (1/2\ \Gamma_L)^2}$$

$$\gamma = \eta \log\left\{\sin\left(\frac{\theta}{2}\right)\right\}$$

$$AR \equiv 2k\ \text{Re}(A) = -\eta\ \csc^2\left(\frac{\theta}{2}\right)\cos(2\gamma) -$$

$$\sum_{L=0}^{L_{max}}\left\{(L+1)\beta^+_L + L\beta^-_L\right\} P^0_L(\cos\theta)$$

$$AI \equiv 2k\ \text{Im}(A) = +\eta\ \csc^2\left(\frac{\theta}{2}\right)\sin(2\gamma) +$$

$$\sum_{L=0}^{L_{max}}\left\{(L+1)\ \alpha^+_L + L\alpha^-_L\right\} P^0_L(\cos\theta)$$

$$BR \equiv 2k\ \text{Re}(B) = -\sum_{L=0}^{L_{max}}\left\{\alpha^+_L - \alpha^-_L\right\} P^1_L(\cos\theta)$$

$$BI \equiv 2k\ \text{Im}(B) = -\sum_{L=0}^{L_{max}}\left\{\beta^+_L - \beta^-_L\right\} P^1_L(\cos\theta)$$

where the (+) and (-) superscripts refer to

$$J = \ell + s \text{ and } J = \ell - s$$

using these expressions we have:

$$\frac{d\sigma}{d\Omega} = \frac{1}{4k^2} \left\{ AR^2 + AI^2 + BR^2 + BI^2 \right\}$$

and

$$P = \frac{2 \cdot \left\{ AR \cdot BR + AI \cdot BI \right\}}{AR^2 + AI^2 + BR^2 + BI^2}$$

In order to account for target thickness effects a numerical integration of these expressions is made over the calculated target thickness using an analytic range - energy relationship. Since these formulae allow for imaginary optical parameters the unitary condition $U_{J,L}^* \cdot U_{J,L} \leq 1$ was calculated and checked.

The elastic scattering cross section excitation functions, previously measured at laboratory angles of $92.4°$, $122.4°$, $152.4°$ and $172.4°$ are shown in Figs. 2 to 5. Note that besides the resonance near 6.8 MeV, there is another smaller resonance near 7.0 MeV. This latter resonance was ignored in the polarization calculations.

The polarization excitation functions are shown in Figs. 6 and 7, at laboratory angles of 60° and 140°. The solid lines in these figures represent calculations assuming the resonance near 6.8 MeV to be $d_{3/2}$. The dashed curves are the corresponding calculations for $d_{5/2}$. From these curves it is obvious that the resonance is $d_{3/2}$ rather than $d_{5/2}$. Only $\ell = 2$ orbital angular momentum was considered since the differential cross section excitation functions are able to unambiguously determine the ℓ-value. The polarization angular distributions at 6.775 and 6.825 MeV with the

339

$d_{3/2}$ calculated curves are shown in Figs. 8 and 9. All of the curves shown in Figs. 6 through 9 are the results of preliminary calculations. However, more sophisticated calculations, described in the next paragraph, improved the fits only slightly.

Using the optical model parameters found in the first column of Table V of Rosen et al.[5], the polarization data were fitted with a modified version of the optical model code OPTIX1[6]. This procedure yielded curves very similar to those shown in Figs. 6 through 9. In addition, parameters for the resonance near 6.8 MeV were found to be the following:

$$\text{Resonance energy } E_L = 6.78 \text{ MeV}$$
$$\text{Total width } \Gamma_L = 55 \text{ keV}$$
$$\text{Partial width } \Gamma_L^P = 15 \text{ keV}$$

DISCUSSION

There are other resonances near the one studied in this paper. These are most clearly seen in the differential cross section excitation curves at 172.4°. However, the effect which they have on the resonance considered is small. No attempt has been made to fit the polarization data at the analogue resonance near 7.0 MeV. The experimental statistics are not good enough because no concentrated data taking efforts have been made in this region. This state is the analogue of the 2.22 MeV level in Zr^{91} and has been assigned to be $g_{7/2}$ by Cohen[7].

One of the interesting features of this work is the result that the spin assignment via polarization measurements for the $d_{3/2}$ level investigated could have

been made even if the partial width ration Γ_L^P/Γ_L had
been much smaller than the observed ratios of about
0.3. In general, polarization measurements are a sensitive test of the j-value and assignments can be made
using much less data than reported in this experiment.
Besides these spectroscopic tool advantages, it is
well to note that the data are consistent with our
present understanding of analogue states in resonance
reactions.

In concluding, we wish to remark again on the
simple analysis needed to determine the spin of a level
using polarization techniques as compared to the more
formidable, still to be explained, j-dependent effects
of d-p stripping. The data taking requirements in
both cases are somewhat tedious and perhaps one who is
familiar with (d,p) studies may find polarization measurements difficult to justify, but with the advent of
good polarized proton beams the experimental case
should swing in favor of this latter technique.

ACKNOWLEDGMENTS
We wish to thank Dr. E. Bernstein for use of
his calibrated polarimeter and Dr. B. B. Kinsey for
his encouragement and assistance in making accelerator
time available for this experiment.

REFERENCES

1) C. F. Moore, Dissertation, Florida State University, (1964), unpublished.

2) B. L. Cohen and O. V. Chubinsky, Phys. Rev. $\underline{131}$ (1952) 2184.

3) L. L. Lee, Jr., and J. P. Schiffer, Phys. Rev. $\underline{136}$ (1964) B405.

4) S. J. Moss and W. Haberli, Nucl. Phys. $\underline{72}$ (1965) 417.

5) L. Rosen, J. G. Beery and A. S. Goldhaber, Annals of Phys., (New York) $\underline{34}$ (1965) 96.

6) W. J. Thompson and E. Gille, Technical Report No. 9, Tandem Accelerator Laboratory, Florida State University, (1965).

7) B. L. Cohen, Phys. Rev. $\underline{125}$ (1962) 1358.

DISCUSSION

SHAFROTH, Bartol: I'd like to say that I think
this is very nice work in the first place. In the
second place, besides being able to get the j as you
showed, do you think there is anything further you can
get, about the reaction mechanism, from this sort of
work? Would it be possible to study polarization of
the inelastically scattered protons? A further question I had was that in a recent preprint of Jones,
Schiffer, Lee, Marinov and Lerner, where elastic scattering of protons on Ca^{48} was observed to study analogue state resonances in Sc^{49}, they showed optical
model fits to a p-wave resonance with j = 3/2 or 1/2
and these curves were strikingly different. Doesn't
this mean that polarization measurements are not really
necessary to pin down j?

MOORE: One of the big hopes in this polarization work is that with the advent of these high intensity polarized beams that people hope to get, that you
would really be able to clobber polarization measurements, whereas I have a lot of problems with resolution
after you do a second scattering that would pretty
much inhibit trying to do inelastic studies, but I
think that you can extend it quite a bit more than
what this first attempt does.

And besides that, as I mentioned before, it
also helps you to determine what the total width, partial width and the resonant energy are, since they are
all parameters in the fitting on this whole polarization data.

SCHIFFER, Argonne: As far as the J-dependent
effect goes, I think you give us more credit than we

deserve. We did not determine the spins. In fact, this state plus two others like it in the other zirconium isotopes were the ones we used to say that there may be a j-dependence in this region.

BRENTANO, Max Planck, Heidelberg: I just want to know how many hours does it take to get this data?

MOORE: Well, we have a lot of machine time.

INGLIS: There are lots of machines in Texas.

MOORE: That's right, The University of Texas is on a corner of LBJ's ranch. One remarkable thing is that the first measurement took two hours. After this point, we felt we knew the spin to be $3/2^+$. We measured this point where we were expecting an optimum polarization.

I was very interested in seeing the polarization excitation curves come out correctly. We took a lot of data involving a lot of time, but I think once you have seen that things are working correctly, you can probably spend six or eight hours and get the spin for any effect this large.

ZAIDI, Max Planck, Heidelberg: How does the polarization depend on the optical phases?

MOORE: That's a good question. We are 2 MeV below the Coulomb barrier here. One of my interests in worrying about this optical problem is that we have data on other isotopes at much higher energies where the effect is very important. However, without using any optical phases at all in these calculations, the black lines you saw on the slide wouldn't change much.

ZAIDI: Is it true that you always expect the two values of j to yield polarizations of opposite sense?

MOORE: Right.

ZAIDI: Is it also true if you don't have pure Coulomb scattering?

MOORE: I don't really know. Perhaps Robson does.

ROBSON, Florida State: The calculations we have done on polarization here indicate that for this $d_{3/2}$ level, the difference between Coulomb and optical is very small. To answer somebody else's question on the same subject, the measurement of polarization could be reduced, I think, to one energy and one angle to tell you what the spin of the level is, provided that you have enough of what you could call universal curves calculated to tell you what angle and what energy to look at.

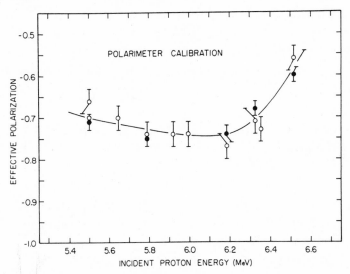

Fig. 1. Polarimeter calibration. The full circles represent the results using the geometry and carbon target of the present experiment. The open circles represent a previous calibration with a slightly different geometry and somewhat thicker carbon target.

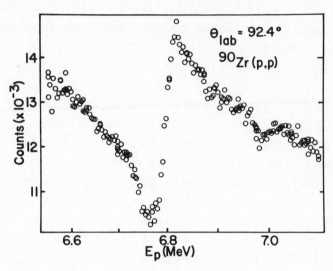

Fig. 2. Differential cross section excitation function of elastically scattered protons from a Zr^{90} target at a laboratory angle of 92.4°.

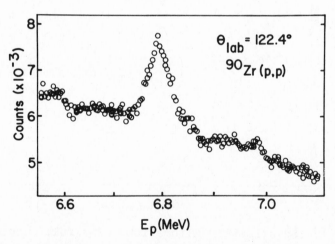

Fig. 3. Differential cross section excitation function of elastically scattered protons from a Zr^{90} target at a laboratory angle of 122.4°.

346

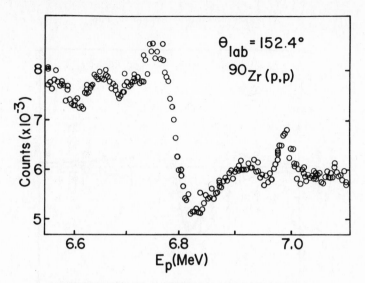

Fig. 4. Differential cross section excitation function of elastically scattered protons from a Zr^{90} target at a laboratory angle of 152.4°.

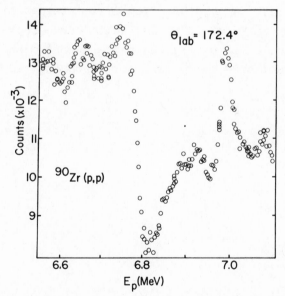

Fig. 5. Differential cross section excitation function of elastically scattered protons from a Zr^{90} target at a laboratory angle of 172.4°.

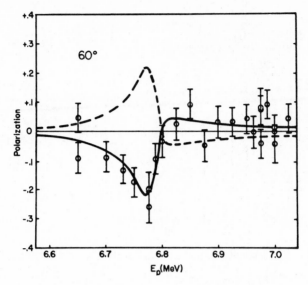

Fig. 6. Polarization excitation function of elastically scattered protons from a Zr^{90} target at a
laboratory angle of 60°. The solid curve represents a
calculation assuming the resonance near 6.8 MeV to be
$d_{3/2}$. The dashed curve is a corresponding calculation
for $d_{5/2}$.

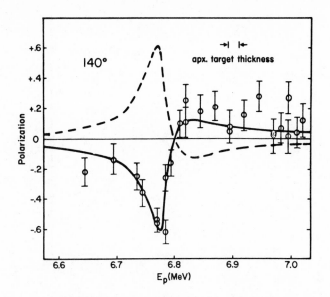

Fig. 7. Polarization excitation function of elastically scattered protons from a Zr^{90} target at a laboratory angle of 140°. The solid curve represents a
calculation assuming the resonance near 6.8 MeV to be
$d_{3/2}$. The dashed curve is a corresponding calculation
for $d_{5/2}$.

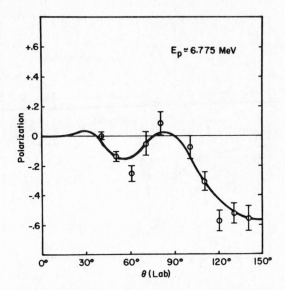

Fig. 8. Polarization angular distribution of elastically scattered protons from a Zr^{90} target at an incident proton laboratory energy of 6.775 MeV. The solid curve represents a calculation assuming the resonance near 6.8 MeV to be $d_{3/2}$.

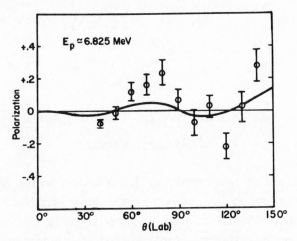

Fig. 9.   Polarization angular distribution of elastically scattered protons from a Zr^{90} target at an incident
proton laboratory energy of 6.825 MeV.   The solid curve
represents a calculation assuming the resonance near
6.8 MeV to be $d_{3/2}$.

351

C7. REMARKS BY H. MORINAGA

Max Planck Institut für Kernphysik

Heidelberg, Germany

I think our analogue friends are being punished because everyone has to study the very difficult theory by Robson. If one studies theory at all, one should study Robson's theory very carefully. However, everybody says the theory is so difficult it is impossible to understand. For an experimentalist one of the most interesting things is the asymmetry of the resonance which we see in the case of (p,n) cross sections:

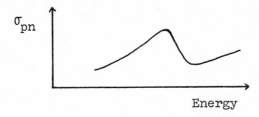

I have an explanation for this which is rather qualitative and which I myself don't think is necessarily true. The idea could be wrong but it is in some sense an easy way to understand things so I should like to present it and then ask for your opinion.

The way of thinking is as follows: if we take a (p,n) cross section then this should be proportional to the square of some matrix element, i.e.

$$\sigma_{pn} = | < ? | ? | \phi(E) \; \Phi_t > |^2$$

On the right hand side we have a target nucleus and a
scattering state of a proton, the latter being a function of energy. Now this couples to higher isobaric
spin states and then I have an interaction which I
don't really know so let's make it a ?. The final
state I don't know either but there is one thing of
which I can be quite sure; that this part is exponentially decreasing with radius increase.

Let us now draw pictures of the wave function
$\phi(E)$ at three values of E, i.e., $E_R - \Delta E$, E_R, $E_R + \Delta E$
with E_R being the analogue resonance energy:

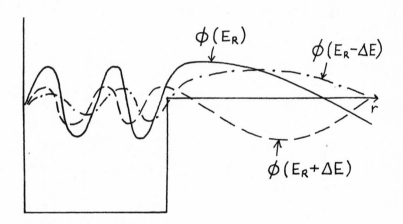

Inside the nucleus the wave function oscillates
and at resonance joins onto the normalized function
outside as shown. Now $\phi(E_R - \Delta E)$ being the function
below the resonance energy has a slightly longer wavelength inside the nucleus and so it does not turn over
just outside the nucleus. However, the wave function
$\phi(E_R + \Delta E)$ turns over a little bit before E_R and has
an important zero just outside the nucleus. Now if we

take integrals of the function for the various energies and assume as Dr. Robson says, that all the mixing
comes from outside the nucleus then we get a large
overlap at $E = E_R$. If we go down to slightly below the
resonance energy the magnitude of the integral should
decrease because the external wave function is pushed
further out. On the high side of the resonance the wave
function has a zero so that the integral may have a
zero. Eventually as one goes up in energy the negative
part of $\phi(E_R + \Delta E)$ will dominate, i.e. the zero moves
into the nucleus. If you represent this graphically
one gets a curve like this for the matrix element M:

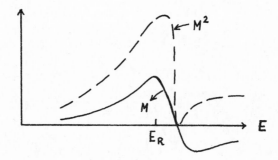

The dotted curve is essentially the σ_{pn} cross section
and exhibits the type of asymmetry observed. This may
be the same thing as what Dr. Robson says, or it may
be different, I don't know. For experimentalists it
may be an easier way to understand the phenomena.

DISCUSSION

ROBSON, Florida State: When you were talking about this last night, I was in a better mood because I had had several stimulants. Now I don't understand the matrix element. What happened to the neutron? After all, the neutron has to come out somewhere. Does it come out in your question marks?

MORINAGA: Probably through the final state question mark.

ROBSON: How can that be exponentially decaying if the neutron gets out?

MORINAGA: I see that is a big question. Maybe it is the other question mark! It doesn't matter. The argument which I am using is that this part doesn't have any zero close to the nucleus.

ROBSON: Okay, well neglecting that and going on then to the second part, it does require, however, a very strong correlation between the analogue state and the entrance channel. It must be essentially an entrance channel state. Otherwise, this model will not work?

MORINAGA: Right, I use the property of this one.

ROBSON: So we get the same effect under the same considerations.

MORINAGA: Right, so maybe it amounts to the same thing.

HAMBURGER, Pittsburgh: Doesn't this argument apply to any resonance? Should all resonances we ever see have this shape? I don't see what is specific to the isobaric analogue states here.

MORINAGA: Well, actually, this kind of thing

should exist in any kind of reaction. For example, you can take the reaction like neutron capture. If you take $\sigma(n,\gamma)$, in this case again, it is the same story. The γ emission is dipole, the capture involves slow neutrons with size resonances. Presuming one has a bound p-state then the entering neutron drops into this one by dipole. In this situation we have the same kind of radial matrix element to calculate which can give zero.

HAMBURGER: Is it experimentally observed?

MORINAGA: In some sense, yes. This means that sometimes a cross section drops very small.

C8. ISOBARIC SPIN EFFECTS IN B^{10} + p[*]

P. P. Singh[+]

Indiana University and Argonne National Laboratory

R. E. Segel, S. S. Hanna[++], M. A. Grace[+++]

Argonne National Laboratory
Argonne, Illinois

We wish to report on a study of the formation
of all the gamma ray emitting states that are formed
by bombarding B^{10} with protons of energy from 4 to 12
MeV. Figure 1 shows the states involved. These consist of the five states of B^{10} excited through (p,p')
reaction; two of C^{10} formed through (p,n) reaction and
the first excited state of Be^7 from the (p,α) reaction.
The variety of available final states makes it possible
to investigate the degree to which various factors
(isobaric spin, energy, configuration) influence the
decay of states at energies corresponding to states in
C^{11} at excitations from 12 to 19.5 MeV.

Thin metallic boron targets, 96% B^{10}, were bombarded by a well collimated beam of protons from the
ANL Tandem Van de Graaff. Gamma rays were detected by
two large NaI detectors which were operated separately

[*] Partly supported by Atomic Energy Commission and
partly by National Science Foundation
[+] Present Address: Indiana Univ., Bloomington, Indiana
[++] Present Address: Stanford Univ., Stanford, California
[+++] Present Address: Clarendon Laboratory, Oxford, Eng.

or in coincidence. Figure 2 shows a typical singles
spectrum while Fig. 3 shows a gamma spectrum in one
detector in coincidence with a 0.72 MeV γ-ray observed
in the second detector. The intensities of the gamma
rays were extracted from the peaks in pulse height
spectrum by correcting for the background of higher
energy γ-rays, efficiencies of NaI detectors and the
geometry of the experimental arrangement[1]. The coincidence (with 0.72 MeV) and the singles spectra were
taken at 50 keV intervals between 4.0 MeV and 10.7 MeV
bombarding energies and in 100 keV steps up to 12 MeV.
From these spectra and the measured decay scheme (details are given in Ref. 1) the yield curves for the
formation of the final states in B^{10}, C^{10} and Be^7 were
obtained. For comparison all the cross sections as a
function of proton energy (and excitation in C^{11}) are
given in Fig. 4 along with those of $B^{10}(p,\alpha_0)Be^7$ and
$B^{10}(p,He^3)Be^8$ taken from Jenkin et al.[2].

The particles emitted from B^{10} + p appear to
fall into at least two distinct classes: (1) those
that show a strong 3 - 4 MeV wide resonance (with some
finer structure) in 4 - 10 MeV region, namely, the
alpha and He^3 particles and the inelastic protons
forming the 0.72-, 2.15- and 3.58-MeV states in B^{10},
and (2) those that show a much weaker resonance (in
7 - 10 MeV region) or none at all in this region, namely
the neutrons and the inelastic protons forming the 1.74-
and 5.10-MeV states of B^{10}. Note that the weak reactions are those for which the residual nucleus is left
in a T = 1 state. Table I lists the maximum cross
sections for the exit channels together with various
quantities that could influence the cross sections.
Channels with higher Q-value have higher cross-sections.

The orbital angular momenta of the initial, ℓ_i, and
the final particle, ℓ_f, (the smallest possible sum of
these is given) seem to have little effect on the
reaction[4]. The last column of the table gives the
Clebsch-Gordan coefficients for forming the final states
with isobaric spin Tf_1 and Tf_2, from the initial system of isobaric spin $(0,1/2)$. It is obvious that some,
but not all, of the inhibition of the $(1,1/2)$ channels
can be attributed to the Clebsch-Gordan coefficients.
The difference in Q-values cannot explain this inhibition since the C^{10} ground state and the 1.74 MeV
state in B^{10} both have Q-values comparable to those of
T = 0 states having maximum cross section an order of
magnitude larger.

The cause of the suppression of T = 1 states
therefore will have to be found in the dynamical char-
acteristics of the $(B^{10} +p)$ system. For example if
B^{10} is considered to consist of clusters of $(Li^6 + \alpha)$
(or as $(\alpha + \alpha + d)$) then the giant resonance observed
in this study could be a resonance[3] in the excitations
of the oscillation of one cluster relative to the others
without any internal excitation of the clusters themselves. Such a resonance, due to two or more T = 0
particles, must have T = 0. On this picture only
those B^{10} states whose wave functions contain an appreciable amount of $(Li^6 + \alpha)$ cluster configuration
would be strongly coupled to the above mentioned giant
resonance. (And it seems that T = 1 states have small
amounts of the appropriate cluster configuration in
their wave functions.)

Though the exact nature of the observed giant
resonances in this study has still to be established,
it is obvious that one should be careful in drawing

any precise conclusions as to the violation (or otherwise) of the isobaric spin selection rules from the
study of reactions of the type (d,α) and (α,α) without
taking the dynamic nature of the reaction under study.

REFERENCES

1) R. E. Segel, P. P. Singh, S. S. Hanna, and M. A.
   Grace, (in press), Physical Review.

2) J. G. Jenkin, L. G. Earwaker and E. W. Titterton,
   Nucl. Phys. 50 (1964) 516; Phys. Letts. 4 (1965)
   142.

3) K. Wildermuth and Th. Kanellopoulos, CERN report
   59-23, 1959.

4) From the angular distribution of inelastically
   scattered protons it seems that the reaction
   mechanism is predominantly through Compound Nucleus
   Formation. (P. P. Singh, B. Watson, J. J. Kroepfl
   and R. E. Segel - private communication).

TABLE I. Maximum cross sections observed for the various channels in the B^{10} + p reactions. The reaction energy is given by Q, the orbital angular momenta of initial and final particles by ℓ_i and ℓ_f, and the isobaric spins of the final nuclei by T_{f_1} and T_{f_2}. The vector addition coefficient for forming the final isobaric state from the initial state is denoted by CG

Final state	σ_{max} (mb)	Q (MeV)	$(\ell_i + \ell_f)_{min}$	T_{f_1}, T_{f_2}	CG
$Be^7 + \alpha$	160	1.15	1	1/2,0	1
$Be^7_{0.43} + \alpha$	55	0.72	3	1/2,0	1
$Be^{10}_{0.72} + p$	45	-0.72	2	0,1/2	1
$Be^8 + He^3$	35	-0.53	2	0,1/2	1
$B^{10}_{2.15} + p$	20	-2.15	2	0,1/2	1
$B^{10}_{3.58} + p$	20	-3.58	0	0,1/2	1
$B^{10}_{5.16} + p$	5	-5.16	0	1,1/2	1/3
$C^{10} + n$	3	-4.56	2	1,1/2	2/3
$B^{10}_{1.74} + p$	2	-1.74	2	1,1/2	1/3
$C^{10}_{3.35} + n$	2	-7.91	0	1,1/2	2/3

DISCUSSION

INGLIS: It seems to suggest that one can't always conclude that it's the isobaric spin selection rule that's doing it.

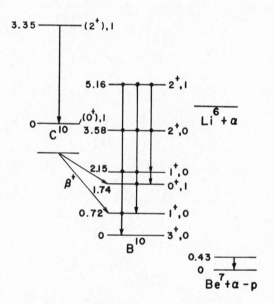

Fig. 1. Energy levels and gamma rays observed in the proton bombardment of B^{10}.

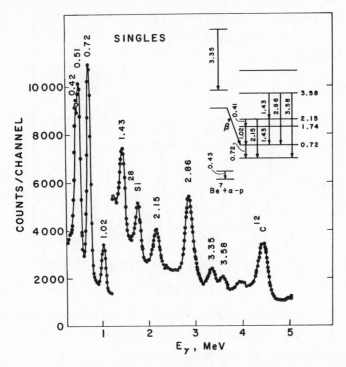

Fig. 2.   Pulse-height spectrum of gamma rays observed in the B^{10} + p reaction at 10 MeV.

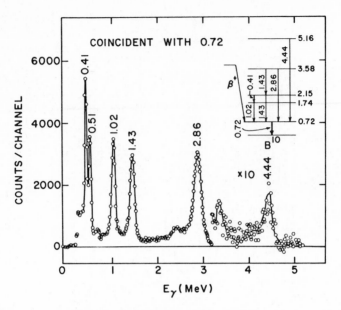

Fig. 3. Pulse-height spectrum of gamma rays observed in coincidence with the 0.72 MeV gamma ray in the B^{10} + p reaction at 10 MeV.

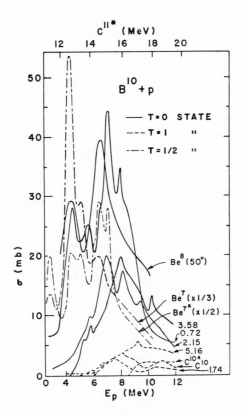

Fig. 4. Comparison of yield curves for the states produced in the proton bombardment of B^{10}. The curves labeled by energies refer to final states in B^{10}. The curves for Be^7 and Be^8 are taken from Ref. 2.

C9. ANALOGUE STATES IN Pb ISOTOPES

A. Adam, G. Bassani, N. Cindro, C. Levi,
M. Mermaz and L. Papineau
Centre d'Etudes Nucleaires de Saclay

The total width Γ of an analogue state is proportional to the Coulomb force between the analogue state (of spin and parity J^π and isobaric spin $T + 1$) and the compound nucleus "normal" states of the same spin and parity and isobaric spin T.

Only a few efforts have been made so far to calculate theoretically the total width Γ of analogue states. In a preliminary model calculation, C. Bloch and V. Gillet (private communication) have evaluated the total width of the analogue of the Tl^{208} ground state in the Pb^{208} compound nucleus. In the calculation of the Coulomb matrix elements giving the coupling between the analogue and the normal states through the T-mixing Coulomb operator V_c

$$M = \langle \psi^{J^\pi,T}_{Pb^{208}norm.st.} | V_c | \psi^{J^\pi,T+1}_{Tl^{208}gr.st.} \rangle$$

they have taken for the Tl^{208} ground state a pure particle-hole shell model configuration. As a model for the Pb^{208} normal states wave functions they have used a complicated admixture of particle hole configurations obtained from spectroscopic calculations in Pb^{208} of Green, Sanderson and Gillet.[2] Although many of the Coulomb matrix elements give contributions of a few hundred keV each, the incoherent superposition of all contributions gives a total width Γ of 130 keV. This value should be taken as purely indicative when compared with the experimental widths. It is anyway at least by a factor of two larger than the Γ that have been observed experimentally, but on much lighter nuclei. Up to the present, analogue states have been observed in (or near) singly closed shell nuclei, where the normal states are much more complicated than in a doubly closed shell nucleus. It is then not surprising that the Pb^{208} model calculation gives a larger width than the observed ones. It seemed interesting to test this assumption by measuring the total width of analogue states in Pb isotopes. As we approach the doubly closed Pb^{208}, the complexity of normal states decreases and then we should expect an increase of the total width. It is evident that these considerations may be perturbed or even invalidated by the variations of the level density. Moreover the study of analogue states in the Pb isotopes is also of particular interest because reasonable models exist for the low-lying states.

We present here some preliminary results relative to the Pb^{206} and Pb^{207} nuclei.

The Pb^{207} and Pb^{206} elastic and inelastic scattering excitation functions (Figs. 1-4) have been obtained by bombarding isotopically enriched Pb targets with the proton beam of the Saclay Tandem Van de Graaff accelerator. The resonances corresponding to the analogues of the Pb^{208} (Fig. 1) and Pb^{207} (Fig. 2) ground states have been clearly observed in the elastic scattering. The analogues of the two first Pb^{207} excited states (Fig. 2) were not excited sufficiently to be identified in the elastic scattering excitation

functions. This is probably due to their small reduced
width, in agreement with what has already been observed
in (d,p) experiments[1]. The energy of the resonances
E_{res}(lab) and their total widths have been obtained from
the inelastic excitation functions. In the case of the
Pb^{207}(p,p$_2$) resonance (Fig. 3) we have E_{res}(lab) =
11.57 MeV and Γ = 200 keV. This value of Γ is in agreement with the results obtained by Booth et al. in
Copenhagen (private communication). From the Pb^{206}(p,p$_1$)
(p,p$_3$ + p$_4$) and (p,p$_5$+p$_6$) excitation functions (Fig. 4)
we obtain E_{res}(lab) = 12.28 MeV and Γ = 150 $\pm$ 20 keV.
A one-level Breit-Wigner fit on the elastic scattering
resonance has confirmed this value of Γ and gives also
the partial width Γ_p = 50 keV.

The values obtained for the total widths are much
larger than what has been observed so far and compare
favorably with the value given by C. Bloch and V. Gillet
for the Pb^{208} compound nucleus. It seems premature to
draw conclusions from the observed variation of Γ without the results on Pb^{204} (at present under study in our
laboratory) and Pb^{208}. A more complete analysis of this
experiment will be published soon.

We wish to thank C. Bloch and V. Gillet for interesting and helpful discussions and their interest in
this experiment.

REFERENCES

1) J. Peleger, U. Schmidt-Rohr, V. Spiegel, P. Turek
   and W. Zuckschwerdt, Nucl. Phys. 48 (1963) 22.
2) V. Gillet, A. M. Green and E. A. Sanderson, (to
   be published).

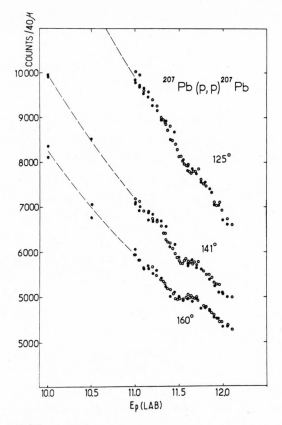

Fig. 1.   Pb^{207} elastic scattering excitation functions.

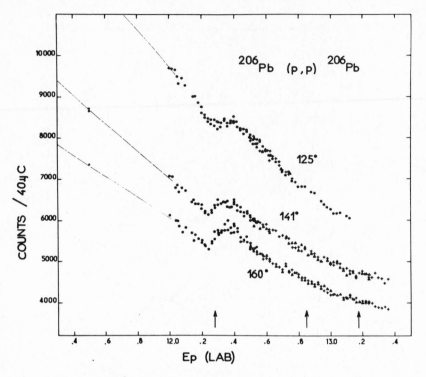

Fig. 2. Pb^{206} elastic scattering excitation functions. The arrows indicate the energies where we should have observed the resonances of the analogues of Pb^{207} two first excited states.

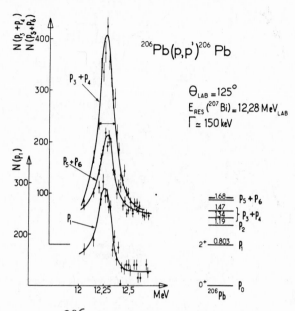

Fig. 3. Pb^{206} inelastic scattering excitation functions.

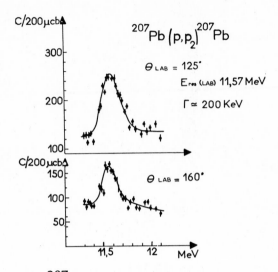

Fig. 4. Pb^{207} inelastic scattering excitation functions.

C10. SPECTROSCOPIC INFORMATION ON Sm ISOTOPES FROM ANALOGUE STATE EXPERIMENTS

G. Bassani, Y. Cassagnou, C. Levi and L. Papineau
Centre d'Etudes Nucleaires de Saclay, France

From a spectroscopic point of view, the study of analogue states by elastic proton scattering does not provide in principle additional information to the corresponding (d,p) stripping reaction if the (d,p) energy resolution is smaller than the analogue states total width. If analogue states are instead observed by inelastic proton scattering it is possible to obtain from their study unique spectroscopic information and, in particular, to investigate the importance of the coupling of a quasi-particle with an excited even-even configuration.

We present here some elastic and inelastic proton scattering experiments on Sm^{148}, Sm^{150} and Sm^{152}. The elastic and inelastic (p,p_1) Sm^{148} and Sm^{150} excitation functions are shown in Fig. 1 and Fig. 2. For Sm^{152} we have only elastic scattering preliminary results.

In the Sm^{148} elastic scattering we observe the analogue of the Sm^{149} ground state at $E_p(lab) = 9.98$ MeV and another strong resonance at $E_p(lab) = 10.50$ MeV, corresponding to an excitation of 250 keV in Sm^{149}. The (p,p_1) excitation function resonates strongly only at the same energy as the strong second elastic resonance. From the resonance analysis of the elastic scattering we obtain an unambiguous determination for the ℓ values

of the strong resonances, i.e., $\ell = 3$ for the ground
state analogue, (in agreement with the $7/2^-$ spin of
Sm^{149}) and $\ell = 1$ for the second one. A tentative fit
with a single level formula, neglecting the weak resonances appearing between the two strong ones, gives an
approximate value for the widths. We obtain for both
resonances $\Gamma \sim 100$ keV, $\Gamma_p \simeq 30$ keV, in agreement with
the total widths deduced from (p,p') results.

In the Sm^{150} elastic scattering we observe two
strong resonances, the first one ($\ell = 3$) at $E_p(lab) =$
10.30 MeV and the second one ($\ell = 1$) at $E_p(lab) =$
10.55 MeV. In the (p,p_1) excitation function we observe
only one resonance (of total width $\Gamma \simeq 100$ keV) at
an energy corresponding to the second one observed in
elastic scattering. For Sm^{152} we do not observe any
resonance around the energy expected for the analogue of
Sm^{153} ground state. Two strong resonances with similar
shapes appear at 10.3 and 10.6 MeV on the 160° excitation function. They probably do not correspond to
single levels. The 141° and 125° excitation functions
suggest that they include $\ell = 3$ and $\ell = 2$ contributions.

The only measured ground state spins in the odd Sm
isotopes are 7/2 for $Sm^{147,149}$ and 3/2 for Sm^{153}. Spin
assignments for the excited states of odd Sm isotopes
still remain very uncertain. We have compared our results with recent (d,p) stripping results [1] which are
the most complete existing. Nevertheless in this experiment relative cross-sections are given at only one angle
and no unique ℓ determination is reported.

We would like to emphasize that our experiment
gives to some extent gross-structure information, since
the spacing of levels is smaller than the total width of
the analogue resonances. The correspondence between our

results and the (d,p) experiments appears very clearly
(Fig. 3). The first strong excited Sm^{149} level in the
(d,p) reaction lies at 535 keV. In Sm^{151} the (d,p)
cross-section of the ground state is very small. The
first strong level has been seen at 60 keV and the second at 307 keV. These two states lie 250 keV apart,
and this is the energy difference we observe between the
two strong resonances. Since no states are reported at
an excitation of 250 keV we conclude that we did not observe the ground state analogue but the analogue of the
60 keV excited state, which is very probably a 7/2$^-$
spherical state.

If we compare our results with the analogue state
experiments on Sm^{144} [2,3], we see that the resonance
picture for the three isotopes (144, 148, 150) is strikingly similar. There are two strong resonances in the
elastic scattering, the first one with $\ell = 3$, the second
one with $\ell = 1$. The second one is preferentially excited in the inelastic scattering to the first 2$^+$ state.
In Sm^{145} the corresponding excited state lies at 895 keV
and has spin 3/2$^-$. It is supposed to be the $p_{3/2}$ shell
model neutron state. The excitation energy of the three
preferentially excited states presents linear variation
with mass number (Fig. 3). This variation, characteristic of a simple underlying shell model structure,
suggests that these neutron states are of the same
nature. In Sm^{147} the possible corresponding state lies
at 700 keV. For this level, strongly excited in
$Sm^{147}(p,p')Sm^{147}$, a tentative spin assignment (7/2$^-$ to
11/2$^-$) has been given. In Sm^{153} the line (Fig. 3)
crosses a level at 125 keV assigned to the 3/2$^-$ (521)
Nilsson orbit (as the ground state of Sm^{155}). If we
suppose that the selected excited state is due to the

coupling of a quasi-particle to the spherical 0^+ ground state, then the linear variation has some significance only up to the Sm^{151}. In fact the Sm^{152} ground state is deformed and Sm^{151} lies in the transition between spherical and deformed ground states. The results on $Sm^{152}(d,p)Sm^{153}$ and our results on $Sm^{152}(p,p)Sm^{152}$ confirm that the state at 125 keV in Sm^{153} is not of the same nature as the selected $3/2^-$ level in the lighter isotopes.

In addition, the first 2^+ level in Sm^{144}, Sm^{148} and Sm^{150} has approximately the same excitation energy as the selected level in the even-odd neighboring nuclei. The same is true for Sm^{146} with respect to the level at 700 keV in Sm^{147}. The fact that the (p,p') excitation functions resonate very strongly for the analogues of states lying at an excitation energy similar to the one of the final state has already been observed in the two previous (p,p') experiments published.[4,5]

We conclude that in odd Sm isotopes, A = 145 to A = 151, we select the same $3/2^-$ neutron state. In addition it appears that its wave function has strong overlap with the 2^+ state of the neighboring nucleus.

REFERENCES

1) R. A. Kenefick and R. K. Sheline, Phys. Rev. 139 (1965) B1479.

2) C. F. Moore, R. K. Jolly, Phys. Letts. 19(1965)133.

3) P. von Brentano, (private communication).

4) D. L. Allan, G. A. Jones, G. C. Morrison, R. B. Taylor, R. B. Weinberg, Phys. Letts. 17 (1965) 56.

5) P. von Brentano, N. Marquardt, J. P. Wurm and S. A. A. Zaidi, Phys. Letts. 17 (1965) 124; S. A. A. Zaidi, P. von Brentano, D. Rieck and J. P. Wurm, Phys. Letts 19 (1965)45.

DISCUSSION

ROBSON, Florida State: Just one comment on your total width calculation. You referred to R-matrix calculations as giving - I think your phrase was - several hundred keV.

BASSANI: I don't know who did it.

ROBSON: I think you are referring back to the article by Lane and Soper. Perhaps Tony Lane would like to comment on that. But first, I don't think that their work is based on R-matrix theory, and second, the work done here with R-matrix theory gives us the right answers for those cases where you expect it to work.

BASSANI: Okay, I wasn't expecting to talk, so I didn't control exactly my information sources.

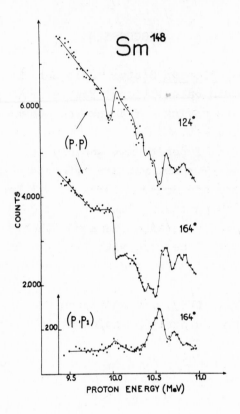

Fig. 1. Excitation functions for elastic scattering of protons on Sm^{148}, and inelastic scattering to the first 2^+ state.

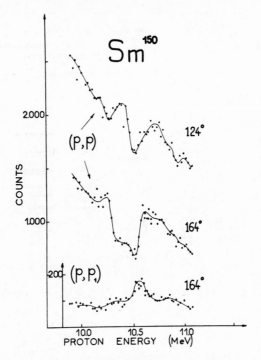

Fig. 2. Excitation functions for elastic scattering of protons on Sm^{150}, and inelastic scattering to the first 2^+ state.

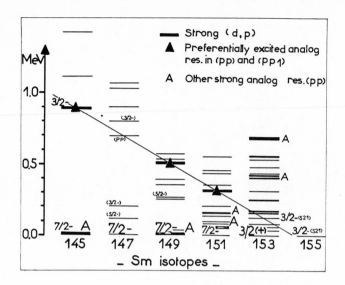

Fig. 3. Level schemes for odd Sm isotopes.

SESSION D

I. Talmi, Chairman

D1. THE ISOBARIC-SPIN SPLITTING
OF NUCLEAR EXCITATIONS[+]

Malcolm H. Macfarlane
Argonne National Laboratory, Argonne, Illinois

INTRODUCTION

Many interesting varieties of nuclear excitation
carry non-zero isobaric spin. In nuclei which are not
self-conjugate, such excitations can produce final
states with several possible values of isobaric spin T.
Since nuclear forces are isobaric-spin dependent the
various T-fragments of the excitation under consideration may be widely separated in energy. This T-splitting of nuclear excitations is the subject of my talk.

NUCLEAR EXCITATIONS

The wave function of a complex nuclear state is
too complicated to be calculated accurately. Nevertheless experiment has shown that nuclei possess simple
and systematic modes of excitation--single quasi-particle states, rotations and vibrations of various sorts.
The theory of nuclear structure therefore makes no
attempt to produce accurate wave functions; it focuses
attention instead on the simple observed excitations
and attempts to relate their properties to the forces
between free nucleons.

[+]Work performed under the auspices of the U. S. Atomic
Energy Commission.

A nuclear excitation is characterized by an operator θ_μ^λ whose tensorial character with respect to ordinary angular momentum and isobaric spin is given by the composite indices (λ,μ). The operator θ_μ^λ may or may not change particle-number. It acts on the nuclear ground state $|\psi_o\rangle$ to produce a state

$$|\sigma\lambda\rangle = \theta^\lambda |\psi_o\rangle \tag{1}$$

of the residual nucleus, where σ denotes any additional labels necessary to specify the state $|\sigma\lambda\rangle$ completely. The state $|\sigma\lambda\rangle$ is then defined to be the excitation produced on the target state $|\psi_o\rangle$ by the operator θ_μ^λ. The excitation so defined is, of course, of physical interest only if the operator θ_μ^λ can be realized experimentally.

Details of angular-momentum coupling have been omitted from the definition (Eq. 1) of a nuclear excitation. We shall assume in this connection that the part of the rank λ of the excitation which refers to ordinary angular momentum couples to the target spin J_o to produce a definite resultant angular momentum J. Since we shall have no occasion to distinguish different final-state spins the various pertinent strengths and sums-over-strengths will be averaged over J; the entire discussion then proceeds as if the target spin J_o were zero. Note however that we do not assume that the target isobaric spin T_o is zero nor that the isobaric spins of excitation operator and target state are coupled to a definite resultant.

Only in special circumstances is the excitation $|\sigma\lambda\rangle$ an eigenstate of the nuclear Hamiltonian. Usually it is distributed over many final states $|\psi_f\rangle$ as illustrated in Fig. 1, where the transition strength

$$\mathcal{G}_f = |\langle\psi_f||\theta^\lambda||\psi_o\rangle|^2 \tag{2}$$

384

of angular-momentum coupling have **again** been omitted.[2]

The sum rules for small values of m have obvious physical interpretations. When m = 0, Eq. (4) states that the total strength of the excitation $\mathcal{O}^\lambda |\psi_0\rangle$ is given by its Hilbert-space norm. The m = 1 sum rule gives the centroid energy of the excitation $|\sigma\lambda\rangle$ as the expectation value of H in the normalized state $[\mathcal{L}^{(0)}]^{-1/2} |\sigma\lambda\rangle$. The m = 2 sum rule yields a simple expression for the width of the excitation.

The complete set of energy moments $\mathcal{L}^{(m)}$ obviously contains exactly the same information as the complete ensemble of strengths $\mathcal{L}_f$ and energies E_f. The moment representation, however, has the major advantage of suggesting a criterion of significance in comparisons with experiment. This criterion is simply that attention should be directed first to the <u>lowest</u> energy moments; once a model disagrees with experiment for a given energy moment it is meaningless to discuss higher moments. In practice, this limits attention to the three lowest energy moments, or, in other words, to the strengths, centroid positions and widths of nuclear excitations.

So far our discussion has not been specialized to any particular nuclear model. Let us from now on represent nuclear states by shell-model wave functions. The main limitation here is that the overwhelming complexity of many-particle wave functions forces us to work within violently truncated shell-model Hilbert spaces. Thus when we speak of the successes and failures of the shell model we have in mind the shell-model limited by present day powers of computation.

There have been multitudes of shell-model studies of nuclear transition rates. These studies have revealed impressive agreement with experiment in some

of the state $|\psi_f\rangle$ in the reaction which produces the excitation $|\sigma\lambda\rangle$ is sketched as a function of excitation energy E_f. The strength $\mathcal{G}_f$ is proportional to the intensity of the component in $|\psi_f\rangle$ of the excitation $|\sigma\lambda\rangle$ under consideration; it is defined by a matrix element reduced (in the sense of the Wigner-Eckart theorem[1]) with respect to both spin and isobaric spin.

To summarize, then, a nuclear excitation is simply the "giant resonance" produced by the action of a definite excitation operator $\mathcal{O}^\lambda_\mu$ on a target state $|\psi_0\rangle$.

SUM RULES AND MODEL WAVE FUNCTIONS

We have said that a theory of nuclear structure seeks to describe the properties of simple excitations in terms of a nuclear model. The conventional procedure here is to carry out detailed model calculations of the excitation energies E_f and their associated strengths $\mathcal{G}_f$. Theory and experiments are then compared energy by energy and strength by strength. The trouble with this procedure is that it carries with it no reasonable criterion by which to distinguish what is significant from what is not.

An alternative procedure[2] is to characterize the distribution of strengths $\mathcal{G}_f$ by its energy moments:

$$\mathcal{G}^{(m)} = \sum_f E_f{}^m \mathcal{G}_f. \tag{3}$$

The mth energy moment is related to the expectation value of the mth power of the Hamiltonian in the state $|\sigma\lambda\rangle$ by the "mth energy-weighted sum rule"

$$\mathcal{G}^{(m)} = \langle \psi_0 | \bar{\mathcal{O}}^\lambda H^m \mathcal{O}^\lambda | \psi_0 \rangle \tag{4}$$

where $\bar{\mathcal{O}}^\lambda$ is the hermitian adjoint of $\mathcal{O}^\lambda$ and details

cases and serious disagreement in many others. The
moment representation yields a simple summary of the
situation. The shell model reproduces rather well the
variations of total strength from nucleus to nucleus
over limited ranges of mass number and gives a reasonably accurate account of centroid energies. Widths,
however, it seriously and consistently underestimates.[3]
This discrepancy is probably an indication that, with
the possible exception of light nuclei (A ≤ 20), shell-
model studies have worked within severely over restricted Hilbert spaces.

There is little doubt that small fragments of
any real nuclear excitation are spread far and wide
across the spectrum of the residual nucleus. No reasonably restricted shell-model wave function can be expected to describe such small isolated fragments of a
giant resonance. Furthermore, the reaction theories
which relate the strengths defined by Eq. 2 to observed
cross sections are usually reliable only for transitions
close to the centroid of the excitation. Thus any
shell-model analysis of nuclear excitations must explicitly confine itself to those fragments of each excitation which lie within 5 or 10 MeV of the centroid. It
must then of course be assumed that the width of the
excitation in question is considerably less than 5 or
10 MeV, and that the missing fraction of the total
strength varies little in magnitude from nucleus to
nucleus. Under those conditions it is reasonable to
discuss variations in total strength from one nucleus
to another and the centroid position and width of the
accessible part of the nuclear excitation under consideration.

These restrictions stem from deficiencies in shell-model wave functions and in nuclear and electromagnetic reaction theories. They are in no sense peculiar to the moment representation of transition rates but are equally important, although concealed, in the conventional item-by-item comparisons between theory and experiment.

ISOBARIC-SPIN SPLITTING

Let the isobaric spin rank of the excitation operator $\mathcal{O}_\mu^\lambda$ be λ_T with projection μ_T and let the target isobaric spin be T_0. Now unless T_0 or $\lambda_T = 0$, λ_T and T_0 can couple to several different resultant isobaric spins T_f;

$$\left[\lambda_T \times T_0\right]_{T_f} : T_f = |T_0 - \lambda_T|, \ |T_0 - \lambda_T| + 1, \ldots T_0 + \lambda_T. \tag{5}$$

The excitation $\mathcal{O}_\mu^\lambda |\psi_0\rangle$ therefore contains several isobaric spin components. If nuclear forces have a sufficiently strong isobaric spin dependence, the various T-components will be clearly separated in energy; in other words the excitation $\mathcal{O}_\mu^\lambda |\psi_0\rangle$ will exhibit a T-splitting. The situation for a two-component excitation ($T_f = T_<$ or $T_>$) is illustrated schematically in Fig. 2.

Whether or not a T-splitting is worth discussing depends, of course, on its magnitude; how widely separated are the various T-centroids? In fact, it is well known that single particle and single hole excitations have large T-splittings - about 1 MeV per excess neutron[4]. There is also some indication of a rather smaller T-splitting - about 0.5 MeV per excess neutron - of the E1 photonuclear giant resonance. It is therefore well worthwhile to discuss T-splittings.

Since the isobaric spin splitting of single particle and single hole excitations will be discussed at this conference by Bayman[*], I will concentrate on generalities and on the nuclear electric dipole excitation.

T-SPLITTING OF DIPOLE EXCITATION;
GEOMETRICAL CONSIDERATIONS

In this section we distinguish between geometrical and dynamical factors in the sharing of strength between the T-fragments of nuclear excitations. To do this, let us consider the isovector nuclear electric dipole excitation operator[5)]

$$\vec{D}_q^{\,1} = - e \sum_{i=1}^{A} \vec{r}(i) \, t_q^{\,1}(i) \qquad (6)$$

which produces the well-known giant resonance in the absorption of low energy photons by nuclei. The tensor indices in Eq. 6 refer to isobaric spin.

Let us consider, then, dipole excitations of target states $|\psi_o\rangle$ for which

$$T_0 = T_{z0} = 1/2 \, (N - Z) \qquad (7)$$

where N and Z are the target neutron- and proton-numbers. All low-lying nuclear states satisfy these conditions to sufficient accuracy. There are three isobaric spin components of the dipole excitation $\vec{D}_q^{\,1}|\psi_o\rangle$; these have $T = T_f = T_0 + 1$, T_0, and $T_0 - 1$. Their total strengths $\mathcal{G}^{(o)}(T)$ are defined by an appro-

---

[*] See Paper E1

priate modification of Eq. 2,

$$\mathcal{G}^{(0)}(T) = \sum_{\substack{f \\ T_f = T}} \mathcal{G}_f \tag{8}$$

where the summation is restricted to final states of isobaric spin T.

Now of course these dynamical strength factors $\mathcal{G}^{(0)}(T)$ are not the whole story. They are defined in Eq. 2 in terms of matrix elements which are reduced both in spin and isobaric spin; nuclear reactions on the other hand are polarized in T. In other words we consider excitations of definite isobaric spin projection q according to the scheme

$$\begin{pmatrix} T_0 \\ T_{z0} = T_0 \end{pmatrix} + \begin{pmatrix} 1 \\ q \end{pmatrix} \longrightarrow \begin{pmatrix} T \\ T_0 + q \end{pmatrix}. \tag{9}$$

The observed dipole excitation strength $G(T,q)$ therefore contains an obvious additional geometrical factor;

$$G(T,q) = \left[C \begin{array}{ccc} T_0 & 1 & T \\ T_0 & q & T_0+q \end{array} \right]^2 \mathcal{G}^{(0)}(T) \tag{10}$$

where [C] is a vector-coupling coefficient.

The various possible dipole excitations and their T-fragments are shown in Fig. 3. Let us summarize them.

$\underline{q = 1}$. The $\Delta T_z = 1$ dipole excitation $\vec{D}\,^1_1 |\psi_0\rangle$ is realized as the El part of μ^- capture on the target state $|\psi_0\rangle$ and is closely related to the El part of the direct (p,n) reaction. Since the $\Delta T_z = 1$ excitation has $T_z = T_0 + 1$ its only possible T-component is that with $T = T_0 + 1$.

390

$\underline{q = 0}$. The $\Delta T_z = 0$ dipole excitation $\vec{D}_o{}^1 |\psi_o\rangle$ is the giant El resonance in photon absorption and in-elastic electron scattering. It has $T_z = T_0$ and two T-fragments, with $T = T_0$, $T_0 + 1$.

$\underline{q = -1}$. The $\Delta T_z = -1$ dipole excitation is of less direct physical interest, but is related to the El part of the direct (n,p) reaction. There are three T-fragments ($T = T_0 - 1$, T_0, $T_0 + 1$).

It is clear from Fig. 3 that not only does a given excitation (definite q) have several T-fragments but each T-fragment appears as an isobaric-spin multiplet of isobaric-analogue excitations. For example, the $T = T_> = T_0 + 1$ fragment of the $\Delta T_z = 0$ (photonuclear) El excitation is the isobaric analogue of the $\Delta T_z = 1$, μ^--capture El excitation. The observed strengths $G(T, \Delta T_z)$ of isobaric analogue excitations differ only in their geometrical factors whose influence for the isovector operators under consideration is summarized in Table I. For given ΔT_z, the geometry obviously favors lower values of T; each unit increase in T is associated with a retardation factor of about $T_0 = 1/2 (N - Z)$.

The discussion of this section obviously applies with minor modifications to any excitation which carries non-zero isobaric spin. The essential points are these:

(1) A given nuclear excitation ($\lambda_T, \Delta T_z$) has, in general, several T-components.

(2) Each such T-component appears in general as an isobaric spin multiplet of isobaric analogue excitations with varying ΔT_z.

(3) The total observed strength $G(T, \Delta T_z)$ of a T-component is the product of a dynamical factor $g^{(o)}(T)$

391

defined as in Eq. 3 and a geometrical factor

$$\left[\, c \, \begin{array}{ccc} T_0 & \lambda_T & T \\ T_0 & \Delta T_z & T_0 + \Delta T_z \end{array} \right]^2 \, .$$

The geometrical factor favors lower T-values by roughly 1/2 (N - Z) (multiplicatively) per unit increase in T.

T-SPLITTING OF DIPOLE EXCITATION;
DYNAMICAL CONSIDERATIONS

Let us now complete our discussion of the sharing of strength between the T-components of the $\Delta T_z = 0$ electric dipole excitation. To do this we first evaluate the total dipole strength

$$G(\Delta T_z = 0) = G(T_<,0) + G(T_>,0) \tag{11}$$

where $T_< = T_0$ and $T_> = T_0 + 1$. $G(T_>,0)$ is then evaluated by observing that the $\Delta T_z = 0$, $T_>$ excitation is the isobaric analogue of the $\Delta T_z = 1$, $T_>$ El μ^--capture excitation. Equation 10 yields

$$G(T_>,0) = \frac{2}{(N - Z + 2)} \, G(T_>,1). \tag{12}$$

$G(T_>,1)$ is evaluated in the same fashion as $G(\Delta T_z = 0)$ and then Eqs. 11 and 12 combine to give the desired ratio $G(T_>,0)/G(T_<,0)$.

The total $\Delta T_z = 0$ strength follows from a simple application of the sum rule Eq. 4. We shall simply quote the result[2]. Let us divide the shell-model orbits in the target state $|\psi_0\rangle$ into three distinct categories:

(1) The filled orbits (f), completely filled

392

for both neutrons and protons.

    (2)   The valence orbits (v).

    (3)   The empty orbits (e), containing neither neutrons nor protons.

Four sorts of transition then can contribute to the total dipole strength; these may be described schematically as $f \to v$, $v \to e$, $f \to e$ and $v \to v$. The situation is illustrated in Fig. 4. A simple expression for $G(\Delta T_z = 0)$ can now be obtained if there are no $f \to e$ and $v \to v$ transitions; in most situations of physical interest we can come close to satisfying these conditions by judicious reclassification of certain filled and empty orbits as valence orbits. The remaining anomalous transitions can then be taken into account explicitly. In the absence of $f \to e$ and $v \to v$ transitions the total $\Delta T_z = 0$ strength is given as the sum of contributions G_v from all valence orbits v by

$$G(\Delta T_z = 0) = \sum_v G_v$$

$$9G_v = \frac{< N_v >}{2(2j_v + 1)} \sum_e d_{ve}^2 + \frac{< N_v^{holes} >}{2(2j_v + 1)} \sum_f d_{vf}^2 \tag{13}$$

where $\langle N_v \rangle$ is the expectation value in the target state $|\psi_o\rangle$ of the number of particles in orbit v, and $\langle N_v^{holes} \rangle$ is the mean number of holes. j_v is the total angular momentum of orbit v. The quantity

$$d_{rs} = < \phi_r \ || \ \vec{r} \ t^1 \ || \ \phi_s > \tag{14}$$

is simply the matrix element of the dipole operator $\vec{r} \ t_q^{1}$, reduced with respect to both spin and isobaric spin, between the single particle states ϕ_r and ϕ_s.

Thus in the approximation that f → e and v → v transitions can be neglected, the total $\Delta T_z = 0$ dipole strength depends on the target wave function only through the occupation numbers of the valence orbits.

Consider now the $\Delta T_z = 1$ excitation, which has $T = T_> = T_0 + 1$. The total strength $G(T_>,1)$ of this excitation can be evaluated under the same assumptions and restrictions which led to Eq. 13. The two kinds of contributing transition are now f proton → v neutron, and v proton → e neutron as indicated in Fig. 5. The total $\Delta T_z = 1$ strength is then given as a sum of contributions $G_v(T_>,1)$ from all valence orbits v by

$$G(T_>,1) = \sum_v G_v(T_>,1)$$

$$9G_v(T_>,1) = \frac{< \text{neutron holes} >_v}{(2J_v + 1)} \sum_f d^2_{vf}$$

$$+ \frac{< \text{protons} >_v}{(2J_v + 1)} \sum_e d^2_{ve} \qquad (15)$$

The notation is self-explanatory. Equations 11, 12, 13 and 15 combine to yield the strength ratio $G(T_>,0)/G(T_<,1)$.

Two factors combine to suppress the $T_>$ component of the excitation. The first is the geometrical factor $2/(N-Z+2)$ that appears in Eq. 12. The second stems from the fact that in a heavy nucleus the neutron orbit v fills before the corresponding proton orbit; consequently both the expectation values $< \text{neutron holes} >_v$ and $< \text{protons} >_v$ are diminished.

To assess the relative importance of geometrical

and dynamical suppression factors, consider the even mass isotopes of Nickel with $Z = 28$ and $N = 30$ to 36 (Ni^{58} to Ni^{64}). The pertinent filled, valence, and empty orbits are shown in Fig. 6. Since to a good approximation the dipole excitation operator $\vec{D}_q^1$ cannot connect single particle states more than one major oscillator shell apart, it is clear that the condition that there be no $f \rightarrow e$ and $v \rightarrow v$ transitions is well satisfied.

If we assume that the various orbit occupation numbers have their maximum possible values, Eqs. 11 to 15 yield for the purely geometrical contribution to the strength ratio

$$\frac{G_{obs}^>}{G_{obs}^<} = \frac{G(T_>,0)}{G(T_<,0)} \tag{16}$$

the value $\frac{1}{T_0} = \frac{2}{(N-Z)}$. To estimate the dynamical suppression factors let us use for the orbit occupation numbers the values obtained from stripping and pick-up reactions[6] on the isotopes of Ni, with square-well values[7] for the single-particle dipole matrix elements d_{rs}. Results are shown in Fig. 7, where the geometrical strength ratio $1/T_0$ is indicated by a dashed line. The dynamical suppression factor increases with $(N-Z)$; by Ni^{64} it contributes an additional factor of 2.

A rough estimate of the strength ratio for Pb^{208} yields the tiny value

$$\frac{G_{obs}^>}{G_{obs}^<} \sim \frac{1}{3000}$$

compared with the geometrical value $2/(N-Z) = 1/22$.

This very small relative value for the $T_>$ strength is
not of course to be taken literally. The point is
simply that for the heaviest nuclei the dynamical suppression factor is at least as important as the geometrical factor and that the two combine to suppress
the $T_>$ fragment of the dipole excitation by about three
orders of magnitude.

T-SPLITTING OF DIPOLE EXCITATION;
EXPERIMENTAL DATA

There is no convincing direct experimental evidence of the T-splitting of the E1 giant resonance.
However, information[8,9] of a rather tentative sort can
be inferred on the basis of (γ,n) and (γ,p) selection
rules discussed at this conference by Segel.* The
situation is outlined in Fig. 8. It is clear that neutron decay of the $T_>$ part of the dipole resonance is
isobaric spin forbidden ($\Delta T = 3/2$). On the other hand,
although the proton decays of both T-components of the
dipole excitation are allowed by isobaric spin selection rules, the $T_<$ decays are strongly inhibited by the
Coulomb barrier. Thus for heavier nuclei ($A \gtrsim 90$)
(γ,n) reactions should proceed mainly through the $T_<$
component of the giant E1 resonance, (γ,p) through
the $T_>$ component.

The observed fact that (γ,p) cross sections in
heavy nuclei tend to peak 3 to 8 MeV higher than (γ,n)
suggests a T-splitting of the giant dipole resonance
ot perhaps 0.5 MeV per excess nucleon. This conclusion
must be regarded as very tentative since (γ,p) cross
sections in heavy nuclei peak at an excitation energy
of around 20 MeV. This is close to the expected energy

*See Paper B5

of the E2 giant resonance. Indeed angular distribution measurements suggest strong dipole-quadrupole interference in this energy region. Thus the higher energy peak in the (γ,p) reactions might be a pure quadrupole effect having nothing to do with the T-splitting of the dipole resonance. The strong suppression of the $T_>$ resonance in heavy nuclei, combined with the fact that the proton decays of the $T_>$ quadrupole excitation are not similarly suppressed might conceivably lead to such an effect. It is however more probable that the peak in the (γ,p) cross section is a mixed dipole-quadrupole phenomenon, with the $T_>$ component of the E1 excitation competing on roughly equal terms with an E2 resonance. Our estimate of the size of the dipole T-splitting would then be roughly correct.

It might be possible to locate the $T_>$ part of the E1 excitation by detecting its isobaric analogue in μ^- capture. The difficulty here is that the dipole contribution is not predominant in μ^- capture on heavy nuclei; indeed all first-forbidden processes $(\Delta J^\pi = 0^-, 1^-, 2^-)$ contribute significantly[10]. However, for light nuclei ($A \lesssim 40$), the various first-forbidden excitations peak at about the same excitation energy. If this can be shown to hold for heavy nuclei reasonably precise estimates of the T-splitting of the dipole resonance could be obtained.

Note finally that, since they involve $\Delta T_z = 1$ and a change of parity, all the first-forbidden contributions to μ^- decay are subject to the dynamical suppression discussed in the previous section. This dynamical suppression, it will be recalled, stems from the fact that neutron orbits in heavy nuclei fill ahead of the corresponding proton orbits. Such effects

on total μ^- capture rates in heavy nuclei are of course
well known; they have been estimated[11] approximately
and found to yield an excellent account of the observed[12] dependence of capture rates on neutron excess.

ISOBARIC-ANALOGUE STATES AND THEIR USES

The sharing of strength between the two T-
components of the giant dipole excitation depends on
the target state $|\psi_o\rangle$ mainly through the occupation
numbers of the valence orbits. These occupation numbers can be obtained from measurements of the total
strength of single particle and single hole excitations
and of their T-components. The two alternative ways
of determining occupation numbers are in fact comple-
mentary; the nucleon transfer reactions are most reliable for orbits of low angular momentum while the
El strengths are dominated by orbits of high spin.

The magnitudes of the energy spacings between
T-components of nuclear excitations yield information
about the isobaric spin dependence of nuclear forces.
Such detailed studies of T-splittings have been carried out only for single particle and single hole excitations. The situation is discussed in detail in
Ref. 4 and we therefore pursue the matter no further.

We have seen that T-components of nuclear excitations span isobaric spin multiplets. Thus a given
nuclear excitation recurs in a series of different
isobaric analogue manifestations and can therefore be
studied in a variety of different nuclear reactions.
This possibility opens the door to the study of many
kinds of nuclear phenomena and, incidentally, opened
the door to the present conference.

398

I shall conclude my talk by mentioning three points of particular interest.

Measurement of Differences in Shape

(a) There is compelling evidence[13] that although the 0^+ ground state of Sm^{150} is spherical, there is a deformed 0^+ state at an excitation energy of 1256 keV. This difference in equilibrium shape can be tested by studying the isobaric analogue 0^+ states in Gd^{150}.

Apart from the neutron-proton mass difference and other small charge-dependent effects, the energy difference between a state and its isobaric analogue is the change in Coulomb energy produced by changing a neutron into a proton. We refer to this as the Coulomb-energy shift ΔE_c between a state and its analogue. The point here is that, other things being equal, ΔE_c is markedly smaller for a deformed than for a spherical state. In fact the influence of deformation on Coulomb-energy shift is given by

$$\Delta E_c(\delta) \approx (1 - 4/45\ \delta^2)\ \Delta E_c(0) \qquad (17)$$

a result which should be insensitive to the details of the nuclear charge distribution. Using the expected Coulomb energy shift[14] for Sm^{150} and $\delta \sim .3$ we find that

$$\Delta E_c(0) - \Delta E_c(\delta) \sim 100\ \text{keV}. \qquad (18)$$

Thus if the above assumptions about equilibrium shapes are correct, then the analogue of the excited 0^+ state should be sought at around 1160 - 1200 keV rather than at 1256 keV above the analogue of the ground state.

(b) (d,p) reactions excite $\Delta T_z = 1/2$, $T = T_0 + 1/2$ single-nucleon excitations. Their isobaric analogues can be studied in proton-induced resonant reactions on the same targets[15]. As a result the same spectroscopic factors ($\mathcal{S}_f$ of Eq. 2) can be measured in completely different sorts of nuclear reaction. Thus not only can the reaction models used to extract spectroscopic factors be tested but also the possibility arises of determining reliable absolute spectroscopic factors. Such quantities would tell us how much of a given single-nucleon excitation is lost as it spreads far and wide over the nuclear excitation spectrum.

(c) Having been formed by resonant proton capture, the isobaric analogue of a (d,p) excitation can now decay by proton emission to excited states of the original target or by γ-emission to excited states of the compound nucleus. In either case a spectroscopic factor is measured analogous to one <u>connecting two excited nuclear states</u>. The possibility thus exists[16] of studying excitations based on excited nuclear-states - a feat of arms hard to achieve in any other way.

REFERENCES

1) D. M. Brink and G. R. Satchler, Angular Momentum, Oxford University Press (1962).

2) Energy moments and sum rules for nuclear excitations have been discussed by J. B. French, University of Rochester Report UR-875-111 (1965). See also R. K. Bansal and J. B. French, Phys. Letts. 19 (1965) 223.

3) M. H. Macfarlane, "The Nuclear Shell Model - Comparison of Theory and Experiment", Proceedings of Conference on Bases for Nuclear Spin-Parity Assignments, Academic Press, (to be published).

4) J. B. French, "Isobaric-Spin Effects in Nuclear Reactions", p. 184 of Nuclear Spectroscopy with Direct Reactions, II. Proceedings, Argonne National Laboratory Report ANL-6878 (1964).

5) In this case the strength factor $\mathcal{G}_f$ of Eq. 2 is simply the conventional reduced transition probability $B(E1: 0 \rightarrow f)$ as defined, for example, in Ref. 1.

6) R. H. Fulmer and A. L. McCarthy, Phys. Rev. 131 (1963) 2133; R. H. Fulmer, A. L. McCarthy, B. L. Cohen and R. Middleton, Phys. Rev. 133 (1964) B955; R. H. Fulmer and W. W. Daehnick, Phys. Rev. 139 (1965) B579.

7) D. H. Wilkinson, Physica XXII, (1956) 1039.

8) The T-splitting of the giant E1 resonance and its relation to isobaric-spin selection rules for (γ,n) and (γ,p) reactions were first discussed by H. Morinaga, Zeit. f. Phys. 188 (1965) 182.

9) S. Fallieros, B. Goulard and R. H. Venter, Phys. Letts. 19 (1965) 398.

10) L. L. Foldy and J. D. Walecka, Il Nuovo Cimento, XXXIV, (1964) 1026.

11) H. Primakoff, Revs. Mod. Phys. 31 (1959) 802.

12) J. C. Sens, Phys. Rev. 113 (1959) 679.

13) R. K. Sheline, R. A. Kenefick, C. L. Nealy and T. Udagawa, Phys. Letts. 18 (1965) 330.

14) C. J. Batty, R. S. Gilmore and G. Stafford, Nucl. Phys. 75 (1966) 599.

15) J. D. Fox, C. F. Moore and D. Robson, Phys. Rev. Letts. 12 (1964) 198.

16) G. A. Jones, A. M. Lane and G. C. Morrison, Phys. Letts. 11 (1964) 329.

TABLE I. Geometrical strength factors $\left[C^{T_0 \; 1 \; T}_{T_0 \; q \; T_0 + q} \right]^2$ for isovector excitations.

q \ T_0	$T_0 - 1$	T_0	$T_0 + 1$
-1	$\left(\dfrac{2T_0 - 1}{2T_0 + 1} \right)$	$\dfrac{1}{(T_0 + 1)}$	$\dfrac{1}{(T_0 + 1)(2T_0 + 1)}$
0		$\left(\dfrac{T_0}{T_0 + 1} \right)$	$\left(\dfrac{1}{T_0 + 1} \right)$
1			1

DISCUSSION

BLOOM, Livermore: I would like to ask what is the order of magnitude of the shifts implied by the isobaric spin mixtures found from these experiments?

MACFARLANE: First of all, the experimental shifts are observed to be small. It is hard to be exact about the size of the shifts produced by Gillet and Sanderson, because they do not give in detail the shell model results before they switched on the Coulomb force. But by switching on this particular mixing effect they get a depression on the order of, as I recall, certainly three or four hundred kilovolts for the 3^- state, so when one state goes down others have had to go up. I would say on the order of 150 to 200 kilovolts at least.

HAMBURGER, Pittsburgh: What would you predict for the giant dipole resonance in medium weight nuclei?

MACFARLANE: I haven't done any specific calculations for medium weight nuclei.

BAYMAN, Minnesota: You showed us those $T = 1$ levels in Ca^{40} or O^{16}; now can you tell us about the $T = 0$ levels? Do they have the right angular momentum and what are their energies?

MACFARLANE: As I remember, three of the spin states are mostly concentrated in one state with spectroscopic factors somewhere in between 1.7 and 1.3. That would be excellent although they are within 2 MeV of being unbound, so that the analysis is a little bit doubtful. I think the $J = 4$ state does not show up in sufficient strength unless one starts pressing into service various mixed components which seem to be obscured by $\ell = 1$ mixing as seen by $\ell = 1$ stripping.

There is one thing about them and that is that
the degree of splitting implied is the degree of fragmentation of the single particle strength, which is
in rough agreement with what Gillet and Sanderson
would have got if they had not added in this extra
Coulomb mixing term.

BLOOM: Has there been some experience in O^{16}
that some of these states are really three particle-
three hole states as opposed to one particle-one hole?
Is it possible here also that some of the states in
O^{16} that are $T = 1$ may be really three particle-three
hole states?

MACFARLANE: You are worried about the fact that
my T-splitting analysis is in terms of one particle-
one hole.

BLOOM: That is correct.

MACFARLANE: Let me say that all that is necessary is the dipole excitation and it has to be a
single particle excitation if O^{16} is a closed shell.
All shell model calculations I have heard of calculate
this way. It is clear that the $T = 0$ states in Erskine's
experiment do not show up isolated just one at a time.
You get pieces of it, two or three pieces that you
can see. There may be others that you can't see. And
then, of course, you average over all of them, so
presumably you are talking about one-particle excitations.

MARGOLIS, McGill: Have you thought at all about
whether inelastic electron scattering would be useful
for detecting the two components of the giant dipole
resonance?

MACFARLANE: With heavy nuclei - I am not too

sure about the electron scattering technology - but
what is needed is something that can resolve states
and that measures spins, and it just looks like the
dipole excitation in heavier nuclei is such a dreadful
mixture, I think that would be pretty difficult too.
I mean, I can make the obvious statement that it might
be useful, but, frankly, I have not thought about it
enough to make any positive statement.

MARGOLIS: It occurs to me that at small momentum transfers you might separate the dipole from the
quadrupole.

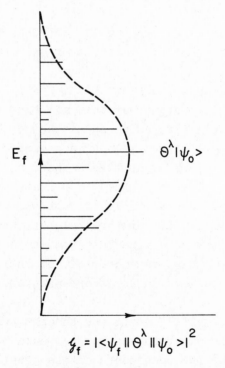

$$\mathcal{G}_f = |<\psi_f \| \Theta^\lambda \| \psi_o >|^2$$

Fig. 1. Sketch of a nuclear excitation.

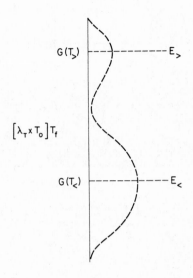

Fig. 2.   T-splitting of a nuclear excitation.

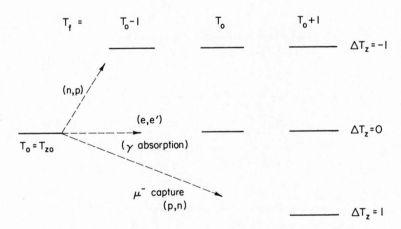

Fig. 3.   T-components of an isovector excitation.

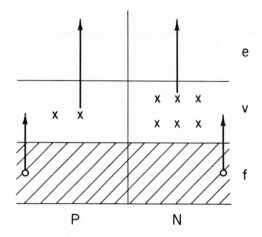

Fig. 4.   Orbit diagram for $\Delta T_z = 0$ dipole excitations.

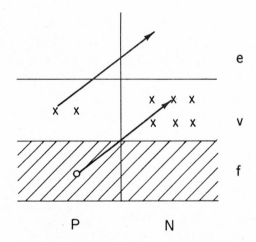

Fig. 5.   Orbit diagram for $\Delta T_z = 1$ dipole excitations.

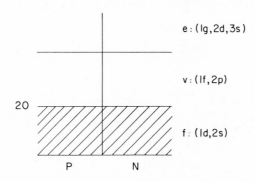

Fig. 6.   Orbits for Nickel.

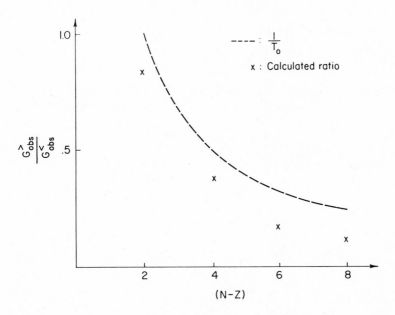

Fig. 7.   T-splitting of dipole strengths for Nickel isotopes.

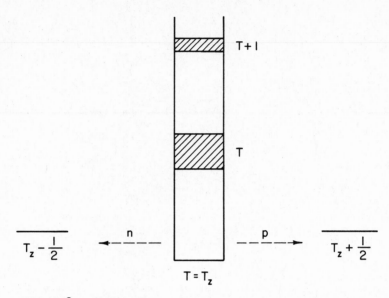

Fig. 8. Isobaric spins involved in the nucleon decay of E1 resonance.

D2. RESONANCE REACTIONS AND ISOBARIC SPIN PURITY[*]

D. Robson

Florida State University
Tallahassee, Florida

TOTAL ISOBARIC SPIN IMPURITY

When isobaric analogue resonances were shown to exist a few years ago[1,2] the first question asked by most nuclear physicists was "how pure is the isobaric spin quantum number for these resonances?" Unfortunately this question is easier to ask than to answer. In particular the conventional description[3] of isobaric spin mixing involving bound shell model states leads one into difficulties when as in the present case the states involved are in the continuum. In the usual perturbation approach a Coulomb interaction V^c mixes into an isobaric spin state $\Psi_0(T)$ an amplitude $a_\nu(T')$ of a state $\Psi_\nu(T')$ which has the same spin and parity, but $T' \neq T$. i.e.,

$$\Psi_0 = \Psi_0(T) + \sum_{\mu \neq 0} b_\mu(T)\ \Psi_\mu(T) + \sum_{\nu, T' \neq T} a_\nu(T')\Psi_\nu(T'), \tag{1}$$

$$a_\nu(T') = \langle \Psi_\nu |V^c| \Psi_0 \rangle\ (E_0 - E_\nu)^{-1}. \tag{2}$$

The second term in Eq. 1 is isobaric spin conserving and we will ignore it. The last term is the total admixture of states with $T' \neq T$ and it is usual

[*]Supported by the Air Force Office of Scientific Research.

411

to call

$$I_{T'} = \sum_{\nu} a_\nu^2(T') = \sum_{\nu} \frac{|< \Psi_\nu | \ V^c \ | \ \Psi_o >|^2}{(E_o - E_\nu)^2} \qquad (3)$$

the total impurity of type T'. Clearly difficulties arise when $\Psi_\nu(T')$ are continuum states since the energies involved become complex in some fashion and the sum becomes an integral.

CHOICE OF FORMALISM

A further obstacle arises in discussing isobaric spin mixing in the continuum, namely that no unique theory of resonance phenomena exists. Let us briefly mention those approaches which have been tried.

R-Matrix Type Theory

This method, favored by the author[4], has proved useful in understanding many of the detailed features of isobaric analogue resonances. Advantages of the separation of configuration space into an inner and outer region are the following: (a) the continuum states are replaced in the inner region by a discrete set of states which in principle are model independent, (b) the isobaric spin representation can be used in the inner region and the physical n-p representation in the outer region, these two representations being matched at the boundaries of the inner region by known surface operators, and (c) antisymmetrization is included.

Main criticism of this method is that a radius a_c has to be introduced in each channel in order to define the inner region. This is not a serious criticism in the present situation because the radii a_c have a defi-

nite meaning. The radii a_c are to be chosen such that
the isobaric spin representation is optimized.

Channel-Coupling Theory

In the channel coupling theory a model is introduced to describe the interaction between a specific
nucleon and the target nucleus states. The main feature is the introduction of an isobaric spin dependent
potential which in its simplest form is involved with
a $\vec{t} \cdot \vec{T}_c$ interaction, i.e.

$$U_1(r) \; \vec{t} \cdot \vec{T}_c$$

such as introduced by Lane[5]. This type of interaction
leads to coupled differential equations the solution of
which is discussed by Tamura[6]. Similar work has also
been carried out at Copenhagen[7]. Such calculations
are of some interest as a test of the isobaric spin potential model and have the advantage that a radius parameter is not invoked. On the other hand the method is
not suitable for direct analysis of data due to the use
of a simple model. Clearly the channel coupling model
does not include antisymmetrization explicitly. It is,
however, relatively easy to include inelastic scattering leading to collective states by using a deformed
isobaric spin potential.

Shell-Model Resonance Theory

Several authors have attempted to introduce a
resonance formalism based on the shell model, however
very little quantitative work has been reported as yet.
Work on this type of approach has recently been discussed in some detail by Weidenmüller[8]. Related work
based on Feshbach's formalism has been discussed by
Venter and Fallieros[9] and at this conference by

413

Stephen[10]. The major difficulty with such theories is that continuum states are involved so that a diagonalization of the continuum appears necessary such as indicated by the work of Bloch and Gillet[11]. Moreover the basis set in practical calculations will not be eigenstates of $\vec{T}^2$ due to the necessity of using different shell model potentials for protons and neutrons. This necessity arises because of the difficulty otherwise of representing asymptotic Coulomb functions by asymptotic neutron functions. Nevertheless such calculations should prove interesting from a nuclear structure point of view.

ANALOGICITY

In the remainder of this work we shall adopt the comprehensive nuclear reaction formalism recently introduced by Lane and Robson[12] and outline how a rigorous theory of isobaric analogue resonances can be developed. In this approach we try to relate the analogue resonances in the nucleus $(N - 1, Z + 1)$ with the low lying bound states of the nucleus (N, Z). The basic concept we are trying to make use of is that of "analogicity" which it seems is best defined according to the following prescription.

Suppose we have an eigenstate of the Hamiltonian H for the nucleus (N, Z) denoted by $\Psi_{\alpha Z}$ wherein α denotes all other quantum numbers including the total number of nucleons $A = N + Z$. In a similar fashion to total angular momentum expansions for scattering problems we expand $\Psi_{\alpha Z}$ in terms of isobaric spin states $|TT_Z\rangle$ which depend only on charge co-ordinates, (we suppress all other isobaric spin quantum numbers τ necessary to define the complete set of isobaric spin states $|\tau T T_Z\rangle$

414

since they are unimportant for the present discussion), i.e.

$$| \Psi_{\alpha Z} > = \sum_{T=T_Z}^{T_Z+Z} A_{\alpha T} | TT_Z >, \qquad (4)$$

the nice feature being that the sum is a finite one due to T having a minimum and maximum value, viz.

$$T_{MIN} = T_Z = 1/2(N - Z), \qquad (5)$$

$$T_{MAX} = T_Z + Z = 1/2(N + Z). \qquad (6)$$

For convenience we reserve the notation T_Z for the nucleus (N,Z). The most appropriate definition of analogicity (in our opinion) is that an isobaric analogue state in the nucleus (N - 1, Z + 1) satisfy the relation

$$| \Psi_{\alpha Z+1} > = \sum_{T=T_Z}^{T_Z+ Z} A_{\alpha T} | TT_Z - 1 >, \qquad (7)$$

which can be written in the more symbolic form

$$| \Psi_{\alpha Z+1} > = \vec{\mathcal{J}}_- | \Psi_{\alpha Z} > \qquad (8)$$

wherein $\vec{\mathcal{J}}_-$ is a modified isobaric lowering operator i.e.

$$\vec{\mathcal{J}}_- = \vec{T}_- (\vec{T}^2 - \vec{T}_Z^2 + \vec{T}_Z)^{-1/2} \qquad (9)$$

with

$$(\vec{T}^2 - \vec{T}_Z^2 + \vec{T}_Z)^{-1/2} |TT_Z> \equiv \left[(T + T_Z)(T - T_Z + 1) \right]^{-1/2}$$
$$X |TT_Z > \qquad (10)$$

415

The content of the analogicity relation is that the states $\Psi_{\alpha Z}$, $\Psi_{\alpha Z+1}$ <u>only differ in their charge number</u>, the space-spin parts being unchanged. The operator $\vec{\mathcal{J}}_-$ is necessary in this regard rather than the conventional operator $\vec{T}_-$. The inverse relation to Eq. 8 is obtained using the operator $\vec{\mathcal{J}}_+$ defined by

$$\vec{\mathcal{J}}_+ = (\vec{T}^2 - \vec{T}_Z^2 + \vec{T}_Z)^{-1/2}\vec{T}_+ = \vec{\mathcal{J}}_-^+ \tag{11}$$

such that $(\vec{\mathcal{J}}_+ \vec{\mathcal{J}}_-) = 1$ for all nuclei of interest here. Note that $(\vec{\mathcal{J}}_- \vec{\mathcal{J}}_+)$ although usually replaceable by the unit operator is zero when operating on states of the type $| T_Z T_Z \rangle$.

Let us now turn to the <u>physical</u> states of the nucleus (N - 1, Z + 1) and denote them by $\phi_{\beta Z+1}$. Again we can make an isobaric spin expansion, i.e.

$$| \phi_{\beta Z+1} \rangle = \sum_{T=T_Z-1}^{T_Z+Z} B_{\beta T} | T T_Z - 1 \rangle \tag{12}$$

and note an important difference between the physical states and analogue states (Eq. 7 above), i.e. the limits of the summation over T are different. What does this mean?

This question is best answered by considering the two nucleon system. In comparing n-p states with n-n or p-p states one finds an extra set of states arising from the additional degree of freedom in the deuteron. The point is that even if there are no charge-dependent interactions operating in the deuteron one can still distinguish the neutron from the proton in that they are allowed to occupy the same space-spin states. Otherwise one is led to "mixed" charged states contrary to any experimental evidence. Such configurations are of course the $T = 0$ states which are not allowed for the dineutron or diproton systems.

ANALOGUE HAMILTONIAN

Returning to the analogue state problem we see that $\Psi_{\alpha Z+1}$ cannot, a priori, be regarded as an eigenstate of the physical Hamiltonian because one of the possible basis states $\mid T_Z - 1, T_Z - 1 >$ is not included in the isobaric spin expansion given by Eq. 7. We now ask for the operator which does have $\Psi_{\alpha Z+1}$ as an eigenstate. Our notation is considerably simplified by introducing projection operators in isobaric spin space, viz.

$$D = \mid T_Z - 1, T_Z - 1 > < T_Z - 1, T_Z - 1 \mid,$$

(isobaric spin "down")

$$U = 1 - D = \sum_{T \neq T_Z - 1} \mid TT_Z - 1 > < TT_Z - 1 \mid$$

(isobaric spin "up")

$$(13)$$

which are clearly orthogonal since $UD = DU = 0$.

With these definitions we write the Hamiltonian H as

$$H = \left\{ \begin{array}{ccc} [\ DHD + UH^oU \ ] & + & [\ DHU + UHD + U(H-H^o)U] \\ H_o & + & H_1 \end{array} \right. \quad (14)$$

and note that one gets two sorts of eigenstates for H_o, namely pure isobaric states $\mid \mu T >$ of the type $T = T_Z - 1 = T_<$ and eigenstates $\mid \alpha Z + 1 >$ of the operator UH^oU which is chosen below to yield only the analogue states. The Hamiltonian H_1 only involves isobaric spin mixing <u>over and above</u> the isobaric spin mixing already existing in the states $\Psi_{\alpha Z+1}$. We shall refer therefore to H_1 as the "interaction" source of <u>relative</u> isobaric spin mixing which arises in going from the system (N,Z) to the system $(N-1, Z+1)$. Clearly we are really only talking about <u>relative</u> isobaric spin purity when we compare the systems (N,Z) and $(N-1, Z+1)$. The question of the <u>absolute</u> isobaric spin impurity can therefore be removed from the discussion on hand and treated as a separate problem.

The operator UH^OU is easily constructed using the requirements

$$(UH^OU - E_\alpha)\,\Psi_{\alpha Z+1} = 0, \quad (H - E_\alpha)\,\Psi_{\alpha Z} = 0, \quad \Psi_{\alpha Z+1} = \vec{J}_-\Psi_{\alpha Z},$$
$$(15)$$

which yields

$$UH^OU = \vec{J}_- H \vec{J}_+ \equiv H^O, \tag{16}$$

the last result being evident from the relations $U = 1 - D$ and $T_+D = 0$. We see therefore that the analogue state is an eigenstate of an operator represented only by a <u>limited</u> basis rather than the complete basis of isobaric states. At this stage one might be misled into thinking the problem is best solved by taking all the eigenstates of H_0 and diagonalizing H_1 with them. This is not the case. The point is that a correct result will be achieved in that way <u>only if the basis set is used over all configuration space</u>. A little thought will show that this corresponds to trying to construct asymptotic Coulomb functions (in the case of proton channels) out of asymptotic neutron type functions, which corresponds to diagonalizing the continuum.

BOUNDARY CONDITIONS

We turn, therefore to the generalized R-matrix method[12] and define eigenstates within a confined region of space wherein protons and neutrons in equivalent orbits may be expected to behave in a similar manner. In the confined region, analogicity is only maintained if we suitably define the boundary conditions at the surfaces of this region. Each surface corresponds to a channel $|c\rangle$ wherein the two groups[*] of nucleons c_1, c_2 making up channel c are regarded as non-interacting except via non-polarizing interactions. Analogicity is then maintained if we use essentially the same boundary conditions for the states $\Psi_{\alpha Z}$, $\Psi_{\alpha Z+1}$.

The boundary matching problem is most elegantly expressed by the use of the $\mathscr{L}$ operator introduced some time ago by Claude Bloch[13]. For the (N,Z) system one has

$$\mathscr{L}_Z \Psi_{\alpha Z} = 0,$$

$$\mathscr{L}_Z = \sum_{c(Z)} |c(Z)\rangle \frac{\hbar^2}{2m_c} \delta(r_c - a_c) \left[\frac{d}{dr_c} - \frac{b_{c(Z)} - 1}{a_c} \right] \langle c(Z)|$$

(17)

wherein $c(Z)$ indicates the various physical channels appropriate to the (N, Z) system. The properties of the $\mathscr{L}$ operators and the various terms defining them are

---

[*] We restrict ourselves to "two-body" channels only, as in the conventional R-matrix theory, and use isobaric spin representations for the separated pairs, viz. $c_1 = \sum_{T_1} c_{1T_1} |T_1 T_{1Z}\rangle$. Usually, at least one of the groups will have pure isobaric spin, e.g. nucleon channels.

discussed in considerable detail elsewhere[12,13].
Space being limited here we simply note that $\mathscr{L}_Z$ en-
sures the correct joining of the inner and outer regions, the factors $b_{c(Z)}$ being the appropriate logarithmic derivatives of the radially outgoing waves in
channels $c(Z)$. The radial variable r_c is assumed to be
independent of Z, e. g., for nucleon channels the boundary $r_c = a_c$ is chosen independently of whether the nucleon is a neutron or a proton.

Analogicity requirements are satisfied by use of
the boundary matching operator $\mathscr{L}^o_{Z+1}$, i.e.

$$\mathscr{L}^o_{Z+1} \, \Psi_{\alpha Z+1} = 0, \tag{18}$$

$$\mathscr{L}^o_{Z+1} = \vec{\mathcal{J}}_- \, \mathscr{L}_Z \vec{\mathcal{J}}_+ = \sum_{\overline{c}} |\overline{c}\rangle \, \frac{\hbar^2}{2m_c} \delta(r_c - a_c)\left[\frac{d}{dr_c} - \frac{b_{c(Z)} - 1}{a_c}\right] \langle \overline{c} |$$

$$\tag{19}$$

with $\overline{c} = \vec{\mathcal{J}}_- \, c(Z)$ defining a set of <u>fictitious</u> channels
for the $(N - 1, Z + 1)$ system. The physical states
$\phi_{\beta Z+1}$ for the $(N - 1, Z + 1)$ system are defined via
$\mathscr{L}_{Z+1}\phi_{\beta Z+1} = 0$, with

$$\mathscr{L}_{Z+1} = \sum_{c(Z+1)} |c(Z + 1)\rangle \frac{\hbar^2}{2m_c} \delta(r_c - a_c)\left[\frac{d}{dr_c} - \frac{b_{c(Z+1)} - 1}{a_c}\right]$$

$$\langle c(Z + 1)| \tag{20}$$

in terms of physical channels $c(Z + 1)$ and their corresponding logarithmic derivatives $b_{c(Z + 1)}$.

Most of the foregoing can be summarized in terms of the combined operators

$$\mathcal{H}_{Z+1} = H + \mathcal{L}_{Z+1} \, ,$$

$$\mathcal{H}_{Z} = H + \mathcal{L}_{Z} \quad ,$$

$$\mathcal{H}^O_{Z+1} = H^O + \mathcal{L}^O_{Z+1} = \vec{J}_- \, \mathcal{H}_Z \, \vec{J}_+ \, , \qquad (21)$$

so that Fig. 1 schematically shows the $(N,Z) \rightarrow (N-1, Z+1)$ flow diagram and summarizes the Schrodinger and boundary condition requirements simultaneously for the region $r_c \le a_c$, (all c).

MIXING

We now need to describe the mixing between $T_<$ states and the analogue states and so we write,

$$\mathcal{H}_{Z+1} = \mathcal{H}_o + h \qquad (22)$$

in which

$$\mathcal{H}_o = D\mathcal{H}_{Z+1}D + U \, \mathcal{H}^O_{Z+1}U \qquad (23)$$

provides the basic set $|\mu T_< >$, $|\alpha Z + 1>$ for $r_c \le a_c$ and

$$h = D \, \mathcal{H}'U + U \, \mathcal{H}'D + U \, \mathcal{H}'U,$$

$$\mathcal{H}' = \mathcal{H}_{Z+1} - \mathcal{H}^O_{Z+1} \qquad (24)$$

leads to the mixing between them. This mixing may be separated into two parts using

$$\mathcal{H}' = H' + \mathcal{L}'_{Z+1} = (H - H^O) + (\mathcal{L}_{Z+1} - \mathcal{L}^O_{Z+1}) \qquad (25)$$

421

the first term being the source of <u>interaction</u> or "<u>internal</u>" mixing and the second being the source of <u>boundary condition</u> or "<u>external</u>" mixing.

Using the methods of Lane and Robson[12] one can obtain an <u>exact</u> expression for the S-matrix corresponding to the usual Breit-Wigner "single" level formula[*], i.e.

$$S_{cc'} = \bar{S}_{cc'} + 2ie^{i(\omega_c + \omega_{c'} - \phi_c - \phi_{c'})} \frac{P_c^{1/2} \bar{\gamma}_{ac} \bar{\gamma}_{ac'} P_{c'}^{1/2}}{E_\alpha - E + \Phi_\alpha}$$

(26)

where ω_c, ϕ_c, P_c are the usual Coulomb phase, hard sphere phase and penetrability respectively. $\bar{S}_{cc'}$ is the scattering matrix arising from all levels other than the analogue state so that if the analogue states are widely spaced $\bar{S}_{cc'} \approx \bar{S}_{cc'}(T_<)$ = scattering matrix via $T_<$ states alone. Eq. 26 is of course, independent of the radii a_c.

The effects of mixing are contained in the <u>observable</u> reduced widths $|\bar{\gamma}_{ac}|^2$ which are given by

$$\bar{\gamma}_{ac} = \left(\frac{\hbar^2 a_c}{2m_c} \right)^{1/2} < \frac{1}{r_c^2} \delta(r_c - a_c)c \mid \bar{a} >, \quad (27)$$

---

[*] The use of channel radii can be avoided in the formalism of Ref. 12 by use of a "volume" basis $|\mathcal{J}_c>$ instead of the surface functions $|c>$ and leads to an alternative form for the S-matrix. The surface factors $g_{ac} = e^{i(\omega_c - \phi_c)} P_c^{1/2} \bar{\gamma}_{ac}$ are replaced (except for constants) by matrix elements $< \mathcal{J}_c |V_c| \bar{a}(Z+1)>$ which are independent of the radii a_c provided a_c are greater than the ranges of the "channel interactions" V_c. However, Eq. 26 is most pertinent to the present discussion and appears to be the simplest form for data analysis.

with

$$|\bar{\alpha}> = |\alpha(Z + 1) > - \bar{g}\, h \mid \alpha(Z + 1) > \qquad (28)$$

and

$$\bar{g} = \Big[\, (1 - |\alpha> <\alpha| \,) \; \mathcal{H}_{Z+1} \; (1 - |\alpha> <\alpha| \,) - E \Big]^{-1}$$

$$x \; (1 - |\alpha><\alpha| \,) \qquad (29)$$

being the Green's operator as represented by all states other than the analogue state of interest $|\alpha(Z+1)> \equiv |\alpha>$.

The factor Φ_α may be written as

$$\left.\begin{array}{rcl} \Phi_\alpha &=& < \alpha|h|\alpha > \quad - \quad < \alpha|h\bar{g}h|\alpha > \\[2mm] &=& (\Delta_\alpha - 1/2 \; i \; \Gamma_\alpha) + (\Delta_M - iW_\alpha) \end{array}\right\} \qquad (30)$$

wherein

$\Delta_\alpha \;\; = \;\;$ Coulomb displacement energy

$\Gamma_\alpha \;\; = \;\;$ "natural" width

$\Delta_M \;\; = \;\;$ shift due to Coulomb mixing (mainly with $T_<$ states)

$W_\alpha \;\; = \;\;$ "theoretical spreading width" due to mixing.

Note that in general this is a theoretical spreading width since it cannot be observed experimentally[*] whenever $\Gamma_\alpha \neq 0$. The differences between the various definitions of spreading widths is discussed elsewhere[12] so we shall not pursue this aspect here.

It is interesting to try and make an estimate of the relative isobaric spin mixing coefficient defined in a similar fashion to the conventional expression (Eq. 3) i.e. from Eq. 28 the total impurity $I_{T_<}$

---

[*] The special case where $\Gamma_\alpha = 0$ so that W_α (= total width) is observable is discussed below.

in the analogue resonance state $|\bar{a}\rangle$ is clearly given by; ($\tilde{\mu}$ = time reverse of μ),

$$I_{T_<} = \sum_\mu |\langle \tilde{\mu} | \bar{g} h | a \rangle|^2 \tag{31}$$

This is not very useful however because of the high density of $T_<$ states in the vicinity of the analogue resonance.

We make the following approximation therefore:

$$\bar{g} \approx \sum_{Sc'} \frac{|Sc'T_< \rangle \langle Sc'T_<|}{E_{Sc'} - E - i W_{Sc'}} \qquad (c' = \text{nucleon channels only}) \tag{32}$$

wherein $|Sc'T_< \rangle$ are a set of single particle states (S) in each channel c' of the type considered by Lane, Thomas and Wigner[14]. These $T_<$ giant resonances have widths $2W_{Sc'}$, usually of order 1 - 10 MeV. Assuming that $h = h^*$ (which can be achieved using large channel radii) and using the approximate form of $\bar{g}$ above we have the interesting relations

$$I_{T_<} \approx \sum_{Sc'} \frac{|\langle Sc'|h|a\rangle|^2}{(E_{Sc'}-E)^2 + W_{Sc'}^2} = \sum_{Sc'} |a_{Sc'}(T_<)|^2 , \tag{33}$$

$$W_\alpha \approx \sum_{Sc'} W_{Sc'} |a_{Sc'}(T_<)|^2 , \tag{34}$$

or for $W_{Sc'} \approx W_{opt} = \text{const.}$ we have

$$I_T \sim \frac{W_\alpha}{W_{opt}} . \tag{35}$$

From a survey of analogue resonances we find $W_\alpha \sim 50$ keV,

424

$W_{opt} \sim 5$ MeV so that $I_{T_<} \sim 1\%$. Consequently we expect that the "analogicity" relation is not much affected by mixing with the $T_<$ states, although it is hard to make general statements in view of the approximations made.

REDUCED WIDTHS OF ANALOGOUS CHANNELS

Consider the particular system described by a set of states $|C(Z)>$ which involves one less neutron than the (N,Z) system. Clearly then by adding a neutron to $C(Z)$ we can form the state $|\alpha Z>$, the probability of such a channel existing at $r_c = a_c$, being characterized by the neutron reduced width $\gamma^2_{\alpha Zn}$. Similarly the addition of a proton to $C(Z)$ leads to the analogue state $|\alpha(Z+1)>$ with a probability at $r_c = a_c$ related to $\gamma^2_{\alpha Z+1p}$. We refer to these two processes as "analogous channels" because they are related in a very simple manner:

$$\frac{\gamma_{\alpha Z+1p}}{\gamma_{\alpha Zn}} = < p_o C(Z)|\ \vec{\mathcal{J}}_- |n_o C(Z)> = <\vec{\mathcal{J}}_+ p_o C|n_o C> \qquad (36)$$

the integrations being over all co-ordinates except r_c.[*]

If we expand $|C(Z)>$ as a series of isobaric spin states:

$$|C(Z)> = \sum_{T_c} C_{T_c} |T_c T_{Zc} >, \qquad (37)$$

then we find

$$\frac{\gamma_{\alpha Z+1p}}{\gamma_{\alpha Zn}} = \frac{<C_{T_c}|C_{T_c}>}{(2T_c+1)^{1/2}} \delta_{T_c T_{Zc}} +$$

$$\sum_{T_c > T_{Zc}, T} <C_{T_c}|C_{T_c}> C(T_c 1/2\ T, T_{Zc}, -1/2\ T_Z - 1) \ \times \ C(T_c 1/2\ T, T_{Zc} 1/2\ T_Z), \qquad (38)$$

---

[*]The channel notation $|n_o C>$ with subscript o indicates that the n,p particles are labelled, (i.e. distinguishable)

which yields the usual result:

$$\frac{\gamma^2_{\alpha Z+1p}}{\gamma^2_{\alpha Zn}} \approx \frac{1}{2T_c + 1} \, , \tag{39}$$

when C has nearly pure isobaric spin $T_c = T_{Zc}$ as expected[15] for nuclei with a large value of T_Z.

From a spectroscopy point of view we wish to know under what conditions the rule given by Eq. 39 can be utilized. From Eqs. 27 and 28 we have

$$\gamma_{\alpha Z+1p} = \overline{\gamma}_{\alpha Z+1p} + \gamma^M_{\alpha Z+1p} \, , \tag{40}$$

with

$$\gamma^M_{\alpha Z+1p} = \left(\frac{\hbar^2 a_c}{2m_c} \right)^{1/2} < \frac{1}{r_c^2} \delta(r_c - a_c) pC(Z) |\overline{g}h| \alpha(Z+1) > \tag{41}$$

being the reduced width amplitude arising via mixing between the analogue state and all states in the spectrum of $\overline{g}$. The condition for Eq. 39 to be utilized easily is clearly:

$$\gamma^2_{\alpha Z+1p} \gg | \gamma^M_{\alpha Z+1p} |^2. \tag{42}$$

However, it is important to point out that this condition will <u>not</u> be satisfied when the proton separation distance is taken according to the usual R-matrix prescription: $a = 1.45(A_1^{1/3} + A_2^{1/3})$. The point is that $\gamma_{\alpha Zn}$ decreases exponentially as the neutron separation distance is increased and from Eqs. 38 or 39 we

see that $\gamma_{\alpha Z+1p}$ also must decrease exponentially in a
similar fashion. This is related to the fact that if
the state $|\alpha(Z)\rangle$ is bound then by analogicity the state
$|\alpha(Z+1)\rangle$ is also bound, so that $|\alpha(Z+1)\rangle$ only involves
closed channels. The choice of radii $a_c = R_c^+$ (say)
wherein closed channels can be ignored leads therefore
to the opposite conclusion to Eq. 42, i.e.

$$|\overline{\gamma}_{\alpha Z+1p}(R_c^+)|^2 \; \approx \; |\gamma_{\alpha Z+1p}^M(R_c^+)|^2 \tag{43}$$

In this event we also have

$$\mathcal{L}'_{Z+1}(R_c^+) \; |\alpha(Z+1)\rangle \; \approx \; 0 \tag{44}$$

and $h \equiv H'$ in Eq. 41. The removal of boundary condition
mixing also leads to $\Gamma_\alpha = 0$ such that:

$$W_\alpha = \text{Im.} \; \langle \alpha|H'\mathcal{G}H'|\alpha \rangle = \text{observed width} \tag{45}$$

In the situation $a_c \geqslant R_c^+$ we see that one cannot
expect to simply relate the parameters of the analogue
resonance to spectroscopic factors appropriate to the
(N,Z) system. We must therefore, consider other
choices of a_c since otherwise the whole aim of analogicity arguments which lead to Eq. 39 becomes a waste
of time.

As we decrease the value of a_c, $\gamma^2_{\alpha Z+1p}$ increases
exponentially so that if we could choose a_c at the surface of the target system then presumably $\gamma^2_{\alpha Z+1p}$ becomes a large part of the observed reduced width, i.e.
Eq. 42 becomes feasible. The choice which appears to
be most useful for proton channels is the outer charge
radius[16] R_c^- (say) $\approx [1.05 \; A_1^{1/3} + 1.5] \times 10^{-13}$ cm

which in heavy nuclei hugs the surface of the target. Of course, by using radii so close to the nucleus the usual channel orthogonality may become invalid due to direct reactions being possible in the "external" region $r_c > R_c^-$. Some lack of orthogonality may occur due to antisymmetization requirements and although the magnitude of this effect will usually be small it need not be negligible in certain cases. Further investigation of this type of non-orthogonality is being carried out. For most situations the proton channels will be dominated by transitions in the region $r_c < R_c^-$ so that the lack of orthogonality will be a small error.

One other feature of the choice $a_c = R_c^-$ is that mixing via H' may be reduced as suggested in Ref. 4. In such cases $\gamma_{\alpha Z+1p}^M$ may be estimated using only boundary condition mixing via $\mathcal{L}_{Z+1}'$. Assuming $\bar{\mathcal{G}}$ is diagonal in channel space and replaceable by the optical model Green's function then one obtains

$$\gamma_{\alpha Z+1p}^2(R_c^-) \approx \left| \frac{f_p - S_n}{f_p - S_p - iP_p} \right|^2 \times \left| \bar{\gamma}_{\alpha Z+1p}(R_c^-) \right|^2,$$

(46)

wherein f_p is the logarithmic derivative of the optical model wave function in the proton channel p; S_p, P_p are the usual proton shift and penetrability and S_n is the equivalent (bound) neutron shift function evaluated at $E_n = E_p - E_c$ (E_c = Coulomb energy). This method is currently under investigation at Florida State University. Preliminary results indicate that $|\bar{\gamma}_{\alpha Z+1p}|^2$ and $\gamma_{\alpha Z+1p}^2$ differ by about 20% for analogue states in nuclei with A ~ 100. In such cases $\gamma_{\alpha Zn}^2$

can be obtained to better than 20% accuracy provided
the proton width $\Gamma_p = 2P_p|\bar{\gamma}_p|^2$ can be extracted ac-
curately from the data. For strong states and a care-
ful least squares analysis the extraction of Γ_p should
be accurate to about 10%, so that spectroscopic factors
for the (N,Z) levels obtained via analogicity relations
should be as accurate as those obtained in neutron capture via (d,p) reactions.

NEUTRON CHANNELS

Finally we consider neutron decay of analogue
resonances. The "resonant" state $|\bar{\alpha}\rangle$ can be written
as a sum of three terms, i.e.

$$|\bar{\alpha}\rangle = |\alpha(Z + 1)\rangle - \tfrac{1}{g}H'\,|\alpha(Z + 1)\rangle - \tfrac{1}{g}\mathcal{L}'_{Z+1}|\alpha(Z + 1)\rangle,$$

$$(47)$$

so that neutron decay in general can arise from three
sources. If $a_c = R_c^+$ is chosen however, only the second
term contributes and this appears to be the term investigated by Bloch and Schiffer[17]. Accurate estimations
of the second term are difficult to make no matter what
value of a_c is used due to a knowledge of wave functions in the interior of the nucleus being required.

Now if $a_c = R_c^-$ is chosen then all three terms
can contribute. The first term only contributes via
isobaric impurities in the residual nucleus $|R\rangle =$

$$\sum_{T_R} R_{T_R} \left|T_R T_{ZR}\right> \text{ since the state } R_{T_{ZR}} \left| T_{ZR} T_{ZR}\right> \text{ has}$$

zero overlap with $|\alpha(Z+1)\rangle$ as is well known. This effect
should be very small since impurities in $|R\rangle$ are ex-
pected to be small provided $|R\rangle$ is a low-lying state
in the residual nucleus. The last term has non-negli-

gible contributions for $a_c = R_c^-$ and has been used[18] to describe the $Zr^{92}(p,n)$ reaction near the s-wave resonance at 6.0 MeV proton energy. Remarkable agreement is obtained which suggests that for $a_c = R_c^-$ the third term is dominant for the particular case investigated. It should be emphasized, however, that detailed calculations of neutron decay are in general quite difficult so that general conclusions are not possible at present.

REFERENCES

1) J. D. Anderson and C. Wong, Phys. Rev. Letters 7 (1961) 250.
   J. D. Anderson, C. Wong and J. W. McClure, Phys. Rev. 126 (1962) 198.

2) J. D. Fox, C. F. Moore and D. Robson, Phys. Rev. Letters 12 (1964) 198.

3) W. M. MacDonald, Nuclear Spectroscopy, Part B, p.932 (Academic Press, New York and London, 1960).

4) D. Robson, Phys. Rev. 137 (1965) B535.

5) A. M. Lane, Nuclear Phys. 35 (1962) 676.

6) T. Tamura, Paper D3.

7) J. P. Bondorf, S. Jägare and H. Lütken, Paper E5.

8) H. A. Weidenmüller, preprint (to be published in Nucl. Phys.).

9) R. Venter and S. Fallieros, Bull. Am. Phys. Soc. 10 (1965) 53.

10) R. O. Stephen, Paper D4.

11) C. Bloch and V. Gillet, Phys. Letters 16 (1965) 12, 18 (1965) 58.

12) A. M. Lane and D. Robson, (to be published).

13) C. Bloch, Nuclear Phys. 4 (1957) 503.

14) A. M. Lane, R. G. Thomas and E. P. Wigner, Phys. Rev. 98 (1955) 693.

15) A. M. Lane and J. M. Soper, Nuclear Phys. 37 (1962) 663.

16) B. Hahn, D. G. Ravenhall and R. Hofstadter, Phys. Rev. 101 (1956) 1131.

17) C. Bloch and J. P. Schiffer, Phys. Letters 12 (1964) 22.

18) D. Robson, J. D. Fox, P. Richard and C. F. Moore, Phys. Letters 18 (1965) 86.

DISCUSSION

MacDONALD, University of Maryland: Do I understand in the calculation of the number that you quoted
for the isobaric spin impurity, that you take the neutrons and protons to be the same? As I understand,
you take them to be the same in the isobaric spin states
that you use.

ROBSON: My answer to that is that the modified
lowering operator and the fact that we use complete
sets of isobaric spin states take any distortion of
that type into account.

MacDONALD: As I understand your T-lowering
operator, that will simply give you essentially the
change of neutrons into protons without changing the
radial wave functions.

ROBSON: Only for each "last" particle, corresponding to each term in the T_- expansion as a sum of
single particle operators.

MacDONALD: But the definition that you gave
uses the ordinary spin lowering operator, with simply
a normalizing factor, and in that case if you apply a
lowering operator to a filled proton shell you don't
get zero with the ordinary isobaric spin formalism.

ROBSON: Neither do I claim that you do.

MacDONALD: Then if I understand it correctly
you do not change the proton to a neutron because if
you did you should get zero, since it is an occupied
state.

ROBSON: Only if you have a pure isobaric state,
and I have a complete set of them.

MacDONALD: If you have a core with neutron

432

wave functions, which have different wave functions from the protons, then are you assuming that this is then expanded in terms of isobaric spin states?

ROBSON: I am assuming that you really are not using isobaric spin at all, other than as a formal basis, and this clearly must be equivalent to any other basis that you want to introduce, because I have used a complete set. I can see no problem in this respect.

MacDONALD: Let me ask you this way. If you have only closed shells, with neutron number equal to the proton number, will you get zero or will you get a number for the isobaric spin impurity?

ROBSON: I assume you get a number if the proton function is in any way different from the neutron function.

MacDONALD: That is what I wanted your comment on. Then it just becomes a question of whether this is a reasonable expectation value to calculate because normally the T_- operator gets from one nucleus to the next. If you get an impurity in a nucleus which has N neutrons and Z protons, you know the neighboring nuclei, with $N \pm 1$ neutrons and $Z \mp 1$ protons, still stay in the same orbitals, do they not?

ROBSON: I did miss this point during the talk. I wasn't trying to talk about absolute isobaric spin impurity at all, only the relative purity of one nucleus as compared to the other.

MacDONALD: That was the point I wanted to get cleared up. Thank you.

MOORE, University of Texas: I think we all accept what analogue states are, the fact that the various states are analogue states, and that in (d,p) you are adding a neutron to a core whereas in (p,p) you are adding a proton to a core for which you have coined the phrase, "analogous channels".

ROBSON: Analogous channels, yes.

MOORE: In most of the work that I have seen there is a direct correspondence between states seen in the (d,p) studies and those seen as resonances in (p,p) scattering. However, in some of the work done at Harwell, this was questioned a little bit, in that they saw more resonances than perhaps were seen in the (d,p) studies; I wonder if you would care to comment a little on just how analogous these so-called analogous channels are.

ROBSON: I am not sure I understand the question, but if you have more than a core plus a particle, such as an excited core plus a particle, then through isobaric spin mixing you have a very good chance of seeing that also, provided that you have good detection equipment to see a small cross-section, so you can see the extra states.

GARVEY, Princeton: I asked a question previously that I didn't feel was adequately answered, and I would like to ask Robson now. With all this formalism perhaps you could make the answer very clear. The question is essentially as follows: If you look at the isobaric analogue states, with varying amounts of resolutions, will the spectroscopic factor that you extract depend on the resolution?

ROBSON: It depends on the widths of the T-lower states compared to the resolution whether this matters at all. If these states are fairly broad compared to the resolution, then it doesn't matter one iota. If the states are narrow then the thing to do, actually, is to determine the strength as Bilpuch suggested,

434

simply subtract the background strength that is around
it, and then you have the analogue strength left.
There is no need to use poor resolution in such cases.

GARVEY: The answer is if I am not at Duke, I
should stay away from that region?

ROBSON: I think you would find it quite hard
to find such an experiment to do. There are very few
places where you can actually get fluctuations of this
type. You have to have essentially only one open
channel. These are rare.

LANE, Harwell: On the question of isobaric spins
in ground states: this may be an academic question or
it may not be. I think it is quite conceivable that
the existence of analogue relations between states
could exist even though isobaric spin is a bad quantum
number. Well, one can easily imagine that this could
be the case if isobaric spin impurities build up as a
result of $Z(Z-1)$ proton interactions. However when you
go to a target state you just change one neutron into
a proton and you do have a special problem.

Originally, I thought there were no experiments
that could be done to check it in the spirit of electric
dipole selection rules in light nuclei. However I
think there may be experiments now; for instance from
the work at the Rutherford Laboratory on (p,n) reactions
for Zr^{90} one knows the position of the $T = 6$ level,
and therefore we can try to do inelastic α scattering
and then appeal to the selection rules usually used,
i.e. that isobaric spin is good, if you do not have a
change of isobaric spin in your target. Then maybe it
is no longer an academic question, one really can measure the isobaric spin impurities of nuclear states.

435

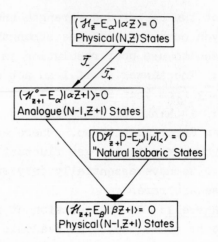

Fig. 1. $(N,Z) \to (N-1,Z+1)$ Flow Diagram.

D3. REMARKS BY E. P. WIGNER

Princeton University

Princeton, New Jersey

I would like to make a few comments on the nature of the isobaric spin resonances when these occur at an energy at which the density of the "normal" levels, that is the levels with $T = T_z$, is high. Under this condition, the state, the isobaric spin of which would be $T = T_z + 1$ if the interaction between all pairs of nucleons were strictly equal, dissolves, in my opinion, under the influence of the Coulomb forces, into a giant resonance. This means that the wave function with $T = T_z + 1$ is not the wave function of a single resonance but appears as an admixture to the wave functions of several resonances -- those which are close on the energy scale to the place where the $T = T_z + 1$ resonance would be in the absence of Coulomb forces and other violations of the strict equality of the proton-proton, proton-neutron and neutron-neutron interactions. The properties of the levels which possess an admixture from the $T = T_z + 1$ state are different from the properties of the states which have no such admixture or only a very small one. They form the giant resonance. The picture which I just projected was proposed by both J. B. French and myself at the Argonne meeting on Nuclear Spectroscopy with Direct Reactions (ANL Report 6878) and I wish to report on some calculations on the subject. It was a rather

437

unusual experience that these calculations could be carried out so easily. Actually, much of what I am going to say will be a repetition of what we heard from Drs. Robson and Macfarlane.

If we consider the problem from the point of view of R-matrix theory, then the principal problem concerns, as I see it, the internal region. We wish to find wave functions in this region which are stationary states with zero derivative on the surface. In order to calculate we proceed in the following way: assume that we initially have a Hamiltonian in which charge dependent forces are neglected and then introduce the charge dependent forces. The basic states will have, before the introduction of the charge dependent forces, the eigenvalues ε_{-2}, ε_{-1}, ε_0, ε_1, ε_2... etc., wherein ε_0 belongs to a state with higher isobaric spin $T = T_z + 1$ and all the surrounding states ε_{-2}, ε_{-1}, ε_1, ε_2 (there are many of these) have lower isobaric spin $T = T_z$. If we neglect the charge dependent forces, then the matrix representing the Hamiltonian will be diagonal.

Now introducing charge dependent forces produces only matrix elements v between ε_0 and all the other ones and so we end up with the Jacobi matrix,

$$
J = \begin{Vmatrix}
\cdots & \cdots & \cdots & \cdots & \cdots & \cdots & \cdots \\
\cdots & \varepsilon_{-2} & 0 & v_{-2} & 0 & 0 & \cdots \\
\cdots & 0 & \varepsilon_{-1} & v_{-1} & 0 & 0 & \cdots \\
\cdots & v_{-2} & v_{-1} & \varepsilon_0 & v_1 & v_2 & \cdots \\
\cdots & 0 & 0 & v_1 & \varepsilon_1 & 0 & \cdots \\
\cdots & 0 & 0 & v_2 & 0 & \varepsilon_2 & \cdots \\
\cdots & \cdots & \cdots & \cdots & \cdots & \cdots & \cdots
\end{Vmatrix} \tag{1}
$$

This matrix has a horizontal row and a vertical column plus a diagonal part; all the other matrix elements vanish. It can be diagonalized easily. The net effect is to shift the levels -- none of them is shifted quite to the next level.

Let us denote by ϕ_λ the unperturbed state with energy ε_λ. Let us further denote a characteristic value of the matrix (1) with ε. If we assume its characteristic vector in the form

$$\psi = \phi_o + \sum_{\lambda \neq o} c_\lambda \phi_\lambda \qquad (2)$$

then $J\psi = \varepsilon\psi$ yields the equations

$$\varepsilon_\lambda c_\lambda + v_\lambda = \varepsilon c_\lambda \qquad (3a)$$

and

$$\sum_{\lambda \neq o} v_\lambda c_\lambda + \varepsilon_o = \varepsilon \qquad (3b)$$

One can obtain c_λ from Eq. 3a and substitute it into Eq. 3b. This gives an implicit equation for ε

$$\sum_{\lambda \neq o} \frac{v_\lambda^2}{\varepsilon - \varepsilon_\lambda} = \varepsilon - \varepsilon_o . \qquad (4)$$

If one plots both left and right sides of Eq. 4 as functions of ε, one can determine the possible ε, the characteristic values of J, graphically. There is an ε between each pair of ε_λ, $\varepsilon_{\lambda+1}$, except that there is only one between ε_{-1} and ε_1. For a large $|\varepsilon - \varepsilon_o|$ the solution of Eq. 4 will lie very close to one ε_λ and the corresponding term of Eq. 4 will be much larger than all other terms. Hence, for this ε, one has

$$v_\lambda^2/(\varepsilon - \varepsilon_\lambda) = \varepsilon - \varepsilon_0.$$

If one now calculates the square of the norm of Eq. 2, one has

$$(\psi,\psi) = 1 + \sum_{\lambda \neq 0} \frac{v_\lambda^2}{(\varepsilon - \varepsilon_\lambda)^2} \approx \frac{v_\lambda^2}{v_\lambda^4/(\varepsilon - \varepsilon_0)^2}$$

$$= \frac{(\varepsilon - \varepsilon_0)^2}{v_\lambda^2} \tag{5}$$

It follows that the square of the coefficient of ϕ_0, the $T = T_z + 1$ state, in the normalized ψ of the state with energy closest to ε_λ becomes

$$a_{\lambda 0}^2 = \frac{1}{1 + \sum \dfrac{v_\lambda^2}{(\varepsilon - \varepsilon_\lambda)^2}} = \frac{v_\lambda^2}{(\varepsilon - \varepsilon_0)^2} \tag{6}$$

It decreases with the square of the distance of the level in question from the unperturbed level with $T = T_z + 1$. This is illustrated in the Figure:

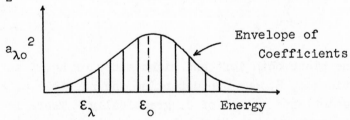

The sum of the $a_{\lambda 0}^2$ is unity and as a result the admixture of the $T = T_z + 1$ state into the $T = T_z$ states will be such as to leave the latter states reasonably pure.

We learned today from Dr. Robson that if we look at the reduced widths of the giant resonance states they will contain two parts -- the original reduced width and the reduced width admixed in from the higher isobaric state. These two are comparable because the $T = T_z$ states are complicated states, the reduced widths of which are quite small. The unperturbed $T = T_z + 1$ state ϕ_o has a large reduced width which, according to Eq. 6, is distributed among the $T = T_z$ states such that the two contributions have the same phase on the low side of the resonances and opposite phase on the high side.

Assuming that the perturbation terms v_λ are of electrostatic origin, one can calculate everything in detail except the interference which one cannot calculate because the reduced widths of the states ϕ_λ with $\lambda \neq o$ will fluctuate according to the Porter-Thomas distribution, whereas the coefficient of ϕ_o will be quite regular.

The next question is, how large are the coefficients $a_{\lambda o}$ and how are they spread out? We learned from Dr. Macfarlane how to calculate the sum of the squares $\sum v_\lambda^2$: this amounts to calculating

$$(C \, \phi_o, \, C \, \phi_o) \qquad\qquad (7)$$

where C is the charge dependent part of the Hamiltonian (assumed to be Coulomb here) and ϕ_o is the eigenstate with eigenvalue ε_o. This is not quite correct because we should subtract out from $C \, \phi_o$ that part which is a multiple of ϕ_o. This follows from the fact that we

441

wish to calculate the matrix element into the $T = T_z$ states and not into the $T = T_z + 1$ state. Even this is quite easy, if we assume the nucleus is uniformly charged. What is surprising is that the so-called Einstein rule is violently violated. The Einstein rule says that the order of magnitude of the numerical coefficients is always unity. This is violated in the present situation because the Coulomb force is a long-range force and because most of it is a constant. If you subtract this constant, and you have to subtract it because it does not give transitions into the $T = T_z$ state, the remainder is quite small.

I have here the results showing the aforementioned violation of Einstein's rule:

$$\sum v^2 = \frac{0.00107 \, e^4}{r_o^2} \, (A - 2) \, [A(A - 4) + 12T_z^2]$$

$$+ \frac{0.0506 \, e^4}{r_o^2} \, [\, A(A - 2) + 4T_z^2] \tag{8}$$

wherein r_o is the nuclear radius and the sum involves all the two-body Coulomb matrix elements.

The next step is to calculate to what extent the mixing is spread out in energy. There again we can use the formula which Dr. Macfarlane told us, i.e. we calculate essentially

$$\frac{(C \, \phi_o, \, HC \, \phi_o)}{(C \, \phi_o, \, C \, \phi_o)} \, , \tag{9}$$

which is the average energy of the states contained in $C \, \phi_o$. Again one must correct for the constant term

and what we really want to calculate in the numerator
is:

$$(\phi_o, [C, [H,C] \ \phi_o),$$ (10)

wherein the square brackets indicate commutation.
Since the potential energy commutes with C only the
kinetic energy term is left and so the whole integral
can again be evaluated.

The next result you can obtain is for the total
width of these giant resonances because you can calculate what the average value of v^2 is for regularly
spaced levels. You find around mass twenty (e.g. Ne^{20})
it is about 5 keV, which I think is rather smaller
than the experimental value. This may be an indication
of the same thing we heard earlier, namely that the
Coulomb potential may not be the only part of the Hamiltonian which is charge dependent. Nuclear forces may
also be charge dependent, but a complete discussion
has not been carried out and the experimental value
around mass 20 may also be uncertain.

The value 5 keV which is obtained by carrying
out the calculation is quite crude because it was
assumed that the nucleus has a definite size and that
it is uniformly filled with protons. These are very
crude assumptions. It is unlikely that the result is
greatly affected by these assumptions but it could
change easily by a factor of three.

I think it is quite amusing that in this case
the giant resonance which Dr. Robson has described for
us can be followed through in detail to the very end.
Even a numerical value can be obtained for the width.
In contrast to the original giant resonance situation

the giant resonance calculated in this case turns out
to be perhaps even narrower than the observed width.
It is not quite clear what this means, but at least
the calculations here are on somewhat safer grounds
than the original ones. After all, most of us believe
that the principal part of the charge dependent interaction is electrostatic and we do know the magnitude
of that.

DISCUSSION

AXEL, <u>Illinois</u>: I have just a couple of minor questions, to clear up a doubt in my mind. One was you mentioned what your estimate was around $A = 20$.

WIGNER: Yes.

AXEL: I wondered if the A dependence is as you have it written up there. The other which is very trivial is: Is r_o, as I think it is, the radius divided by A to the one third?

WIGNER: No, r_o is the whole radius. The A-dependence increases terribly, but, of course, this again is not surprising because ψ contains essentially A^2 terms and ψ^2, A^4 terms. After integration over the two body interactions $1/r_{ij}$, $1/r_{\ell m}$, etc., one gets the result but it is rather crude. It would be better to calculate it with MacDonald's method.

BAYMAN, <u>Princeton</u>: Would you please explain again the meaning of the symbols in your matrix. I did not understand when you were reading your paper.

WIGNER: Yes. This is the matrix that I calculate, using the various functions within the internal region which are supposed to have zero derivative on the surface. I first consider the matrix without the charge dependent forces, and then I diagonalize it. Before diagonalization there are many, many of the $T - 1$ states, and there is but only one T-state. Now, there is the situation when the charge dependent forces are not taken into account.

The charge dependent matrix elements between this and the others is the v written here. There will be another ϵ_o and another T, but I don't worry about

that anymore, because that is too far away. Did I
answer your question?

BAYMAN: Yes.

MARGOLIS, McGill: Can you see, or do you expect
any difference between the cases where the fine structure states are well spaced and where they overlap?

WIGNER: The calculations of the ϵ_λ are always
discrete. However, if we go to the collision matrix,
then we don't have discrete levels, but wide levels,
and if we have wide levels, the situation will be more
complicated, and I did not look into it, but, as I
say, essentially, when I interpret these levels as
actual fine structure, then I assume implicitly that
they are well separated. I think that is the way
Robson explained it to us this afternoon.

446

D4. DIRECT SOLUTION OF LANE EQUATION AND THE ANALOGUE STATE RESONANCE IN PROTON SCATTERING[*]

Taro Tamura

Oak Ridge National Laboratory
Oak Ridge, Tennessee

In order to explain the peaks in the spectrum of neutrons from (p,n) reaction[1], Lane[2] introduced a new term of the form

$$U_1(t \cdot T), \tag{1}$$

into the usual optical model potential. Robson[3] formulated an R-matrix theory by taking into account Eq. 1, not explicitly, but somewhat implicitly, and achieved a beautiful success in explaining the experimental excitation functions around the analogue state resonances in the (p,p),(p,n) and other cross sections[4]. In particular the observed asymmetry of the peaks in the excitation functions was very well accounted for.

If Eq. 1 is considered explicitly in an optical model calculation, it gives rise to a set of coupled equations between the proton (p) and the neutron (n) channels[5]. If the proton energy is sufficiently low, the corresponding neutron energy becomes negative, and at a certain energy the neutron is strongly coupled into a bound eigenstate, which has a much larger

[*]Research sponsored by the United States Atomic Energy Commission under contract with Union Carbide Corp.

amplitude than at energies off this resonance. Because of the coupling between the (p) and (n) channels, this resonance is reflected into the proton channel and a narrow resonance is expected to occur in the (p,p),(p,n) and other reactions. The purpose of the present paper is to show that, with a reasonable set of the optical model parameters, such resonances are indeed predicted at the right energies and that the excitation functions thus derived are in good agreement with experiment.

The coupled equation to be solved may be written, in the upper (u)- and lower (ℓ)-spin representation, as

$$\left[T - E + \Delta_c - U_o + \frac{T_o}{2} U_1 \right] \chi_u = (\Delta_c - V_c)(t_1^2 \chi_u + t_1 t_2 \chi_\ell),$$

$$(2.1)$$

$$\left[T - E + V_c - U'_o - \frac{T_o + 1}{2} U_1 \right] \chi_\ell = (\Delta_c - V_c)(t_1 t_2 \chi_u - t_1^2 \chi_\ell)$$

$$(2.2)$$

where $t_1 = (2T_o + 1)^{1/2}$, $t_2 = (2T_o/(2T_o + 1))^{1/2}$ and the other notations are the same as used by Robson, except that the sign in front of U_1 has been reversed so that in Eq. 2 U_o and U_1 have the same sign, and that in Eq. 2.2 a potential U'_o has been introduced which is defined as

$$U'_o = U_o + iW_\ell. \qquad (3)$$

Equation 3 means that an imaginary potential is assumed only in the ℓ-channel, an assumption that seems reasonable, because the u-channel corresponds to the ground or a very low-lying state in the system consisting of the neutron and the target.

Since the $(u\ell)$-channel representation is un-physical[3], we shall now transform into the (pn)-channel representation by using the relation

$$\chi_u = t_1\chi_p + t_2\chi_n \quad \text{and} \quad \chi_\ell = t_2\chi_p - t_1\chi_n. \tag{4}$$

The resulting equation is

$$\left[T - E + V_c - U_o - t_2^2 W_\ell - \frac{T_o}{2} U_1\right]\chi_p = -\sqrt{\frac{T_o}{2}}(U_1 + 2i t_1^2 W_\ell)\chi_n, \tag{5.1}$$

$$\left[T - E + \Delta_c - U_o - t_1^2 W_\ell + \frac{T_o-1}{2} U_1\right]\chi_n = -\sqrt{\frac{T_o}{2}}(U_1 + 2i t_1^2 W_\ell)\chi_p. \tag{5.2}$$

The technique and the computer program used previously in computing the (elastic and inelastic) scattering cross sections in terms of the coupled-channel calculations[6] can be used here, with a modification required by the fact that the neutron is in a negative energy state since in our case $E < \Delta_c$.

A detailed numerical calculation has been made to analyze the excitation functions of the differential cross section of the $Mo^{92}(p,p)$ process, for E at around 5.3 MeV, where an analogue state resonance of $1/2^+$ character was found[4]. The explicit form of the optical model potential assumed is the following:

$$U_o = V_o/(1+e(r)), \quad U_1 = V_1 \cdot 4e(r)/(1+e(r))^2,$$

$$W_\ell = W_\ell' \cdot 4\bar{e}(r)/(1+\bar{e}(r))^2, \quad e(r) = \exp((r-r_o A^{1/3})/a) \text{ and }$$

$$\bar{e}(r) = \exp((r-r_o A^{1/3})/\bar{a}), \tag{6}$$

with the parameters

$$V_o = 54.67 \text{ MeV}, \quad W_\ell = 2 \text{ MeV}, \quad V_1 = 54T_o/A \text{ MeV}, \quad r_o = 1.25 \text{ Fm},$$

$$\Delta_c = 1.33Z/A^{1/3} + m_n - m_p = 13.37 \text{ MeV}, \quad a = 0.65 \text{ Fm},$$

$$\bar{a} = 0.47 \text{ Fm}. \tag{7}$$

The theoretical excitation functions thus obtained are compared with experiment[4,7] in Fig. 1, and the agreement is seen to be very good.

The good agreement obtained in Fig. 1 indicates that our theory predicted not only the correct position of the resonance, but also the correct shape of the resonance, namely, an asymmetry with a longer tail at the lower energy side. It should be noted that we would get an asymmetric resonance with a longer tail at the higher energy side, if a very small W_ℓ had been used, or if W_ℓ were sufficiently large but it was assumed only to appear in the left hand side of Eq. 5 and not in the coupling term in the right hand side.

It should also be remarked here that, in obtaining the theoretical curves in Fig. 1, Eq. 5 was not solved as it stands, but was solved after the operators on the right hand side were multiplied by a constant q, say, and q = 0.8 was used. The reason of this artifice is explained as follows.

It is known that the spectroscopic factor S of the $s_{1/2}$ orbit in the ground state of Mo^{93}, the analogue of which is the resonant state of interest here, is known to be 0.70[8], and we expect that our resonant state has a similar value for S. On the other hand it is clear that Eq. 5 as it stands is an equation in which S = 1 is assumed, since no mechanism is considered

there which prohibits the filling of the $s_{1/2}$ state
with its maximum amplitude. If Eq. 5 were solved as
it stands, we indeed have a resonance which is too
wide, and we cannot fit the experimental excitation
function shown in Fig. 1.

Since the use of q with a value less than unity
gives rise to a resonance which is narrower than that
obtained with q = 1, it can be considered a very practical way of taking account of the fact that S is less
than unity into our calculation. If then it becomes
possible to relate the value of q that gives agreement
between our excitation curves and experiment (q = 0.8
in the present example), with a value of S, this artifice can be considered a useful way of obtaining the
spectroscopic factor from the analysis of the analogue
state resonance in the (p,p) cross sections.

If W_ℓ were put equal to zero in Eq. 5 and if we
plot $|C_{1/2^+}|^2$ as a function of E, ($C_{1/2^+}$ is the ampli-
tude of the scattered $s_{1/2}$ wave as defined by the relation $\chi_p = F_0 + C_{1/2^+} (G_0 + iF_0)$ in the asymptotic
region), then the width that can be read off this plot
is just Γ_p, the partial width for the emission of the
$s_{1/2}$ particle from the analogue state resonance, since
with $W_\ell = 0$ Γ_p equals the total width of that resonance.
We thus computed Γ_p for q = 0.8 and q = 1.0, and obtained the ratio $\Gamma_p(0.8)/\Gamma_p(1.0)$ which is to be interpreted as the value of S that we are seeking. The result is S = 0.53, in close agreement with the (d,p)
data[7].

The role that a non-vanishing W_ℓ plays in data
fitting is to reduce the peak value of $C_{1/2^+}$ from unity
(a value obtained with $W_\ell = 0$) and broaden the resonance (in addition to giving a correct asymmetry in the

resonance curve as mentioned above). It should be
noted that the increase in the width thus obtained is
much smaller than the value of $W_\ell^!$ itself.

In spite of the success of the above artifice,
it is desirable to develop a method in which the derivation of S can be made in a less artificial way. For
that purpose we have extended our basic Eq. 5 so that
in the p- (and n-) channel the state, in which an $s_{1/2}$
particle coexists with the target (and its analogue)
in its ground state, is coupled with another state in
which the particle in a $d_{5/2}$ orbit coexists with the
target in its first excited 2^+ state. In other words
the two-channel coupled Eq. 5 is extended to a four
channel coupled equation. We should now keep q = 1,
but we can get a sufficiently narrow resonance if a
sufficiently large value is taken for β, the coupling
constant between the $s_{1/2}$ -ground and $d_{5/2}$ -2^+
channels[6].

It was found that an equally good fit to the
excitation curves as shown in Fig. 1 can be obtained
in this way, when the optical model parameters as
given in Eq. 7 are used, and β = 0.12 is taken. (This
value of β is in agreement with that derived from a
Coulomb excitation experiment[9]; β = 0.12 ± 0.2). After
this good agreement was obtained we performed calculations of Γ_p with $W_\ell^! = 0$, for β = 0 and β = 0.12 and
obtained S in the same way as was done for the above
artificial treatment. The obtained result is S = 0.55,
very close to the previous value showing that the above
artificial method is indeed a useful, practical way,
even though it seems to lack a formal basis.

When the above four-channel calculation is made,
and the value of β is fixed, another way exists that

allows us to compute S far more definitely than the
above method that evaluated S via the evaluation of
Γ_p. Namely, we can solve a bound state problem of a
neutron in Mo^{93} in which the above coupling of the $s_{1/2}$
ground and $d_{5/2}-2^+$ states are taken into account. The
probability of the former state is nothing but the
value of S, we are seeking. A computer program to
solve this problem has almost been completed and the
result will soon be reported.

In addition to the possibility of this more
reasonable way of calculation of S, another and very
important merit of the four (and more) channel calculation is that it allows one to calculate the effects
of the resonance on the (p,p') process. The above
four channel calculation has already given an indication of a resonant behavior in the inelastic scattering cross section.

The author is indebted to Drs. P. von Brentano,
D. Robson, J. P. Schiffer and G. R. Satchler for stimulating and helpful discussions.

REFERENCES

1) J. D. Anderson and C. Wong, Phys. Rev. Letts. $\underline{7}$ (1961) 250; $\underline{8}$ (1962) 442; J. D. Anderson, C. Wong and J. W. McClure, Phys. Rev. $\underline{126}$ (1962) 2170; $\underline{129}$ (1963) 2718.

2) A. M. Lane, Phys. Rev. Letts. $\underline{8}$ (1962) 171; Nucl. Phys. $\underline{35}$ 1962) 676.

3) D. Robson, Phys. Rev. $\underline{137}$ (1965) B505.

4) J. D. Fox, C. F. Moore and D. Robson, Phys. Rev. Letts. $\underline{12}$ (1964) 198; P. Richard, C. F. Moore, D. Robson and J. D. Fox, ibid $\underline{14}$ (1964) 343.

5) G. R. Satchler, R. M. Drisko and R. H. Bassel, Phys. Rev. $\underline{136}$ (1964) B637; see also P. E. Hodgson and J. R. Rook, Nucl. Phys. $\underline{37}$ (1962) 632.

6) T. Tamura, Rev. Mod. Phys. $\underline{37}$ (1955) 679.

7) The author is indebted to Dr. J. D. Fox for sending the detail of the experimental data.

8) S. A. Hjorth and B. L. Cohen, Phys. Rev. $\underline{135}$ (1964) B920.

9) P. H. Stelson and L. Grodzins, Nucl. Data, (to be published).

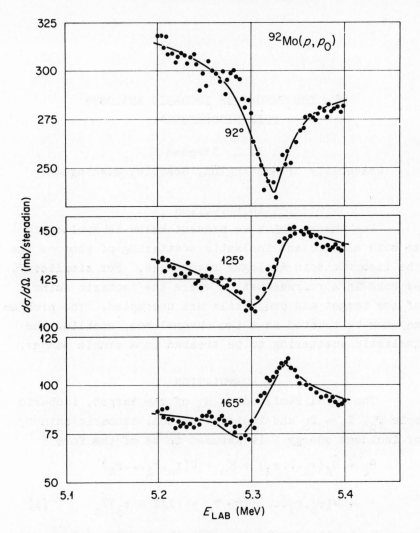

Fig. 1. Comparison between the theoretical and experimental excitation functions.

D5. THE THEORY OF ISOBARIC ANALOGUE SPIN RESONANCES*

R. O. Stephen

University of Washington, Seattle, Washington

INTRODUCTION

The theory which we present below is applicable to both elastic and inelastic scattering of protons via the isobaric spin analogue resonances. For simplicity, we work in a representation where the isobaric spins of the target and projectile are uncoupled. The problem may now be treated as a two channel one, enabling the inelastic scattering to be treated in a simple manner.

FORMULATION

The total Hamiltonian H_o of the target, isobaric spin T_o, $T_3 = T_o$ and incident proton, isobaric spin t, of incident energy E is assumed to be of the form[1]

$$H_o = H_A(r_1 \ldots r_A) + K_o + U(r_o, r_1 \ldots r_A)$$

$$+ W(r_o, r_1 \ldots r_A) t \cdot T_o + (1/2 - t_3) V_c \qquad (1)$$

where H_A is the Hamiltonian for the target nucleus and K_o is the kinetic energy operator for the incident proton with coordinate r_o. The wave function Ψ_o for the total system satisfies

$$H_o \Psi_o = E \Psi_o \qquad (2)$$

*Supported in part by the United States Atomic Energy Commission under RLO-1388B

where Ψ_o has the antisymmetrized form

$$\Psi_o = A \left[\sum_i u_i(p)\, \phi_i(T_o, T_o) + \sum_k w_k(n)\psi_k(T_o, T_o - 1) \right]$$

(3)

The states $\phi_i(T_o, T_o)$ and $\psi_k(T_o, T_o - 1)$ satisfy

$$\psi(T_o, T_o - 1) = T_-\, \phi(T_o, T_o) \tag{4}$$

$$(H_A - \epsilon_i)\, \phi_i(T_o, T_o) = 0 \tag{5}$$

$$\left[H_A + v_c \right] \psi_k(T_o, T_o - 1) = (\epsilon_k + \Delta_c)\psi_k(T_o, T_o - 1) \tag{6}$$

$$v_c = \left[T_-\, ,\, V_{c,A} \right] T_-^{-1} + \Delta_c \tag{7}$$

where T_- is the isobaric spin lowering operator. The states $\psi(T_o, T_o - 1)$ are the isobaric analogues of the normal states $\phi(T_o, T_o)$. Substituting the wave function Ψ_o in Eq. 2 we get the two sets of coupled equations 8 and 9 for u and w. It has been shown by Feshbach[2] that, provided the incident energy E is sufficiently low so that only one-nucleon channels are open the effect of the antisymmetrization of Ψ_o is to introduce exchange potentials into the coupled Eqs. 8 and 9

$$(H_1 - E)u = -W(C|A)w \tag{8}$$

$$(H_2 - E)w = -W^+(C|A)u \tag{9}$$

where H_1, H_2 and $W(C|A)$ are matrix operators

$$H_{1,ij} = (K_o + \epsilon_i + V_c)\, \delta_{ij} + U_{ij} - 1/2\, T_o\, W_{ij}$$

$$H_{2,k\ell} = (K_o + \epsilon_k + \Delta_c) \, \delta_{k\ell} + U_{k\ell} + 1/2 \, (T_o - 1) \, W_{k\ell}$$

$$W(C|A)_{ik} = 1/2 \, W_{ik}$$

where

$$U_{ij} = \, < \phi_i \mid U - U_{ex} \mid \phi_j >$$

$$W_{ik} = (2T_o)^{1/2} \, < \phi_i \mid W - W_{ex} \mid \phi_k >$$

and

$$u = \begin{pmatrix} u_o \\ | \\ u_1 \\ | \end{pmatrix} \qquad w = \begin{pmatrix} w_o \\ | \\ w_k \\ | \end{pmatrix}$$

Eliminating w between Eqs. 8 and 9 yields

$$[H_1 + W(C|A) \, \frac{1}{(E - H_2)} \, W^+(C|A) - E] \, u = 0 \qquad (10)$$

We now expand the second term on the left of Eq. 10 in a complete set of states of H_2 and retain only the bound states. These states correspond to states where a neutron is bound to the analogue. These states have a very small probability for neutron emission and hence the effect of the unbound states of H_2 will not be appreciable. Equation 10 then becomes

$$(H_1 + \sum_n \frac{W(C|A) \, \Phi_n > <\Phi_n \, W^+(C|A)}{E - (\mathcal{E}_n + \Delta_c)} - E) \, u = 0 \qquad (11)$$

where $(H_2 - \mathcal{E}_n) \, \Phi_n = 0$

458

Suppose that E is close to $(\mathcal{E}_n + \Delta_c)$, we then rewrite Eq. 11 as

$$(H'_1 + \frac{W(C|A) \; \Phi_n > <\Phi_n \; W^+(C|A)}{E - (\mathcal{E}_n + \Delta_c)} - E) \; u = 0 \tag{12}$$

$$H'_1 = H_1 + \sum_m{}' \frac{W(C|A) \; \Phi_m > < \Phi_m \; W^+(C|A)}{E - (\mathcal{E}_n + \Delta_c)} \tag{13}$$

The transition amplitude, $\mathcal{J}(\beta|0)$ to a final state β can be easily obtained from the asymptotic behavior of u. We easily find formally

$$\mathcal{J}(\beta|0) = \mathcal{J}_d(\beta|0) + \mathcal{J}_{res}(\beta|0) \tag{14}$$

$$\mathcal{J}_d(\beta|0) = < u_\beta^{(-)} | \; V \; | \; u_o^{(+)} > \tag{15}$$

$$\mathcal{J}_{res}(\beta|0) = \frac{<u_\beta^{(-)}| \; W(C|A) \; | \; \Phi_n > <\Phi_n|W^+(C|A) \; | \; u_o^{(+)}>}{E - (\mathcal{E}_n + \Delta_c) - <\Phi_n|W^+(C|A)\frac{1}{E^{(+)}-H'_1}W(C|A)|\Phi_n>} \tag{16}$$

The potential V includes all the non-resonant potentials in H'_1. The third term in the denominator of Eq. 16 can be further simplified yielding

$$< \Phi_n| \; W^+(C|A)\frac{1}{E^{(+)}-H'_1} \; W(C|A)|\Phi_n > = \Delta + i \; \Gamma/2 \tag{17}$$

where

$$\Delta = < \Phi_n| \; W^+(C|A) \; P \; \frac{1}{E - H'_1} \; W(C|A)| \; \Phi_n > \tag{18}$$

$$\Gamma = 2\pi \sum_\beta | < u_\beta^{(-)} | \; W(C|A)| \; \Phi_n > |^2 \tag{19}$$

459

Δ is the level shift away from resonance and Γ is the total width.

The resonance term may, less formally, be written as

$$\mathcal{J}_{res}(\beta|0) = \frac{-ie^{i\delta}\beta(\Gamma_\beta)^{1/2}(\Gamma_o)^{1/2} e^{i\delta_o}}{E - (\varepsilon_n + \Delta_c + \Delta) - i\,\Gamma/2} \qquad (20)$$

where

$$\Gamma_\beta = \left(\frac{2k_\beta}{E_\beta}\right)(a_\beta)^2 \qquad (21)$$

$$\Gamma = \sum_\beta \Gamma_\beta \qquad (22)$$

$$a_\beta = \left(\frac{T_o W_o^2}{2}\right)^{1/2} \int_0^\infty v_\beta(r)\ f(r)\ h(r)\ r\ dr \qquad (23)$$

$$\Delta = \sum_\beta \Delta_\beta \qquad (24)$$

$$\Delta_\beta = -\left(\frac{T_o k_\beta W_o^2}{2E_\beta}\right)\int h(r)v_\beta(r_<)f(r_<)f(r_>)w_\beta(r_>)h(r')$$

$$r\ r'\ dr\ dr' \qquad (25)$$

where $W_o f(r)$ is the form of the potential $W(C|A)$; $v_\beta(r)$ is the regular part of $u_\beta^{(-)}(r)$, $w_\beta(r)$ the irregular part; $h(r)$ is the bound state radial form factor for the scattered proton.

Figures 1 and 2 show the calculated and experimental data[3] for the inelastic scattering of protons from Pb^{206} via the ground state analogue resonance. The calculation uses the wave functions for Pb^{206} of True and Ford[4]. The effective potential $W_o f(r)$ is

DISCUSSION

TALMI: In connection with Tamura's presentation I would like to submit that a similar paper was presented by Jägare from Copenhagen, and I am sure it would be very interesting to compare these things, but we cannot start it now, of course, because of the shortage of time.

ROBSON, Florida State: What did you do with the continuum?

STEPHEN: The continuum can be taken into account in the same way as you do but I have used perturbation theory. It's really a simple thing to do.

ROBSON: I am glad you think so!

STEPHEN: Well, of course, it depends on how sophisticated you want to be in which case it could be complicated.

ROBSON: How do you possibly get the width correctly unless you treat the continuum correctly?

STEPHEN: The width was not calculated right. I got a width of 70 keV for the widths of those resonances which you saw, which was considerably less than the widths which were measured experimentally, but, clearly, one has to put this in and then there are various degrees of sophistication one can go to.

assumed to have a Woods-Saxon form with a strength of 100 MeV/A.

REFERENCES

1) A. M. Lane, Nucl. Phys. <u>35</u> (1962) 676.
2) H. Feshbach, Ann. Phys. <u>5</u> (1958) 357.
3) C. D. Kavaloski, J. S. Lilley, P. Richard, N. Stein, Paper C4.
4) W. W. True, K. W. Ford, Phys. Rev. <u>109</u> (1958) 1675.

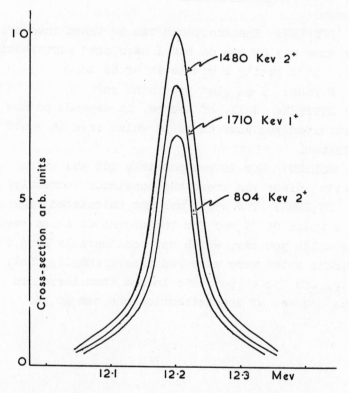

Fig. 1. Calculated cross section for inelastic scattering of protons from Pb^{206} via the ground state analogue resonance.

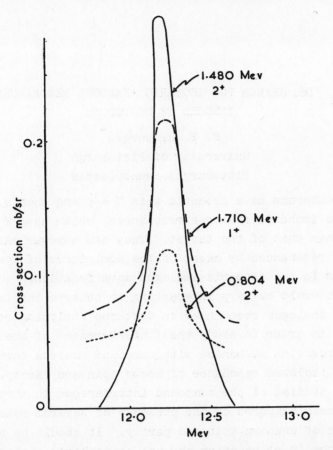

Fig. 2. Experimental cross section for inelastic scattering of protons from Pb^{206} via the ground state analogue resonance.

D6. SEARCH FOR ISOBARIC ANALOGUE RESONANCES INDUCED BY DEUTERONS

E. W. Hamburger[*]

University of Pittsburgh

Pittsburgh, Pennsylvania

Deuterons have isobaric spin $T = 0$ and should not excite isobaric analogue resonances, which have T larger than that of the target. They can however excite these resonances by means of the admixtures of lower T states in the isobaric analogue wave function.

It would be very interesting to observe the isobaric analogue resonances in deuteron stripping reactions in order to study the "interference" of the direct reaction mechanism with compound nucleus formation at an isolated resonance of known spin and parity. Previous studies of the compound interference in stripping have been hampered by the presence of several resonances of unknown spin and parity. It should be noted that the (d,p) reaction through an isobaric analogue resonance is isobaric spin forbidden only in the entrance channel; the exit channel is allowed.

There are only certain target nuclei for which the deuteron channel is open at the resonance energy. The deuteron energy at which the resonance should appear is, for example, for the $Pb^{207}(d,p)Pb^{208}$ reaction to form, in Bi^{209}, the analogue of the Pb^{209} g.s.:

$$E_D^{Lab} = \frac{209}{207}\left[\Delta E_c + 2.22 \text{ MeV} - B(2n) \right]$$

[*]On leave from Universidade de Sao Paulo

where ΔE_c is the Coulomb energy difference between Pb^{209} and Bi^{209}, 2.22 MeV is the deuteron binding energy and B(2n) is the binding energy of the last two neutrons in Pb^{209}: $B(2n) = M(Pb^{207}) + 2M(n) - M(Pb^{209})$. Only the analogues of heavy nuclei having small neutron binding energy can be studied.

The first step in this experiment was to look for big effects. Three readily available targets, Bi^{209}, Pt^{196} and Pr^{141} were bombarded in the energy region where isobaric analogue resonances were expected (11.1 MeV, 6.8 MeV and 4.1 MeV respectively). The (d,p) cross sections are smooth functions of the incident energy within $\pm$ 10%.

The measurements were made with solid state detectors set at scattering angles of 90° and 150° and covered with a thick aluminum foil to stop the elastically scattered deuterons. The incident beam was monitored with an integrator and with two monitor counters set at $\pm$ 25° to the incident beam.

The next step was to study the $Pb^{207}(d,p)Pb^{208}$ reaction with greater precision. For this reaction isobaric analogue resonances have already been observed in the scattering of protons from Pb^{208} [1] at proton energies of 14.94, 16.45, 16.93 and 17.4 MeV (see Fig. 1). The resonances should occur at deuteron energies of 9.8, 11.3, 11.8 and 12.3 MeV respectively. The data near the lowest resonance is shown in Figs. 2 and 3, respectively for the transition to the Pb^{208} g.s. and to the unresolved doublet at 3.198 - 3.475 MeV excitation energy. The target was 200 μg/cm^2 thick, enriched to 92.9% in Pb^{207}. The ordinate scale is proportional to cross section multiplied by energy squared. The absolute cross sections at deuteron energy 9.78 MeV

465

are given in the figures.

There are small fluctuations about a smoothly
varying cross section but no resonance can be identified. The width of the resonance, as observed in proton scattering from Pb^{208}, is 220 keV[1], so that e.g.
the small peak at 9.68 MeV in the 150° Pb^{208}, g.s.
curve is too narrow to correspond to the isobaric analogue state. The fluctuations are almost all less than
3% of the cross section, with a few as high as 5%. For
the transition to the excited states, Fig. 3, where the
statistics are also better, they are mostly smaller
than 3%.

One can estimate an upper limit for the partial
width for deuteron emission from Fig. 2 by assuming
that the resonance cross section is added incoherently
to the direct cross section, using the Breit-Wigner
formula and assuming an isotropic compound angular
distribution. The data show that the peak cross section of the resonance is less than ~ 4 μb/std.

One obtains for the peak resonance cross section

$$(\frac{d\sigma}{d\Omega})_{\substack{\text{reson.} \\ \text{max}}} = \frac{18\Gamma_{p4}(\Gamma_{d3} + \Gamma_{d5})}{\Gamma^2} \text{ mb/std} < 0.004 \text{ mb/std}$$

and using Moore's result[1] for Γ and $\Gamma_{p4} = 18$ keV:
$\Gamma_{d3} + \Gamma_{d5} < 0.6$ keV. The subscripts on the partial
widths give the type of particle and the orbital angular momentum.

The reduced width is less than 1.5% of the Wigner limit:

$$\theta_{d3}^2 = \gamma_{d3}^2 (\frac{\hbar^2}{ma^2}) < 0.015$$

This upper limit is not really very small. For example

in another isobaric spin forbidden reaction Mani and Dutt[2] find for neutrons in $Y^{89}(p,n)Y^{90}$: $\theta_n^2 \sim 0.004$. Actually the deuteron width is probably much smaller than the limit given above because amplitudes, rather than cross sections, should be added; the experimental upper limit would then be reduced by a factor ~ 8 to ~ 0.002.

The higher resonances in Bi^{209} have smaller angular momenta, the deuteron penetrabilities are much larger, so that smaller deuteron reduced widths can be detected. They will be studied next.

REFERENCES

1) C. F. Moore, private communication.
2) G. S. Mani and G. C. Dutt, Phys. Lett. <u>16</u> (1965) 50.

DISCUSSION

WIGNER, Princeton: Do I understand that that is really a serious problem, the fact that you did not find it?

HAMBURGER: No. There might have been a serious problem if we had found something. I should have mentioned that the reason for doing the experiment, at least my main interest in it was that if we could find the resonance we could study the interference of a direct reaction with the compound nucleus formation at an isolated resonance with well-known spin and parity. This has not been possible in stripping in the past.

WIGNER: Why is it that this analogue state does not show up?

HAMBURGER: Because the reduced width for deuteron emission is very small due to isobaric spin conservation. It is forbidden by isobaric spin conservation. Now, neutron emission is also forbidden, but is favored by a very large penetration factor. The deuteron has a very small penetration factor, and that is why it is not observed.

WIGNER: Thank you.

SHAFROTH, Bartol: I was going to ask about the 3^- state. Did you also take data for that state into consideration?

HAMBURGER: Yes, that was considered, however, it is too small. The statistics are too poor to get a good upper limit.

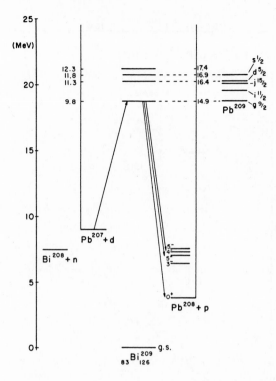

Fig. 1. Energy level scheme for the $Pb^{207}(d,p)Pb^{208}$ reaction through compound states in Bi^{209}.

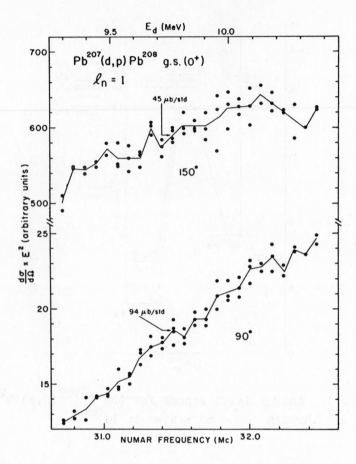

Fig. 2. Data of several runs for the Pb^{207}(d,p)Pb^{208} g.s. reaction. The line is drawn through the averages of the experimental points.

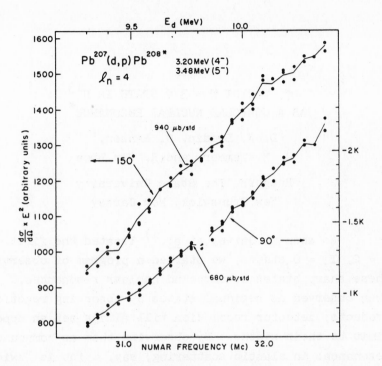

Fig. 3. Data for the Pb^{207}(d,p)Pb^{208} reaction to the unresolved states at 3.20 MeV (4-) and 3.475 MeV (5-) in Pb^{208}. The line is drawn through the averages of the experimental points.

D7. LOWEST T = 3/2 STATE IN N^{13} AS A COMPOUND NUCLEAR RESONANCE[*]

D. J. Bredin, O. Hansen,[+]
G. M. Temmer, and R. Van Bree

Rutgers, The State University
New Brunswick, New Jersey

As soon as Garvey et al.[1] located the first
T = 2, T_z = 0 states, we started a program of observing
these sharp states as compound nuclear resonances.
When observed as residual states by observing reaction
products, detector resolution will always set an upper
limit to their widths. By observing them as compound
resonances in elastic scattering, say, which is "twice
forbidden" as far as isobaric spin is concerned, tandem accelerators with their high beam resolution may
hope to push this limit down to the keV level. Our
first attempts to locate these states in Ne^{20} and Mg^{24}
were inconclusive, mainly owing to unstable beam conditions.

Meanwhile, the location of the T = 3/2 levels
in the A = 13 multiplet excited in T-allowed reactions
became available[2,3], and we investigated the C^{12} + p
channel to form N^{13} (T = 3/2) at the appropriate excitation by twice T-forbidden elastic and inelastic scattering. This state was reported as less than 20 keV

[*]Supported in part by the National Science Foundation
[+]Present address: Niels Bohr Institute, Copenhagen

wide[2]. We scanned the excitation function for elastic
and inelastic scattering (to the 4.43 MeV, 2^+ and 9.64,
3^- states) and found a single sharp anomaly in the 165°
data with a typical dispersion shape, superimposed on
a very broad structure (of the order of 1 MeV wide).
This is shown schematically in Fig. 1, and in detail
in Fig. 2. The main curve represents 10-keV steps over
the crucial region; the insert shows a repeat run with
5-keV steps. The counting statistics are shown for
one point, and the full excursion in the resonance
occurred within one energy increment. Since our target
was 1.6 keV thick, we were presumably limited by beam
resolution. We place an upper limit of 5 keV on the
observed width. The two arrows indicate where angular
distributions were obtained (see Figs. 5 and 6). Figs.
3a and 3b show the spectra observed at 20° and 165°,
respectively. Peaks are identified in the caption.
Our nominal energy for the resonance is 14.212 $\pm$ 0.018
MeV, corresponding to an excitation in N^{13} of 15.047 $\pm$
0.018 MeV. This is to be compared with 15.068 $\pm$ 0.008
MeV obtained by $B^{11}(He^3,n)N^{13}$ time-of-flight determination[2]. Our value is based on calibration with a
known C^{12} + p resonance at 4.808 MeV[4]. A more precise
location will soon be undertaken. Figure 4 gives the
excitation curves at 90° for elastic and inelastic
scattering (2^+). Since this is presumably an $\ell =$
$1(J^{\pi} = 3/2^-)$ resonance, (analogue of B^{13} ground state)
we expect to see small anomalies at 90°. Evidence for
seeing the resonance also in the 3^- inelastic channel
was obtained. For the purpose of doing a proper resonance analysis, we have obtained the elastic and inelastic angular distributions on either side of the resonance (see arrows in Fig. 3) shown in Figs. 5 and 6.

Corresponding curves agree with each other almost completely, and will allow optical model parameters to be extracted for the broad underlying background. They also agree generally with previous cyclotron work in this region[5]. Absolute values were obtained by comparison with Ref. 4.

At this time, we would like to call attention to some related and beautiful work on $T = 3/2$ states in F^{17} from $O^{16}(p,p)O^{16}$, leading to the first and second excited states analogous to N^{17}, obtained several years ago[6]. The ground state analogue was not located then. In our case, the second $T = 3/2$ state was not accessible since it lies 4 MeV higher.

A theoretical estimate of the width of our state produced by mixing with available $T = 1/2$, $J^{\pi} = 3/2^{-}$ states was kindly provided by J. N. Ginocchio[7], making use of Oak Ridge p-shell wave functions[8] and calculating the Coulomb effects by perturbation theory. This involves both $T = 1$ admixture in C^{12} and $T = 1/2$ admixture in N^{13}. He obtains values of 1.4 keV or 5.4 keV for the observed width, using harmonic oscillator size parameters of 1.55 F and 1.8 F, respectively.

A preliminary attempt to locate the first $T = 2$ state in C^{12} at ~ 27.5 MeV[9] by $B^{11} + p$ gave a negative result. In addition to re-examining other similar doubly forbidden reactions, we plan to study the $C^{12}(p,\gamma)N^{13}$ reaction (and similar once T-forbidden reactions) to obtain radiative widths for these sharp states.

We are indebted to G. Lenz, B. Teitelman, and M. Wiesen for their assistance in the long hours of data collection.

REFERENCES

1) G. T. Garvey, J. Cerny and R. H. Pehl, Phys. Rev. Letters 13 (1964) 548.
2) E. Adelberger and C. A. Barnes, Bull. Am. Phys. Soc. 10 (1965) 1195.
3) J. Cerny, R. H. Pehl, G. Butler, D. G. Fleming, C. Maples and C. Detraz, Phys. Rev. Letters 20 (1966) 35.
4) C. W. Reich, G. C. Phillips and J. L. Russell, Phys. Rev. 104 (1956) 143.
5) S. Kobayashi, J. Phys. Soc. Japan 15 (1960) 1164.
6) G. Hardie, R. L. Dangle and L. D. Oppliger, Phys. Rev. 129 (1963) 353.
7) J. N. Ginocchio, (private communication).
8) M. L. Halbert, (private communication).
9) G. T. Garvey, (private communication).

DISCUSSION

SHAFROTH, Bartol: Are you calculating the width just on the basis of the $T = 1/2$ impurity in the $T = 3/2$ state?

TEMMER: No. Both the $T = 1/2$ impurity in N^{13} and the $T = 1$ impurity in C^{12}.

ADELBERGER, Cal. Tech.: I would like to know, if you conduct these experiments with exceedingly high resolution, would you see any kind of fine structure at all?

TEMMER: I would like to say there was one day two weeks ago when we had some troubles and we thought maybe we were seeing that sort of thing.

ROBSON, Florida State: I don't think you could.

ADELBERGER: At what region of the mass table would you expect to see such fine structure?

ROBSON: I don't know.

WIGNER, Princeton: It depends on the energy, the higher the energy the more you see the fine structure. The probability of seeing the fine structure increases as you increase the level density. Of course, if the density of levels is too small then you don't see the fine structure. If you increase it too much the fine structure becomes so fine that you won't see it.

ADELBERGER: You wouldn't see it if they were overlapping, would you?

WIGNER: That is correct; but it is hardly likely that you would see nothing. There would still be something because there would be fluctuations.

HAMBURGER, Pittsburgh: In this case then it would be what? A single level? That way there is no fine structure?

TEMMER: I don't think we will be able to answer that question for a long time to come.

MacDONALD, University of Maryland: With reference to the question whether you see the fine structure or not because of overlapping levels, I would like to call attention to a paper in Physical Review Letters by myself and Richard Ferrell, in which a very simple calculation shows that if one has levels which are not directly coupled to the continuum but which are coupled to such a resonant state one does see the fine structure, the levels do not overlap in between each state. The resonance phase shift goes to the optical value in between each fine resonance.

WIGNER: Is there one channel or several?

MacDONALD: There is one channel. I don't know how general it is, but that was the result we arrived at.

WIGNER: In one channel it is always that way.

SCHIFFER, Argonne: I'm sorry, but I must confess I am rather confused by this. These states are presumably proton decay forbidden, so they should not be observed. They should be sharp states.

TEMMER: They should not be formed nor should they decay.

SCHIFFER: Assuming you get the protons by mixing of the same type that was discussed before except it is opposite here, this state picks up some width from the T-lower states to show up in the elastic scattering, so I don't really understand in what sense it is meaningful to say one sees fine structure in this very narrow state which picks up a little bit of width from the broad T-lower states.

CERNY, Berkeley: I have a very mundane question. What do you think the accuracy is of that particular number?

TEMMER: I would say the accuracy is sort of problematic. We have about as much trouble with the accuracy as you do.

CERNY: I was thinking of the Cal. Tech. number. My number is not very accurate.

TEMMER: Their number is $15.068 \pm .008$. At the present time, however, ours is $15.047 \pm .018$. That is carrying all sorts of errors, due to the way we are calibrating, using other people's results. There are better ways of doing this, I admit, but that is about as accurate as we can be at the moment.

HENSLEY, Cal. Tech.: There is a very good chance that you will be able to see this with the (p,γ) as you say because you have only one forbidden channel. The analogue state in carbon 13 has been seen by $Be^9(\alpha,\gamma)$ so there is a very good chance of doing the (p,γ) experiment.

TEMMER: That is true.

TALMI: Would someone answer Schiffer's question?

TEMMER: The answer is "yes".

WIGNER: Would you state the question over again?

SCHIFFER: My problem was that this state would not have any proton width at all, if it were perfectly pure. It only acquires some proton width by mixing with the T-lower state so that it can be seen in proton scattering.

AXEL, Illinois: I think that can be clarified by asking Temmer a question. How many other states are there in that region for N^{13}? If there are not

many other states, there is no question that any gremlin
will turn up and make any fine structure. If there
were a lot of states then one could ask about the fine
structure. I think what Schiffer is saying - and
correct me if I am wrong - is that one doesn't expect
lots of states within a 5 keV interval, so where is
the fine structure supposed to come from?

TEMMER: As was stated, there is a bump, a
smooth bump, on which this whole thing is located.

AXEL: But is that a lot of states, or one?

TEMMER: I don't know. I think one would have
to make a careful study of this whole structure using
about 2 1/2 keV steps.

ROBSON: When you talk about fine structure you
want to talk about a giant resonance which refers only
to a particular channel before you turn on the mixing.
Here the giant resonance is not in the channel you are
looking at, so you can hardly regard it as being the
source of a giant resonance in the particular channel
you are looking at, and I think that what Schiffer was
saying is quite correct.

SEGEL, Argonne: I just wanted to make the comment that the implication when you look for fine structure is that in this region of the nucleus you have
these very narrow levels as in the A^{40} data where they
were enhanced when you went through the analogue states.
I don't think in N^{13} you would expect the T-lower levels
to be narrower than the analogue state and so there is
no fine structure expected.

TEMMER: From the calculations that have been
made we know exactly where the T-lower levels are.
There are not many - you can count them on your fingers.

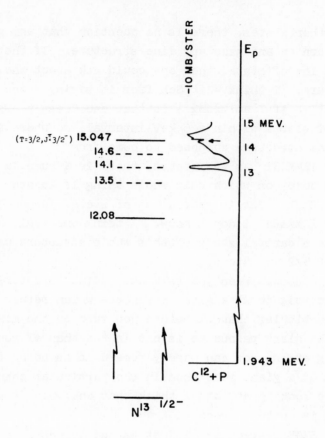

Fig. 1.   Schematic excerpt of N^{13} level diagram.

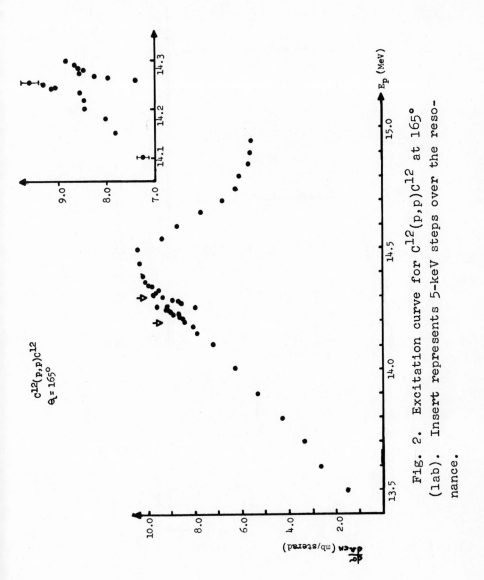

Fig. 2. Excitation curve for $C^{12}(p,p)C^{12}$ at 165°
(lab). Insert represents 5-keV steps over the resonance.

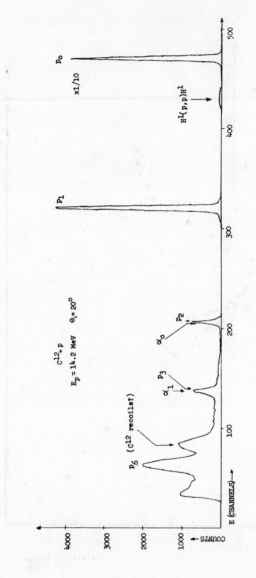

Fig. 3. (a) Spectrum at 20°.

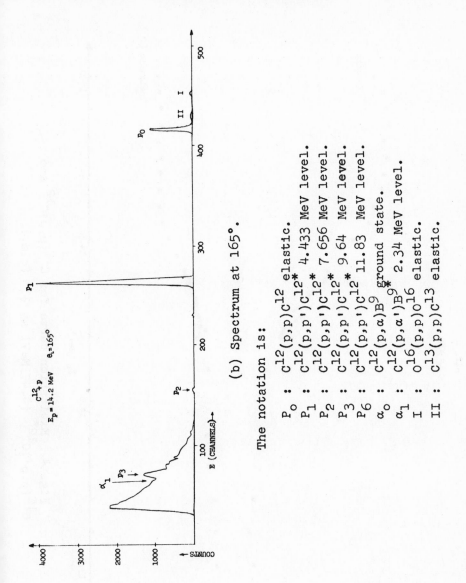

(b) Spectrum at 165°.

The notation is:

P_0 .. $C^{12}(p,p)C^{12}$ elastic.

P_1 .. $C^{12}(p,p')C^{12*}$ 4.433 MeV level.

P_2 .. $C^{12}(p,p')C^{12*}$ 7.656 MeV level.

P_3 .. $C^{12}(p,p')C^{12*}$ 9.64 MeV level.

P_6 .. $C^{12}(p,p')C^{12*}$ 11.83 MeV level.

α_0 .. $C^{12}(p,\alpha)B^9$ ground state.

α_1 .. $C^{12}(p,\alpha')B^{9*}$ 2.34 MeV level.

I .. $O^{16}(p,p)O^{16}$ elastic.

II .. $C^{13}(p,p)C^{13}$ elastic.

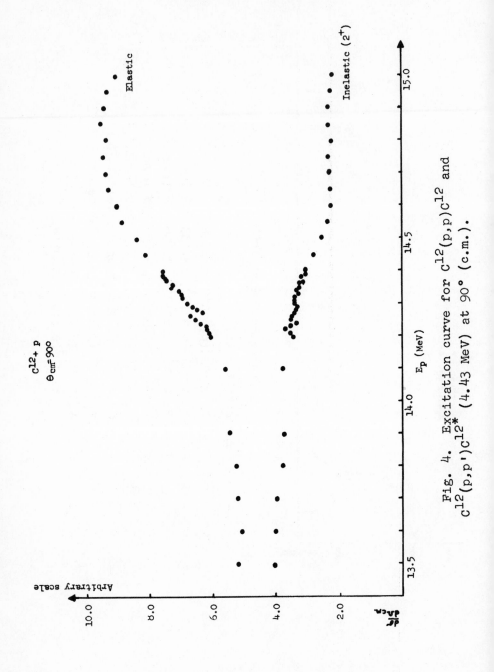

Fig. 4. Excitation curve for $C^{12}(p,p)C^{12}$ and $C^{12}(p,p')C^{12*}$ (4.43 MeV) at 90° (c.m.).

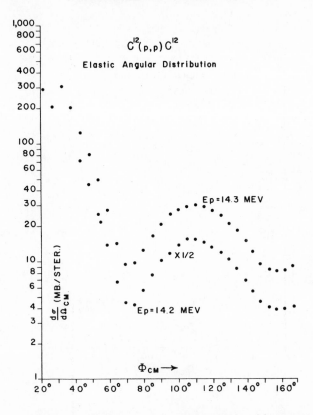

Fig. 5. Elastic angular distributions (center of mass) on either side of resonance (cf. arrows in Fig. 2). 14.2-MeV points arbitrarily lowered by factor 2.

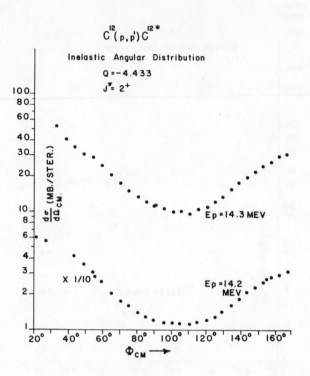

Fig. 6. Inelastic angular distributions (center of mass) at the same energies as in previous figure (cf. arrows in Fig. 2). 14.2-MeV points arbitrarily lowered by factor 10.

486

D8. AN INVESTIGATION OF (p,n) REACTION MECHANISM VIA ISOBARIC ANALOGUE RESONANCES*

H. J. Kim and R. L. Robinson
Oak Ridge National Laboratory
Oak Ridge, Tennessee

The isobaric analogues of low-lying bound states observed by (d,p) reactions are observed as sharp resonances in proton elastic scattering as well as in proton induced reactions such as (p,p') and (p,n). For medium weight nuclei (A ~ 90) the analogue states are observed in the region of excitation energy where the non-resonant background cross-section is due mostly to compound nuclear reactions. Because these analogue states are well separated and fall in the region of densely populated compound nuclear states of normal isobaric spin, one can investigate certain aspects of the non-resonant, background reaction mechanism by studying the effect of the presence of the analogue state on the reaction mechanism. Thus we have investigated the exci-functions and the angular distributions of neutron groups produced by the (p,n) reactions on Sr^{88} and Y^{89} in the energy region of well established[1] $d_{5/2}$ isolated resonances. These resonances are due to the isobaric analogues of the $d_{5/2}$ neutron states of Sr^{89} and Y^{90}. The neutron groups feeding the ground state of Y^{88}, ground state of Zr^{89}, and 590 keV state of Zr^{89} were

*Research sponsored by the U.S. Atomic Energy Commission under contract with Union Carbide Corporation.

detected by time-of-flight methods in conjunction with
a pulsed proton beam accelerated by the ORNL 5.5 MeV
Van de Graaff accelerator. Thin targets ($\sim$8 keV for
5 MeV protons) of normal isotopic abundance evaporated
on thin Pt backing were used.

In the vicinity of an analogue state, the (p,n)
reaction amplitude to a specific final state is $T(i|f)$
$= T_B + T_A$, where T_B is the non-resonant, background
amplitude and T_A is the additional amplitude needed to
account for the presence of the analogue state. We
assume T_A to be given correctly by Robson's theory[2]
and we shall use the same notation as in Ref. 2. Since
the analogue state is isobaric spin forbidden to decay
via (p,n) reactions, T_A is entirely due to "mixing" of
the compound states with the analogue state. The
reaction amplitude is

$$T(i|f) = T_B + f_A \, U^{J^{\pi}_A}$$

where

$$T_B = \sum_J U^{J^{\pi}}, \quad f_A = \frac{E_A - \Delta - E}{E_A - E - i(\Gamma/2)} - 1.$$

$U^{J^{\pi}}$'s are elements of the collision matrix with
$\vec{J} = \vec{I}_I + \vec{J}_p = \vec{I}_f + \vec{J}_n$ and appropriate parity.
I_i, I_f, J_p, J_n are the spins of the initial nucleus,
final nucleus, total particle spin $\vec{\ell} + \vec{s}$ of incident
proton and emitted neutron, and J^{π}_A is the spin and
parity of the analogue state. In this investigation
J^{π}_A is the result of adding a $d_{5/2}$ proton to the initial
nucleus. Assuming $U^{J^{\pi}}$'s to be insensitive to small
changes in the incident energy of order Γ, the differential cross-section near the analogue state is

$$\sigma(E;\theta) = \sigma_B(\theta) + |f_A(E)|^2 \sigma_A(\theta) + \sigma_{Int}(E;\theta) \quad (1)$$

where

$$\sigma_B(\theta) = \frac{\lambda^2}{8(2I_i + 1)} \sum_{J,J'} U^{J^\pi} U^{J'^{\pi'}*} = C \sum_{J,J'} U^{J^\pi} U^{J'^{\pi'}*}$$

$$\sigma_A(\theta) = C |U^{J_A^\pi}|^2$$

and

$$\sigma_{Int(E;\theta)} = 2 \text{ Re} \left\{ Cf_A \sum_J U^{J_A^\pi} U^{J^{\pi*}} \right\}$$

$$= 2\left\{ Ref_A \right\} [\sigma_A(\theta) + Re\Sigma] + 2\left\{ Imf_A \right\} Im\Sigma$$

(2)

where

$$f_A = \left\{ Ref_A \right\} + i\left\{ Imf_A \right\} \text{ and } C \sum_{J \neq J_A} U^{J_A^\pi} U^{J^{\pi*}} = Re\Sigma + i(Im\Sigma).$$

The energy dependence of $\sigma(E;\theta)$ near E_A is determined by the energy dependence of $|f_A|^2$, $\left\{ Ref_A \right\}$ and $\left\{ Imf_A \right\}$. We note that $|f_A|^2$ is symmetric about E_A and $\left\{ Ref_A \right\}$ and $\left\{ Imf_A \right\}$ are asymmetric about E_A. Experimental (p,n) excitation functions are shown in Figs. 1, 2 and 4. The asymmetric nature of the cross-section about the resonance energies can be seen in these figures. If the random phase assumption concerning $U^{J_A^\pi}$ is made, then

$$\sum_J U^{J_A^\pi} U^{J^{\pi*}} = 0 \text{ for } J^\pi \neq J_A^\pi \text{ and}$$

$$\sigma(E;\theta) = \sigma_B(\theta) + (|f_A|^2 + 2\left\{ Ref_A \right\}) \sigma_A(\theta)$$

$$= \sigma_B(\theta) + \left\{ \frac{(E_A - \Delta - E)^2}{(E_A - E)^2 + (\Gamma/2)^2} - 1 \right\} \sigma_A(\theta) \qquad (3)$$

One of the experimental excitation functions is compared to one calculated using Eq. 3, and is shown in Fig. 3. The parameters Δ and Γ were adjusted for a good visual fit to the experimental result and they are also shown in the figure. The calculated $\sigma(E;\theta)$'s were averaged over 8 keV energy interval in order to account for the 8 keV target thickness.

Three resonances studied are superimposed in Fig. 4. It is rather striking to note that the shapes as well as the widths of the resonances are very much the same. From Eq. 3 it can be shown that the observed width of the resonance is mainly determined by Γ if $\Gamma < |\Delta|$ and the skewness to the high or the low energy side of E_A is determined by the sign of Δ. Using the isobaric analogue resonance theory[3] the ratio $|\Delta|/\Gamma_{el}$, where Γ_{el} is elastic partial width, is about 100 and the sign of Δ is determined to be negative for all three resonances. From Fig. 4 we can, therefore, infer that the spreading widths $W = \Gamma - \Gamma_{el}$ are the same for these $d_{5/2}$ analogue states.

If we take $U^{J_A^\pi} \sum_J U^{J^{\pi*}} = |U^{J_A^\pi}|^2$, which seems

reasonable in view of the preceeding resonance shape study, then we can proceed with the inquiry by studying the angular distributions of neutrons. At a given incident energy the angular dependence of the neutron cross-section decaying to a specific final state is $\sigma_{B(\theta)} + K\,\sigma_{A(\theta)}$, where K is an angle independent constant. Furthermore the analogue state is formed by coupling a single $j_p = j_{pA}$ to the initial nuclear spin I_i. Therefore

$$\sigma_{A(\theta)} = \frac{\lambdabar^2}{8} \frac{2J_A + 1}{2I_i + 1} \sum_{J_n, J'_n} U_{(j_{pA}, J_n)}^{J_A^\pi} U_{(j_{pA}, J'_n)}^{J_A^{\pi *}}$$

where
$$\vec{J}_n + \vec{I}_f = \vec{J}'_n + \vec{I}_f = \vec{J}_A.$$

Separating the kinematical factor of U^{J^π} from the dynamical one $\sigma_{A(\theta)}$ becomes

$$\sigma_{A(\theta)} = \frac{\lambdabar^2}{8} \frac{2J_A + 1}{2I_i + 1} \sum_{J_n, J'_n, \upsilon} t(j_{pA}, J_n, J_A) t^*(j_{pA}, J'_n J_A)$$

$$X \ \eta_\upsilon(j_{pA} j_{pA} I_i J_A) \eta_\upsilon(J_n J'_n I_f J_A) P_\upsilon(\theta) \tag{4}$$

where t's contain all the dynamics of the reaction, the η_υ's are the coefficients defined and tabulated by Satchler,[4] and the P_υ's are the Legendre polynomials.

In order to test the randomness assumption of t's, we have calculated $\sigma_A(\theta)$ using Eq. 4 and the randomness assumption, i.e.,

$$t(j_{pA}, J_n, J_A) t^*(j_{pA}, J'_n, J_A)$$

$$= |t(j_{pA}, J_n, J_A)|^2 \delta_{J_n, J'_n} \delta_{\ell_n, \ell'_n}$$

where ℓ_n = the orbital angular momentum of the neutron. The calculated $\sigma(\theta)$'s are compared with the experimental angular distributions in Figs. 5 and 6. The on-resonance $\sigma(\theta)$'s were obtained by simply adding normalized $\sigma_A(\theta)$'s calculated by Eq. 4 to the off-resonance angular distribution measured at the incident energies a few Γ's away from the resonance energy. We have also ignored any contribution from higher partial waves than the lowest partial wave ℓ_n.

491

If the randomness assumption is valid for $U^{J_A\pi}$, which is reasonable in view of good fits shown in Figs. 5 and 6, it can be applied to all relevant $U^{J\pi}(j_p,j_n)$'s. Under this condition $\sigma_B(\theta)$'s are symmetric about $\theta = 90°$ and become the cross-sections given by the Hauser-Feshbach theory $\sigma(\theta)_{H.F.}$. We have calculated on-resonance and off-resonance angular distributions using the Hauser-Feshbach theory and the additional enhancement given by Eq. 4. The calculated $\sigma(\theta)$ are compared to the experimental data in Figs. 5 and 6. The magnitude of the calculated $\sigma(\theta)$'s are arbitrarily adjusted for good visual fits.

In conclusion we have demonstrated that the enhancement of the (p,n) cross-section brought about by the presence of an isolated isobaric spin analogue state can be used as a tool to investigate some aspects of the reaction mechanism and to see if the randomness assumptions in the statistical compound nucleus model are valid for (p,n) reactions on medium weight nuclei at incident proton energies of about 5 MeV.

REFERENCES

1. J. D. Fox, C. F. Moore, and D. Robson, Phys. Rev. Letts. 12 (1964) 198; D. B. Lightbody, G. E. Mitchell and A. Sayres, Phys. Letts. 15 (1965) 155; G. S. Mani and G. C. Dutt, Phys. Letts. 16 (1965) 50.

2. D. Robson, J. D. Fox, P. Richard and C. F. Moore, Phys. Letts. 18 (1965) 86.

3. D. Robson, Phys. Rev. 137 (1965) B535.

4. G. R. Satchler, Proc. Phys. Soc. (London) 56 (1953) 1801.

DISCUSSION

SHAFROTH, Bartol: How does your data compare with the data of Sayres on this?

KIM: I think it is excellent. Ours is more detailed.

SHAFROTH: What values do you get for the widths Γ and Γ_n.

KIM: On the width questions we get twenty kilovolts; the shift factor is minus 80 kilovolts, the latter being consistent with the R-matrix calculation.

HAMBURGER, Pittsburgh: There must be some connection between the two transitions, that in Y^{89} and that in Sr^{88}. Some of them must be the same. Has that been verified?

KIM: Yes. As I said the doublet must add up to the same thing as observed in Sr^{88}. We need absolute cross sections for this and we are investigating this.

BLOOM, Livermore: Will you give us briefly an idea of what you found out about the reaction mechanism in your experiments?

KIM: Yes. I think when you can isolate two elements of the collision matrix for the (p,n) reaction, they do obey the statistical model insofar as random phases are involved, i.e. the interference between different partial waves is taken as zero.

BRENTANO, Max Planck, Heidelberg: You have a slowly rising factor and the resonance is superimposed on it. Why don't you take an interference term between the background and your resonances?

KIM: That is what I have done.

493

BRENTANO: I don't understand.

KIM: May I show you on this fourth slide? The interference taken into account is between the background and the resonance but only for the same spin and parity.

BRENTANO: Thank you. I see now.

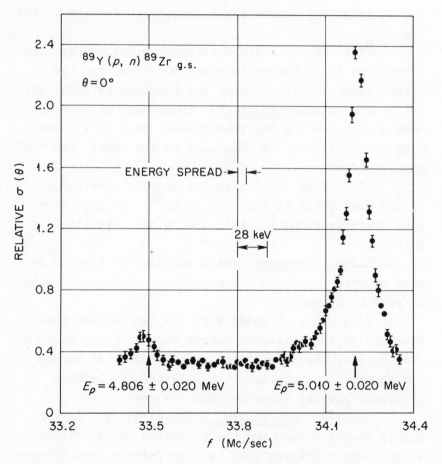

Fig. 1. (ORNL-DWG 66-1817) Excitation function for $Y^{89}(p,n)Zr^{89}$.

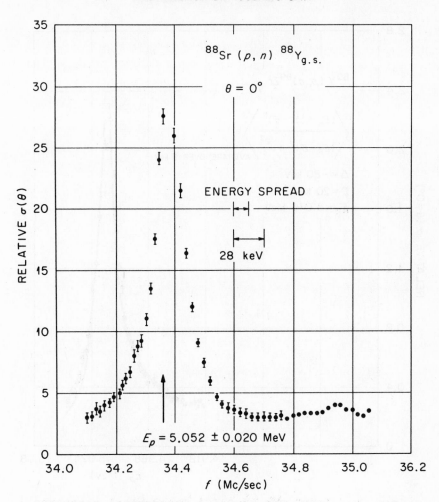

Fig. 2. (ORNL-DWG 66-1818) Excitation function for Sr^{88}(p,n)Y^{88}.

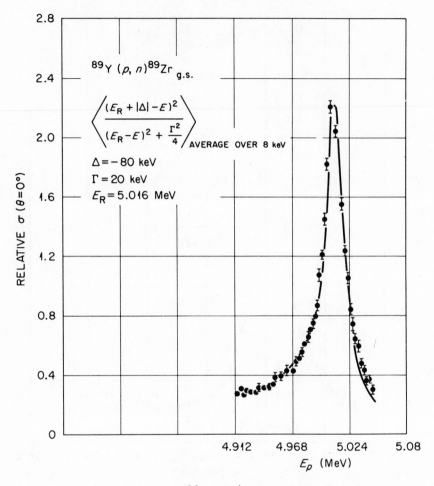

Fig. 3. (ORNL-DWG 66-2159) Theoretical resonance shape for $Y^{89}(p,n)Zr^{89}$.

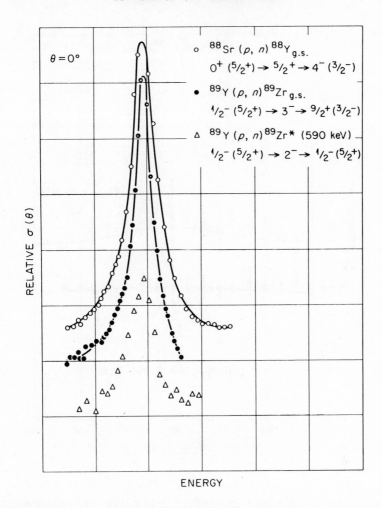

Fig. 4. (ORNL-DWG 66-1822) Superposition of three resonances indicated.

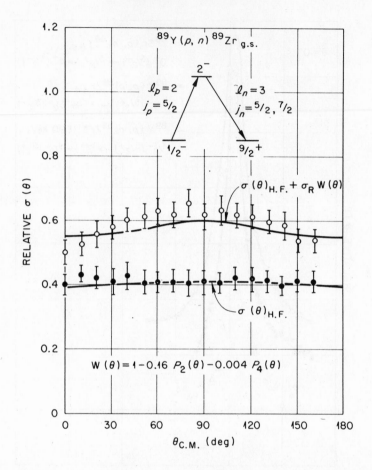

Fig. 5. (ORNL-DWG 66-1819) Open circles are on-resonance data and closed circles are off-resonance data.

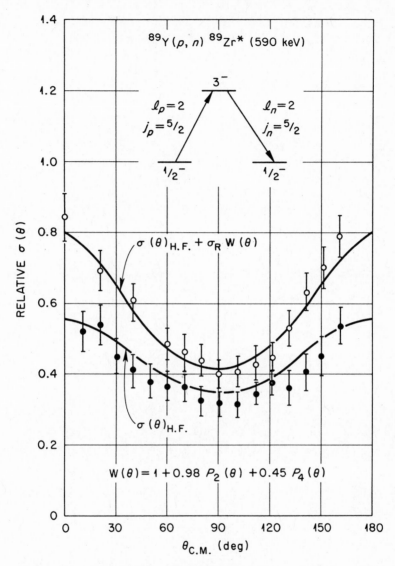

Fig. 6. (ORNL-DWG 66-1821) Open circles are on-resonance data and closed circles are off-resonance data.

SESSION E

J. P. Schiffer, Chairman

E1.   ISOBARIC SPIN IN STRIPPING
AND PICK-UP REACTIONS[+]

B. F. Bayman

School of Physics, University of Minnesota

Minneapolis, Minnesota

To introduce our discussion of isobaric spin in
particle transfer reactions, let us compare the reactions (d,t) and (d,He^3) performed with the same target.
The first reaction removes a neutron from the target;
the second removes a proton.   Let us first neglect any
effects of the Coulomb interaction and the neutron-
proton mass difference.   Figure 1 symbolizes the changes
that take place in the isobaric spin and its z-component.
T_A in Fig. 1 is the isobaric spin of the target.

The (d,t) reaction excites states with isobaric
spin $T_A - 1/2$ ($\equiv T_<$) and $T_A + 1/2$ ($\equiv T_>$).   The isobaric
analogue of each of the $T_>$ states should be excited by
the (d,He^3) reaction.   To compare the relative intensities with which pairs of analogue states are excited,
we consider an expansion of the target wave function in
terms of states of the first A-1 nucleons, coupled to
the last nucleon:

$$\Psi_{1,2,\ldots,A}(A;I_A M_A, T_A T_A) = \sum_{k,n\ell j} (\beta_k I_k T_<; n\ell j | \} I_A T_A)$$

$$\left[\Psi_{1,2,\ldots,A-1}(A-1; \beta_k I_k, T_< T_<)\phi_A(n\ell j; 1/2 \; 1/2)\right]^{I_A}_{M_A}$$

[+]Work supported by AEC Contract No. AT-11-1(1371).

$$+ \sum_{i,n\ell j} (\alpha_i I_i T_> ; n\ell j |\} I_A T_A) \; \times$$

$$\left\{ (T_> \; 1/2 \; T_> \; -1/2 |T_A T_A) \right.$$

$$\left[\Psi_{1,2,\ldots,A-1}(A-1;\alpha_i I_i, T_> T_>) \phi_A(n\ell j; 1/2 \; -1/2) \right]^{I_A}_{M_A}$$

$$+ (T_> \; 1/2 \; T_> -1 \; 1/2 |T_A T_A)$$

$$\left. \left[\Psi_{1,2,\ldots,A-1}(A-1;\alpha_i I_i, T_> T_> -1) \phi_A(n\ell j; 1/2 \; 1/2) \right]^{I_A}_{M_A} \right\}$$

$$\tag{1}$$

The square brackets indicate vector coupling of the angular momentum of the Ath nucleon to that of the first $A-1$ nucleons. The symbol $(; |\})$ is a kind of fractional parentage coefficient, and α_i symbolizes an index that distinguishes between daughter states of the same angular momentum and isobaric spin. The product

$$\left[\Psi_{1,2,\ldots,A-1}(A-1;\beta_k I_k, T_< T_<) \phi_A(n\ell j; 1/2 \; 1/2) \right]^{I_A}_{M_A}$$

automatically has a total isobaric spin of $T_< + 1/2 (\equiv T_A)$.

However the products

$$\left[\Psi_{1,2,\ldots,A-1}(A-1;\alpha_i I_i, T_> T_>) \phi_A(n\ell j; 1/2 \; -1/2) \right]^{I_A}_{M_A}$$

and

$$\left[\Psi_{1,2,\ldots,A-1}(A-1;\alpha_i I_i, T_> T_> -1) \phi_A(n\ell j; 1/2 \; 1/2) \right]^{I_A}_{M_A}$$

have to enter the sum in Eq. 1 with amplitudes given by the vector-coupling coefficients $(T_> 1/2 \; T_> -1/2 |T_A T_A)$ and $(T_> 1/2 \; T_> -1 \; 1/2 |T_A T_A)$ in order to achieve a total isobaric spin of T_A.

From the wave function in Eq. 1 we immediately get the ratio of the spectroscopic factors for exciting the two analogues

$$\Psi_{1,2,\ldots,A-1}(A-1;\alpha_i I_i T_> T_>) \text{ and } \Psi_{1,2,\ldots,A-1}(A-1;\alpha_i I_i T_> T_>-1).$$

It is

$$\frac{S(I_A,T_A T_A \xrightarrow[n\ell j]{(d,t)} \alpha_i I_i,T_> T_>-1)}{S(I_A,T_A T_A \xrightarrow[n\ell j]{(d,He^3)} \alpha_i I_i,T_> T_>)} =$$

$$\frac{(T_> 1/2 \; T_>-1 \; 1/2 | T_A T_A)^2}{(T_> 1/2 \; T_>-1/2 | T_A T_A)^2} = \frac{1}{2T_A + 1} \tag{2}$$

Now let $Z_{n\ell j}$ and $N_{n\ell j}$ be the numbers of $n\ell j$ protons and neutrons in the target. Then

$$Z_{n\ell j} = \sum_i S(I_A,T_A T_A \xrightarrow[n\ell j]{d,He^3} \alpha_i I_i,T_> T_>) \tag{3}$$

so that

$$\sum_i S(I_A,T_A T_A \xrightarrow[n\ell j]{d,t} \alpha_i I_i,T_> T_>-1) = \frac{Z_{n\ell j}}{2T_A+1} \tag{4}$$

a sum rule for the total (d,t) spectroscopic factors leading to daughter states with isobaric spin $T_>$. Further

$$N_{n\ell j} = \sum_i S(I_A,T_A T_A \xrightarrow[n\ell j]{d,t} \alpha_i I_i,T_> T_>-1)$$

$$+ \sum_k S(I_A,T_A T_A \xrightarrow[n\ell j]{d,t} \beta_k I_k,T_< T_<) \tag{5}$$

which yields the corresponding sum rule for daughter states with isobaric spin $T_<$:

$$\sum_k S(I_A,T_A T_A \xrightarrow[n\ell j]{d,t} \beta_k I_k,T_< T_<) = N_{n\ell j} - \frac{Z_{n\ell j}}{2T_A+1} \tag{6}$$

Equations 4 and 6 are examples of a type of sum rule
introduced by French and Macfarlane in 1961.[1]

An attempt to check these sum rules was made by
Sherr, Rost, Rickey, Hoot and myself.[2] The (p,d) reaction was performed on a series of targets from Ti^{48} up to
Ni^{62}, and an attempt was made to determine the sums in
Eqs. 4 and 6 for the pick-up of an $f_{7/2}$ neutron. But to
extract a spectroscopic factor from an experimental angular distribution one requires a DWBA calculation for
the pick-up of an $f_{7/2}$ neutron from the well generated by
all the other nucleons. This is essentially a single-
particle calculation. The spectroscopic factor is the
factor by which this single-particle transfer cross-section
must be multiplied to yield the experimental cross-section.
But to do the DWBA calculation of the pick-up of an $f_{7/2}$
neutron, one needs its radial wave function. The standard
procedure for obtaining it is to assume it is the wave
function in a Woods-Saxon well, of a depth chosen to give
the picked-up neutron the correct separation energy. This
will ensure that the asymptotic tail of the picked-up
neutron has the right shape, which is important for what
is believed to be a surface reaction. This means that
the $f_{7/2}$ neutron radial wave function used for transitions
to highly excited states will be squeezed in more tightly
than the $f_{7/2}$ neutron radial wave function used for transitions to the low-lying states.

The summed spectroscopic factors so obtained are
illustrated in Fig. 2. The ratios S_{exp}/S_{theory} plotted
there should ideally be unity. However, we would not be
disturbed by a value different from unity, provided that
it were constant. It is seen that there is a generally
downward trend with increasing A, but what is more serious
from the present viewpoint is the discrepancy between the

506

ratios for the $T_>$ and $T_<$ summed spectroscopic factors. The $T_>$ spectroscopic factors are too large compared with the $T_<$ ones, and this discrepancy is larger when there is a greater difference in excitation energy between the $T_>$ and $T_<$ states, that is when there is a greater difference between the tails of the picked-up neutron wave functions. We would decrease the $T_>$ spectroscopic factors relative to the $T_<$ ones if we would ignore the effect of binding energy on the radial wave functions, since this would allow the radial wave functions corresponding to excited states to extend further out, which would give a larger DWBA cross-section so that a smaller spectroscopic factor would be needed. The result of such an analysis is shown in the bottom half of Fig. 2, where the same radial wave function is used in the DWBA calculation of low- and high-lying states. There is still a systematic decrease with increasing A, but at least the $T_>$ and $T_<$ spectroscopic factors are consistent with each other.

However, the situation cannot be allowed to rest there because the neutron separation energies for the low-lying and high-lying final states are different, and this difference should reflect itself in the radial wave functions. Moreover, there are other data which favor wave functions appropriate to the separation energy. Table I shows the analysis by Blair and Armstrong[3] of their (He^3,d) data, where they added a proton to Fe^{54}, Ni^{58} and Ni^{60} to make $T_>$ and $T_<$ states, and compared this to the addition of a (d,p) neutron to make the analogous $T_>$ states. Consider the case $Fe^{54}(d,p)Fe^{55}$ versus $Fe^{54}(He^3,d)Co^{55}$. States in Fe^{55} at 0, .417 and .935 MeV are seen in the (d,p) reaction, with angular momenta $3/2^-$, $1/2^-$ and $5/2^-$. The analogous Co^{55} states at 4.71, 5.14 and 5.72 MeV are seen in the (He^3,d) reaction. If we use the French-Macfarlane rule, given by Eq. 2, the neutron spectroscopic factors measured in the (d,p) reaction would imply proton spectroscopic factors of .27, .20, .20. If the proton spectroscopic factors are extracted from the (He^3,d) data using the separation energy procedure, values of .22, .26 and .27 are obtained. However if the radial wave functions are used that explain the (He^3,d) data to the low-lying Co^{55} states, one gets .27, .24 and .43, indicating that it is better to use the radial wave function appropriate to the correct separation energy. It should be noted that apart from the 4.71 MeV state in Co^{55}, all the Co^{55} $T_>$ states are unbound by a few hundred keV to a few MeV. Thus it is not surprising that we see greater sensitivity to the radial wave function than in the (p,d) experiment of Sherr et al., where the final states were all bound except for the case of $Ti^{50}(p,d)Ti^{49}$. Also since the He^3 is strongly absorbed by the nucleus, the (He^3,d) reaction may be more sensitive to the radial wave function at the nuclear surface than is the (p,d) reaction.

A way to understand the apparent insensitivity, observed by Sherr et al., of the neutron wave function to the separation energy was proposed by Pinkston and Satchler.[4] They noted that a neutron moving relative to an (A-1)-particle core with $T_<$ sees a different effective potential than one moving relative to an (A-1)-particle core with $T_>$. This is a consequence of the isobaric spin dependence of the nuclear interactions, and of the fact that the neutron must be antisymmetrized with respect to the neutrons in the core. Lane[5] has shown how this effect may be incorporated into the single-particle picture by the addition of a term proportional to $\vec{t}_A \cdot \vec{T}_c$ to the isobaric-spin-independent shell-model potential U_o:

$$V = U_o + U_1 \, \vec{t}_A \cdot \vec{T}_c \tag{7}$$

Here $\vec{t}_A$ refers to last nucleon and $\vec{T}_c$ to the (A-1)-particle core. If this potential is used in the analysis of the (p,n) reaction to analogue states as a quasi-elastic process, the best fit is obtained if U_1 is positive and is peaked on the nuclear surface. As applied to the (p,d) reaction where $T_>$ and $T_<$ refer to the isobaric spin of the (A-1)-particle core, Eq. 7 becomes

$$V = U_o + 1/2 \; U_1 \; x \begin{cases} T_A - 1/2 \text{ for } T_A(p,d)T_< \\[2mm] -T_A - 1/2 \text{ for } T_A(p,d)T_>. \end{cases} \tag{7'}$$

This has the consequence that the $T_>$ potential effectively has a larger radius than the $T_<$ potential, and this counteracts the tendency of the higher $T_>$ separation energy to pull the radial wave function in. For the (He^3,d) reaction the "core" is the target, and $T_>$ and $T_<$ refer to the final state of target-plus-a nucleon:

$$V = U_o + 1/2 \; U_1 \; x \begin{cases} -T_c - 1 \text{ for } T_c(He^3,d)T_< \\[2mm] T_c \text{ for } T_c(He^3,d)T_> \end{cases} \tag{7''}$$

and here the well is smaller for the $T_>$ state so that the effect of the higher binding is reinforced by the change in the size of the well. Thus the suggestion of Pinkston and Satchler is able to reconcile the apparently conflicting results of Sherr et al. and Blair and Armstrong.

However, the addition of a $\vec{t} \cdot \vec{T}_c$ term gives rise to more than a difference between the $T_>$ and $T_<$

effective single-particle potentials. It also converts the $T_>$ situation into a 2-channel problem, since the t_+T_- component in the potential can change the $(T_>, T_> +$ proton) wave function into a $(T_>, T_> - 1 +$ neutron) wave function. For example, let us return to the comparison of (d,t) and (d,He^3) reactions to analogue states, and consider in particular Cr^{52} as a target. If we write the Cr^{52} ground state wave function schematically as

$$\Psi(Cr^{52}) = \Psi(V^{51})\phi(1/2,-1/2) + \Psi(Cr^{51*})\phi(1/2,1/2), \quad (8)$$

the Schrödinger wave function takes the form given by Lane[5] and by Robson[6],

$$\left[-\frac{\hbar^2 \nabla^2}{2m} + U_o + U_c - 5/4\ U_1 - E \right]\phi(1/2,-1/2)$$

$$+ \frac{\sqrt{5}}{2}\ U_1\ \phi(1/2,1/2) = 0$$

$$(9)$$

$$\left[-\frac{\hbar^2 \nabla^2}{2m} + U_o + \Delta_c + 3/4\ U_1 - E \right]\phi(1/2,1/2)$$

$$+ \frac{\sqrt{5}}{2}\ U_1\ \phi(1/2,-1/2) = 0$$

Here U_c is the Coulomb energy term added to the proton shell-model potential, whereas Δ_c is the Coulomb energy difference between a V^{51} state and its isobaric analogue in Cr^{51} (see Fig. 3)

$$\Delta_c = M(Cr^{51*}) + M_n - M(V^{51}) - M_p \approx 8.1\ MeV \quad (10)$$

Tamura[7], and Bondorf, Jägare and Lütken[8] have solved coupled equations such as these for an energy such that the proton kinetic energy is positive but the neutron kinetic energy is negative. In our case we want both proton and neutron kinetic energies to be negative. If U_c were constant and equal to Δ_c, one would uncouple the

Eqs. 9 by taking linear combinations with the vector coupling coefficients that give Cr^{52} an isobaric spin of 2,

$$\chi_2 \equiv \sqrt{5/6} \ \phi(1/2,-1/2) - \sqrt{1/6} \ \phi(1/2,1/2)$$

$$\chi_3 \equiv \sqrt{1/6} \ \phi(1/2,-1/2) + \sqrt{5/6} \ \phi(1/2,1/2)$$

(11)

$$\left[-\frac{\hbar^2 \nabla^2}{2m} + U_o - 7/4 \ U_1 + \frac{5U_c + \Delta_c}{6} - E \right] \chi_2$$

$$+ \sqrt{5/6}(U_c - \Delta_c)\chi_3 = 0$$

(12)

$$\left[-\frac{\hbar^2 \nabla^2}{2m} + U_o + 5/4 \ U_1 + \frac{U_c + 5\Delta_c}{6} - E \right]\chi_3$$

$$+ \sqrt{5/6}(U_c - \Delta_c)\chi_2 = 0,$$

and this would lead directly to the French-Macfarlane ratio for the (d,t) and (d,He^3) spectroscopic factors. To see this we note that if the coupling terms in Eq. 12 were absent, we could find a solution corresponding to the Cr^{52} ground state for which $\chi_2 \neq 0$ but $\chi_3 = 0$. Since $\chi_3 = 0$, $\phi(1/2,-1/2) = -\sqrt{5} \ \phi(1/2,1/2)$ so that the (d,He^3) spectroscopic factor is 5 times the (d,t) spectroscopic factor, as given by Eq. 2.

However Δ_c and U_c are not equal and an exact solution requires numerical integration of the coupled Eqs. 9 or 12. Thus, to do a complete DWBA analysis of the hypothetical (d,t) - (d,He^3) experiment, we must obtain the $T_>$ form factors by integrating the coupled equations. The $T_<$ form factor is obtained by integrating the single Schrödinger equation

$$\left[-\frac{\hbar^2 \nabla^2}{2m} + U_o + 3/4 \ U_1 - \delta - E \right]\chi_< = 0,$$

(13)

where δ is the difference between neutron and proton separation energies in Cr^{52}, as shown in Fig. 3.

Taro Tamura is planning to do this calculation within the next few weeks. In a contribution to this conference[9], Bock, von Brentano, Duhm and Stock give some interesting speculations about the effect of this coupling on the (He^3,α) form factor, and apply their conclusions successfully to an analysis of their $Cr^{52}(He^3,\alpha)Cr^{51}$ and $Cr^{50}(He^3,\alpha)Cr^{49}$ data.

If we take the view that the relevant nuclear symmetry in these medium-heavy nuclei is the analogue spin discussed by MacDonald,[10] the Eqs. 12 automatically decouple. Let us suppose that the normalized functions $\psi(1/2, \pm 1/2)$ satisfy

$$\left[-\frac{\hbar^2\nabla^2}{2m} + U_o + U_c - 7/4\ U_1 - E\right]\psi(1/2,-1/2) = 0$$
$$\left[-\frac{\hbar^2\nabla^2}{2m} + U_o + \Delta_c - 7/4\ U_1 - E\right]\psi(1/2,+1/2) = 0 \tag{14}$$

with the same eigenvalue E. Following MacDonald, we define analogue spin operators $\vec{w}$ by

$$w \pm \psi(1/2,\mp 1/2) = \psi(1/2,\pm 1/2)$$
$$w \pm \psi(1/2,\pm 1/2) = 0 \tag{15}$$
$$w_z \psi(1/2,\pm 1/2) = \pm 1/2\ \psi(1/2,\pm 1/2).$$

Then the function

$$-\sqrt{1/6}\ \Psi(Cr^{51*})\psi(1/2,1/2) + \sqrt{5/6}\ \Psi(V^{51})\psi(1/2,-1/2) \tag{16}$$

will satisfy the Schrödinger equation, provided that the symmetry term is $U_1\ \vec{W}_A \cdot \vec{W}_c$ and that

$$W_+\Psi(Cr^{51*}) = \sqrt{5}\ \Psi(V^{51}), \quad W_-\Psi(V^{51}) = \sqrt{5}\ \Psi(Cr^{51*}) \tag{17}$$

In dealing with the analogue spin, we absorb the difference $\Delta_c - U_c$ into the formalism so that no coupling
is left over. It will be interesting to compare the
results of this approach to that of the coupled equations.

Let us now turn to the relevance of isobaric spin
to the transfer of two nucleons. Figure 4 is the two-
nucleon counterpart of Fig. 1.

The selection rules implied by Fig. 4 have been
used very effectively by Cerny, Detraz, Garvey and
Pehl[11-14] in their study of the masses of members of
$T > 1$ multiplets. As an example of their method, consider a comparison of the reactions $Be^9(p,t)Be^7$ and
$Be^9(p,He^3)Li^7$. The former reaches Be^7 states with
$T = 1/2$ and $3/2$, in both cases by transfer of two
nucleons with $T = 1$ (and $T_z = 1$) and $S = 0$, assuming
that the transferred nucleons are spatially symmetric.
The $Be^9(p,He^3)Li^7$ reaction also reaches $T = 1/2$ and $3/2$
states in the daughter nucleus. The $T = 3/2$ states are
again reached by $\Delta T = 1$, $\Delta S = 0$ transfer but the $T = 1/2$
states can be reached by both $\Delta T = 1$, $\Delta S = 0$ and $\Delta T = 0$,
$\Delta S = 1$ transfer. Thus the tritons and He^3 particles
that are emitted leaving Be^7 and Li^7 in analogous $T = 3/2$
states should have exactly the same angular distributions, apart from phase space factors and appropriate
isobaric spin vector coupling coefficients. On the other
hand there is no reason to expect the triton and He^3
angular distributions to be simply related if the Be^7
and Li^7 are left in analogous $T = 1/2$ states. Thus a
comparison of the (p,t) and (p,He^3) angular distributions
makes it possible to identify the $T = 3/2$ states in the
daughter nuclei. Figure 5 shows the near-identity of the
$Be^9(p,t)Be^7$ and $Be^9(p,He^3)Li^7$ angular distributions

associated with a T = 3/2 final state. The separation
energies from Be^9 of two neutrons or a neutron and a
proton are evidently close enough that one is not
troubled by differences in radial form factors.

An interesting feature of Fig. 4 is the possibility
of reaching in the (p,t) reaction states whose isobaric
spin exceeds T_z by 2.[15] Table II summarizes the energies
of the $T = T_z + 2$ "double analogue" states that have
been seen[16] until now. In every case where a T = 2
state has been sought in a $T_z = 0$ nucleus it has been
found, with a width of less than 80 keV. No $T = T_z + 2$
states have been seen in nuclei with $T_z > 0$, because the
fraction of the (p,t) strength that reaches $T = T_z + 2$
states is lower in these cases. An argument similar to
that which led to Eqs. 4 and 6 implies that for $(n\ell j)^2$
pick-up, this fraction is

$$\frac{\sum_i S(I_A T_A T_A \xrightarrow[(n\ell j)^2]{p,t} \alpha_i I_i T_A+1, \ T_A-1)}{\sum_i S(I_A T_A T_A \xrightarrow[(n\ell j)^2]{p,t} \alpha_i I_i T_i, T_A-1)} =$$

$$\frac{Z_{n\ell j}(Z_{n\ell j}-1)}{N_{n\ell j}(N_{n\ell j}-1)} \times \frac{1}{(T_A+1)(2T_A+1)} .$$

For $S^{34}(p,t)S^{36}$(T=2) this is 1/6, assuming that the neutrons are taken from doubly-closed shells. For
$S^{36}(p,t)S^{34}$(T=3) this is 1/15.

Reactions involving the transfer of more than two
nucleons have similar selection and intensity rules. It
is clear that future research will make extensive use of
their simplicity and generality to test our understanding

of the reaction process, and to explore the intriguing relationship between isobaric analogue states.

REFERENCES

1) J. B. French and M. H. Macfarlane, Nucl. Phys. 26 (1961) 108.

2) R. Sherr, B. F. Bayman, E. Rost, M. E. Rickey and C. G. Hoot, Phys. Rev. 139 (1965) B1272.

3) A. G. Blair and D. D. Armstrong, Phys. Letts. 16 (1965) 57.

4) W. T. Pinkston and G. R. Satchler, Nucl. Phys. 72 (1965) 641.

5) A. M. Lane, Nucl. Phys. 35 (1962) 676.

6) D. Robson, Phys. Rev. 137 (1965) B535.

7) T. Tamura, Paper D4.

8) J. P. Bondorf, H. Lütkin, and S. Jägare, Paper E5.

9) R. Bock, P. von Brentano, H. Duhm and R. Stock, Paper S35.

10) W. M. MacDonald, Paper B4.

11) J. Cerny and R. H. Pehl, Phys. Rev. Letts. 12 (1964) 619.

12) G. T. Garvey, J. Cerny and R. H. Pehl, Phys. Rev. Letts. 12 (1964) 726.

13) G. T. Garvey, J. Cerny and R. H. Pehl, Phys. Rev. Letts. 13 (1964) 548.

14) C. Detraz, J. Cerny and R. H. Pehl, Phys. Rev. Letts. 14 (1965) 708.

15) G. T. Garvey and B. F. Bayman, Argonne National Laboratory Report 6848,p125,(1964) unpublished.

16) J. Cerny and G. T. Garvey, private communication.

TABLE I

SPECTROSCOPIC FACTORS FOR (He³, d) and (d, p) REACTIONS

(1)	(2)	(3)	(4)	(5)	(6)	(7)
State excited by (d,p) reaction (MeV)	J^π	Analogue state excited by (He³, d) reaction (MeV)	$(c^2S)_{pred}$	$(c^2S)_1$	$(c^2S)_2$	Estimated shell-model position (MeV)
Fe55						
0	3/2⁻	Co55 4.71±0.07	0.27	0.22	0.27	4.0
0.417	1/2⁻	5.14±0.05	0.20	0.26	0.24	5.8
0.935	5/2⁻	5.72±0.05	0.20	0.27	0.43	4.6
Ni59						
0	3/2⁻	Cu59 3.88±0.05	0.17	0.18	0.37	1.5
0.340	5/2⁻	4.30±0.05	0.32	0.33	0.72	2.2
0.471	1/2⁻	4.36±0.05	0.20	0.22	0.29	3.3
3.071	(9/2⁺)	6.86±0.10 a)				
Ni61						
0	3/2⁻	Cu61 6.40±0.05	0.062	0.062	0.26	1.5
0.069	5/2⁻	6.47±0.05	0.12	0.14	0.67	2.2
0.290	1/2⁻	6.65±0.07 b)				
2.133	(9/2⁺)	8.42±0.10 a)				

a) State is too far unbound to allow meaningful analysis.
b) Strongly interfering state present.

TABLE II

ENERGIES OF T=2 STATES

A	$T_Z = 0$	$T_Z = 1$
12	27.52 (MeV)	12.63 (MeV)
16	22.9	9.9
20	16.8	6.43
24	15.355	5.95
40	11.98	4.39
52	8.54	2.79
56	9.85	3.58

DISCUSSION

DIETRICH, Stanford: You mentioned that it is very important to consider the radial dependence of the wave function appropriate to the separation energy, and in the discussion of Sherr et al.'s experiment you also indicated that the results would not be reliable for levels that were too unbound.

BAYMAN: That is correct.

DIETRICH: I was just wondering, could you make some general statement as to how unbound you can let these things be and still get reasonable results? Alternatively, how close to the separation energy your particles can get and still get fairly reasonable results?

BAYMAN: I am afraid I don't know the answer to that question. Blair and Armstrong comment that when applying the DWBA calculations to these unbound levels, they did a kind of extrapolation from DWBA calculations to bound levels, and I am afraid I don't know what they mean by that. I meant to ask Schiffer to explain it to me before the session but I didn't get the chance.

SCHIFFER, Argonne: I think all they mean by it is that they take the dependence on binding energy of the cross-section and draw a smooth curve through it, but whether this has any validity whatsoever is open to question. Perhaps we will hear about this from Stock in just a little while.

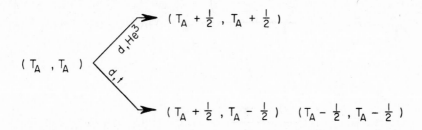

Fig. 1.   Isobaric spin changes associated with one-nucleon pick-up.

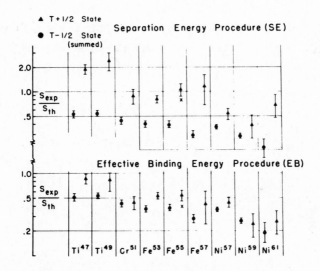

Fig. 2.   Comparison of experimental and theoretical values for the summed $7/2^-$ spectroscopic factors.   The upper part of the figure shows the results obtained by using a form factor determined for each state by the separation energy.   The lower part of the figure shows the results obtained by using a form factor determined by the lowest $7/2^-$ state in each nucleus, and then kept constant for that nucleus.

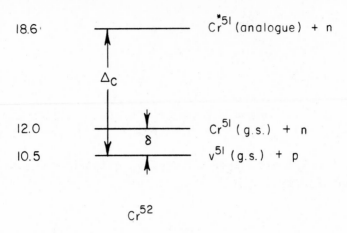

Fig. 3. Separation energies in the Z = 24, N = 28 system.

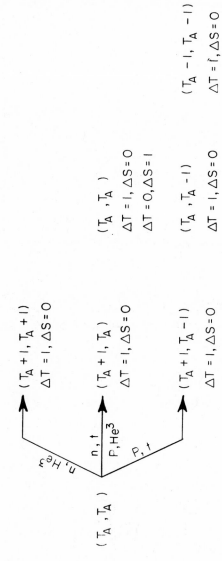

Fig. 4. Spin and isobaric spin changes associated with two-nucleon pick-up. The ΔS and ΔT values are related by the assumed space-permutation symmetry of the transferred nucleons.

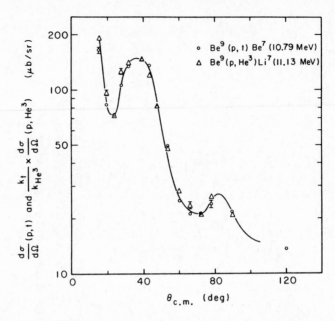

Fig. 5. A comparison of the (p,t) and (p,He^3) reactions to isobaric analogue states of Be^7 and Li^7 (from reference 14).

E2. EVIDENCE FOR A DEPENDENCE OF SINGLE-PROTON TRANSFER REACTIONS ON ISOBARIC SPIN[*]

R. H. Siemssen, G. C. Morrison, and B. Zeidman

Argonne National Laboratory
Argonne, Illinois
and
H. Fuchs

Hahn-Meitner Institut
Berlin, Germany

We have compared the relative spectroscopic factors from (He^3,d) reactions with those from (d,n) reactions for the low $T = 0$ and $T = 1$ states in the odd-odd nuclei B^{10}, N^{14} and Al^{26}. It is widely accepted that the (d,n) and the (He^3,d) reactions are analogous processes involving proton transfer and that they should therefore yield the same spectroscopic factors. In contrast to this expectation, we find in each case that the relative spectroscopic factor for the $T = 1$ state deduced from the (d,n) reaction is less than the spectroscopic factor from the (He^3,d) reaction, the spectroscopic factors for the $T = 0$ states being normalized to each other for the two reactions.

Published data[1-6] have been used wherever possible. In addition, we have measured the $Be^9(He^3,d)B^{10}$ and the $C^{13}(He^3,d)N^{14}$ reactions at 17 MeV at angles

---
[*]Work performed under the auspices of the United States Atomic Energy Commission

around the stripping maximum, and the $C^{13}(d,n)N^{14}$ and
$Mg^{25}(d,n)Al^{26}$ reactions were measured at 5.5 MeV. The
(He^3,d) reactions were studied at the Argonne tandem
Van de Graaff with a counter telescope, while the (d,n)
measurements were done at the Hahn-Meitner Institut
with a pulsed-beam time-of-flight spectrometer. Relative spectroscopic factors have been extracted from
the data (Table I - III) by means of DWBA theory with
reasonable distortion parameters. Since the lowest
T = 1 state in an odd-odd light nucleus is bracketed by
T = 0 states with little difference in excitation
energy, the relative spectroscopic factors should be
rather insensitive to the choice of the distortion
parameters. Furthermore, all final states for which
the spectroscopic factors are compared are formed by
proton capture with the same orbital-angular-momentum
transfer. From Table I - III it is seen that the relative spectroscopic factors for the T = 0 states are
approximately the same for the (He^3,d) and the (d,n)
data, whereas the values for the T = 1 transitions are
less in the (d,n) reaction than those in the (He^3,d)
reaction. It can also be seen that the effect is independent of energy where the reactions have been studied at different energies. The difference is greatest
in the reactions on Be^9 where it is roughly a factor
of 3. In the $C^{13}(d,n)N^{14}$ and $Mg^{25}(d,n)Al^{26}$ reactions,
the relative spectroscopic factors for the T = 1 transitions are smaller than in the corresponding (He^3,d)
reactions by a factor of 1.6 to 1.8. For N^{14}, however,
the relative (d,n) and (He^3,d) spectroscopic factors
for the T = 0 states also differ somewhat. The relative spectroscopic factors for Al^{26} from the (d,n)
reaction have to be taken with some caution. At 3 MeV,

the (d,n) angular distributions show evidence of some
compound-nucleus reaction which probably is still present at 5.5 MeV.

Why the relative yield of the transitions to the
$T = 1$ states should be less in the (d,n) than in the
(He^3,d) reaction is not understood. Originally it was
thought that exchange or cluster effects present in
the (d,n) reaction might be responsible for the observed difference. If exchange stripping in the (d,n)
reaction involves only the low-lying $T = 0$ states of
the core as intermediate parent states, then no contribution from this mechanism is expected to the $T = 1$
final state[2,7]. If exchange effects are **that important** in the (d,n) reaction, however, we would also expect the relative spectroscopic factors from the (d,n)
and the (He^3,d) reaction to the various $T = 0$ states
to differ markedly since the spectroscopic amplitudes
from the direct and the exchange terms are unrelated.

Alternatively, if the radial wave function of
the captured particle depends on whether it is captured
into a $T = 0$ or a $T = 1$ state, this dependence might
explain the observed differences between the (d,n) and
the (He^3,d) reaction. In contrast to the (d,n) process,
the (He^3,d) reaction is a surface reaction and therefore will be more affected by changes in the slope of
the bound-state wave function than will the (d,n) process. DWBA calculations with a 2p wave function instead of the 1p wave function indeed show that the
change in cross section for the (He^3,d) process is
twice that for the (d,n) reaction. At present, however,
there is no theoretical justification for expecting the
wave function for the $T = 1$ state to be very different
from that of the corresponding $T = 0$ state, though a

large difference would be required to reproduce the observed difference between the (d,n) and the (He^3,d) reaction.

Discussions with Drs. D. Kurath, M. H. Macfarlane and J. P. Schiffer are gratefully acknowledged.

REFERENCES

1) S. G. Buccino and A. B. Smith, Phys. Letters 19 (1965) 234.

2) G. C. Morrison, A. T. G. Ferguson and J. E. Evans, in Proc. Rutherford Jubilee Int. Conf., Manchester, 1961, edited by J. B. Birks (Heywood and Co., London, 1961), p. 575.

3) R. H. Siemssen, M. Cosack and R. Felst, Nucl. Phys. 69 (1965) 209.

4) H. E. Wegner and W. S. Hall, Phys. Rev. 119 (1960) 1654.

5) R. E. Benenson and B. Yaramis, Phys. Rev. 129 (1963) 720.

6) S. Hinds and R. Middleton, Proc. Phys. Soc. (London) 75 (1961) 754.

7) V. G. Neudachin, I. B. Teplov and O. P. Shevchenko, Soviet Physics, J.E.T.P. 9 (1959) 599.

TABLE I. Relative spectroscopic factors of B^{10} from the $Be^9(d,n)B^{10}$ and the $Be^9(He^3,d)B^{10}$ reactions.

E_x (MeV)	T	$Be^9(d,n)B^{10}$			$Be^9(He^3,d)B^{10}$		
		E_d = 2.8 MeV[a]	4.0 MeV[b]	7.0 MeV[c]	E_{He3} = 10 MeV[d]	17 MeV	25MeV[e]
0	0	1.0	1.0	1.0	1.0	1.0	1.0
0.72	0	2.24	2.2	2.3	2.0	1.8	1.94
1.74	1	0.85	1.1	1.0	3.35	2.6	2.7
2.15	0	0.60	0.4	0.41	0.57	0.55	0.55

a Reference 3.

b Reference 2.

c Reference 1.

d Reference 6.

e Reference 4.

TABLE II. Relative spectroscopic factors of N^{14} from the $C^{13}(d,n)N^{14}$ and the $C^{13}(He^3,d)N^{14}$ reactions.

E_x (MeV)	T	$C^{13}(d,n)N^{14}$		$C^{13}(He^3,d)N^{14}$
		E_d = 3.9 MeV[a]	5.5 MeV	E_{He3} = 17.0 MeV
0.0	0	1.0	1.0	1.0
2.31	1	0.97	1.1	1.6
3.91	0	0.72	0.8	0.5

[a] Reference 5.

TABLE III. Relative spectroscopic factors of Al^{26} from the $Mg^{25}(d,n)Al^{26}$ and the $Mg^{25}(He^3,d)Al^{26}$ reactions.

E_x (MeV)	T	$Mg^{25}(d,n)Al^{26}$		$Mg^{25}(He^3,d)Al^{26}$
		E_d = 3.0 MeV[a]	5.5 MeV	E_{He3}=22 MeV[b]
0	0	1.0	1.0	1.0
0.23	1	2.0	1.8	2.8

[a] Reference - R. B. Weinberg and R. B. Taylor (private communication).

[b] Reference - A. G. Blair (private communication).

DISCUSSION

Anon: Some of Blair's spectroscopic factors must be wrong because of the poor resolution he used. Some of his states which he assumed to be singlets are actually doublets when one used better resolution. Therefore the spectroscopic factor should be divided between a couple of states. In some cases they say they have mixtures of $\ell = 1$ and $\ell = 3$ states and resort to the DWBA code. It is also worth mentioning that the spectroscopic value for the $\ell = 1$ transition was obtained from the secondary peak and not as usually done from the primary peak.

BAYMAN: In which direction do these correction factors shift the relative spectroscopic factors?

ROBSON, Florida State: I could perhaps direct my question to Schiffer. Is this the same effect which Bayman just discussed, that you have to take into account the difference in the form factor for the $T = 1$ state compared to the $T = 0$ state?

SIEMSSEN: Yes, the idea is you have really a different radial function for the $T = 1$, there is theoretical justification for this, you cannot calculate it just yet, but this could explain the observed effect.

SCHIFFER: Qualitatively it might, but quantitatively it is not at all clear that it would account for this.

E3. THE CHARGE EXCHANGE REACTION [*]

J. D. Anderson

Lawrence Radiation Laboratory
Livermore, California

HISTORICAL RESUME

In January of 1961 at Livermore we began a study
of the statistical model of the compound nucleus. In
particular we measured neutron spectra from proton bombardment of V^{51} and intended to deduce from these
spectra information about the dependence of the level
density of the residual nucleus on excitation energy.
In Fig. 1 we have typical neutron spectra and in Fig. 2
the probability of emitting a neutron of energy E, divided by the neutron energy, i.e. $P(E)/E$, which is proportional to the level density is shown plotted versus
excitation energy. The pronounced peak at an excitation energy of 6.5 MeV which was not in agreement with
the statistical model, is of course the topic of this
paper. We concluded that this level which was selectively populated via the (p,n) reaction was indeed the
analogue state in Cr^{51} corresponding to the ground
state of our V^{51} target [1]. Since for this charge exchange reaction we assume that all the nuclear interactions within the initial and final nucleus are the
same, the Q-value for the isobaric reaction is just the
usual Coulomb displacement energy.

[*] Work performed under the auspices of the United States
Atomic Energy Commission

In the next few years measurements were extended
to include angular distributions both for the (p,n)
reaction (at Livermore[2]) and (He[3],t) reactions (by
Blair and Wegner at Los Alamos[3]) and neutron spectra
measurements were extended to heavier nuclei[4]. The
Coulomb displacement energies derived from the Livermore (p,n) experiments[5] are summarized in Fig. 3. It
should be pointed out that these measurements have been
further extended by Batty et al.[6,7] up to U^{238}. In
all these measurements the width of the neutron group
was determined by detector resolution and target thickness. The best we were able to do was place an upper
limit of 100 keV on the width of the isobaric state for
nuclei up to A $\sim$ 100 and an upper limit of 150 keV for
A $\sim$ 165. During this period also, the existence of
excited isobaric states, corresponding to the excited
states of the target nuclei, was suggested by E. Rost[8]
and were indeed observed in the Livermore experiments[4,8].

As the experiments indicated the persistence of
a "narrow" neutron group even at excitation energies
which were unstable against particle decay, the interpretation of these phenomena particularly by Lane and
Soper[9,10,11], was keeping pace. Indeed with the inclusion of the isobaric spin term in the optical
model[12,13] they were able to account for the proton
potential anomaly and in addition predict that the (p,n)
isobaric cross section can be calculated within the
framework of the optical model.

In Fig. 4 we see the (p,n) cross sections for
all the elements between Sc and Co for a proton bombarding energy of 18.5 MeV. These data[14] indicated a
slow variation of the cross section as a function of
A showing no shell effects. There are no appreciable

differences between odd and even nuclei indicating
that explicit shell model calculations including all
possible multipoles[15] might not be necessary and indeed the cross sections are strongly forward peaked as
one might expect.

How well the detailed calculations[16] agree with
experiment can be seen in Fig. 5. Since the magnitude
of the isobaric spin potential necessary to fit the
(p,n) experiments is in agreement with other estimates
of the symmetry term in the optical potential it seems
fair to say that the isobaric spin term in the optical
model is capable of explaining the diffractive nature
of the (p,n) angular distributions and the absolute
magnitude of the cross sections.

At this point work was begun on three separate
experiments, although seemingly unrelated, we shall
see presently how they all fit together. The first was
an investigation of the (p,n) cross section for the
titanium isotopes A = 46-50. This was meant to yield
a check of the charge independent formulation of the
optical model which was independent of any optical parameters, i.e. the cross section is proportional to the
neutron excess. The second experiment was the investigation of the Mg^{25} and Mg^{26} (p,n) reactions which
Satchler et al.[16] had suggested would shed some light
on the mechanism involved in the (p,n) transitions to
"excited" analogue states.

The third experiment involved the investigation
of the (p,n) cross section on O^{17} and O^{18} in which we
were interested in deducing features of the two body
force from a microscopic description of the (p,n)
reaction. We shall discuss these experiments in re-
verse order for reasons which will soon become obvious.

TWO BODY FORCE

There have been several attempts in the last few years to extract information about the relative strength of the singlet and triplet forces by analyzing (p,n) angular distributions[17,18]. The success of this method unfortunately depends to a large extent on the approximations made in one's microscopic description of the process, e.g. zero range forces, harmonic oscillator wave functions and the cut-off radius. By measuring the O^{17} and O^{18} cross sections a great deal of this model dependence is removed.

In the direct (p,n) reaction on $T = 1$ nuclei such as O^{18} and Mg^{26} a unique possibility exists for detecting the spin exchange process occurring simultaneously with the isobaric spin (charge) exchange process via the

$$V_{\sigma\tau} = \underset{\sim}{a}(\vec{\sigma}_o \cdot \vec{\sigma}_i)(\vec{\tau}_o \cdot \vec{\tau}_i)f(r_{oi}) \qquad (1)$$

two-body potential, where $f(r_{oi})$ is the form factor and $\underset{\sim}{a}$ is the strength parameter. (The subscript o refers to the free nucleon, which is a proton initially and a neutron finally, and $i = 1,2$ refers to the bound nucleons.) Whereas $V_{\sigma\tau}$ can and will cause the transition from the ground state ($J^{\pi} = 0^+$, $T = 1$) in the initial nucleus to the ground state in the final nucleus ($J^{\pi} = 1^+$, $T = 0$), the simple charge exchange potential

$$V_{\tau} = b(\vec{\tau}_o \cdot \vec{\tau}_i)f(r_{oi}) \qquad (2)$$

cannot. V_{τ}, on the other hand, will account for the quasielastic (p,n) process $(0^+,1) \rightarrow (0^+,1)$. Thus a

533

comparison of the cross section to these final states
can give us directly an estimate of the relative
strengths of $V_{\sigma\tau}$ and V_{τ}, i.e. a/b[19].

The level scheme for F^{18}, the final nucleus is
shown in Fig. 6 along with a neutron time of flight
spectrum from a typical run using a 10 meter flight
path. The cross sections for both low lying $(1^+,0)$
levels (n_0 and n_2 of Fig. 6.) were measured and found
to be comparable with each other. The measurement of
the cross section of the isobaric state $(0^+,1)$ is an
upper limit due to the contribution from the three other
states lying nearby. (From an additional experiment
with a 25 meter flight path we were able to resolve the
3^+ and 5^+ levels which indicated the contribution to
n_1 from these levels was not negligible but amounted
to from 20 to 50% of the observed cross section.)

The total cross section for the quasielastic
process (including the contributions from the unresolved
levels) and the total cross section for the population
of the $(1^+,0)$ ground state are shown as a function of
proton energy in Fig. 7(a). The ratio of the $(0^+,1)$
to $(1^+,0)$ cross sections, ρ, is shown in Fig. 7(b).
For energies above 8 MeV a value of $\rho = 5.5 \pm 1.5$ well
encompasses the range of variation observed.

If one makes a number of simplifying assumptions
such as, that the 0^{16} core is inert, allowing only for
an angular momentum transfer of zero, and neglecting
the orbital angular momentum of the coupled particles
we are left with only the spin and isobaric spin parts
of the wave function with which to deal. Thus we
obtain a rather familiar result $\rho = b^2/3a^2$. However
at this point we shall just quote the results of a
more complete shell model calculation using jj coupling

and assuming the ground state of O^{18} is a pure $(d_{5/2})^2$ configuration[20]. This yields

$$\rho = \frac{b^2}{1.4a^2} \quad \text{or a/b} \simeq 0.4.$$

The effects of spin exchange can also be deduced from the ratio of the quasielastic cross sections for O^{17} and O^{18}. The simple optical charge-exchange model leads to a prediction of the ratio of these cross sections of $\simeq 0.5$ independent of the optical parameters used, i.e. the cross section is proportional to the neutron excess. In Fig. 8 we show the observed ratio for proton energies from 6.5 to 13 MeV. For the higher energies the ratio lies in the range 1.1 ± 0.3. The behavior of this ratio over the energy range shown in Fig. 8 makes it evident that the factor-of-two difference between the optical model prediction and experiment must be due to the operation of a fundamentally different mechanism than simple charge exchange. The inclusion of spin exchange appears to be the most plausible explanation.

Still using the monopole approximation but with jj coupling the results are

$$\frac{\sigma(O^{17})}{\sigma(O^{18})} = \frac{b^2 + 7/5a^2}{2b^2} = 0.5 + 0.7\,\frac{a^2}{b^2} \qquad (3)$$

thus $a/b \simeq 0.9$. Since time does not allow we will not discuss the more detailed calculations which include the contributions from higher multipoles and estimates of the exchange integrals but simply note that the present results are essentially unchanged.

At present the most consistent set of data yielding information about the two-body force comes from the $N^{15}(p,n)O^{15}$ experiments at Livermore and the $N^{15}(He^3,H^3)O^{15}$ experiment at Berkeley where the cross sections to the $p_{1/2}$ hole ground state and the $p_{3/2}$ hole state at 6.15 MeV excitation have been measured. These results yield a $\sim$ b with excellent fits to the (p,n) angular distributions[21].

EXCITATION OF EXCITED ISOBARIC STATES

Although the existence of excited isobaric states was observed in the (p,n) and (He^3,H^3) reactions on medium A nuclei as early as 1962, attempts to calculate the (p,n) cross sections have been rather unsuccessful. Since the (p,p') scattering from the target states are well described by a deformed optical potential Satchler et al.[16] have calculated the (p,n') cross section for a deformed isobaric spin potential. The results were disappointing in that for the same deformation parameter as in the analogous (p,p') case the calculated (p,n') cross sections are a factor of 10 (for a surface isobaric spin potential) to 30 (for a volume isobaric spin potential) lower than the measurements. At this point Satchler suggested that one not worry about the magnitude of the cross section but try and determine whether the overall approach made sense. He proposed that one select for measurements two permanently deformed nuclei such as a pair of the Mg isotopes which have well identified rotational bands as shown in Fig. 9.

Since our example is chosen such that there is strong coupling between the odd nucleon and a permanently deformed core, and if the adiabatic approximation is valid, the inelastic cross section within the ground state band is related to the cross section for

536

the even mass nucleus by the expression

$$\frac{d\sigma}{d\Omega} (J \rightarrow J') = \frac{(N-Z)_J}{(N-Z)_o} < J, \ell, K, 0|J', K>^2 \frac{d\sigma(0 \rightarrow \ell)}{d\Omega}$$

$$(4)$$

where K is the projection of the total angular momentum on the symmetry axis. The effects of strong coupling also appear in the quasielastic cross section where the prediction for the odd mass nucleus is

$$\frac{d\sigma}{d\Omega} (J \rightarrow J) = \frac{(N-Z)_J}{(N-Z)_o} \left[\frac{d\sigma}{d\Omega} (0 \rightarrow 0) + \sum_{\ell \text{even}} < J, \ell, J, 0|JJ >^2 \right.$$

$$\left. \frac{d\sigma}{d\Omega} (0 \rightarrow \ell) \right]$$

$$(5)$$

where $\frac{d\sigma}{d\Omega} (0 \rightarrow 0)$ and $\frac{d\sigma}{d\Omega} (0 \rightarrow \ell)$ are the quasielastic and inelastic cross sections respectively for the even mass isotope. The experiment consists of measuring the cross sections for the $Mg^{25,26}$ isotopes and then from the Mg^{26} $(0 \rightarrow 0)$ and $(0 \rightarrow 2)$ T = 1 cross sections predict the excitation of the ground state rotational band for the $Mg^{25}(p,n)Al^{25}$ reaction.

From our previous discussion one problem becomes immediately obvious; our macroscopic description (optical model) has failed to take into account spin-flip which we have just seen from the O^{17} and O^{18} experiments is just as important as the simple charge exchange term. But let us continue on in spite of these difficulties. In Fig. 10 we see the neutron time of flight spectra for 9.3 MeV proton bombardment of Mg^{26}. By now we are not surprised to see the pronounced excitation of the 1^+ state, but we are somewhat taken aback by the largeness of the 3^+ and 5^+ excitations. (Although the (He^3, H^3) experiment of Blair and Wegner[3] has shown similar results the largeness of the 3^+ and 5^+ transition as compared to the 0^+ transition could be ascribed to the large angular momentum brought in by the heavier projectiles.) When corrected for the energy variation of the detector efficiency the 2^+, $T = 1$ level is actually larger than the 0^+, $T = 1$ cross section.

In Fig. 11 we have the time spectra of neutrons resulting from 11.4 MeV protons on Mg^{25}. At first glance this spectra is very encouraging in that the isobaric transition is much larger than any other; however, on closer inspection one notices that the population of the $J^\pi = 7/2^+$ member of the $K = 1/2$ band is comparable to that for the $J^\pi = 7/2^+$ member of the $K = 5/2$ ground state band. Since the $K = 1/2$ to $K = 5/2$ transitions are probably single particle in nature and since single particle effects are not explicitly included in this macroscopic calculation we have an additional complication.

In Fig. 12 are shown a few "characteristic" angular distributions[22]. As is well known the nucleon angular distributions tend to be washed out and characterless as compared to complex projectiles. From a comparison of the data for 12.1 and 13.9 MeV protons (13.1 MeV data is used when the 13.9 MeV data is obscured by overlapping with the target gamma ray) one concludes that the angular distributions are slowly varying with bombarding energy - a necessary criterion of any direct reaction description. One also notes that the $Mg^{25}(p,n)Al^{25}$ ground state angular distribu-

tion is washed out by comparison with the Mg^{26} isobaric
transition and indeed one can account for the angular
shape of the Mg^{25} cross section by adding appropriate
mixtures of Mg^{26} $(0 \to 0)$ and $(0 \to 2)$ transitions.

I do not think anyone will be surprised when I
say that the ratio of cross sections to the higher J
values of the K = 5/2 band are only in crude agreement
with the Clebsch-Gordan coefficient of Eq. 4, for any
detailed agreement would have to be accidental.

Although our macroscopic description (the deformed isobaric spin model) is inadequate for the Mg
isotopes, R. Lawson has noted that there are more than
sufficient measurements to attempt a microscopic,
though phenomenological, description. This approach
again bypasses the problem of calculating matrix elements from more basic considerations by using the fact
that the measured $Mg^{26}(p,n)$ cross sections are proportional to the square of the appropriate matrix elements
in a multipole expansion of the two-body force. Thus
one is left with the somewhat simpler problem of computing the appropriate coupling of these moments in the
$Mg^{25}(p,n)$ reaction from the deformed shell model. One
might ask of what use is such a phenomonological description. From the moment analysis one would hope to
get some idea of just how complex a calculation will
have to be in order to describe the (p,n) data.

In Fig. 13 we have plotted the quantity

$$\frac{\sigma(0 \to J)}{(2J + 1) \, \sigma(0 \to 0)}$$

versus bombarding energy such that one can see directly
the relative importance of the higher multipoles to
the monopole. As one might expect the 1^{+} cross section

has much the same energy variation as the monopole and the 3^+ the same as the corresponding $\lambda = 2$ moment or 2^+. Unfortunately we were unable to obtain measurements on the 4^+, $T = 1$ state (due to experimental limitations) which would have completed the set of moments for the $(d_{5/2})^2$ configuration.

THE TITANIUM ISOTOPES

This experiment[23], which was done with C. D. Goodman, had rather simple objectives. We wanted an experiment which would indicate the applicability of the isobaric spin term in the optical model independent of any parameterization. From DWBA calculations and from optical calculations for volume or surface isobaric spin terms and for volume or surface absorption, all calculations indicated that for the titanium isotopes the (p,n) isobaric cross section is proportional to N - Z.

In Fig. 14 we see the measured angular distributions for Sc^{45} and $Ti^{46,47,48,49,50}$. The solid curve is a Legendre fit to the data. One notices that the angular shape around $\theta = 90°$ varies from isotope to isotope. This variation is not an odd-even effect, i.e. although Ti^{48} and Ti^{49} look quite different, Ti^{49} and Ti^{50} look quite similar. The results are that for the even titanium isotopes the cross section scales vary nicely as N - Z but the odd isotopes have much larger cross sections than expected. Since we do not observe any pronounced excited isobaric states for the even-even targets, the possibility of higher multipole moments (such as $\lambda = 2$) contributing an additional term in the odd isotopes can be immediately ruled out.

My first thought (after the O^{17}, O^{18} experiments) was that this was a clear cut example of the contribution of the spin flip part of the charge exchange force which is neglected in the optical model. This was further strengthened by the fact that Ti^{47} which has the smaller neutron excess of the odd isotopes also shows the largest discrepancy from the expected N - Z variation. These expectations were not, however, borne out by calculations. Assuming that the neutrons and protons are filling a single shell j, and limiting the orbital angular momentum transfer to zero, Madsen[24] obtains for the odd titanium isotopes the following result:

$$\frac{d\sigma}{d\Omega} = \left[1 + \frac{4}{49} \frac{J(J + 1)}{(N-Z)^2} \ X^2 \left(\frac{a}{b} \right)^2 \right] \frac{d\sigma}{d\Omega}_{\text{no-spin-flip}} \tag{6}$$

where J is ground state spin, the ratio of a to b is the ratio of $V_{\sigma\tau}$ to V_τ as in the oxygen experiments and X^2 is unity for pure senority 1 wave functions. Evaluating X^2 from Bayman's[25] wave functions one obtains the results shown in Table I. For values of a/b $\sim$ 1 it is clear that the addition of the spin flip term does not account for the experimental results. The titanium isotopes are currently being investigated using the (He^3, H^3) reaction at both Oak Ridge and Livermore.

Another explanation for the larger cross section for the odd titanium isotopes is the possibility that, for example, in Ti^{47} there is an appreciable amount of higher isobaric spin (T = 5/2) mixed into the ground state (T = 3/2). A 30% admixture would account for the experimental results. Such a large admixture however seems unrealistic on the basis of other experiments[26]. The possibility of large T mixing has resulted in the proposal of Goodman[27] that one should be able to measure the T mixing in Ti^{47} from the (H^3, He^3) reaction to the $J^{\pi} = 5/2^-$, $T = 5/2$, parent state in Sc^{47}.

Another aspect of the titanium experiment was the determination of A dependence of the Coulomb displacement energy for a fixed Z. We were able to obtain measurements with relative errors of about $\pm$ 40 keV which are shown in Fig. 15. These data yield a variation in Coulomb displacement energy from Ti^{46} to Ti^{50} of - 60 $\pm$ 50 keV while an $A^{-1/3}$ variation would predict - 220 keV. Similar experiments have been recently done at Los Alamos by Sherr, Blair and Armstrong[28] using the (He^3, H^3) reaction and they report a variation of - 30 $\pm$ 40 keV. Their work also includes a number of isotopes of Cr, Fe and Ni. Sherr et al. interpret the smallness of the Coulomb shifts as indicating no significant change in the spatial wave function as neutrons are added in the same $(f_{7/2})$ shell. We make no further mention of the Coulomb energies since Yavin will be discussing extensive (He^3, H^3) measurements in a following paper.*

SUMMARY

From the O^{17}, O^{18} and N^{15} data we conclude that the charge exchange part of the effective two-body force is well represented by

$$V_{oi} = V_o(\vec{\tau}_o \cdot \vec{\tau}_i) (1 + \vec{\sigma}_o \cdot \vec{\sigma}_i) f(r_{oi})$$

$$(7)$$

---

* See paper S23.

where V_o is about 12 MeV and the Yukawa form factor, $f(r_{oi})$, has a range of 1.4 Fm. This force can be expanded in multipole moments corresponding to the angular momentum transfer, the relative importance of the moments being strongly shell dependent. The monopole part of the simple exchange term can be included explicitly in the optical model while the monopole part of the spin-flip term accounts for most of the $(0^+, 1 \rightarrow 1^+, 0)$ transition. The quadrupole transitions ($\lambda = 2$) are not well accounted for with the experimental cross sections being larger than calculated. These conclusions are about the same for transitions such as $d_{5/2} \rightarrow 2S_{1/2}$ or $(d_{5/2})^2_{0^+} \rightarrow (d_{5/2})^2_{2^+}$. At least part of this discrepancy is due to our neglect of the exchange integrals. (The existence of a <u>low</u> lying 2^+, $T = 1$ collective core state mixed with the 2^+, $T = 0$ core state could also explain these results.) For the Mg isotopes it is clear that angular momentum transfers as large as $\lambda = 4$ are important and preliminary (He^3, H^3) results on nuclei in the $f_{7/2}$ shell show $0^+ \rightarrow 7^+$ transitions indicating the presence of $\lambda = 6$ components.

The effect of the spin-flip term in the two-body force has been calculated using a microscopic description in the monopole approximation and is found to decrease as $\frac{1}{N-Z}$. The inclusion of spin-flip does not account quantitatively for the measured odd-even effect in the titanium isotopes. It is not clear that including higher multipoles will appreciably alter these results.

It is regrettable that there is insufficient time to discuss (p,n) polarization measurements[30,31], the excitation of "double analogue" states via the (p,n) reaction[32] and the many current (He^3, H^3) experiments now in progress.

ACKNOWLEDGEMENTS

I am indebted to Professor R. Sherr, C. D. Goodman, V. A. Madsen, R. Lawson, C. Wong and S. D. Bloom for making data and calculations available before publication and for many helpful discussions.

REFERENCES

1) J. D. Anderson and C. Wong, Phys. Rev. Letts. 7 (1961) 250.

2) J. D. Anderson, C. Wong, and J. W. McClure, Phys. Rev. 126 (1962) 2170.

3) A. G. Blair and H. E. Wegner, Phys. Rev. Letts. 9 (1962) 168.

4) J. D. Anderson, C. Wong, and J. W. McClure, Phys. Rev. 129 (1963) 2718.

5) J. D. Anderson, C. Wong and J. W. McClure, Phys. Rev. 138 (1965) B615.

6) C. J. Batty, G. H. Stafford and R. S. Gilmore, Phys. Letts. 6 (1963) 292.

7) C. J. Batty, R. S. Gilmore and G. H. Stafford, Nucl. Phys. 75 (1966) 599.

8) J. D. Anderson and C. Wong, Phys. Rev. Letts. 8 (1962) 442.

9) A. M. Lane and J. M. Soper, Phys. Rev. Letts. 7 (1961) 420.

10) A. M. Lane and J. M. Soper, Nucl. Phys. 37 (1962) 506.

11) A. M. Lane and J. M. Soper, Nucl. Phys. 37 (1962) 663.

12) A. M. Lane, Phys. Rev. Letts. 8 (1962) 171.

13) A. M. Lane, Nucl. Phys. 35 (1962) 676.

14) J. D. Anderson, C. Wong, J. W. McClure and B. D. Walker, Phys. Rev. 136 (1964) B118.

15) P. E. Hodgson and J. R. Rook, Nucl. Phys. 37 (1962) 632.

16) G. R. Satchler, R. M. Drisko and R. H. Bassel, Phys. Rev. 136 (1964) B637.

17) S. D. Bloom, N. K. Glendenning and S. A. Moszkowski, Phys. Rev. Letts. 3 (1959) 98.

18) C. Wong, J. D. Anderson, S. D. Bloom, J. W. McClure and B. D. Walker, Phys. Rev. 123 (1961) 598.

19) S. D. Bloom, J. D. Anderson, W. F. Hornyak and C. Wong, Phys. Rev. Letts. 15 (1965) 264.

20) J. D. Anderson, S. D. Bloom, W. F. Hornyak, V. A. Madsen and C. Wong, (to be published).

21) V. A. Madsen, et al., (to be published).

22) C. Wong, J. D. Anderson, J. W. McClure and B. A. Pohl, (to be published).

23) C. D. Goodman, J. D. Anderson and C. Wong, (to be published).

24) V. A. Madsen (private communication). I am especially indebted to Prof. V. A. Madsen for making available the results of his shell model calculation for the titanium isotopes for this conference.

25) J. D. McCullen, B. F. Bayman and Larry Zamick, Phys. Rev. 134 (1964) 515.

26) See for example S. D. Bloom, Paper B1.

27) C. D. Goodman (private communication).

28) R. Sherr, B. F. Bayman, E. Rost, M. E. Rickey and C. G. Hoot, Phys. Rev. 139 (1965) B1272.

29) R. Sherr, A. G. Blair and D. D. Armstrong, (to

be published).

30) B. D. Walker, C. Wong, J. D. Anderson, J. W. McClure and R. W. Bauer, Phys. Rev. $\underline{137}$ (1965) B347.

31) B. D. Walker, C. Wong, J. D. Anderson and J. W. McClure, Phys. Rev. $\underline{137}$ (1965) B1504.

32) C. J. Batty, E. Friedman, P. C. Rowe and J. B. Hunt, Phys. Letts. $\underline{19}$ (1965) 33.

TABLE I. Analysis of (p,n) isobaric cross section data.

Target	σ_t (mb)	$\dfrac{\sigma_t}{N-Z}$	Ratio to Ti^{48}	
			Measured	Calculated
Sc^{45}	7.41	2.47	1.11 ± 0.08	$1 + 0.103\ a^2/b^2$
Ti^{46}	4.42	2.21	0.97 ± 0.08	1.00
Ti^{47}	10.99	3.66	1.61 ± 0.10	$1 + 0.065\ a^2/b^2$
Ti^{48}	9.10	2.27	1.00	1.00
Ti^{49}	14.33	2.87	1.26 ± 0.10	$1 + 0.045\ a^2/b^2$
Ti^{50}	14.20	2.37	1.04 ± 0.06	1.00

DISCUSSION

GREEN, University of Florida: The fact that you use a $(\vec{\tau}_1 \cdot \vec{\tau}_2)(\vec{\sigma}_1 \cdot \vec{\sigma}_2)$ term and you quote a range of 1.4 fermis suggests that you are really sensing the π-meson. The accompanying terms for the π-meson would not be a $(\vec{\tau}_1 \cdot \vec{\tau}_2)$ times a function of r, but would have the tensor force as its companion. It would seem as if this might alter some of your calculations.

ANDERSON: Yes, I should comment that we are well aware of the tensor force but we haven't gotten the exchange integral for this force yet and so Vic Madsen is planning on doing this this summer.

DAEHNICK, Pittsburgh: I would like to point out that the wave function of F^{18} spin 1 ground state is not $(d_{5/2})^2$ always. About half $(d_{5/2})^2$ and half $(d_{5/2}, d_{3/2})$. $(d_{5/2})^2$ is very bad and it is strongly due to these two basis states which causes the ground state to be spin 1.

ANDERSON: Which pushes the 1^+ state down and the other 1^+ state goes up!

SHAFROTH, Bartol: When you do the angular distributions of these groups you look at the place where the peak is. Now if you look off this peak, is the angular distribution isotropic?

ANDERSON: For these cross-sections it doesn't matter. For magnesium there is nothing more, there is no background since we are not in the continuum. For the titanium-vanadium, yes, the background is isotropic except in extreme forward directions, $15°$, something like that. From $30°$ on out it is isotropic. We are not positive yet that we are not seeing some instrumental

effects due to multiple scattering at 15° into the
detector, so we are not sure if that increase in background is real or not.

SHAFROTH: Then for your titanium data, were
those curves calculated curves?

ANDERSON: No. The calculated curves are on
the very last slide, these are Legendre polynomials.
Also, some (He^3,t) work just finished at Oak Ridge by
Luderman et al. confirms the $(N - Z)$ relationship for the
even titanium isotopes. They hope to do (He^3,t) on
Ti^{47} and Ti^{49}.

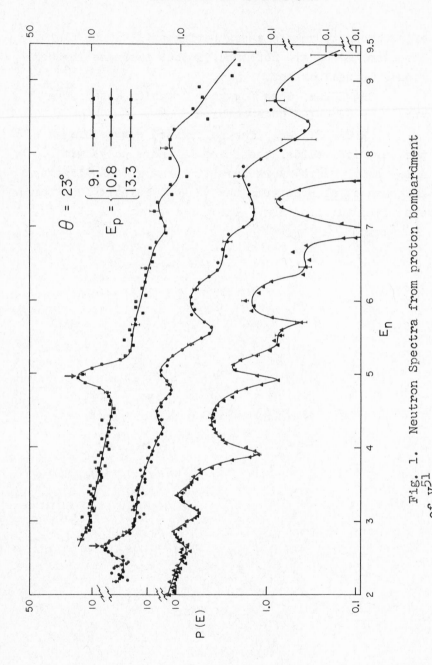

Fig. 1. Neutron Spectra from proton bombardment
of V^{51}.

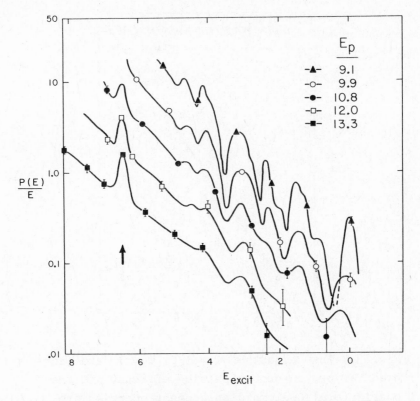

Fig. 2. The neutron spectra transformed to the center-of-mass system and divided by the energy of the emitted neutron are plotted as a function of the excitation of the residual nucleus Cr^{51}. The arrow denotes the position of the analogue state.

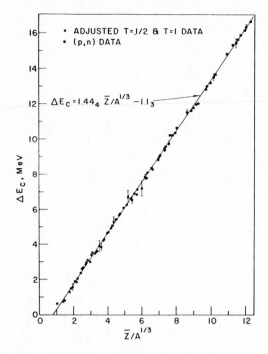

Fig. 3. The "adjusted" T = 1/2, T = 1 data (corrected for proton-proton pairing effects) and the isobaric (p,n) Coulomb displacement energies are plotted versus $\overline{Z}/A^{1/3}$ where $\overline{Z} = \dfrac{Z_{initial} + Z_{final}}{2}$.

A least-squares fit to the data is also shown. For the "adjusted" data, only errors larger than 150 keV are shown.

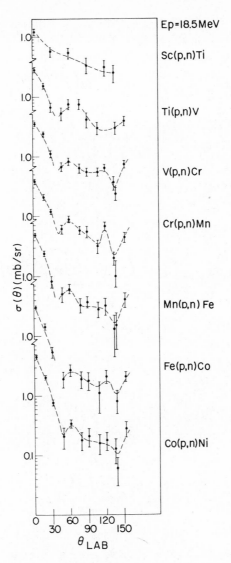

Fig. 4. Angular distributions of the neutrons from the isobaric (p,n) reaction on medium-A nuclei between Sc^{45} and Co^{59} for an incident proton energy of 18.5 MeV.

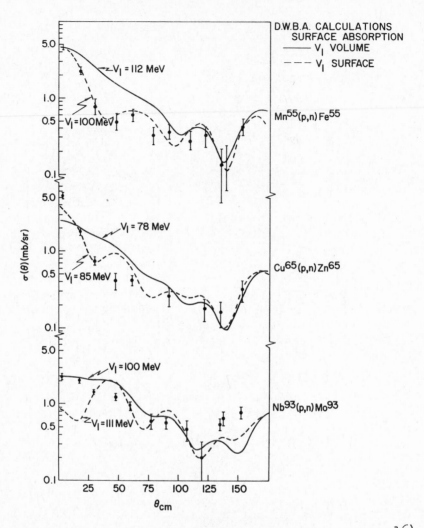

Fig. 5. The DWBA calculations of Satchler et al.[16] are shown both for a volume and a surface-centered isobaric spin optical potential together with the experimental data.

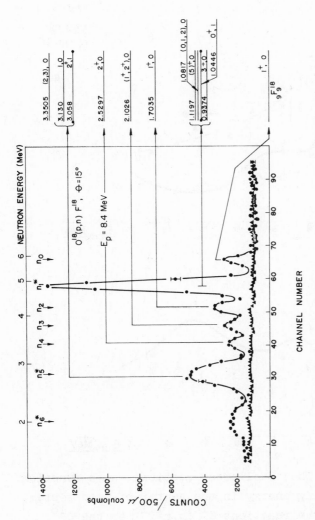

Fig. 6. Time-of-flight spectrum from 8.4-MeV proton bombardment of O^{18}. The levels in F^{18} corresponding to the observed neutron groups are shown in the level diagram on the right. The analogue of the O^{18} ground state is the level at 1.04 MeV in F^{18}.

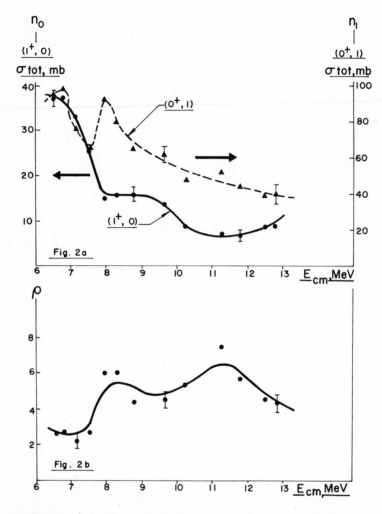

Fig. 7. (a) The total cross sections, as a function of the bombarding energy in the center-of-mass system, are shown for the reactions $O^{18}(p,n)F^{18}$ to the O^{18} analogue state ($J^\pi = 0^+$, T = 1) and the F^{18} ground state ($J^\pi = 1^+$, T = 0). (b) The ratio (ρ) of the $(0^+,1)$ to $(1^+,0)$ cross sections is shown as a function of bombarding energy.

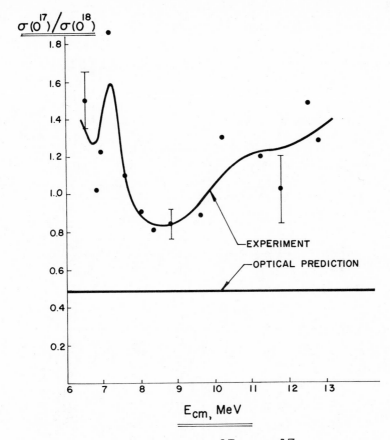

Fig. 8. The ratio of the $O^{17}(p,n)F^{17}$ ground state cross section to the $O^{18}(p,n)F^{18}$ (0^+,1) cross section is shown as a function of the bombarding energy in the center-of-mass system. The optical model predictions (0.5) is also shown.

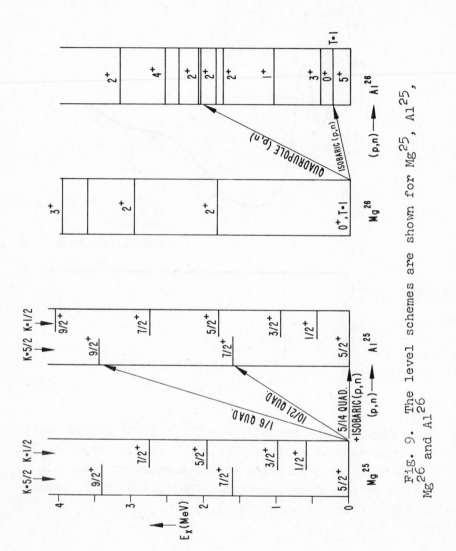

Fig. 9. The level schemes are shown for Mg^{25}, Al^{25}, Mg^{26} and Al^{26}.

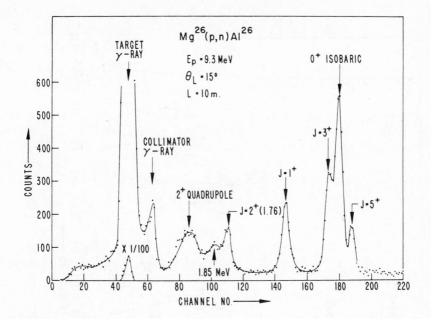

Fig. 10. Time-of-flight spectrum from 9.3-MeV proton bombardment of Mg^{26}.

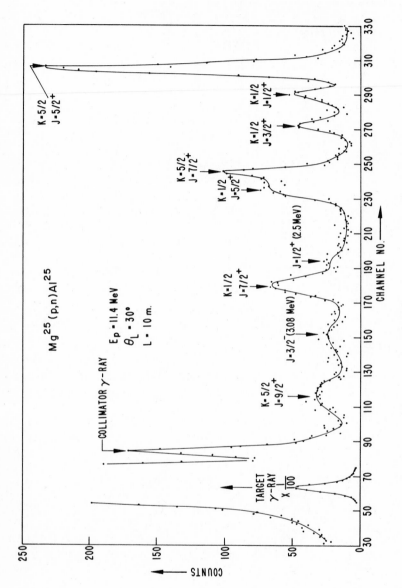

Fig. 11. Time-of-flight spectrum from 11.4-MeV
proton bombardment of Mg^{25}.

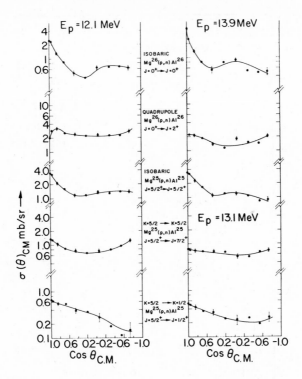

Fig. 12. Characteristic angular distributions for the (p,n) reaction on Mg^{26} and Mg^{25} are shown for two bombarding energies.

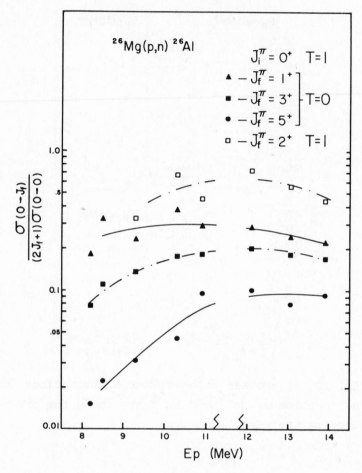

Fig. 13. The quantity $\dfrac{\sigma(0 \to J)}{(2J+1)\ \sigma(0 \to 0)}$ is shown

for the $Mg^{26}(p,n)Al^{26}$ reaction as a function of proton bombarding energy. The data between 11 and 12 MeV is omitted because of a resonance in the $\sigma(0 \to 0)$ cross section.

Fig. 14. Angular distributions of the neutron groups
leading to the analogues of
the target states for 15.2-Mev
proton bombardment of Sc^{45} and
$Ti^{46,47,48,49,50}$. The solid
curves are Legendre polynomial
fits to the data.

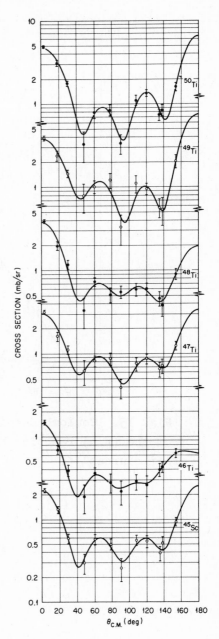

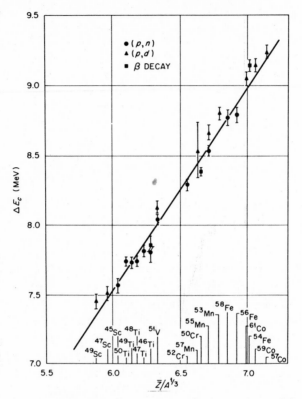

Fig. 15. Coulomb displacement energies obtained from the (p,n) reaction on the titanium isotopes and other sources[28].

E4. ISOBARIC SPIN AND THE OPTICAL MODEL

J. M. Soper[+]

Atomic Energy Research Establishment, Harwell

Over the years the optical model has accumulated
more and more terms in the potential it uses to describe
the scattering of nucleons by nuclei. These refinements
have been made possible by the great increase, both in
volume and accuracy, of the available experimental evidence. One such term is the isobaric spin term in the
real potential; I shall here review briefly the evidence
that bears upon it. I shall then look at a possible
suggestion for a further simple extension of the optical
potential.

The strength of the real central potential currently contains the following terms[1]

$$V_p = V_0 - \beta E + \beta V_c + V_1 (\frac{N - Z}{A})$$

$$V_n = V_0 - \beta E \qquad\qquad - V_1 (\frac{N - Z}{A}) \qquad\qquad (1)$$

for protons and neutrons respectively. There is a constant term. There is a velocity dependence which is
well established and can be represented for most purposes by a linear variation with energy with coefficient
β. The proton sees the Coulomb potential V_c, which we
do not include here since it has a different radial

[+]On leave of absence at the Argonne National Laboratory
and at California Institute of Technology.

variation from the other terms. It gives rise however to the Coulomb correction term, βV_c in the proton potential; since the proton has less kinetic energy (because of the Coulomb interaction) when it reaches the nucleus than does a neutron of the same lab energy, and because the potential is velocity dependent, the proton sees a potential differing by βV_c from the neutron potential.

The final term, $\pm V_1 \left(\frac{N-Z}{A}\right)$ is the symmetry potential, or isobaric spin potential. The latter name arises from a suggestion by Lane[2] that the term be written as

$$\frac{4}{A} V_1 \; (\vec{t} \cdot \vec{T}) \tag{2}$$

This is clearly charge independent. It reduces to the forms in Eq. 1, immediately in the case of neutron scattering, and after averaging over the isobaric spins of the scattering state for proton scattering. In the latter case it will, of course, describe each state separately; it also provides a very simple way of describing the "cross channel" i.e. (p,n) scattering to the isobaric analogue of the ground state. This process, known as quasi-elastic scattering, provides in its turn a very convenient way of measuring V_1.

The determination of V_1 was treated at length by Hodgson[3] at the Paris Conference two years ago. There are two main methods that promise accuracy; analysis of proton elastic scattering and quasi-elastic (p,n) reactions.

The elastic scattering typically involves the determination of average optical model parameters that describe well a chosen range of nuclei. For each nucleus separately the real potential depth is varied to give a best fit to the data. The resulting potentials

plotted against $(\frac{N - Z}{A})$ should yield a straight line of
slope V_1. Several such analyses were quoted by Hodgson.
More recent ones, such as those by Baugh et al.[4]
Picard,[5] Rosen et al.[6] and Satchler[7] are consistent
with the earlier data; the concensus remains at the
value quoted by Hodgson, namely

$$V_1 = 24 \pm 4 \text{ MeV} \tag{3}$$

Care has, of course, to be exercised in the choice
of nuclei to be analyzed. Thus Durisch et al.[8] found
no evidence for a term in $\frac{N - Z}{A}$ among the tin isotopes.
Sood[9] has interpreted this result as arising from the
effect on V_p of the crossing of a subshell gap at about
Sn^{114}; he argues that the three isotopes heavier than
this are consistent with $V_1 = 18$MeV, which is close to
the accepted range of values. Such experiments as these,
however, serve as a warning that by analyzing different
nuclei we may be introducing extraneous effects which
may introduce errors into determinations of V_1 by these
means.

The quasi-elastic scattering experiments, direct
(p,n) reactions going to the analogue of the ground
state, are free of this objection. Because the isobaric
term is the only one acting, they also permit a more
searching analysis of its radial dependence. Satchler
et al.[10] find from their analysis of the Livermore
data[11] using DWBA that a surface form for the potential
is strongly favored, with

$$V_1 = 25 \pm 5 \text{ MeV} \tag{4}$$

The agreement with the proton scattering result is re-
assuring. Analyses of (p,n) data are also underway by
Thurlow and Hodgson[12] (DWBA) and by Gutfreund and

Unna[13] who are computing the solution of the coupled
channels equations[2] numerically.

One possible fly remains in our ointment. Rosen
et al. [6], as well as analyzing their scattering of
polarized protons (obtaining $V_1 = 27$ MeV) also considered
neutron data. Knowing $V_p - V_n - \beta V_c$ for a particular
nucleus at a single energy, we can deduce V_1, free again
from uncertainties due to variations between nuclei.
They do this and obtain $V_1 = 9$ MeV. This discrepancy
depends heavily, of course, on the accuracy of the neutron data. If it is real it poses a serious and unsolved
problem. The authors point out that the discrepancy
will vanish if the Coulomb correction term is ignored,
and Sood[14] has emphasized this feature, also pointing
out that this term does not appear in the bound-state
problem. Its appearance in a velocity-dependent potential is difficult to avoid, however, and we should perhaps sit on the fence for a while longer.

The isobaric spin potential (Eq. 2) is now a familiar and quite accurately known part of the optical
potential. It is interesting to speculate on the introduction of other, equally simple, terms into the expression. I shall confine myself here to a brief consideration of a spin-spin term:

$$\frac{4}{A} V_2 \, (\vec{s} \cdot \vec{S}) \tag{5}$$

This will arise from the spin dependence which is undoubtedly present in the central interaction.

This potential suffers some disadvantages of course
It makes no contribution at all to elastic scattering in
the usual (i.e. unpolarized) case. The usual case for
the isobaric spin potential by contrast is usually completely polarized both in projectile and target

(**separated** isotope). We therefore have to go to the cross channel and look at spin-flip scattering as a quasi-elastic process. Another objection would be that while T becomes very large in heavy nuclei, S will never build to large values, because "spins pair off". This is not altogether true, and while S never rivals T as we go to heavy nuclei it is not always near zero. It is strictly zero if an (n ℓ) shell is completely full of course, but if only the j = ℓ + 1/2 component of a shell is full we have:

$$\langle \vec{S}^2 \rangle = \frac{2\ell(\ell + 1)}{2\ell + 1} \tag{6}$$

Remembering that Pb^{208} has a proton 1h shell and a neutron 1i shell in just this condition, we see that we may get appreciable effects.

The quasi-elastic process corresponds to the spin-flip transition of a nucleon from j = ℓ + 1/2 to j = ℓ - 1/2. All the nucleons in the j = ℓ + 1/2 shell contribute coherently to this amplitude which can thus become "semi-collective" in nature; clearly any nucleons present in the j = ℓ - 1/2 state will tend to supress the transition through the Pauli principle. This is the physical reason for the maximum at the closing of the j = ℓ + 1/2 shell.

For an even-even nucleus the spin-flip analogue of the analogue state in isobaric spin is a J = 1$^+$ ΔT = 0 state at an excitation energy of approximately the spin-orbit splitting for the ℓ state involved.[15] Since this is a monopole excitation the emergent projectile will be peaked in the forward direction. Kawai et al.[16] have considered this sort of process in the s-d shell; although in that work the chief interest was in the T = 1 excitations which come from the $(\vec{\sigma}_1 \cdot \vec{\sigma}_2)(\vec{\tau}_1 \cdot \vec{\tau}_2)$

569

part of the potential. This part also gives rise to the spin-flip (p,n) reactions considered theoretically by Ikeda[17] in heavy nuclei.

Compared with the isobaric spin term, the spin term may seem small (S is appreciable, but not enormous), uncertain (S is not a good quantum number), and cumbersome (we need a model calculation to evaluate S). However it would seem worthwhile to try to give the optical potential an "exchange character"; the parameters involved would then be further numbers for many-body theory to aim at, in the way that Brueckner and Dabrowski[18] have discussed the isobaric spin term.

My warmest thanks are due to the authors mentioned below who communicated results prior to publication; also to P. E. Hodgson and G. R. Satchler for their comments.

REFERENCES

1) F. G. Perey, Phys. Rev. 131 (1963) 745.

2) A. M. Lane, Nucl. Phys. 35 (1962) 676.

3) P. E. Hodgson, Proc. of the Paris Conf. on Nucl. Physics, 257 (1964).

4) D. J. Baugh, G. W. Greenlees, J. S. Lilley and S. Roman, Nucl. Phys. 65 (1965) 33.

5) J. Picard, Nucl. Phys. 68 (1965) 153.

6) L. Rosen, J. G. Beery, A. S. Goldhaber, and E. H. Auerbach, Ann. of Phys. 34 (1965) 96.

7) G. R. Satchler, private communication.

8) J. E. Durisch, R. R. Johnson and N. M. Hintz, Phys. Rev. 137 (1965) B904, See also ibid., B906.

9) P. C. Sood, Phys. Letts. 19 (1965) 52.

10) G. R. Satchler, R. M. Drisko and R. H. Bassel, Phys. Rev. 136 (1964) B637.

11) J. D. Anderson, C. Wong, J. W. McClure and B. D. Walker, Phys. Rev. 136 (1964) 118.

12) N. Thurlow and P. E. Hodgson, private communication.

13) H. Gutfreund and I. Unna, private communication.

14) P. C. Sood, to be published.

15) C. F. Clement, A. M. Lane, and J. M. Soper, unpublished.

16) M. Kawai, T. Terasawa and K. Izumo, Nucl. Phys. 59 (1964) 289.

17) K. Ikeda, Progress of Theoretical Physics, 31 (1964) 434.

18) K. A. Brueckner and J. Dabrowski, Phys. Rev. 134 (1964) B722.

DISCUSSION

COHEN, Pittsburgh: There is one other way, at least one other way, to determine V_1, or at least something very closely related to it, and that is from the location of the single particle states of the shell model. When you do this - there are two ways of doing this - one is if you go through a whole periodic table then you get V_1 something like 27 MeV. On the other hand, if you do it over a very short range, say over the Zr isotopes, you get something like 16 or 18 MeV, and I am just wondering if anything like this happened in the optical model.

SOPER: This is difficult to say. If you do it with the optical model over a short range of nuclei, as has been done by some people in the Sn isotopes, then in the first place they run into this possible shell effect. They couldn't find any variation with $N - Z$ at first. If you follow Sood and ignore Sn^{112} then he got a value of 18 MeV, which is in the same direction that you obtained. I don't know what the other numbers are on this. Whether this is significantly lower than what we find in general use here, I really don't know.

GREEN, University of Florida: I would like to make a remark which bears on the V_1 potential. In our old work this is the form factor for the V_1 and we got the estimate about $\pm 26 \frac{(N-Z)}{A} \xi(r)$. It was suggested that

it was a relatively rapidly changing potential function, something like the nuclear potential, perhaps a little bit different. On the other hand, the Coulomb correction is a relatively slow-varying potential. When you consider the influence of both terms, the Coulomb potential and this symmetry term, you found that this had a greater influence on the wave function than the Coulomb did. It seems as if this would bear on many of the comments made in earlier lectures here as to how one should look at the radial wave functions of neutrons and protons. This term certainly has to be given a great deal of consideration.

SOPER: You are suggesting then that the symmetry potential ought to be taken into account in calculating the Coulomb correction?

GREEN: That is right. The Coulomb potential has a bigger effect on the energy - in fact, almost twice as big an effect on energy as this term, but it does not have as big an effect on the wave function.

SOPER: Isn't it true though that as you go along the stability line the symmetry potential and the Coulomb potential both follow the same pattern, i.e. the $Z/A^{1/3}$ law?

GREEN: They do approximately.

ANDERSON, Livermore: I'd like to mention that if one calculates the exact equations for a surface peaked isobaric spin potential the cross section does not scale as V_1^2 which it does for a volume isobaric spin potential. I don't think we can stress too strongly the importance of the form factor of the isobaric spin potential. In preliminary calculations at this time solving the equations for bound neutron channels, it would appear that the width that one predicts may again be sensitive to the form of the isobaric spin potential.

SOPER: I should mention something which Anderson, I think, also said in his talk. The fits to the (p,n) data are certainly very much better if a surface peaked form factor is used for the V_1 potential.

WIGNER, Princeton: I would like to understand Green's comment. The way I thought about it is that the main part of the isobaric spin potential commutes with T^2. There may be deviation from this symmetry which does not commute but this, I think, has very little effect on the average potential. It may have large effects or correlations, but I don't think you can express it very well with a significant isobaric spin dependent potential.

GREEN: Well, I look on the origin of this term as being the $\vec{\tau}_1 \cdot \vec{\tau}_2$ terms of the π-meson and possibly the ρ-meson. If you have a large neutron excess this would go into the Lane $\tau_3 \times (N - Z)$ type term. The neutron excess giving a deeper attraction to protons but a weaker attraction to neutrons.

WIGNER: What you say is correct I think for the normal states, but for the analogue states the effect of the symmetry term is exactly the same because the symmetry term commutes with T^2, of course, if there are short range deviations which do not commute with T^2 then this effect will spoil the T-quantum number more vigorously than the Coulomb term which is equally large but mainly flat,which part doesn't do anything.

GREEN: I guess the question is whether you would have second order influences through changes in the wave function and this I think is the main point.

WIGNER: Thank you.

BLOOM, Livermore: I want to ask Soper about the very interesting suggestion he made that there might be an $\vec{s} \cdot \vec{S}$ term in the total potential. I was wondering if you wanted to believe in the two-body potential describing residual interactions in nuclei?

This would be associated with the $\vec{\tau} \cdot \vec{T}$ interaction just as in the work described by Anderson.
Would it perhaps not be possible that the $\vec{s} \cdot \vec{S}$ term
that you have there would in fact be associated with
the $\vec{\tau} \cdot \vec{T}$ term and might be exactly the same thing that
we are attempting to investigate at Livermore.

SOPER: This is certainly true. If you look
at the inelastic scattering to a nucleus with neutron
excess, those terms will contribute to the cross-
section of the 1^+ state. If you are going to the 1^+
state in a (p,n) reaction, then you will only get this
$(\vec{\sigma} \cdot \vec{\sigma})(\vec{\tau} \cdot \vec{\tau})$ term, and one would hope that one could
sort these out in this sort of way.

E5. A POTENTIAL MODEL FOR ISOBARIC ANALOGUE STATES

J. P. Bondorf and H. Lütken
The Niels Bohr Institute, Copenhagen

and

S. Jägare
Nordita, Copenhagen

Isobaric analogue states in heavy nuclei were for the first time observed as final states in (p,n) reactions by Anderson et al.[1] The reaction mechanism was explained by Lane,[2] who assumed that the reaction is a quasi-elastic scattering process in which the charge is exchanged by the isovector potential $V_1\vec{t}\cdot\vec{T}$, where $\vec{t}$ and $\vec{T}$, respectively, are the isobaric spin operators of the projectile and the target. Fox et al.[3] have also observed isobaric analogue states as resonances in elastic and inelastic proton scattering and in (p,n) reactions. It was shown by Robson,[4] how these resonances were naturally interpreted by the same potential model as that describing quasi-elastic (p,n) scattering to final analogue states, the only change being that the neutron energy is negative in the resonance case, and thus direct neutron emission is forbidden.

Robson's discussion is performed in the R-matrix formalism, in which the formal aspects of the potential model can be investigated. It is, however, also possible to describe the effect of the compound nucleus formation in terms of an optical potential. The scattering problem can then be solved directly by numerical integration of the coupled equations for the one-particle motion. The treatment can also be extended so as to take into account the coupling of the scattered nucleon to specific degrees of freedom of the target nucleus (vibrations, rotations, one-particle excitations, etc.), which may be important for the structure of the resonance state.

The extension of the optical model to include charge exchange effects leads to a Schroedinger equation of the form

$$(H_{nucleus} + H_{nucleon} + H_r - E)\Psi = 0 \qquad (1)$$

The first term $H_{nucleus}$ is the Hamiltonian for the intrinsic motion of the A nucleons in the target system. We must include states of this system with isobaric spin component $M_T = T_o$, the isobaric spin of the initial state of the target, as well as the analogue states with $M_T = T_o - 1$. In the simplest approximation, which neglects the coupling to specific internal degrees of freedom, the nuclear Hamiltonian can be represented by the two-by-two matrix

$$H_{nucleus} = \begin{Bmatrix} 0 & 0 \\ 0 & \Delta \end{Bmatrix} \begin{matrix} M_T = T_o \\ M_T = T_o - 1 \end{matrix} \qquad (2)$$

where Δ is the energy difference between the analogue states. The second term, $H_{nucleon}$, in Eq. 1 is the mass of the nucleon. The last term in the Hamiltonian is

$$H_r = \frac{\vec{p}^2}{2\mu} + V_o + \vec{t} \cdot \vec{T} \, V_1 + (1/2 - t_z)V_c \qquad (3)$$

where V_o and V_1 are the nuclear isoscalar and isovector potentials, and V_c the Coulomb potential. In terms of

V_o and V_1 the nuclear potentials acting in the $T_o \pm 1/2$ channels of the total system (for definition of these channels, see Ref. 4) are

$$V_{T_o + 1/2} = V_o + 1/2 \; T_o \; V_1$$
$$V_{T_o - 1/2} = V_o - 1/2 \; (T_o + 1)V_1$$

$$(4)$$

In the $T_o - 1/2$ channel, we assume an optical potential similar to that determined from proton scattering experiments. For the $T_o + 1/2$ channel, however, we assume a real potential like that for the low energy bound states in nuclei. This assumption requires a complex symmetry potential V_1. The total wave function for the two-channel system is of the form

$$\Psi = \phi_p \chi_p \Phi(T_o, T_o) + \phi_n \chi_n \Phi(T_o, T_o - 1)$$

$$(5)$$

where ϕ_p and ϕ_n are space-spin wave functions and χ_p and χ_n the isobaric spin functions for the nucleon. The nuclear states Φ are assumed to have spin zero and are labeled by the isobaric spin quantum numbers (T, M_T). Inserting Eqs. 2, 3 and 5 into Eq. 1 one obtains the coupled equations

$$\left(\frac{\vec{p}^2}{2\mu} + V_c + V_o - V_1 \frac{T_o}{2} - E + m_p\right)\phi_p = -V_1 \sqrt{\frac{T_o}{2}} \; \phi_n$$
$$\left(\frac{\vec{p}^2}{2\mu} + \Delta + V_o + V_1 \frac{T_o - 1}{2} - E + m_n\right)\phi_n = -V_1 \sqrt{\frac{T_o}{2}} \; \phi_p$$

$$(6)$$

In the energy region of interest, the neutron energy $E_n = E - \Delta - m_n$ is negative, while the proton energy $E - m_p$ is positive.

The one-particle approximation is expected to be satisfied if the target nucleus has a closed neutron shell and the best cases are those for which the proton shell is also closed. As an example, we have chosen

Ca^{48} with $T_o = 4$ as target. The following parameters were used

$$\text{Re } V_o(r) = (-52f(r) + 15 \frac{1}{r} \frac{df(r)}{dr} \vec{\ell} \cdot \vec{s})\text{MeV}$$

$$\text{Re } V_1(r) = 2.17f(r)\text{MeV}$$

$$\text{Im } V_{T_o-1/2} = -2f(r)\text{MeV}$$

$$\Delta + m_n - m_p = 7.32 \text{ MeV}$$

$$f(r) = \left\{1 + \exp\left[(r - 4.54\text{fm})/(0.65\text{fm})\right]\right\}^{-1}$$

With this choice of parameters we have numerically integrated the coupled radial wave equations for each value of the orbital and total angular momenta (ℓ, j) of the nucleon, with the boundary condition that the wave function in the closed neutron channel decreases exponentially for large r. From the phase shifts determined in this manner, the cross sections shown in Figs. 1 - 4 were obtained. The parameters (Eq. 7) are not too realistic due to the lack of experimental data and the numerical results are therefore somewhat uncertain. The differential cross section shows resonances in the $p_{3/2}$, $p_{1/2}$ and $f_{5/2}$ channels (Figs. 1 - 3). The position of these analogue states, which are analogous to the lowest states in Ca^{49}, are determined by the position of the bound states in the neutron well. This is easily seen from Eqs. 6. When the neutron energy E_n is near the energy of a bound state, ϕ_n becomes large and thus affects strongly the proton wave function through the coupling. The reaction cross section in the different (ℓ, j) channels is shown in Fig. 4 and it can be seen how it varies with typical asymmetry over a resonance.

The authors wish to express their gratitude to Professors A. Bohr and B. R. Mottelson, Copenhagen, and

Dr. P. v. Brentano, Heidelberg, for stimulating discussions. One of us (S.J.) wishes to thank NORDITA for their hospitality.

REFERENCES

1) J. D. Anderson and C. Wong, Phys. Rev. Letts. $\underline{7}$ (1961) 250.

2) A. M. Lane, Nuclear Phys. $\underline{35}$ (1962) 676.

3) J. D. Fox, C. F. Moore and D. Robson, Phys. Rev. Letts. $\underline{12}$ (1964) 198.

4) D. Robson, Phys. Rev. $\underline{137}$ (1965) B535.

DISCUSSION

SCHIFFER, <u>Argonne</u>: I would like to ask whether the fact that you see a difference in two states could not be attributed to the different partial waves rather than a difference in energy?

BONDORF: It might be.

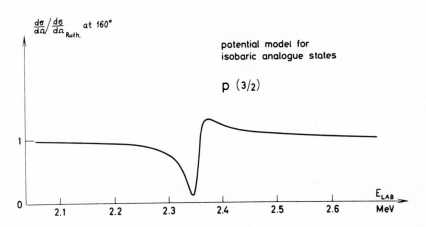

Fig. 1. Differential elastic proton cross section for $Ca^{48}(p,p)$ showing the resonance at the isobaric analogue of the ground state of Ca^{49}.

$Ca^{48}(pp)$

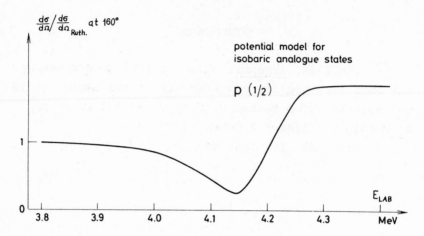

Fig. 2. Differential elastic proton cross section for $Ca^{48}(p,p)$ showing the resonance at the isobaric analogue of the first excited state of Ca^{49}.

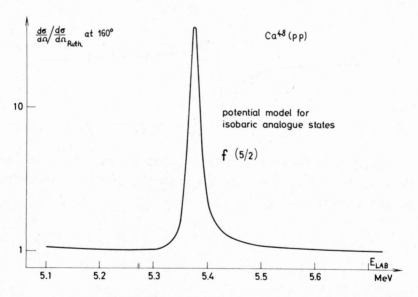

Fig. 3. Differential elastic proton cross section for $Ca^{48}(p,p)$ showing the resonance at the isobaric analogue of the second excited state of Ca^{49}.

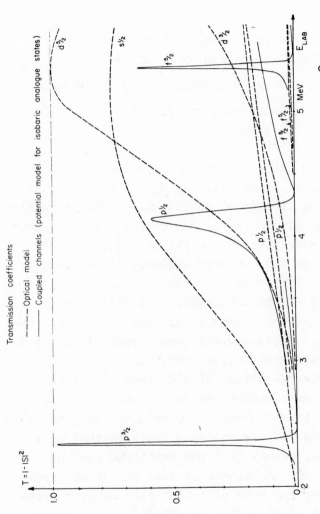

Fig. 4. Transmission coefficients $T_{\ell j} = 1 - |S_{\ell j}|^2$ for Ca^{48}(p,p). The full-drawn curves are calculated from Eqs. 6 with the potentials given by Eqs. 7. The dotted curves are calculated from an optical potential corresponding to the potentials in Eqs. 7.

583

E6. (p,n) REACTION ON Zr^{91}
FOLLOWED BY PROTON EMISSION[*]

A. I. Yavin, R. A. Hoffswell, and T. M. Noweir

University of Illinois
Urbana, Illinois

Analogue states in medium-weight nuclei have
been investigated by Anderson et al.[1], who observed
neutron spectra from (p,n) reactions. A strong neutron
group of well-defined energy was observed in all nuclei
at an energy corresponding to the excitation of the
final nucleus to the isobaric analogue of the target
ground state. They suggested that the reaction is direct and involves the conversion of a target neutron into a proton, leaving unchanged all quantum numbers except E and T_Z. Coulomb displacement energies derived
from the reactions were also computed.

The primary purpose of the present experiment
was to investigate another method of measuring the
Coulomb displacement energy by observing, when feasible,
the proton decay of the analogue state reached by a
(p,n) reaction, rather than the scattered neutrons.
The advantage of this method is that proton spectroscopy is easier and more efficient than neutron spectroscopy. The reaction $Zr^{91}(p,n)Nb^{91*}$ was selected,
and protons from the decay of Nb^{91*}, where Nb^{91*} represents the analogue of the ground state of Zr^{91}, were

[*]Supported in part by the United States Office of
Naval Research

observed. Once the energy of protons from the decay of Nb^{91*} is known, the Coulomb displacement energy E_c may be determined from the relation: $E_c = \Delta E + T + \delta$, where $\Delta E = E(Zr^{90} + p) - E(Zr^{91})$, $T = T(p) + T(Zr^{90})$ is the total kinetic energy in the Nb^{91*} system, and δ is the neutron-proton mass difference in energy units. It was hoped that the experiment would enable the observation of excited analogue states in Nb^{91} and the subsequent determination of their energies.

The center of mass (p,n) threshold for the desired reaction is equal to the Coulomb energy, which was taken, for Zr^{91}, to be 11.75 MeV[2]. A Zr^{90} target was also used in order to demonstrate that the proton group of interest was indeed from the decay of Nb^{91*}, (Nb^{90*} is proton stable). The Zr^{91} and Zr^{90} targets used had isotopic purities of 91% and 98%, respectively and had considerable carbon and oxygen surface contaminants. Target thicknesses were 750 Mg/cm^2 and 590 Mg/cm^2, respectively.

The experiment used a proton beam of 100 na from the University of Illinois isochronous cyclotron. A detector telescope, consisting of 90 μ and 2100 μ detectors in conjunction with a particle identifying system to provide both energy and mass information, was used. The solid angle for particle detection was approximately 2.5 x 10^{-4} sterad. To avoid excessive counts from Coulomb scattering at forward angles, the detector telescope was positioned at 135° to the incident beam.

Figure 1 shows the relevant level diagram for the reaction which can be written schematically as

$$p + Zr^{91} \rightarrow Nb^{91*} + n$$
$$\quad\quad\quad \hookrightarrow Zr^{90} + \bar{p}_o,$$

in which $\bar{p}_o$ is the proton from the decay of Nb^{91*} to the ground state of Zr^{90}. Also shown are other possible protons from decays to excited states of Zr^{90}, ($\bar{p}_1$, $\bar{p}_2$ and $\bar{p}_3$), as well as a possible proton decay from the first excited analogue state in Nb^{91} to the ground state of Zr^{90}, ($\bar{p}_o'$).

Typical pulse height spectra of protons resulting from 13.0 MeV, 13.15 MeV, and 13.3 MeV proton bombardment of Zr^{91} are shown in Fig. 2. Each spectrum displays the expected $\bar{p}_o$ peak. Also shown are peaks corresponding in energy to elastic scattering from Zr^{91} as well as to elastic and inelastic scattering from O^{16} and C^{12} target contaminants. A slight indication of a peak corresponding in energy to $\bar{p}_o'$ protons may also be seen; however, the statistics are too poor to warrant definite conclusions.

An interesting feature in these data is that by increasing the energy of the incoming protons, all prominent peaks such as elastic and inelastic ones were displaced to higher energies, with the exception of the $\bar{p}_o$ peak, indicating, as expected, that the $\bar{p}_o$ energy is independent of the incident proton energy. Proton spectra from the Zr^{90} target were taken under the same conditions mentioned above and are plotted below the spectra from the Zr^{91} target. As expected, there is no indication of a peak consistent with $\bar{p}_o$ in the spectra from Zr^{90}. The sums of the three spectra from both Zr^{91} and Zr^{90} are shown in Fig. 3. This summing process has the effect of broadening all peaks except the $\bar{p}_o$ peak, which is effectively accentuated in the case of Zr^{91}.

Calibration of all spectra was accomplished through the use of a separate energy spectrum taken at

12.8 MeV incident proton energy. The requirements
that the detected particle be a proton and stop in the
2100 μ detector was removed for this run. This permitted observation of 6.05 MeV and 8.78 MeV α particles
from a thorium source, as well as scattered charged
particles. This spectrum is displayed in Fig. 4 and
shows that the removal of the coincidence requirement
resulted in a very small added contribution from scattered charged particles other than protons. The removal of the coincidence requirement also permitted detection of low energy protons (those which were stopped
in the 90 μ detector and, therefore, not recorded in
Figs. 2 and 3), resulting in the observation of two
weak peaks which are energetically consistent with $\bar{p}_1$
and $\bar{p}_3$, (see Fig. 1). Unfortunately, the peaks due
to $\bar{p}_0$ and scattered protons from O^{16} (6.1) accidentally
coincided for this run.

The total observed energy T of the $\bar{p}_0$ proton was
4.70 ± 0.10 MeV, the uncertainty being largely due to
the accidental overlap of the $\bar{p}_0$ and O^{16} (6.1) peaks
in the calibration run. (The neutrons from the primary (p,n) process are low in energy and scatter in all
directions, causing only a slight broadening of the observed peak). Since $\Delta E = 6.42 \pm 0.01$ MeV[3], the analogue state is at an excitation energy of 11.12 MeV in
Nb^{91}. Adding δ = 0.78 MeV gives a Coulomb displacement
energy for Zr^{91} of 11.90 ± 0.10 MeV. The absolute
cross section was calculated by integrating the area
under the $\bar{p}_0$ peak. Assuming isotropic distribution of
the protons from the decay of Nb^{91*} ($\bar{p}_0$), the integrated
cross section is approximately 5 mb.

In conclusion, we can say that our preliminary
results indicate that the (p,n$\bar{p}$) process is relatively

easy to detect. Our measured Coulomb displacement energy for Zr^{91} is in good agreement with the value of 11.75 $\pm$ 0.15 MeV measured by Anderson, et al. for Zr. The (p,n$\bar{p}$) experiment is inherently an accurate tool for the determination of Coulomb displacement energies, and would compare favorably with the (p,n) experiment, especially when magnetic spectrometers are used. Its main advantage over the corresponding (He^3,t) investigation is in counting rate. (The cross section for the (He^3,t) reaction is 10 - 100 times smaller than the cross section for the primary (p,n) reaction and the competition from charged particles is much more severe).

Unfortunately, we are unable to determine, on the basis of the present experiment, whether the (p,n$\bar{p}$) process can identify analogues of excited states, via the observation of $\bar{p}_o^!$, and subsequently determine the corresponding Coulomb displacement energies. We have probably observed the $\bar{p}_1$ proton transition to the 0^+ first excited state of Zr^{90} from the Nb^{91*} analogue of the ground state of Zr^{91}. We might also have seen the $\bar{p}_3$ proton transition to the 5^- third excited state of Zr^{90}. These transitions have recently been observed in inelastic proton scattering from analogue resonances[4]. The $\bar{p}_3$ transition, if genuine, is surprising in view of the configurations involved. However, the low energy part of the spectrum was observed only at one proton energy; the statistics of that part of the spectrum are poor and an uncertainty exists due to the C^{12} and O^{16} contaminants. No conclusive statement can, therefore, be made concerning these transitions on the basis of this experiment.

Apart from the determination of Coulomb displacement energies, the (p,n$\bar{p}$) method should serve, as

a spectroscopic tool in at least two additional ways:
(1) Coefficients of fractional parentage might be determined via the observation of branching ratios in the proton decay of analogue states. This would supplement similar measurements on the ground states of the corresponding nuclei via (p,d), (d,t) and (He^3,α) reactions, with the possible added advantage of a smaller dependence on the reaction mechanism. (2) Whenever the analogue state reached by the primary (p,n) process is both proton and neutron unstable, neutron decay could result due to isobaric spin impurity of the analogue state (and to a lesser degree, due to the isobaric spin impurity of the residual state). An accurate determination of the cross section for the $(p,n\bar{p})$ process as well as for the primary (p,n) process would then yield information on both the total width and the proton width of the analogue state, and, therefore, on the neutron width as well.

We are grateful to Professor P. Axel for his many useful suggestions and discussions, and to Professor T. Hecht for helpful comments. We also wish to thank Mr. L. E. Ernest and the cyclotron crew.

REFERENCES

1) J. D. Anderson, C. Wong, J. W. McClure and B. D. Walker, Phys. Rev. 136 (1964) B118.

2) J. D. Anderson, C. Wong, and J. W. McClure, Phys. Rev. 138 (1965) B615.

3) R. R. Ries, R. A. Damerow, and W. H. Johnson, Jr., Phys. Rev. 132 (1963) 1662.

4) J. C. Legg, M. A. Crosby and G. Roy, Bull. Am. Phys. Soc. 11 (1966) 100.

DISCUSSION

SEGEL, Argonne: I didn't understand the point
about the high resolution spectroscopy. Isn't there
about a hundred kilovolts of broadening from the recoil?

YAVIN: I said if you are about 2 MeV above
threshold. What recoil do you mean?

SEGEL: The recoil of the Zr.

YAVIN: Yes; if you are just about at the
threshold, the neutron would sort of spill off, the
remainder being just left behind.

SEGEL: Yes, but what happens at higher energies?

YAVIN: Then there will be a Zr recoil. My
suggestion was to try to go down lower if you want to
look with better resolution and if the cross section
is still appreciable slightly above threshold then you
should be able to do it.

SEGEL: Thank you.

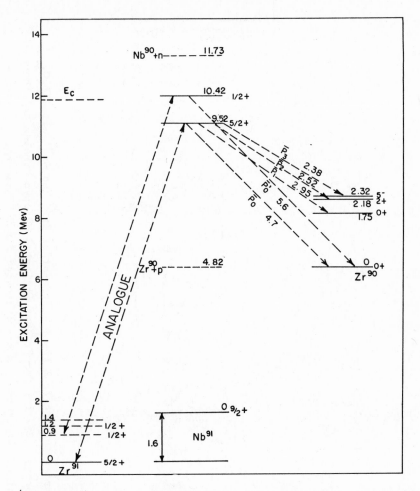

Fig. 1. Level diagram showing the analogue states of Zr^{91} in Nb^{91}, and possible proton decays of these states to various levels in Zr^{90}.

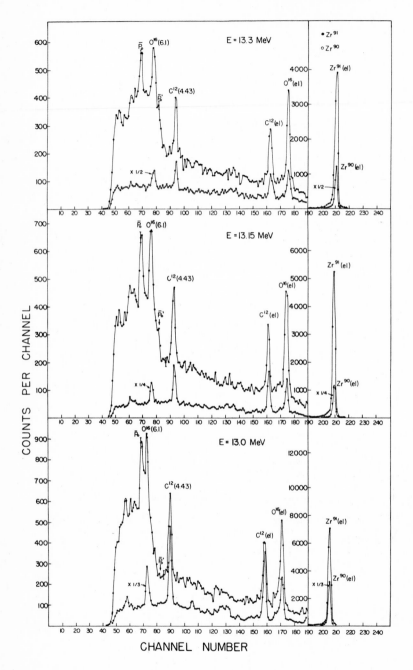

Fig. 2. Proton spectra resulting from the bombardment of Zr^{90} and Zr^{91} with 13.0, 13.15, and 13.3 MeV protons. Spectra for Zr^{90} are indicated by open circles and those for Zr^{91} by closed circles. Scale changes are indicated for Zr^{90} spectra.

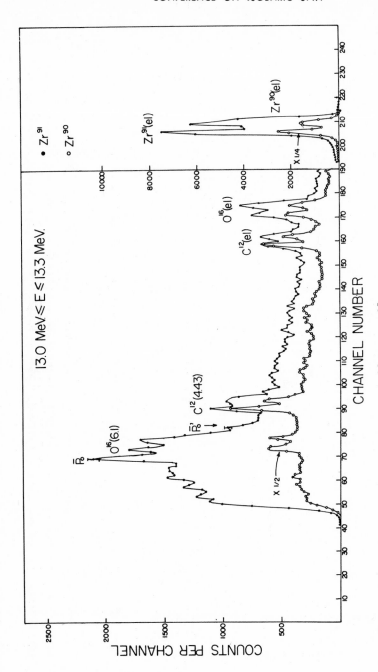

Fig. 3. Summed proton spectra for Zr^{90} and Zr^{91} produced by adding individual proton energy spectra for 13.0, 13.15, and 13.3 MeV incident proton energies. The spectrum for Zr^{90} is indicated by open circles, and for Zr^{91} by closed circles. The scale is reduced by a factor of 2 for the Zr^{90} spectrum.

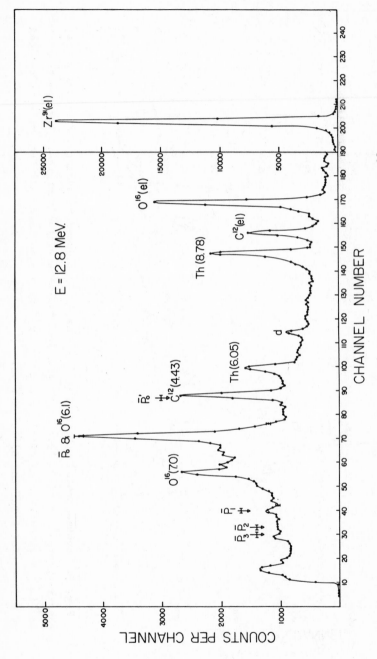

Fig. 4. Complete charged particle spectrum from the bombardment of Zr^{91} with 12.8 MeV protons. The spectrum includes two alpha peaks from a thorium source. The $\bar{P}_0$ and O^{16} (6.1) peaks overlap. Arrows indicate the expected positions of the $\bar{P}_0$, $\bar{P}_1$, $\bar{P}_2$ and $\bar{P}_3$ peaks.

E7. ANALOGUE STATES IN $Co^{55,57}$ AND $Cu^{59,61}$ EXCITED BY (He^3,d) REACTIONS*

B. Rosner, C. H. Holbrow and D. J. Pullen

University of Pennsylvania
Philadelphia, Pennsylvania

The (He^3,d) reaction on a target nucleus with isobaric spin T can excite both $T - 1/2 = (T_<)$ and $T + 1/2 = (T_>)$ isobaric spin states in the final nucleus. Furthermore, at suitable bombarding energies transitions to many states proceed by stripping in a proton, and the deuteron angular distributions can be analyzed using DWBA theory.

For the present purposes we may distinguish between two classes of (He^3,d) reactions. In the first the target nuclei have a small neutron excess and the reactions lead to $T_>$ levels at quite low excitation energies and both $T_>$ and $T_<$ states are excited with comparable intensities. In the second class the target nuclei have a larger neutron excess and the lowest-lying $T_>$ states occur at higher excitations. These tend to be strongly excited compared to the nearby $T_<$ states and thus stand out prominently in the deuteron spectra. Examples of the first class are the $Fe^{54}(He^3,d)Co^{55}$ and $Ni^{58}(He^3,d)Cu^{59}$ reactions, whereas the reactions $Fe^{56}(He^3,d)Co^{57}$ and $Ni^{60}(He^3,d)Cu^{61}$ are examples of the second class.

---

*Supported by the National Science Foundation.

These four reactions have been studied using a
16.5 MeV He^3-beam from the University of Pennsylvania
Tandem Accelerator, and deuteron spectra were recorded
over a range of angles with a broad-range magnetic
spectrograph. For each reaction two exposures were
made with better than 20 keV resolution to determine
excitation energies. Complete angular distributions
were measured with thicker targets ($\sim$ 45 keV) to reduce the duration of the measurements.

RESULTS

A spectrum obtained at 30° with the Ni^{58} target
is shown in Fig. 1. On the basis of excitation energy,
and also ℓ-value and spectroscopic factor, the 3.90 MeV
level of Cu^{59} has been identified as the analogue of
the Ni^{59} ground state. The other levels for which excitation energies are given were similarly determined
to be analogues of four of the low-lying states of
Ni^{59}. A deuteron spectrum measured at 30° with the
Fe^{56} target is shown in Fig. 2. In this case the analogues are quite strongly excited relative to the
neighboring $T_<$ states. Using this fact, and the relative spacing of the levels, the analogue of the Fe^{57}
ground state is found to lie at 7.27 MeV excitation
energy in Co^{57} and two other levels at 7.43 and 7.66
MeV are identified as the analogue states corresponding
to the 0.136 and 0.366 MeV levels in Fe^{57}. Similar
criteria were used to locate analogue states in Co^{55}
and Cu^{61}.

Angular distributions corresponding to the
strongly excited analogue states are shown in Fig. 3.
The curves serve only to guide the eye and were not
calculated from theory. Uncertain ℓ - value assignments

are indicated in brackets.

The experimental results for all four reactions
are summarized in Table I. In the first column the excitation energies for the analogue states are given,
and their excitation energies relative to the first
analogue state in each sequence are shown in the next
column. These may be compared with the sequence of
excitation energies of corresponding states in Fe^{55},
Fe^{57}, Ni^{59} and Ni^{61} determined from (d,p) reactions
and listed in the third column. Values of ℓ_p and ℓ_n
characterizing the (He^3,d) and (d,p) transitions to
analogue pairs are shown in columns 4 and 5 respectively.
For cases in which the Q-value for the transition was
not less than ∼ -6 MeV it was possible to extract
transition strengths from the present data with an
uncertainty of about 30%. These are presented in
column 6 and should be compared with the $(2J + 1)c^2S$
values obtained for the corresponding levels in the
(d,p) work and given in the last column.

When comparing the (He^3,d) data with the (d,p)
data, all corresponding sequences of $\ell = 1$ analogue
levels can be lined up to within 25 keV. However, in
the two cases where the analogue states occur at comparatively low excitation energies, the $\ell = 3$ states
observed in this study lie about 80 keV above their
corresponding states in Fe^{55} and Ni^{59}.

Differences between Coulomb energies of analogue pairs, i.e. the Coulomb displacements, were
evaluated from the excitation energies of the ground
state analogues and the atomic masses of Mattauch et
al.[1]. The results, listed in Table II, agree well
with the values interpolated from the (p,d) studies of
Sherr et al.[2].

From Table II it can be seen that the Fe^{55}-Co^{55} Coulomb displacement is 110 keV more than the Fe^{57}-Co^{57} Coulomb displacement. If this difference is attributed to an $A^{-1/3}$ mass dependence, the calculated difference between the Coulomb displacements is 109 keV. The close agreement with experiment is probably fortuitous. It is interesting that no such difference between Coulomb displacements is observed when the results for the analogue pairs Ni^{59}-Cu^{59} and Ni^{61}-Cu^{61} are compared. Sherr[3] also has reported sequences of isobars exhibiting an $A^{-1/3}$ mass dependence in their Coulomb displacements and a few which do not.

It is also noteworthy that the ground state analogue at 3.90 MeV in Cu^{59} has an observed width of 38 keV which is just twice the experimental width of 19 keV. The present data and those of Schiffer[4] indicate that this width may arise from an unresolved doublet with a relatively weak $T_<$ member.

REFERENCES

1) J. H. E. Mattauch, W. Thiele and A. H. Wapstra, Nucl. Phys. 67 (1965) 1.
2) R. Sherr, B. F. Bayman, E. Rost, M. E. Rickey and C. G. Hoot, Phys. Rev. 138 (1965) B1272.
3) R. Sherr, A. G. Blair, and D. D. Armstrong, (PUC-937-66-k92).
4) G. C. Morrison and J. P. Schiffer (private communication).

TABLE I. Experimental results for (He^3,d) and (d,p) reactions.

Analogue States Excited by (He^3,d) Reaction — Nucleus Ex(MeV)	Energy Sequence of Analogue States	States Excited by (d,p) Reaction — Nucleus Ex(MeV)	ℓ_p	ℓ_n	$(2J+1)C^2S$ Calculated from (He^3,d) data	$(2J+1)C^2S$ Predicted from (d,p) data
Co^{55} 4.76±.03	0	(a) Fe^{55} 0	1	1	0.92	1.08
5.20	0.44	0.417	1	1	0.48	0.40
5.78	1.02	0.935	3	3	1.56	1.20
6.85	2.09	2.061		1		0.13
6.93	2.17	2.159		3		0.30
Co^{57} 7.27±.04	0	(b) Fe^{57} 0	1	1		0.44
7.43	0.16	0.136	(3)	–		–
7.66	0.39	0.366	1	1		0.20
Cu^{59} 3.90±.02	0	(a) Ni^{59} 0	1	1	0.64	0.68
4.32	0.42	0.340	} 1+3	3	1.50	1.86
4.37	0.47	0.471		1	0.28	0.39
4.78	0.88	0.887		1		0.11
5.24	1.34	1.318	(1)	1		0.17
Cu^{61} 6.45±.03	0	(b) Ni^{61} 0	1	1		0.25
6.54	0.09	0.069	(3)	3		0.74
6.71	0.26	0.290	1	1		
7.66	1.21	1.195				
8.56	2.11	2.135	1+4	1+4		

(a) Fulmer et al., P.R. 131 (1963) 2133; (b) Cohen et al., P.R. 126 (1963) 698.

TABLE II. Coulomb displacement energies ΔE_c, obtained from the experimental observed excitation energies of the isobaric analogue states. All energies in MeV.

Residual Nucleus	Co^{55}	Co^{57}	Cu^{59}	Cu^{61}
Ex	$4.76 \pm .03$	$7.27 \pm .04$	$3.90 \pm .02$	$6.45 \pm .03$
ΔM^a	$3.46 \pm .01$	$.84 \pm .02$	$4.80 \pm .02$	$2.24 \pm .01$
(n-H)	.78	.78	.78	.78
ΔE_c	$9.00 \pm .03$	$8.89 \pm .04$	$9.48 \pm .03$	$9.47 \pm .03$

a) J. H. E. Mattauch et al., Nucl. Phys. 67 (1965) 1.

DISCUSSION

SCHIFFER: I would just like to make a very brief comment. Morrison and I have measured one of the same reactions that Rosner has spoken about, with a little bit better resolution, and seemed to see an effect which might be interesting.

Could you just show us that slide again, please?[*] The point I would like to make here is that there is one analogue state showing up as in the work of Rosner but there seems to be a group of states in the high resolution data. This might have some bearing on the sort of spreading of analogue strength that was discussed yesterday by Robson. There is some indication that even in these very nearly bound states such effects persist.

*Fig. 1, Paper E7.

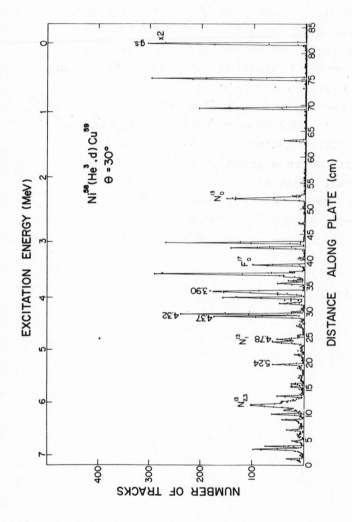

Fig. 1. Deuteron spectrum for the $Ni^{58}(He^3,d)Cu^{59}$ reaction taken at $\theta = 30°$. Excitation energies of the analogue states are indicated in MeV.

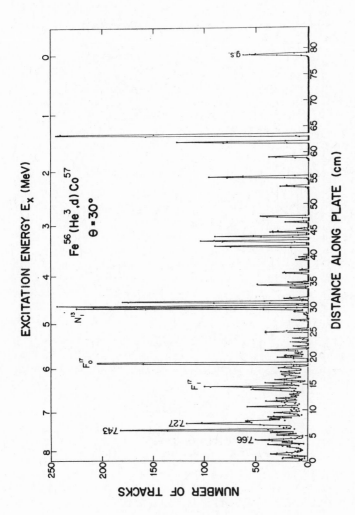

Fig. 2. Deuteron spectrum for the $Fe^{56}(He^3,d)Co^{57}$ reaction taken at $\theta = 30°$. Excitation energies of the analogue states are indicated in MeV.

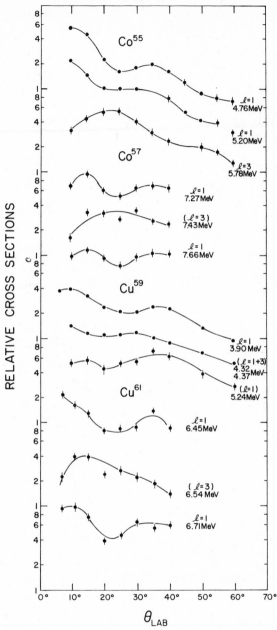

Fig. 3. Angular distributions of deuterons for some of the strongly excited analogue states in the (He³,d) reactions. The lines serve only as a guide to the eye.

604

E8. EXCITATION OF ISOBARIC ANALOGUE STATES IN MEDIUM-WEIGHT NUCLEI BY THE (He^3,α) REACTION[*]

T. H. Braid, L. Meyer-Schützmeister and D. D. Borlin[+]

Argonne National Laboratory
Argonne, Illinois

Since the (He^3,α) reaction has large positive Q values for nuclei in the $1f_{7/2}$ region, it provides a very convenient means of studying the formation of both the $T_0 - 1/2$ and $T_0 + 1/2$ states which can be excited in the pickup of a neutron from a target of isobaric spin T_0. In most of our measurements we have used a 13-MeV He^3 beam from the ANL Tandem and have recorded the α-particle spectra in nuclear track plates in a magnetic spectrograph. In a few cases, however, we have used the 33-MeV beam from the 60-in. cyclotron and have observed the spectra with semiconductor counters. The energy resolution width was about 40 keV at best because of the thickness of the rolled metal targets for most of the data taken with the spectrograph.

For most of the even-Z, even-N target isotopes of Ti, Cr, Fe, and Ni and for the odd-Z, even-N isotopes Sc^{45} and V^{51}, spectra have been taken at a few angles to find the energies of the levels. In the case of V^{51} and Fe^{56}, angular distributions have been

[*] Work performed under the auspices of the United States Atomic Energy Commission

[+] Permanent address: Washington University, St. Louis

measured from 8° to 57° so as to provide comparisons with DWBA calculations.

Figure 1 shows three typical spectra, with Fe^{54}, Fe^{56} and V^{51} targets. The strong background at small angles and low α-particle energy is at least partly due to He^3 ions scattered in the spectrograph.

The spectra from the two Fe targets are typical of the data from even-even targets. There is only one highly excited (4 - 10 MeV) level formed by $\ell = 3$ pickup, which is the analogue of the lowest $7/2^-$ state (normally the ground state) of the corresponding isobar. The positions of these states, which are known from the (p,d) reaction[1], are in agreement with the present measurement. This state in Ti^{45} appears at an excitation of 4.73 MeV. Hence the Coulomb shift $E_c = 7.57 \pm$ .020 MeV, in agreement with the values from the Ti isotopes when corrected for the $A^{1/3}$ dependence.

In the case of the odd-Z, even-N targets, $\ell = 3$ pickup leads to the analogues of excited states as well as to the ground state. The spectrum from a Sc^{45} target shows several levels in Sc^{44} which are analogues of known levels in Ca^{44} formed by $\ell = 3$ proton pickup from the same target. In V^{50}, four $\ell = 3$ levels have been found (Fig. 1) corresponding to the $J = 0^+$ ground state and the $J = 2^+$, 4^+ and 6^+ excited states of Ti^{50}. They occur at $E_x = 4.83$, 6.40, 7.54 and 8.08 MeV. Relative spectroscopic factors for these levels and for the $T_<$ levels have been extracted by DWBA fits to the angular distributions. Table I shows that the ratios of spectroscopic factors agree fairly well with those expected. The parameters that gave the best fit to the data are those reported by Blair and Wegner[2]. We used the conventional "separation energy" for the bound-state wave function. Use of the "effective binding"[1] prescription yields incorrect ratios. For instance, the value of S for the 8.08-MeV state is low by a factor of almost two. On the other hand, the ratio of the total $T_>$ strength to the total $T_<$ strength is too high by 50% when calculated by the conventional method.

More highly excited states which can be seen in Fig. 1 correspond to the pickup of different orbitals, principally $2s_{1/2}$ and $1d_{3/2}$, and these are seen in a number of nuclei. The positions and spacings of these levels show some differences from those of the excited states in the corresponding isobar. The d and s levels are particularly distinct in the case of Ti^{45} ($E_x = 4.79$ and 5.71 MeV) and Ti^{47} ($E_x = 8.15$ and 8.77 MeV). In Sc^{45} the corresponding states at 13 keV[3] and 0.92 MeV excitation are believed to represent the total $1d_{3/2}$ and $2s_{1/2}$ strengths[4]. It is possible, therefore, to make a simple calculation to estimate the extent to which the shift in the d and s states relative to the f state can be accounted for simply as a different Coulomb effect on the different wave functions, the nuclear charge distribution being assumed to be the same. The calculation is similar to that of Jones, et al.[5]. On the assumption of a uniformly charged sphere, a radius was found which produced the observed Coulomb shift for a $1f_{7/2}$ particle bound in a Woods-Saxon potential by the average binding energy of the $f_{7/2}$ neutrons in Sc^{45}. Then the Coulomb shifts were found for $1d_{3/2}$ and $2s_{1/2}$ wave functions (bound so as to represent the excited states) with the same charge radius. Since the analogue of the d hole state has two components, one with a d proton hole and one with a d neutron hole, it follows that

$$E_c = 1/3 \; E_c(d_{3/2}) + 2/3 \; E_c(f_{7/2}),$$

and similarly for the analogue of the s state.

Table II shows that for the d state the predicted f-d separation is about twice as large as observed while the f-s separation is also over-estimated but not as much. Considering the simplicity of the calculation, it is satisfactory that the effects are of roughly the right magnitude and in the right direction. This limited agreement shows that the energy differences between the states in Sc^{45} and their analogues in Ti^{45} may well be due simply to the effect on the different wave-functions of overall charge distribution which remains essentially unchanged.

REFERENCES

1) R. Sherr, B. Bayman, E. Rost, M. E. Rickey and C. G. Hoot, Phys. Rev. 139 (1965) B1272.

2) A. G. Blair and H. E. Wegner, Phys. Rev. 127 (1962) 1233.

3) J. L. Yntema and J. R. Erskine, Phys. Letts. 12 (1964) 26.

4) J. L. Yntema and G. R. Satchler, Phys. Rev. 134 (1964) B976.

5) K. W. Jones, J. P. Schiffer, L. L. Lee, Jr., A. Marinov and J. L. Lerner, Phys. Rev., (in press).

TABLE I. Relative spectroscopic factors for $l = 3$ analogue states in V^{50}.

E_x	l	S	
		Relative	Theoretical
4.83	3	1.0	1.0
6.40	3 (+1)	0.4	0.55
7.54	3 (+1)	0.9	1.0
8.08	3	1.6	1.4

TABLE II. Coulomb shifts for d and s hole states in Ti^{45}.

$E_x(Ti^{45})$	l	$E_x - E_x^f$		$E_x(Sc^{45})$
		Obs.	Calc.	
4.73	3	0		0
4.79	2	0.060	0.119	0.013
5.71	0	0.98	0.995	0.94

DISCUSSION

TEMMER, Rutgers: I would just like to make a statement concerning the concept of charge parity. This is a concept due to Wigner and Feenberg around 1937 and was last looked at by Kroll and Foldy in 1952. It says that the evenness and oddness of isobaric spin itself is very often a sufficient principle for eliminating transitions to certain states in self-conjugate nuclei. For instance, in the work of Browne reported two days ago all the reactions of the type (α,d), (d,α) and such in self-conjugate nuclei are strictly self-mirrored reactions. Consequently you do not get transitions from an odd T to an even T (in this case we are only talking about T = 0 and T = 1 so this is automatically satisfied). Now that we have the benefit of Garvey's work in this field where the first T = 2 states are we can really check this thing for the first time. It sounds unbelievable but you should be able to go from T = 0 to T = 2 if charge symmetry holds. Of course, if charge independence holds you should not go to T = 2. We all know the answer more or less but it certainly is worth checking to see just what the limits are on this.

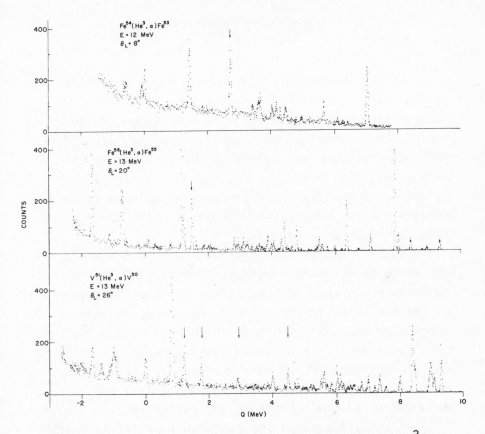

Fig. 1. Typical spectra of α-particles from (He^3, α) reactions on targets of Fe^{54}, Fe^{56} and V^{51}. The peaks corresponding to analogue states resulting from pickup of a $1f_{7/2}$ neutron are indicated by arrows. The strong peak near $Q = 1$ MeV is a contaminant from a light element.

CONFERENCE SUMMARY
D. H. Wilkinson

It has become usual for conference summarizers to talk exclusively about their own work - in a different field. Unfortunately, the organizers of this conference only wished me into this hot seat about two weeks ago, and so deprived me of the opportunity of making the usual preparations, and so I am actually driven to summarizing this conference. I hope you will forgive me this breach with tradition. I wouldn't like it to be taken as a precedent.

There is, however, one tradition that I shall adhere to in actually naming the participants to the conference who made contributions; and that tradition is the tradition of the British Judiciary, in which judges, on handing down their judgement, only actually name the authorities on which the judgement is based, if those authorities are either exceedingly distinguished, or dead. So I leave it to those whom I name and do not name to do the arithmetic appropriately.

I will summarize the conference as far as I can, in the form of my personal impressions of what we have learned, as the chairman said I would, and I will do this under a number of headings:

I.   What We Know
II. What We Believe
III. Doubts

I will take these headings in order.

Turning now to my second heading, I think that we believe in analogue states. Turning next to my third heading I will discuss the conference. The first section we had was on the basis of the analogue business, namely, charge dependence and charge symmetry, and we there had a review of the present status of our knowledge about the actual nucleon-nucleon forces, without any mention of the possible importance of the three body forces, because we are still astonishingly - almost completely - ignorant of the possible importance of the three body forces in nuclei. This will be important for the complex systems we have been talking about chiefly, and of course no information comes from the two nucleon system.

First of all, we had a look at the proton-proton singlet scattering length, and saw values for that ranging from -16.6 to -16.9 fm. This is to be compared with the neutron-neutron scattering length, which is -16.5 $\pm$ 1.3 fm. This is not the actual number given at the conference. It is one which I think is a little more recent and a little more accurate, that was given at the Williamsburg conference five weeks ago.

This corresponds then to a possible departure from charge symmetry of about one percent, or something of this sort and perhaps we can just remember that a somewhat similar statement can be made about the degree of charge symmetry on the basis of Coulomb energy comparisons of isobaric doublets.

WIGNER, Princeton: What is this comparison of now?

WILKINSON: This is a comparison of the singlet scattering length in the proton-proton and neutron-neutron systems. The charge symmetry comparisons.

WIGNER: What about symmetry?

WILKINSON: That includes symmetry, and thank you for saving me at least one minute of my summary by the remarks you made before I began.

If one compares the proton-proton and neutron-proton singlet scattering length, of course there is a big difference, say, 6.83 ± 0.15 fm, and this corresponds then to a difference of potential strength of about 4.3 percent for a Yukawa potential, but very much less than this for a square well, and it is not quite clear why the difference between these two potentials is so great.

This is something which will bear further investigation. Certainly, we cannot simply assume that the effective form of the interaction is going to be well represented by a Yukawa potential. Again, let us remember that somewhat similar information, in the sense that the neutron-proton interaction seems to be a little stronger than the proton-proton, again comes from Coulomb energies with an indication which at the moment is very crude but which is certainly consistent with somewhere between zero and a 4% difference.

These are comparisons in the singlet scattering lengths. Another comparison can come by a quite different form of analysis which has been done, particularly by Breit, which takes into account the whole body of information (all spin states), and analyzes it in terms of a coupling constant, g^2.

This again was not mentioned at this conference, but I will give you the information that from the proton-proton data, the best current figure for the coupling constant is 15.1, and from the neutron-proton data, $13.9 \pm .9$, which are not really inconsistent. The magnetic moment and Coulomb corrections remain quite strong to these figures and for example, represent about one unit of correction in the case of the neutron-

proton coupling constant. We are still rather unsure
about the best way to make these rather delicate electromagnetic corrections.

We were given some discussion of the possible
meaning of these departures, or possible departures,
from charge symmetry and charge independence. It seems
as though differences of this magnitude are very reasonable, just in view of the differences between $\pi^{\pm}$
and π^{0} mesons. If one considers the possible potential
associated with pion exchange, they are not equal in
mass, their interactions will not be quite the same, so
there will be differences on those grounds. It seems
as though the expected magnitude of those differences
is quite reasonably in accord with these empirical observations here.

We also saw some mention of a possible π^{0} - η^{0}
mixing. This is essentially a Coulomb mixing of
isobaric spin in the exchange particle itself, and if
one has such a mixing the real exchange particle, the
virtual particle, that is really exchanged, is a mixture of these two, then we shall have a breakdown of
charge independence and also a breakdown of charge symmetry. It is rather difficult at the moment to make
more than just that qualitative observation.

So what one gets from looking at the fundamental
interactions is the go ahead to talk about more complicated systems. Such departures as there are from charge
independence are quite small. I think one should remember, in discussing the more complicated systems,
that these departures from charge independence are
roughly on the order of the Coulomb forces, and if
Coulomb forces are important in breaking down the charge
independent wave functions, then so also may be the

specifically nuclear differences. The form of the potential is totally different, and I don't think one can simply assume that there is not going to be a significant contribution to isobaric spin mixing and associated effects from the charge dependence of specifically neutron forces. Perhaps it should be looked at more directly.

We have then, as the second chapter, taken quite an extensive look at the traditional methods for determining isobaric spin purity or charge parity following Georges Temmer's comment.

We looked at electromagnetic transitions, β-decay and also the type of reaction symbolized by (d,α). That last type of reaction, let us remember is not really an investigation of charge independence in the case of self-conjugate nuclei.

What we learned from this is that everything is more or less all right and more or less as we thought it was for several years now, namely, that the low-lying states do appear to be quite decent eigenstates of "T"-certainly to better than a percent or so, which is roughly the limit of our experiments - maybe a few tenths of a percent. The more highly excited states do get progressively less pure from an isobaric state point of view, although as of today our knowledge of this is not too extensive, (on the quantitative aspect of isobaric spin impurity). To get a number you always have to guess what is the reduced width of the state which is mixed in. You don't know what state is mixed in of the other isobaric spin, so you are driven to using systematics and systematics always have an extensive spread of about an order of magnitude.

Except when making an identification of states,

specific states, to be mixed in, it is rather difficult to get an actual number for the isobaric spin
impurity.

One or two warnings were voiced in a salutary
way about all these methods, particularly this (d,α)
type of reaction, in which the spin effect in inhibiting
the transition of the isobaric spin forbidden states,
can be very important just because this is the way the
spins run - one is often exciting states of spin zero,
as the isobaric spin forbidden transition, and this
will produce an inhibition.

Also, we have seen a number of examples which
are by no means fully understood of, as it were, the
coyness of the $T = 1$ states, (talking now about self-
conjugate nuclei), in their excitation by methods
which are not isobaric spin dependent. At least they
do not have isobaric spin selection rules associated
with them. So, for example, (p,p') and other reactions,
leading to $T = 1$ states, are often rather weak, even
when there is no obvious reason why they should be, so
this kind of thing has to modulate the enthusiasm with
which we interpret the apparently isobaric spin forbidden transitions.

Another point which was made, though not at all
extensively, is that even though reactions such as this
are fast, that does not mean that the Coulomb forces
will not be important. Let me just remind you of the
old argument here; if we take the system such as A + B,
going to C + D, and if both initial particles are $T = 0$,
then before the system comes together we have, let us
say, a good $T = 0$ state, but when the systems come together the Coulomb forces start growing in other isobaric spins and they will grow them in as a function of

time something like this:

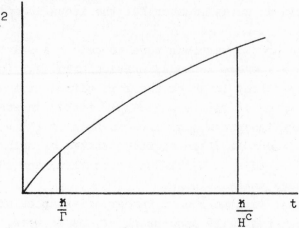

If I denote by α^2 the measure of the amounts
and intensity of other isobaric spin that is grown in,
it will rise as a function of time, something like
this, where the time constant at t_2 is presumably on
the order of the Coulomb matrix element, i.e. $t_2 \sim \dfrac{\hbar}{H^c}$.
So if now this system, A + B, stays together for
a long time, as it would if it went through a compound
nucleus, then the other isobaric spin grows, and in
the decay the isobaric spin is not conserved as from
the initial state.

If, on the other hand, the reaction is very fast,
the system breaks up very quickly, and not much mixing
takes place and the rules work. So the growing-in
time t_1 will be something on the order of the characteristic width of the levels through which the reaction
is passing, i.e. $t_1 \sim \dfrac{\hbar}{\Gamma}$.

So if one has a direct interaction, this is a
relatively short interaction, there is no time for the
Coulomb forces to work in the intermediate state, and
so the rules should work. Now if we go to forward

angles, and do a direct reaction there is a strong
tendency to interpret the excitation of $T = 1$ states
as being a good measure of isobaric spin impurities in
the initial and final states. The argument here is
that the intermediate system has been cut out of the
reckoning by the short time scale.

This may not be valid, this sort of diagram I
have drawn here rather refers to the nuclear reaction
times, the time for which the nuclear forces are at
work, which in the case of direct interaction, of
course, is a short time, because nuclear forces are
short range. However, the Coulomb forces are not, and
all the time particle A is cruising up to particle B,
they are in Coulomb communication for a period of time,
which is long compared to the actual nuclear reaction
time which we imagine to be associated with this sort
of distance.

Because of the longer time scale of the Coulomb
interaction, one may effectively go up the curve rather
more than one thinks.

Of course, the Coulomb is very flat across each
nucleus (projectile and target); on the other hand, it
is time varying so it is not very easy to say, qualitatively, how important this effect might be. Probably
it is susceptible to a reasonably quantitative guess,
but I have not seen such a guess made.

I turn now to the analogue states as we more
normally think of them. But, first, perhaps, before
talking about analogue states as seen in the compound
nucleus, or intermediate system, just one or two words
about analogue states as seen as residual nuclei. We
want, of course, as I have mentioned, to be able to use
compound nucleus analogue states as spectroscopic tools.

This involves us in all sorts of analyses and one wants
to have confidence in the analysis procedures that one
is using.

When one sees analogue states as residual states
that one knows all about, then one can apply what are now
conventional methods, e.g. DWBA and so on, and extract
relative spectroscopic factors and these had better agree.
So it is good to remember, before talking about the compound nucleus analogue states, where our difficulties are
of a more novel character, that we are not yet completely
squared away on the older problem of properly understanding direct reactions.

We saw this morning a couple of examples of the difficulty that one gets into in getting the correct ratio
between spectroscopic factors for analogue residual states,
and it is quite clear that this is not a completely solved
problem. Also, in comparing, for example, the (d,n) and
(He^3,d) reactions, we saw that the relative spectroscopic
factors for T=1 and T=0 states may be different, as excited in these two reactions, although from the point of
view of our model they are essentially identical. This problem is probably linked with the earlier one that I mentioned, of exciting different analogue states and understanding their relative spectroscopic factors, but here
we have a problem that we are not completely clear on.

Now I will go to the compound nuclear analogue
states, and draw a very familiar diagram (following page).
Take a nucleus (A,Z) and add to it a neutron, for example
by stripping, and make (A+1,Z) or add a proton and form
the analogue state, (A+1,Z+1). These are T-upper states
and somewhere down here are T-lower states. I have taken
out the Coulomb energy difference in comparing the $T_>$
states in (A+1,Z+1) and (A+1,Z).

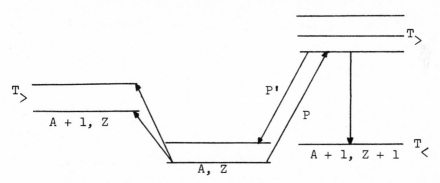

These are now very well-established phenomena, and
perhaps before I talk at all about the hopes one has for
these, I might just say one or two things very briefly
about the actual phenomenon of the compound nuclear
formation of the analogue states.

We have had a little bit of, not confusion at this
meeting, but a little bit of uncertainty, about how one
related the shape of the analogue states seen in real life
with the reduced width of the proton that is exciting it.
Let's consider the region of excitation in which we have
the analogue state which, primitively would be excited at
the arrow position, and note that there are a great number of T-lower states right along here into which it
dissolves.

Now, as a rule, one doesn't know the anatomy, as
it were, of the analogue state in detail. One just sees
an envelope, as it were, Except perhaps in the one case
of the Duke work, which was reported, i.e.
$A^{40} + p \to K^{41}$, where one really does see these fine
structure states as separated - almost completely

separated - states. If I could use a modest expression in describing this Duke work, I would call it
stupendously beautiful. I have never seen such an
experiment before. It gave me an immediate sensual
thrill, if one may be so bold to say.

So if one can start talking about the analogue
state from that starting point in which these are completely well separated one from another, which presumably only happens in rather rare cases of single-
channel phenomena and so on, how does one understand
the relationship between that and the gross envelope
of the analogue states as we normally think of them?
This is perhaps a little bit puzzling. Suppose we can't
be like Duke, and do it properly but have to use poor
resolution. One is now averaging over many of these
completely separated fine structure elements of the
analogue state. How does it come about then that one
observed the overall envelope? Well, this is entirely
because of the complete coherence between the fine
structure states here.

If you look at them one by one, if you look at
one on the left hand side of the diagram, what we really
see is that it goes up like that, and down like that
so one should not draw these just as little lines like
this, but as lines that go up more than they go down.
Then when we get on the right side of the center of
the analogue state, we find that they go the other way.
They go down more than they go up, as you can see.

Now when we average over this with poor energy
resolution then in this region we tend to be up, and
in this region we tend to be down, and the analogue
state, as we would then see it, would go something
like the smooth curve.

I would rather not draw it outside of the fine structure amplitudes because it can't get outside their envelope; in fact, it should be considerably below it, if the sharpness of these states is much better than the separation.

So if now we can only do the experiment this way, we see that it does not matter whether we know or do not know what the fine anatomy is, because if these underlying states are really broad and not sharp - broad now compared with the fine structure width as I have drawn it here, but still narrow compared to the fine analogue widths, then we get just the same picture as before. They tend to be plus on the low side, and minus on the high side.

So if there are many channels open and the individual fine structure states are broad, we get the same gross envelope in poor resolution as if the individual fine structure states are exceedingly narrow. In other words, there is no real worry about this in extracting the parameters of the overall analogue states, entirely due to the complete coherence that exists between the fine structure states. In discussing the interpretation of this envelope here one could be unlucky and get fluctuations and that sort of thing, but this is something which is relatively simple to handle, or, if one cannot handle it, one can move on to nuclei where it looks nicer.

The point now is can we, with confidence, interpret the strengths that we get for the proton width in through the analogue state, in terms of spectroscopic factors?

Well, it is really more or less a matter of taste. One can say that the object of this analogue

state business is to understand the mechanism and really
to understand how the dissolving of the analogue state
into the fine structure comes about. As I say, it is
a matter of taste. It is not my own personal taste.
My personal taste is that I am much more interested in
the nuclear structure information, i.e. the spectroscopic factors. I am not very interested in the mechanism. But, obviously, one must understand the mechanism before you can turn it around and use the phenomena to give you the spectroscopic information. So
it is very important to check whether the apparent
properties of this proton as you put it into the compound nucleus forming the analogue state are really
the same as the properties of the neutron, as one put
it into there by stripping. In making that comparison
I go back to my earlier remark that one is not going to
have real confidence in making this comparison unless
one has coped with the easier problem of straightforward
direct interactions insofar as that is used for extracting spectroscopic factors.

So, perhaps, not trying to run on this difficult
problem, before we learn to crawl on the other one
would be a good idea.

We cannot say that there is no future in analogue state work, because it merely tells us what the
reduced width is here when we know what it is there
anyway. The point was made several times very properly that if we can understand the simple process of
elastic scattering we can also try and understand the
inelastic scattering in which the p' comes out to an
excited state of the target nucleus, and this is, of
course, an equivalent to (d,p) stripping using an
excited state of the target nucleus as target. As

some theoretician said in a flash of perception this
is a difficult experiment.

We can indeed learn something by the inelastic
scattering that we can't by stripping, if we can really
master the details of the inelastic scattering process.
Similarly for (p,n) and more complicated reactions.

The inelastic scattering does not seem to be in
completely good shape yet. For elastic scattering you
expect cockeyed shapes because of the interference
with the Coulomb or direct scattering mechanisms.
Offhand, one might expect to get a nice symmetrical
Breit-Wigner shape. However, for (p,p') through analogues one does not. As a rule it is lopsided. One
does see interference effects and at this point I would
like to make two remarks. One is that one is getting
interference with other levels nearby. The other is
that one is getting interference with the background,
and, of course, there is no real difference between the
two.

We did see some quite good signs both in (p,p')
and (p,n) of a quantitative understanding of the asymmetry of the inelastic groups in terms of specific calculations, done in relation to the specific model for
the background. So this is something that presumably
will get understood if perhaps only semi-empirically.
I don't think one wants a very deep theory of the background interference - an empirical understanding will
do.

So there seems there to be very good hope that
one can turn this into a good spectroscopic tool, and
one can look forward very much to that being done. I
should also perhaps mention the question of the gamma
decay of the analogue state although only briefly. This

is obviously a somewhat difficult technique, but also
can be a very valuable one because one will get just
as important spectroscopic information by the gamma
transitions as one does from the inelastic scattering.
So a thorough investigation of gamma transitions from
analogue states, I think, is going to be very interesting and valuable in the future.

And now, a very interesting possibility that has
come out of this conference, and again something that
impressed me very much, is the possibility of finding
spins of analogue states when one doesn't know the spin
of the corresponding states in the rather more conventional nucleus. One quite often will find one's self
in a position where the spin of the well-defined isolated gamma emitting levels of the parent analogue is
unknown, and where one can then fix it by going to the
analogue state and finding its spin. The point here
being that one has the possibility of doing this, as
shown by the extremely nice work from the University
of Texas by measuring polarization of the scattering
through the analogue states. Here we have the advantage, that we have a background, namely, the Coulomb,
or optical model scattering, against which the polarization through the analogue state can establish itself.
This will, as it were, write its signature on the
background, yielding a polarization which we understand.
So, as is often the case, if you can do an interference
experiment, you get more information than if you study
the object of interest in isolation.

So, by these means, and they are obviously capable of considerable extension, one should be able to
do the spectroscopy of low-lying states by going to
the analogue better than by studying them directly.

626

There may well be a significant future in this for
ordinary conventional nuclear structure physics when
one will, without further mentioning it, use the analogue state properties just as another tool for determining the spins of states.

My impression after this part of the conference
was that I am very much in agreement with Peter Axel's
historical remark that we are probably now in the analogue state business at about the same stage as we were
in the early days of Butler stripping. It was not at
all clear then whether that would ever be a valuable
tool. I think it is now becoming somewhat clearer that
it may become a valuable tool.

Similarly, we are now guessing, in the same way
as we did then, about the analogue state business. It
may become purely a spectroscopic tool long after we
are interested in its actual mechanism. I expect it
will be a very valuable spectroscopic tool, and I think
that will probably turn out to be correct.

I have for very obvious reasons failed to say
anything at all about the theory of this business. The
theory, as we have been told, is very difficult, and
that I believe. The only historical remark that I
would make about the theory is that - and it is a very
obvious one, I'm afraid - before analogue states were
discovered we did not think that they existed. We
thought that isobaric spin was so ill-defined; correspondingly, the definition of the analogue state, as we
knew it, was likewise so ill-defined, so broad, that it
wasn't worth thinking about. Now, of course, they have
been discovered; theoretically it is going to be quite
difficult to understand how they are as broad as they
are. This is just the way theory goes, it oscillates

627

and sometimes converges on the right answer.

One thing that did come out of the theoretical discussions is the possibility in some instances of defining the isobaric spin purity of an analogue state, and we also saw some experimental possibilities of making a meaningful measurement here. I think we will all be looking forward to that with considerable anticipation.

Having now discharged the duty that was laid upon me by the organizers of the conference, I would like at this time to discharge a very much more pleasant duty which they did not lay upon me, and that is thanking them very much, and I am sure this is on your behalf too, for arranging this conference, in getting us here, and in being so very efficient and pleasant about it.

I think we must all be very grateful to them for this, and for enabling us to spend these very pleasant few days in sunny Florida, the Analogue State.

CONTRIBUTED PAPERS
(Not Presented)

S1. ISOBARIC ANALOGUE STATES IN I^{131}

J. Burde, L. Birstein, G. Engler, A. Ginsburg
A. A. Jaffe and A. Marinov

The Hebrew University
Jerusalem, Israel

The isobaric analogue states of Te^{131} have been investigated with the (p,p) and (p,p') reactions on a target enriched in Te^{130}. Excitation functions for both the elastically and inelastically scattered protons have been measured in the bombarding energy range of 7.5 to 12.6 MeV using the proton beam of a Tandem Van de Graaff accelerator. Spectra from two solid state detectors (Li-Si) were recorded simultaneously in multichannel analyzers. Absolute cross sections were measured by comparison with elastic scattering of 3-MeV protons at 60° to the incident beam which was assumed to be due to Rutherford scattering only. Proton spectra were observed in the above range of energies for angles of 90°, 125° and 165° to the incident beam.

Figure 1 shows the results obtained at 165° for the elastic group and the inelastic groups leading to the 0.846-MeV (2^+), 1.588 + 1.633-MeV [unresolved, (4^+), (2^+)] and 1.982-MeV excited states in Te^{130}. A fourth inelastic group leading to 1.815 + 1.885-MeV states (unresolved) in Te^{130} was also observed, having a much smaller cross section. Figure 2 shows the excitation functions obtained for the elastically scattered protons at $90°$, $125°$ and $165°$.

A resonance identified to be the analogue of the ground state of Te^{131} was found for $E_p^{c.m.} = 7.96$ MeV corresponding to a Coulomb displacement energy between Te^{131} and I^{131} of 13.87 MeV. Thirteen further resonances were observed and are also identified as corresponding to analogues of low-lying states of Te^{131}. A further resonance at an incident proton energy of $E_p^{c.m.} = 11.38$ MeV is observed clearly only for the inelastic proton group leading to the 850 MeV level in Te^{130}, and does not correspond to a level in Te^{131} found in the (d,p) reaction[1].

Figure 3 shows the correspondence between the levels in Te^{131} obtained by the Te^{130}(d,p) reaction and the levels in I^{131} obtained in our work. The results are summarized in Table I; column 2 gives the observed energies of the resonances in the center of mass system. Where strong inelastic resonances were observed, the energies of the resonances were taken as the positions of the maxima of the peaks, while in the low-energy region where the inelastic peaks are weak but strong resonances are observed in the elastic scattering, the energies of the resonances were obtained by the method of Haeberli[2]. The total widths of the resonances (Γ, column 3) were similarly obtained from the peaks in the excitation curves for the inelastic channels where possible, or else from the excitation curves for elastic scattering by the above method.

For the prominent resonances in the elastic scattering (at $E_p^{c.m.} = 7.96$; 8.27; and 10.18 MeV respectively) theoretical values for the excitation functions at various angles were calculated assuming a real potential well of Woods-Saxon shape. The method

of calculation was similar to that of Jones et al.[3,4].
The depth of the real potential was adjusted in each
case to give the proper resonance in the proton bombarding energy and the parameters for spin-orbit
strength, the radius and diffuseness were V_{SO} = 7.5 MeV,
r_0 = 1.25 F, and a = 0.65 F respectively.

The theoretical shapes so obtained, are in good
agreement with the experimental results for values of
orbital angular momentum identical to those found for
the analogues of the states in the reaction
$Te^{130}(d,p)Te^{131}$ [1].

The single particle proton width ($\Gamma_{s.p.}$) was
obtained from the same calculations.

The ratio of the proton width to the total
width (Γ_p/Γ) was obtained from the elastic scattering
data at 165° by using the relation

$$k\left[(d\sigma/d\omega)_{max}^{1/2} \pm (d\sigma/d\omega)_{min}^{1/2} \right] = \frac{\Gamma_p}{\Gamma} (J+1/2)P_\ell(\cos\theta)$$

and the results for Γ_p are given in Table I. Column 5
in Table I gives the ratios of Γ_p to $\frac{1}{2T_0+1}$ $\Gamma_{s.p.}$
where T_0 is the isobaric spin of the target nucleus,
Te^{130}; these values should be equal to the spectroscopic factors for the corresponding states obtained
in the (d,p) reaction[1], given in the last column.
Also included in Table I are the energies, the values
of l_n, and the spins of the low-lying states in Te^{131}
as obtained in the $Te^{130}(d,p)Te^{131}$ reaction.

It is seen that the (p,p') reaction allows the
identification of analogue states which are much less
pronounced in the elastic scattering data. The values
of $\frac{\Gamma_p \times (2T_0+1)}{\Gamma_{s.p.}}$ obtained from the analysis of the

elastic proton scattering agree with the spectroscopic factors for the analogues of these states from the (d,p) reaction to within a factor of two, which is satisfactory agreement considering the uncertainties involved in the calculations used to derive these quantities from the experimental data.

REFERENCES

1) R. K. Jolly, Phys. Rev. <u>136</u> (1964) B683.

2) W. Haeberli, Phys. Rev. <u>99</u> (1955) A640.

3) K. W. Jones, J. P. Schiffer, L. L. Lee, Jr., A. Marinov and J. L. Lerner, (to be published in Phys. Rev.).

4) We are indebted to Mr. Y. Tikochinsky for a computer program for optical model calculations which was used in our analysis.

TABLE I. Results of (p,p) and (p,p') reactions on Te^{130} and comparison with results from the Te^{130}(d,p)Te^{131} reactions.

	$(E_p^{c.m.} - 7.96)$ (MeV)	Γ (keV)	Γ_p (keV)	$\dfrac{(2T_0 + 1) \times \Gamma_p}{\Gamma_{s.p.}}$	Data from Te^{130}(d,p)Te^{131} [a]			
					E (MeV)	l_n	J^π	S
1.	0.00	78	13	0.64	0.00	2	$3/2^+$	0.28
2.	0.31	60	35	0.53	0.29	0	$1/2^+$	0.31
3.	2.22	70	27	0.58	2.27	3	$7/2^-$	0.40
4.	2.47	90			2.49	{1}	{$3/2^-$}	0.032
						{5}	{$9/2^-$}	0.074
5.	2.54	75			2.56	1	($3/2^-$)	0.18
6.	2.94	120			2.99	1	($3/2^-$)	0.064
7.	3.15				3.15	1	($3/2^-$)	0.039
8.	3.33	85			3.38	(3)	($5/2^-$)	0.051
						(5)	($9/2^-$)	0.078
						(6)	($13/2^+$)	0.19
9.	3.42	100				(3)	($5/2^-$)	0.10

TABLE I continued

	$(E_p^{c.m.} - 7.96)$ (MeV)	Γ (keV)	Γ_p (keV)	$\dfrac{(2T_0 + 1) \times \Gamma_p}{\Gamma_{s.p.}}$	Data from $Te^{130}(d,p)Te^{131}$ [a]			
					E (MeV)	l_n	J^π	S
10.	3.53				3.53	(5)	($9/2^-$)	0.17
						(6)	($13/2^+$)	0.40
11.	3.63				3.68	1	($1/2^-$)	0.25
12.	3.88				3.93	1	($1/2^-$)	0.10
13.	3.98				4.02	3	($5/2^-$)	0.17
						(1)	($1/2^-$)	0.20
14.	4.24				4.30	(5)	($9/2^-$)	0.12
15.	4.51	110			4.55	(6)	($13/2^+$)	0.25
						(3)	($5/2^-$)	0.12
						(6)	($9/2^-$)	0.61

[a] See Ref. 1

636

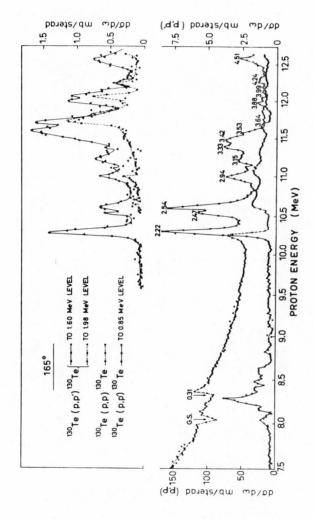

Fig. 1. Excitation curves for elastic and inelastic proton scattering by Te[130] at a laboratory angle of 165°.

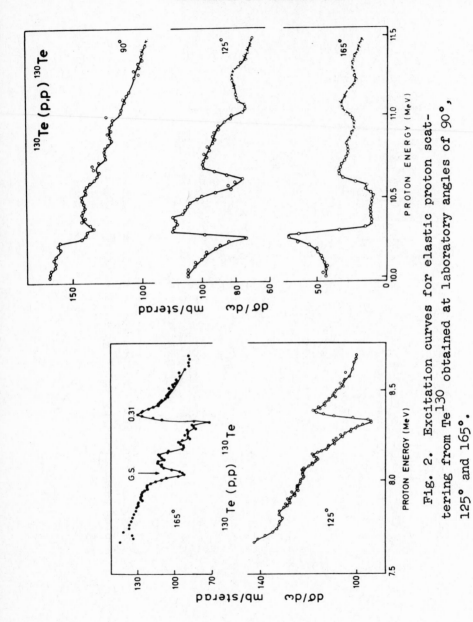

Fig. 2. Excitation curves for elastic proton scattering from Te^{130} obtained at laboratory angles of 90°, 125° and 165°.

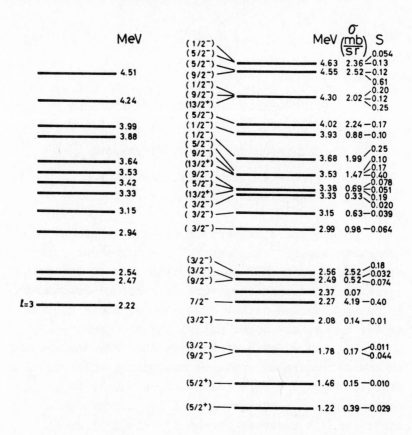

Fig. 3. Comparison between levels in Te^{131} obtained by the Te^{130}(d,p)Te^{131} reaction[1] and levels in I^{131} obtained from the present work. The energies of the levels in I^{131} are given as E = (E$_p^{c.m.}$ - 7.96) MeV.

S2. ISOBARIC ANALOGUE RESONANCES OF THE $V^{51}(p,\gamma)Cr^{52}$ AND $V^{51}(p,n)Cr^{51}$ REACTIONS

E. Teranishi and B. Furubayashi

Electrotechnical Laboratory
Tanashi-cho, Kitatama-gun, Tokyo

Since the discovery of isobaric analogue resonances in the Sr^{88} + p and Y^{89} + p reactions, many efforts have been made in investigations of isobaric correspondences and structure of analogue resonances in heavy compound nuclei of A = 80 to 140. However, as far as medium-weight nuclei are concerned, only quite limited numbers of experiments have been reported on the structure of analogue resonances as compound states. We report here analogue resonances in Cr^{52} corresponding to the ground and low-lying excited states in V^{52} observed in the $V^{51}(p,\gamma)Cr^{52}$ and $V^{51}(p,n)Cr^{51}$ reactions.

Excitation curves of the (p,γ) reaction in the E_p = 0.6 to 2.7 MeV region and the (p,n) reaction in the E_p = 2.0 to 2.6 MeV region were measured using the protons from a 3 MeV Van de Graaff accelerator and a vacuum evaporated natural vanadium target. The bombarding protons had an energy spread less than 2 keV and the absolute energy scale was accurate to ± 5 keV. The thickness of the target was 6 keV to 1.6 MeV protons. Gamma rays were detected with a 11 cm diameter x 10 cm thick NaI scintillation counter having an energy bias of 2.5 MeV, and neutrons were measured with a BF_3 long counter.

Several strong resonances were observed in the excitation curves well separated from each other and distinguished from numerous fine resonances as shown in Figs. 1 and 2. Strong resonances in the (p,n) reactions were also observed in the (p,γ) excitation curve in the same energy region[1].

Excitation energies of analogue states in Cr^{52} can be estimated from the level scheme of low-lying states of V^{52} [2-6] and the Coulomb displacement energy[7]

$$\Delta_c = (1.444 \pm 0.005) \left(\frac{\overline{Z}}{A^{1/3}} \right) - (1.13 \pm 0.04)$$

$$= 7.96 \pm 0.07 \text{ MeV}.$$

Table I shows comparisons between the excitation energies of the observed strong resonances in Cr^{52} and expected energies of isobaric analogue states. The differences are always 80 to 100 keV. Such a systematic appearance of strong resonances at a constant Coulomb displacement energy from the levels of V^{52} would strongly suggest that these resonances actually correspond to isobaric analogue states in the compound nucleus Cr^{52}. The average value of the observed Coulomb displacement energy is 8.05 ± 0.02 MeV.

Angular distribution of the ground state neutrons (n_o) at the 2.33 MeV resonance, measured with a shape-discriminated stilbene scintillation counter, is fitted by $1 + (0.22 \pm 0.06) \times P_2 (\cos \theta)$. This distribution is compatible with an $\ell_p = 1$ assignment for the resonance required from $\ell_n = 1$ of the corresponding state of V^{52} [2,4].

One of the structures of analogue resonances is

641

shown in Fig. 3, which has been obtained for the (p,n) resonance at E_p = 2.33 MeV in measurements with higher energy-resolution using a 1.5 keV thick target. The energy resolution is still insufficient to resolve individual fine resonances but one can observe a "gross structure" enveloping nearby fine resonances, the width of which is about 15 keV. The observed width of any fine resonance included in this structure does not seem to differ appreciably from those of normal states in a distant region. Furthermore, it should be noted that the gross structure has a slightly asymmetric shape. Those structures have been observed also on the resonance peaks Nos. 4, 8, 10, 12 and 13, while other peaks, Nos. 3, 5, 6 and 7, do not show observable structure in the present experiment.

Such aspects of the structure of analogue resonances are analogous to the fine structure of the analogue resonance observed in the $Mo^{92}(p,p)Mo^{92}$ reaction[8] and these are expected to be interpreted in terms of an enhanced amplitude fluctuation of narrow normal states by the analogue state. According to Robson's theoretical treatment[9,10], an isolated analogue resonance of the total (p,n) cross section is to be expressed approximately by

$$\sigma \propto \frac{(\varepsilon_\lambda - E)^2}{(\varepsilon_\lambda + \Delta - E)^2 + 1/4\ \Gamma^2}, \quad E_0 = \varepsilon_\lambda + \Delta \tag{1}$$

If one estimates an adequate zero-level of the neutron yield as illustrated by the dotted line in Fig. 3, Eq. 1 offers a reasonable fitting to the observed gross structure as shown by the broken line using parameters E_0 = 2.331 MeV, Δ = 25 keV and Γ = 14

642

keV. The fitting is normalized at the peak point of the resonance.

If an analogue resonance is assumed to be dominated by the proton channel, the resonance shape should be the same for the (p,n) and (p,γ) reactions as a consequence of the theory[10]. In our preliminary experiments on this prediction, approximately the same width and asymmetry of the gross structure have been actually observed for the (p,n) and (p,γ) resonances at E_p = 2.33 MeV, although some difference is observed between the fine structures of both reactions.

REFERENCES

1) E. Teranishi and B. Furubayashi, Phys. Letts., (to be published).

2) H. A. Enge, MIT Laboratory of Nuclear Science Progress Report, (May 1960), p. 98.

3) J. H. Bjerregaad, P. F. Dahl, O. Hansen and G. Sidenius, Nucl. Phys. 51 (1964) 641.

4) J. Catalá, A. García, J. M. Bolta, S. Hinds, H. Marchant and A. E. Forest, Nucl. Phys. 74 (1965) 1.

5) O. A. Wasson, K. J. Wetzel and C. K. Bockelman, Phys. Rev. 136 (1964) B1640.

6) D. H. White, B. G. Sanders, W. John and R. W. Jowell, Jr., Nucl. Phys. 72 (1965) 241.

7) J. D. Anderson, C. Wong and J. W. McClure, Phys. Rev. 138 (1965) B615.

8) P. Richard, C. F. Moore, D. Robson and J. D. Fox, Phys. Rev. Letts. 13 (1964) 343.

9) D. Robson, Phys. Rev. 137 (1965) B535.

10) D. Robson, J. D. Fox, P. Richard and C. F. Moore, Phys. Letts. 18 (1965) 86.

TABLE I. Isobaric analogue states in Cr^{52}.

| States in V^{52} | Analogue states in Cr^{52} | | | | |
| calculated | observed | | | | |
E_x (MeV) ($\pm$ 0.008 MeV)	E_x (MeV)	Peak No.	E_p(lab.) (MeV) ($\pm$ 0.006 MeV)	E_x (MeV)	E_x(obs.)$-$ E_x(calc.) (keV)
0	11.172	1	0.763	11.263	91
0.021	11.193	2	0.781	11.281	88
0.146	11.318	3	0.910	11.407	89
0.431	11.603	4	1.210	11.702	99
(0.768)	(11.940)	5	(1.558)	(12.043)	103
0.787	11.959	6	1.565	12.050	91
0.839	12.011	7	1.629	12.113	102
0.873	12.045				
1.282	12.454				
1.410	12.582	8	2.203	12.676	94
1.486	12.658	9	(2.273)	(12.744)	86
1.554	12.726	10	2.333	12.803	77
1.577	12.749				
1.732	12.904	11	2.521	12.983	79
1.756	12.928	12	2.538	13.003	75
1.791	12.963	13	2.583	13.048	85

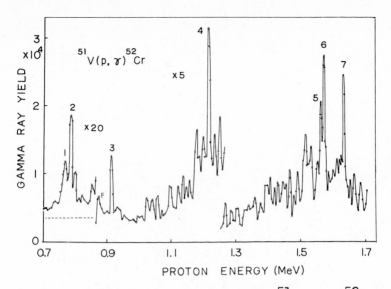

Fig. 1. Excitation curve of the $V^{51}(p,\gamma)Cr^{52}$ reaction measured with overall energy resolution about 8 keV. The dotted line in the lowest proton energy region expresses the background level of γ-rays.

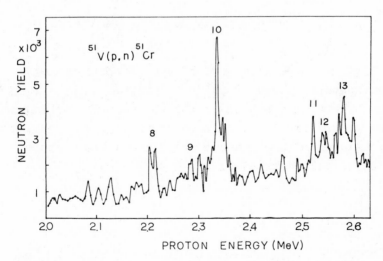

Fig. 2. Excitation curve of the $V^{51}(p,n)Cr^{51}$ reaction measured with overall energy resolution of about 6 keV.

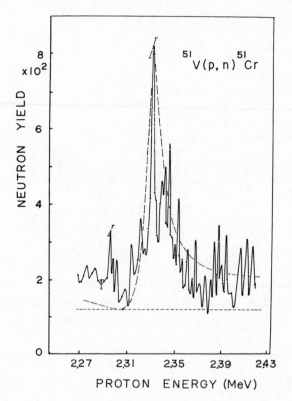

Fig. 3. Fine structure of the isobaric analogue resonance of the $V^{51}(p,n)Cr^{51}$ reaction at E_p = 2.33 MeV. The broken line expresses the theoretical fitting to the gross structure. The dotted line is the estimated zero-level of the neutron yield. The flags express statistical accuracies.

S3. STUDY OF THE LOW-LYING ISOBARIC ANALOGUE STATES OF Sr^{89}*

E. R. Cosman, A. K. Kerman, H. A. Enge and A. Sperduto

Massachusetts Institute of Technology

Cambridge, Massachusetts

The analogue states of the low-lying levels in Sr^{89} are studied via the (p,p) and (p,p') reactions on Sr^{88}. The information from conventional Breit-Wigner fits to the elastic data is compared with the results of a DWBA analysis of the $Sr^{88}(d,p)Sr^{89}$ reaction. In addition, an analysis of the $Sr^{88}(p,p)$ data is discussed, and preliminary results are given. This involves a solution of the two coupled channel equations that describe the analogue state excitations.

EXPERIMENTAL RESULTS

Figure 1 shows a $Sr^{88}(p,p)$ excitation curve from 4.9 to 7.5 MeV obtained with the proton beam from the MIT-ONR Van de Graaff accelerator. The target thickness was about 35 $\mu g/cm^2$, and the scattered protons were detected by surface barrier counters. The first two pronounced and well-separated resonances correspond to analogues of the $d_{5/2}$ ground state and $s_{1/2}$ first excited state of Sr^{89}, and the disturbance at 7.1 MeV is caused by interference between two d-wave

---

*This work has been supported in part through funds provided by the U. S. Atomic Energy Commission under AEC Contract AT(30-1)-2098

resonances. Several energy sweeps have revealed consistent fine deviations from a smooth cross section curve. One example is the sharp "spike" at the bottom of the 90° s-wave dip.

Figure 2 displays the proton spectrum up to 2.5-MeV excitation from the $Sr^{88}(d,p)Sr^{89}$ reaction at 7.0-MeV incident energy. Level Nos. 2, 4 and 5 had not been resolved from level No. 3 by previous investigators. Also shown are the angular distributions of the lowest six transitions, as obtained with the MIT multiple-gap spectrograph. The circles are the data, and the curves were calculated by the DWBA code JULIE. The stripping transitions 0, 1, 2 and 3 correspond to the $Sr^{88}(p,p)$ resonances mentioned above. The non-stripping levels, Nos. 4 and 5 (marked "n.s." in the figure), probably have large collective components orthogonal to $Sr^{88}(0)$ and therefore did not appear in the elastic data.

Results from inelastic proton scattering to the 1.820-MeV, 2^+ state in Sr^{88} are shown in Fig. 3. In the top of the figure, the arrows indicate the incident energies on and off resonance at which this 2^+ transition was studied; at the bottom of the figure are shown the angular distributions obtained in the multiple-gap spectrograph for this transition. By monitoring the elastic yield near resonance and by narrowing the entrance and exit slits of the analyzing magnet, it was possible to keep the energy drift of the incident beam to less than 1 keV throughout these exposures. Off resonance (E_4), the yield is low, and the angular distribution is flat. On the resonances, the yields are much higher, and the angular distributions seem to deviate from symmetry around 90°. This

648

is particularly true for E_2 = 5.056 MeV on the $d_{5/2}{}^+$ resonance for which the transition shows a pronounced peaking in the back angles. This effect seems to vary rapidly with incident energy, since for E_1 and E_3, 30 keV to each side of E_2, it has disappeared. The shapes at E_1, E_3, E_5 and E_6 all suggest a forward-angle bump at about 60°. In the case of E_6 = 7.120 MeV, the energy was not precisely at the center of the large 7.10 analogue resonance, and therefore a back-angle peaking may have been missed. These behaviors may be due to an interference of the analogue state exciting mechanism and other reaction processes, such as Coulomb excitation.

A (p,p') excitation function for the 2^+ state at 157° has also been recorded on the nuclear-track plates, but the data had not been extracted at the time of this meeting.

ANALYSIS OF THE RESULTS

The Sr^{88}(p,p) data have been compared with Breit-Wigner shapes using the equations of Blatt and Biedenharn[1] where the adjustable parameters are E_{res}, Γ_p, Γ_{tot}, ℓ, j^π. Figure 4 shows the results of this comparison at 90°. In the $d_{5/2}$ case, this method does not reproduce the asymmetry of the shape at 90°, whereas for the other resonances, the 90° fit is good.

Table I compares the information derived from the (p,p) and (d,p) reactions. The (d,p) spectroscopic factor was derived from the relationship

$$d\sigma/d\Omega = 1.48 \ (2j + 1)S_{\ell_n j} \ \sigma(\ell_n, Q, E_d, \theta)$$

where σ is calculated from the DWBA code JULIE, and

$d\sigma/d\Omega$ is the experimental cross section. The d and p optical-model parameters used were obtained from Perey.[2] The equation used to relate θ_n to Γ_p is[3]

$$\theta_n^2 = (2T_0 + 1) \frac{\Gamma_p}{2P_\ell} \cdot \frac{m_p R^2}{\hbar^2}$$

where P_ℓ is the penetrability, T_0 = isobaric spin of target, and R = nuclear radius.

An attempt has been made to generate the analogue state resonances by coupling the proton-plus-target channel $|pT>$ to the neutron-plus-analogue state of the target channel $|nA>$. The two coupled equations describing neutron and proton wave functions, u_n and u_p, are

$$\left[E - T_p - (V_0 + iW + V_c + \frac{T_0}{2} V_1) \right] u_p = \left(\frac{T_0}{2} \right)^{1/2} V_1 u_n$$

$$\left[E - \Delta - T_n - (V_0 - \frac{T_0 - 1}{2} V_1) \right] u_n = \left(\frac{T_0}{2} \right)^{1/2} V_1 u_p$$

and the resulting exact transition matrix for the proton scattering is

$$\tau = \tau_p + \frac{T_0}{2} < \phi_p^{(-)} V_1 g V_1 \phi_p^{(+)} >$$

where τ_p gives rise to the potential scattering and the Green's function is

$$g = \frac{1}{(E - \Delta - T_n - V_0 + \frac{T_0 - 1}{2} V_1 - \frac{T_0}{2} V_1 \frac{1}{E^{(+)} - H_p} V_1)}$$

From this, one sees that the approximate position of the resonance is always at the energy of the bound neutron plus Δ, the Coulomb energy difference between $|T >$ and $|A >$.

Figure 5 shows a comparison of the experimental data to curves derived from the coupled-channel calculation. Adjusting the shapes with this method was found to be more difficult than with the previous procedure because of their very sensitive dependence on V_o, W, and V_1. The results are preliminary. To produce the curves shown, well parameters had to be used that seem unacceptable because of their deviation from values derived from optical-model analysis.

REFERENCES

1) J. M. Blatt and L. C. Biedenharn, Rev. Mod. Phys. 24 (1952) 258.

2) F. G. Perey, Phys. Rev. 131 (1963) 745.

3) D. Robson, Phys. Rev. 137 (1965) B535.

TABLE I. Comparison of spectroscopic information derived from $Sr^{88}(p,p)$ and $Sr^{88}(d,p)$.

| | $Sr^{88}(p,p)$ | | | | | | | $Sr^{88}(d,p)$ | | | | | |
| | | States in Y^{89} | | | | | | | | States in Sr^{89} | | | |
Level No.	E_p (MeV)	E_x (MeV)	ℓ, J^{π}	Γ_{tot}	Γ_p	θ_n^2		E_x (MeV)	Q (MeV)	$(2J+1)S_{\ell j}$	J^{π}	$S_{\ell j}$	ℓ_n
0	5.056	0.000	2, $5/2^+$	16	8	1.20		0.000	4.133	4.76	$5/2^+$	0.80	2
1	6.062	1.006	0, $1/2^+$	70	46	0.96		1.031	3.102	1.81	$1/2^+$	0.91	0
2	7.030	1.974	2, $(5/2^+, 3/2^+)$	50	11	0.30		1.931	2.202	0.55	$(5/2^+)$ / $(3/2^+)$	0.092 / 0.14	2
3	7.100	2.044	2, $3/2^+$	50	23	0.63		2.000	2.133	1.85	$(5/2^+)$ / $(3/2^+)$	0.31 / 0.46	2
4	not seen							2.057	2.076				n.s.
5	not seen							2.071	2.062				n.s.

652

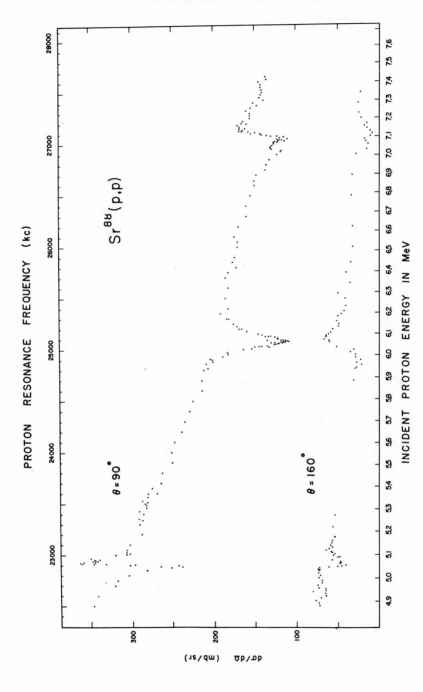

Fig. 1. Sr⁸⁸ excitation function.

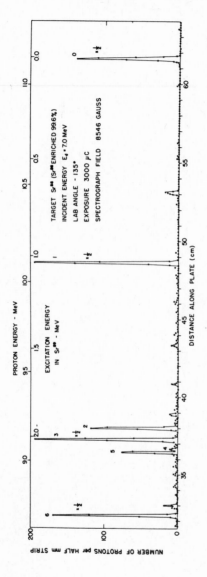

Fig. 2a. Spectrum from Sr88 (d, p) Sr89 measured in M. I. T.

Multiple Gap Spectrograph.

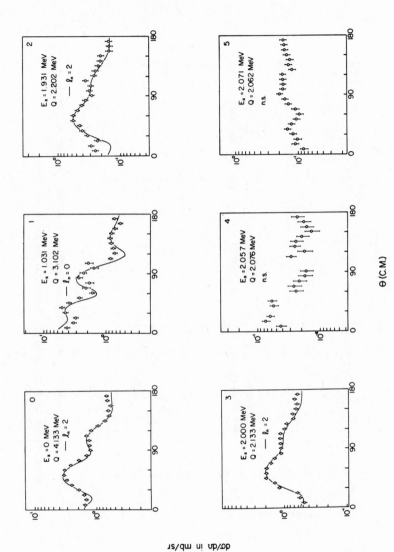

Fig. 2b. Proton angular distributions from the Sr^{88} (d, p) Sr^{89} reaction.

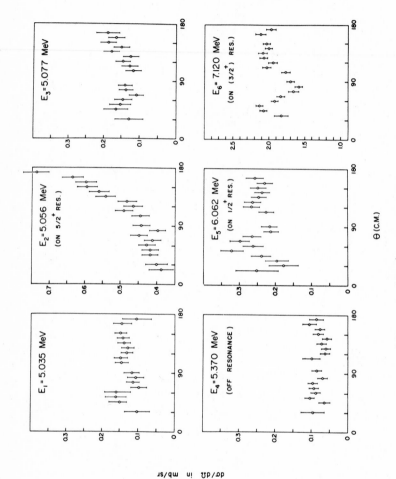

Fig. 3. Sr^{88} (p, p') Sr^{88} (2^+_1) – Angular distributions from transitions to the 2^+ state in Sr^{88} at several incident energies.

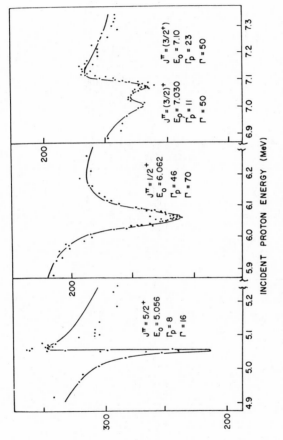

Fig. 4a. Sr^{88} (p,p) — Breit–Wigner fits to analog state resonances.

Fig. 4b. Sr^{88} (p,p) - Elastic scattering at 90°.

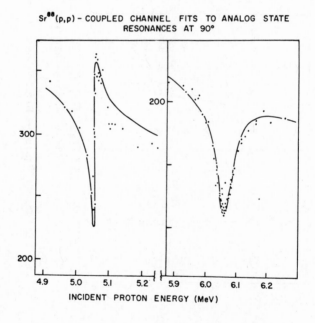

Fig. 5. Comparison of the experimental data to curves derived from the coupled-channel calculation.

S4. CHARGE ASYMMETRY OF NUCLEAR FORCES
AND THE PURITY OF ISOBARIC SPIN
K. Okamoto
University of New South Wales
Kensington, Australia

CHARGE ASYMMETRY OF NUCLEAR FORCES
Evidences for Charge Asymmetry

Three-body system.

It has been a well-known fact that the Coulomb energy (referred to as E_c) of He^3 is almost equal to the binding energy difference (referred to as Δ) of H^3 and He^3. The experimental value of Δ is given as[1]

$$\Delta = B(He^3) - B(H^3) = 0.76384 \pm 0.00026 \text{ MeV} \tag{1}$$

This fact is usually regarded as the strongest evidence in favor of charge symmetry.

However latest investigations show that E_c is not necessarily equal to Δ[2,3]. In almost all calculations on E_c in the past, He^3 was assumed to be a pure (or almost pure) S-state. However, recent studies of the form factors of H^3 and He^3 have revealed that there exists a so-called mixed symmetry S-state (S' state) in H^3 and He^3 with the probability of about 4%[4,5]. The existence of this S' state has an important consequence on the value of E_c.

It was shown[2] that the interference term between the S' state and the dominant S-state, which we shall call the SS' interference, is to decrease E_c by 20% or more if we assume the S' state probability as 2% and the resultant value of E_c is

$$E_c = (0.52 \rightarrow 0.57) \text{ MeV} \tag{2}$$

This is of course considerably smaller than Δ of Eq. 1.

However there are three short-comings of Ref. 2. (1) The sign of the S' state; although in Ref. 2 it was taken to decrease E_c, it might be opposite in the case of realistic nuclear potentials which include strong tensor forces, (2) The magnitude of the S' state; although its probability was assumed to be 2% it might be smaller than 2%[6-9] in which case the SS' interference might not decrease E_c so seriously, and (3) Error of variational calculations. The final result was based on the calculations of Pappademos[10] which is a kind of variation. Usually the accuracy of variation is low, so that the final result may not be reliable, although this point was discussed briefly after Eq. 13 of Ref. 2.

Therefore it is desirable to estimate E_c using some other methods which are free from these ambiguities. This was made later[3], in which E_c was estimated directly from the observed form factor of He^3 without assuming the S' state. Such a procedure is allowed, because the S' state is necessary only to explain the difference of the form factors of H^3 and He^3, so that if one wants to fit the form factor of He^3 only, the S-state alone is enough. The error due to neglect of the D-state would be only several percent, and be within the error of a crude estimate of this kind. The result is

$$E_c = (0.50 \rightarrow 0.56) \text{ MeV} \tag{3}$$

This is in excellent agreement with Eq. 2, which shows that the conclusion of Ref. 2 is probably reasonable.

Many-body system.

We have seen $E_c < \Delta$ for A = 3. If this is correct, the same tendency should appear also for heavier mirror nuclei with A > 3. This problem was discussed very recently[11], and it was shown that also for heavier nuclei with A > 3 E_c is generally smaller than Δ by a sizeable fraction (20 - 30%). The detailed discussion of this problem is given in Ref. 11, and here we merely quote the results in Table I.

For the sake of comparison we list the results of other authors for A = 3, 7, 11 and 14 in brackets. For A = 3, the E_c of other authors are also more or less smaller than Δ. But the difference is not so large as in our case, although it is generally the same order of magnitude. For A = 7, 11 and 14 the discrepancy we found is larger than those in previous work by one to two orders of magnitude, which shows that a serious re-investigation of this problem is necessary. In any case the fact of $E_c < \Delta$ indicates that there exists charge asymmetry of nuclear forces such that the n-n interaction is stronger than the p-p interaction.

Estimate of Charge Asymmetry

The next problem is to estimate the magnitude of charge asymmetry. Although it is very difficult to do it exactly, a crude estimate could be obtained in the following way.

Estimate from the three-body system.

(a) Method using the results of variation. This was already made by Blin-Stoyle and Yalgin[12]. They used the charge dependent potential of the following type:

$$V_{C.D.} = V_0 \ [(p+r\vec{\sigma}_1 \cdot \vec{\sigma}_2)(\tau_{1z}+\tau_{2z}) + (q+s \ \vec{\sigma}_1 \cdot \vec{\sigma}_2)T_{12}] \tag{4}$$

where $T_{12} = (\tau_{1z}\tau_{2z} - 1/3\vec{\tau}_1 \cdot \vec{\tau}_2)$, p, q, r and s are charge dependent parameters. Then, the difference between the n-n and p-p potentials is given by

$$d = \frac{V_{nn} - V_{pp}}{V_0} = 4(3r - p) \qquad (5)$$

Since $V_{nn} - V_{pp} = E_c - \Delta$ which is - (0.1 → 0.2) MeV, and the expectation value of V_0 is - (25 → 35) MeV, they obtained

$$3r - p \cong 0.1 \sim 0.3\% \qquad (6)$$

$$\therefore \quad d \cong 0.3 \sim 1\% \qquad (7)$$

(Blin-Stoyle and his collaborators usually define the magnitude of charge asymmetry by using r and p, or 3r - p. Of course the definition is completely up to the individual, but if one wants to define it as a difference of the <u>strengths</u> of the n-n and p-p interactions, then the definition must be Eq. 5 and the factor 4 in front must be included. In the following we will use this definition.)

But Eqs. 6 and 7 would probably be an underestimate, because, as pointed earlier, the effect of the SS' interference decreases E_c by 20 - 30%. Then it would probably decrease $|< V_0 >|$ also. This decrease would be even larger than the case of E_c, because nuclear forces are of shorter range and more singular near the origin than the Coulomb force, and the effect of the S' state increases the distance between like particles. Since $\underline{d} = (E_c - \Delta)/< V_0 >$, the decrease of $|< V_0 >|$ means an increase of d. We assume $|< V_0 >|$ would be decreased by 30% or more, and multiply Eq. 6 by 1.5.

$$\underline{d} \cong 0.5 - 1.5\% \qquad (8)$$

(b) Two-body approximation. In this case H^3 (or He^3) are regarded as deuteron and neutron (or proton), and deuteron is replaced by a potential which acts on neutron (or proton). Then the three-body problem is reduced to the two-body problem. We assume $\Delta - E_c = 0.2$ MeV. Then, since the neutron separation energy, S_n, of H^3 is - 6.267 MeV, S_p of a fictitious He^3 after the Coulomb force is switched off would be - 6.067 MeV. We assume appropriate potentials between deuteron and neutron (or proton), keep the ranges unchanged, and adjust the depths so as to reproduce the two values of S_n and S_p. Then the difference of the two potentials corresponds to charge asymmetry. In order to see whether the results depend on the form of the potential, we choose three types of potentials. The results are:

$$
\begin{array}{lll}
\text{Square well} & d = 2.3\% & (9) \\
\text{Hulthén potential} & d = 1.8\% & (10) \\
\text{Square well + Hulthén} & d = 2.3\% & (11)
\end{array}
$$

These results show that the treatment is rather model-independent. Further it seems to support our agreement that Eq. 7 is probably an underestimate.

Estimate from the many-body system.
This was already made by Altman and MacDonald[13]. They analyzed the $A = 14$ triad and obtained the following equations:

$$
\begin{aligned}
-250.96\, p + 247.1\, r &= -0.018 \\
-\ 0.243\, p +\ 1.376\, r &= 2.4 \times 10^{-3} \ \text{(Case I)} \\
&= -10.2 \times 10^{-3} \ \text{(Case II)}.
\end{aligned}
$$

They solved these equations and obtained p and r. However the right hand side of the first equation corresponds to $\Delta - E_c$, which in our case is 1.26 MeV from Table I. Moreover Case II leads to the conclusion that the p-p force is stronger than the n-n force, which is inconsistent with $E_c < \Delta$. Therefore in our case the equations to be solved are:

$$-250.96 \, p + 247.1 \, r = 1.26 \qquad (12)$$

$$-243p \quad + 137r \quad = 2.40 \qquad (13)$$

We solve these equations and obtain

$$r \cong 0.03\% \qquad (14)$$

$$p \cong -0.4 \% \qquad (15)$$

Inserting these into Eq. 5 we get

$$d \cong 2\% \qquad (16)$$

This is consistent with Eqs. 9, 10 and 11 and again supports our discussion after Eq. 7.

Although all of these estimates are very crude and should not be trusted literally, we could say that charge asymmetry is of the order of 1 - 2%. This is consistent with the conclusion of Lin[14], who obtained $\underline{d} = (0.4 - 2)\%^*$ from the analyses of the A = 6 triad. This conclusion seems surprising, because an intuitive guess about charge asymmetry is that it is of the order of the n-p mass difference, which is about 0.1%. Our estimate is, however, larger than this by an order of magnitude, which would be interesting from more fundamental viewpoints.

---

*These values are obtained from his Table III. The last row of this table corresponds to $d \cong 7\%$, which seems to be too large, and is excluded.

The n-n Scattering Length

Although direct measurement of the n-n scattering length, a_{nn}, is impossible, it can be obtained indirectly from some kinds of nuclear reactions. There are two kinds of such reactions that are usually cited.

(a) $n + d \rightarrow 2n + p$ $a_{nn} = -21.7 \pm 1f$[15], $-23.6^{+2}_{-1.6}f$ [16]

$$(17)$$

(b) $\pi^- + d \rightarrow 2n + \gamma$ $a_{nn} = -16.4 \pm 1.9f$[17] (18)

On the other hand Heller et al. calculated a_{nn} assuming charge symmetry and obtained[18]

$$a_{nn} = -16.6 \sim 16.9 \ f \ (\text{theory}) \qquad (19)$$

for realistic nuclear potentials. Then a question arises. If (a) is correct, charge asymmetry is expected, but if (b) is correct, charge symmetry holds. Our conclusion is rather consistent with (a) but we will investigate if it is really inconsistent with (b). We use the formula for the well depth parameter derived by Blatt and Jackson[19],

$$s = 1.0 + (0.6 \rightarrow 0.8) \ \frac{b}{a} + \ . \ . \ . \qquad (20)$$

where a and b are the scattering length and the intrinsic range, respectively. Since $b/a \cong 0.15$ for the 1S state, higher order terms can be neglected, and so

$$s \cong 1.0 + (0.09 \rightarrow 0.12) \ a^{-1} \qquad (21)$$

where a is in f. Then we see that a change of s by 1% corresponds to a change of a by 8 - 10%.

If added to Eq. 19 this corresponds to $a_{nn} = (-18 \rightarrow -19)f$. It is to be noted that the error in Eq. 18 does not include that of theory, so if added,

the error could be $\pm$ (2.5 → 3)f namely a_{nn} = (-13.4 →
-19.4)f. Then charge asymmetry up to 1% would be
within the error a_{nn}. According to the detailed calculations by Lin[14] charge asymmetry of (0.4 → 2)% corresponds to a_{nn} = (-19 → -20)f, which is in agreement
with our estimate. Thus we see our conclusion is not
necessarily inconsistent with (b), and is certainly
consistent with (a). Moreover if we take into account
the possibility of the inequality of n-n and p-p force
ranges, one cannot draw a definite conclusion about
the validity of charge symmetry from these experiments,
because s depends not only on a but also on b.

EFFECT OF CHARGE ASYMMETRY
IN LOW ENERGY NUCLEAR PHYSICS

Level Systematics of Mirror Nuclei

It is well-known that there exists a beautiful
correspondence between levels of mirror nuclei. This
fact is always regarded as a strong evidence in favor
of charge symmetry. But is it really necessary to
assume strict charge symmetry to explain this fact?
Simple considerations show that it is not.

Suppose that the depth of one of the mirror nuclei is V and that of the other is V'. We assume that
the difference, $\Delta V = V' - V$, is much smaller than V.
Then, since V is usually deep enough to contain many
bound levels, if ΔV is added to V, positions of all
bound levels move by a constant ΔV, their relative distance being unchanged, so do positions of levels which
are high up in the continuum. Their properties, such
as spins and parities, are also scarcely affected.
Then if one normalizes the bottoms of V and V' at the

666

same position, one finds the beautiful correspondence
of the levels mentioned above. (Of course if there
happens to be a level very near the zero energy, its
position would seriously be affected by addition of ΔV,
and the beautiful correspondence would be destroyed.
This fact is already known as the Thomas-Ehrman shift,
and is explained theoretically[20]). Note that the necessary and sufficient condition for this argument is
$|\Delta V| \ll |V|$, and the origin of ΔV is completely arbitrary. One could attribute ΔV to the Coulomb potential,
as is usually done, but one could also divide ΔV into
two, $\Delta V_c + \Delta V_n$, where ΔV_c is the Coulomb potential and
ΔV_n is the charge asymmetric nuclear potential. One
could even assume $\Delta V = \Delta V_n$. Of course the fact $|\Delta V| \ll |V|$
itself already means approximate validity of charge
symmetry, but since d defined by Eq. 5 is of the order
of $\Delta V/V$ and the above-mentioned argument probably holds
as far as $|\Delta V|$ is less than, say, 1/10 of $|V|$, one can
conclude that charge asymmetry up to 10% would not
affect the beautiful correspondence of levels of mirror
nuclei. Therefore this correspondence is by no means
a proof for the validity of strict charge symmetry,
although it is usually believed to be so.

Purity of the Isobaric Spin

If charge asymmetry of nuclear forces exists at
all, one might think that the purity of the isobaric
spin would be seriously affected, and as a result rates
of transitions or reactions which are forbidden from
charge symmetry would be considerably increased and be
observed experimentally. This argument also is not
necessarily true because of the following reasons.

Charge dependence of nuclear forces.

It is well known from the two-body scattering that the n-p interaction in the ^1S state is stronger than the p-p interaction in the same state by a few percent. Then if charge symmetry is assumed, we get

$$|V_{pp}| = |V_{nn}| < |V_{np}|^* \qquad (A)$$

$$(V_{np} - V_{pp})/V_{pp} = 2\sim3\% \qquad (21)$$

But we assumed $d = (V_{nn} - V_{pp})/V_{pp} \cong 1\sim2\%$; therefore in our case

$$|V_{pp}| < |V_{nn}| \cong |V_{np}| \qquad (B)$$

Then we take the simplest case, H^3. One might think that there is no isobaric spin impurity in H^3 because there is no Coulomb interaction. But even in the complete absence of the Coulomb interaction there exists a certain amount of the isobaric spin impurity due to charge dependence in the case of (A). However, in our case (B), the amount of the impurity is considerably reduced in H^3 because there exist only n-p and n-n pairs, which are almost equal in our assumption. In other words introduction of charge asymmetry rather makes n-p and n-n pairs charge independent, and as a result the isobaric spin impurity in H^3 is decreased. For heavier nuclei n-p, n-n and p-p pairs all appear and the situation becomes much more complicated, but essentially the same conclusion is expected. If one compares (A) and (B), it is understood that the expected

---

*Since all V's are negative (attractive), absolute values must be used.

amount of the impurity would be roughly the same in both cases, because the impurity is after all caused by the difference between either one and the other two of the three interactions.

Destructive interference between singlet and triplet states.

The charge asymmetric part of the charge dependent potential of Eq. 4 is

$$V_{CAS} = [(p + r(\vec{\sigma}_1 \cdot \vec{\sigma}_2)] \, (\tau_{1z} + \tau_{2z})V_0$$

Then the factor in the first bracket is p - 3r and p + r for the singlet and the triplet states, respectively. For sufficiently small nuclei the relative state of like particles is predominantly the ^{1}S state, but as the nucleus becomes larger, ^{3}P and higher states come in. Then there might exist a destructive interference between the two states due to the opposite sign of the second term, and as a result the isobaric spin impurity would not be increased.

Short range nature of nuclear forces.

Since the Coulomb force is of longer range than the nuclear forces, the relative importance of contributions from the Coulomb force to the isobaric spin impurity becomes larger than those from charge asymmetric nuclear forces as the nuclear size is increased. For sufficiently large nucleus, therefore, the isobaric spin impurity would be determined mainly by the Coulomb force.

Because of these reasons we conclude that the isobaric spin impurity is not affected very much by the presence of charge asymmetry that we have assumed. But this is of course a <u>general</u> argument. In certain special cases the effect of charge asymmetry might be appreciable. Serious break down of the isobaric spin selection rule in some (<u>d</u>,α) reactions[21], or large discrepancies between the neutron and proton reduced widths for levels of a self conjugate nucleus[22], might have some relation to this point. This problem is, however, beyond the scope of this work.

Relation to the G-Parity Non-Invariance
in the Beta-Decay

The isobaric spin impurity induced by charge asymmetry has its effect on the ft values of the β decay. As is well-known, the ft values of N^{12} and B^{12} are fairly different, although they are mirror nuclei. This problem was recently studied by Blin-Stoyle and Rosina in great detail[23].

They defined the following quantity:

$$\delta_{exp} = \frac{ft(N^{12}) - ft(B^{12})}{ft} = (11 \pm 1 \rightarrow 16 \pm 3)\%$$

$$(22)$$

They calculated the corrections for δ due to many effects, and concluded $\delta_{calc} \cong 7\%$ at most, so that the remaining discrepancy is possibly due to the G parity non-invariance (abbreviated as GPN). However we shall point out that they underestimated contributions from charge asymmetry, and if corrected, the assumption of GPN may not be necessary.

According to their calculations contributions from charge asymmetry and the Coulomb interaction are δ_0 and $\delta_{2\hbar w}$, which are due to the isobaric spin impurities by the two interactions. In the case of the Soper mixture they are given as

$$\delta_0 = -0.27 \; p + 1.17 \; r + 0.0022^{*}$$

$$\delta_{2\hbar w} = -3.05 \; p - 2.46 \; r + 0.0062$$

$$\therefore \; \delta_0 + \delta_{2\hbar w} = -3.32 \; p - 1.29 \; r + 0.0084$$

$$(23)$$

where the first and second terms are due to charge asymmetry in Eq. 4, and the last term is due to the Coulomb force. If we insert Eqs. 14 and 15, we get

$$\delta_0 + \delta_{2\hbar w} \cong 2\% \qquad (24)$$

This is clearly larger than their estimate by an order of magnitude. If inserted into their Eq. 24 we obtain $\delta_{calc} \cong 9\%$, which is very close to the lower limit of δ_{exp}. Of course their Eq. 24 is the maximum possible value, so that the possibility of $\delta_{calc} \ll \delta_{exp}$ still remains, in which case GPN is necessary. But on the other hand it should be pointed out that δ_{exp} is also decreasing as the accuracy of the experiment is improved, and there is also a possibility that δ_{exp} goes down to coincide δ_{calc} without assuming GPN. Therefore the necessity of GPN is now not yet clear. This conclusion is consistent with that of Fujii and Otsubo[24],

---

* In their Eq. 12 the last term is 0.022, but if one inserts p' = p - 0.0083, cited after their Eq. 11 into Eq. 12, the last term should be 0.022. This is clearly consistent with the sentence after their Eq. 12, because if it were 0.022, δ_0 would be 2.2% even if p = r = 0.

who also concluded that the necessity of GPN is not yet
definite.

SUMMARY AND CONCLUSION
Therefore we conclude as follows:

(a) The Coulomb energy difference of mirror nuclei is
in general considerably smaller than their binding
energy difference, and the discrepancy is probably
20 - 30%.

(b) This corresponds to charge asymmetry of the type
in which the n-n interaction is stronger than the p-p
interaction.

(c) It is difficult to estimate the magnitude of charge
asymmetry, but crude estimates using various methods
show that it would reach 1 ~ 2%. This is larger than
the n-p mass difference by an order of magnitude, and
should be surprising.

(d) This charge asymmetry is not necessarily inconsistent with the experimental data on the n-n scattering length.

(e) Contrary to the ordinary belief, the beautiful
correspondence of levels of mirror nuclei is by no
means a proof for strict charge symmetry. Presence of
charge asymmetry up to 1 ~ 2% cannot be excluded from
this argument.

(f) The purity of the isobaric spin of nuclear states
is probably not affected very much by the presence of
such charge asymmetry.

(g) If such charge asymmetry exists at all, the
assumption of the G parity non-invariance in the β
decay might not necessarily be needed, although present
theoretical and experimental uncertainties do not allow
us to draw a definite conclusion.

Finally we would like to emphasize the following point. Some of the above-mentioned facts, such as (a) and (e), are completely opposite to the common knowledge that are cited in any text book of nuclear physics. Our investigations, however, have revealed that these "common knowledge" are not necessarily true. It would be certainly desirable to re-investigate these so-called "well established" facts to see if our knowledge in nuclear physics is certainly on a firm basis.

REFERENCES

1) J. H. E. Mattauch, W. Thiele, and A. H. Wapstra, Nucl. Phys. $\underline{67}$ (1965) 1.

2) K. Okamoto, Phys. Letters $\underline{11}$ (1964) 150.

3) K. Okamoto, Progr. Theoret. Phys. (Kyoto) $\underline{34}$ (1965) 326.

4) H. Collard et al., Phys. Rev. $\underline{138}$ (1965) B57.

5) L. I. Schiff, Phys. Rev. $\underline{133}$ (1964) B802.

6) R. J. Blin-Stoyle, Phys. Rev. Letters $\underline{13}$ (1964) 55.

7) T. A. Griffy and R. J. Oakes, Phys. Rev. $\underline{135}$ (1964) B1161.

8) J. M. Blatt and L. M. Delves, Phys. Rev. Letts. $\underline{12}$ (1964) 544.

9) J. S. Levinger and B. K. Srivastava, Phys. Rev. $\underline{137}$ (1965) B426.

10) J. N. Pappademos, Nucl. Phys. $\underline{42}$ (1963) 122; $\underline{56}$ (1964) 351.

11) K. Okamoto, Phys. Letts, (to be published).

12) R. J. Blin-Stoyle and C. Yalgin, Phys. Letts. $\underline{15}$ (1965) 258.

13) A. Altman and W. M. MacDonald, Nucl. Phys. $\underline{35}$ (1962) 593.

14) D. L. Lin, Nucl. Phys. $\underline{60}$ (1964) 192.

15) M. Cerino et al., Phys. Rev. $\underline{133}$ (1964) B948.

16) V. K. Voitovetskii et al., Nucl. Phys. $\underline{69}$ (1965) 513.

17) R. P. Haddock et al., Phys. Rev. Letts. $\underline{14}$ (1965) 318.

18) L. Heller, P. Signell and N. R. Yoder, Phys. Rev. Letts. $\underline{13}$ (1964) 577.

19) J. M. Blatt and J. D. Jackson, Phys. Rev. $\underline{76}$ (1949) 18.

20) e.g. J. M. Blatt and V. Weisskopf, "Theoretical Nuclear Physics", p. 257-259.

21) G. M. Matous and C. P. Browne, Phys. Rev. $\underline{136}$ (1964) B399; references of previous work are cited in this paper.

22) e.g. H. W. Newson et al., Phys. Rev. $\underline{108}$ (1957) 1294; R. L. Macklin and J. H. Gibbons, Phys. Rev. $\underline{109}$ (1958) 105; P. R. Bevington, W. W. Rolland and H. W. Lewis, Phys. Rev. $\underline{121}$ (1961) 871.

23) R. J. Blin-Stoyle and M. Rosina, Nucl. Phys. $\underline{70}$ (1965) 321.

24) A. Fujii and H. Ohtsubo, Progr. Theoret. Phys. (Kyoto) $\underline{34}$ (1965) 873.

TABLE I. Comparison of the binding energy difference and the Coulomb energy difference of mirror nuclei taken from Ref. 11 (all in MeV). Values in brackets are those of other authors.

A	Pair	Δ	E_c	$\Delta - E_c$	$(\Delta-E_c)/\Delta$(%)
3	$H^3 - He^3$	0.76384 ± 0.00026	$0.50 \sim 0.57$ [a,b]	$0.19 \sim 0.26$	$25 \sim 34$
			$(0.645 \sim 0.736)$[c]	$(0.03 \sim 0.12)$	$(4 \sim 16)$
			$(0.505 \sim 0.685)$[d]	$(0.08 \sim 0.26)$	$(10 \sim 34)$
			$(0.67 \sim 0.69)$[e]	$(0.07 \sim 0.09)$	$(9 \sim 12)$
			(0.663)[f]	(0.10)	(13)
6	$He^6 - Be^6$	2.3336 ± 0.0126	1.80	0.53	23
7	$Li^7 - Be^7$	1.6440 ± 0.0017	1.21	0.43	26
10	$Be^{10} - C^{10}$	4.6166 ± 0.0132	(1.613)[g]	(0.031 ± 0.0017)	(1.9 ± 0.1)
			3.34	1.28	28
11	$B^{11} - C^{11}$	2.7631 ± 0.0017	< 2.28	> 0.48	> 17
14	$C^{14} - O^{14}$	6.5531 ± 0.0015	(2.644)[g]	(0.119 ± 0.0017)	(4.3 ± 0.1)
			5.29	1.26	19
			(6.576)[h]	(0.0229 ± 0.0015)	(-0.35 ± 0.02)

References for TABLE I

[a] Ref. 2.

[b] Ref. 3.

[c] Ref. 10.

[d] L. M. Delves, Phys. Rev. 135 (1964) B1316.

[e] Y. C. Tang and R. C. Herndon, Phys. Letts. 18 (1965) 42.

[f] B. D. Srivastava, Nucl. Phys. 67 (1965) 236.

[g] P. C. Sood and A. E. S. Green, Nucl. Phys. 5 (1957) 274.

[h] Ref. 13.

S5. CONTRIBUTION OF SECOND FORBIDDEN MATRIX ELEMENTS TO ISOBARIC SPIN FORBIDDEN BETA-TRANSITIONS : Ga^{66}

L. Van Neste[*], (introduced by J. P. Deutsch),
R. Coussement, J. P. Deutsch

Louvain University
Louvain, Belgium

INTRODUCTION

The isobaric spin forbidden (0+) - (0+) beta-transitions are considered as useful tools to measure the isobaric spin impurity of nuclear states: it is usually stated that the transition probability is directly related to the impurity coefficient α[1].

In the case of high ft-values however, this procedure becomes questionable, because a strong depression of the Fermi matrix element $\int 1$ could render the contributions from the second forbidden matrix elements $\int i \, \bar{\alpha} \cdot \bar{r}$ and $\int r^2$ non-negligible. These contributions may be detected through the energy dependency, they eventually introduce in the beta spectrum shape factor.

Langer[2] reported a non-statistical spectrum shape factor for the (0+) - (0+) ground state transition from Ga^{66} to Zn^{66}, but did not furnish a satisfying theoretical explanation of his experimental results. We thought it worth while to re-investigate this transition both from the experimental and theoretical point of view.

---

[*] Aspirant of the N.F.W.O.; in partial fulfillment of the requirements of a Ph.D. Thesis

In the following we describe:

(a) the measurement of the shape factor performed with a short lens magnetic spectrometer,

(b) the χ^2 - analysis of our results using a more complete theoretical formula than the one of Ref. 2,

(c) the information one can obtain from measurements of other observables.

DESCRIPTION OF THE SPECTROMETER

The features of the spectrometer, in which the positron spectrum of Ga^{66} has been measured, are discussed in detail in Ref. 3. The power supply of the magnetic lens was stabilized to 0.2% up to the highest current values. Because of its little sensitivity to gamma-rays a Geiger detector was used in this experiment. Partial transmission through the edges of the spectrometer baffles is believed to be negligible: replacing the exit baffle in aluminium by a brass one had no influence on the shape factor.

For calibration the conversion lines of In^{114m}, Bi^{207} and Cs^{137} as well as the end points of the continuous spectra of In^{114m} and Cl^{38} were used: a linearity of better than 0.1% was confirmed. In order to check for systematic experimental distortions the shape factors of the In^{114m} and Cl^{38} beta-decays were extensively investigated in a series of different measurements. Within the experimental errors they proved to have the statistical resp. unique first forbidden shape (cfr. Figs. 1 and 2).

The FWHM of the mentioned conversion peaks in addition to the one measured with a Tl^{208} source indicated no energy dependence of the resolution.

SOURCE PREPARATION

Ga^{66} was produced by bombarding a copper target with 24 MeV α-particles in the cyclotron of Louvain University. The Ga^{66} was extracted carrier free. Zapon films recovered with a carbon foil of 15 $\mu g/cm^2$ were used as source backing: thicker mylar backings were also used and led to the same experimental results. Diameter of the source was always inferior to 3 mm. Purity of the source was checked by a life-time measurement in the spectrometer for various values of the energy. The life-time used for half-life correction was 9.35 h.

MEASUREMENTS

A series of measurements was carried out, each of which consisted of different runs with the same source. The accuracy of the dead-time corrections was checked by using alternatively sources of high and low intensity: although the latter do not allow high statistical accuracy the same behavior of the shape factor was found. In order to investigate the effects of an eventual erroneous half-life correction, measurements both with increasing and decreasing energy were performed: for each source at least one run of each type was done. Usually different runs in the same direction were added for obtaining better statistics.

An important correction in this case is background subtraction. Although background never exceeded 2% of the total counting rate, the momentum-dependent part of it (spurious annihilation radiation detection) could introduce distortions into the shape factor. Therefore two runs were made during each measurement: in the first all the positrons and the background were counted, in the second we stopped the positrons by an aluminium absorber just in front of the detector. This introduced a number of counts due to annihilation in the absorber, proportional to the primary spectrum.

If $N_1(p)$ and $N_2(p)$ are the number of counts, dependent on the positron momentum p, registered in the first, resp. the second run, we can state:

$$N_1(p) = N_{1+}(p) + N_{B.G.}(p)$$
$$N_2(p) = \alpha N_{1+}(p) + N_{B.G.}(p)$$

where $N_{1+}(p)$ = number of positrons reaching the detector

$N_{B.G.}(p)$ = background

Then $N_1(p) - N_2(p) = (1 - \alpha)N_{1+}(p)$: thus, from the difference of two separate runs, we get a number proportional to $N_{1+}(p)$ and have not to determine the constant α.

TREATMENT OF THE DATA

The spectrum shape $C(W)$ was calculated correcting for the finite resolution (3%) of the spectrometer (see Ref. 3,4). In order to determine $C(W)$, one should keep in mind that the behavior of $C(W)$ and the value taken for the end point energy W_o are correlated. Lacking any external precise information on W_o, we have to choose a criterion in order to extract it from the spectrum shape measurement. We adopted as criterion the absence of an abrupt change of slope near the spectrum's end point. Following this criterion we admit a range for possible values of W_o from 9.120 mc^2 to

9.142 mc^2. The shape factors corresponding to these extreme values of W_0 and an intermediary one are plotted in Fig. 3.

THEORETICAL ANALYSIS

As the transition is strongly hindered (log ft = 7.9) we expect eventual contributions of the second forbidden matrix elements to the spectrum shape (cfr. Ref. 5,6):

$$C(W) = L_0 + 2(q\ N_0/3 - q^2 L_0/6) \int r^2 \Big/ \int 1 + 2(N_0 - q\ L_0/3)$$

$$\int i\ \overline{\alpha} \cdot \overline{r} / \int 1 + 2(q\ M_0/3 - 4q^2 N_0/9) \int i\ \overline{\alpha} \cdot \overline{r} \int r^2 / (\int 1)^2$$

$$+ q^2 M_0/9\ (\int r^2 / \int 1)^2 + (M_0 - 2\ q\ N_0/3$$

$$+ q^2 L_0/9 - q^2 R^2 M_0/3)\ (\int i\ \overline{\alpha} \cdot \overline{r} / \int 1)^2$$

where q is the energy of the neutrino, R the nuclear radius (in n.u.) and L_0, M_0, N_0 the usual combinations of the electron radial wave functions. As the end point energy of the transition is relatively high, the lepton parts of the terms quadratic in the second forbidden matrix elements become important because of the factor q^2, and should not be neglected. In order to check the adequacy of particular sets of $\int r^2 / \int 1$ and $\int i\ \overline{\alpha} \cdot \overline{r} / \int 1$ to describe the experimental shape factor, separate χ^2 - analyses were done for the three shape factors represented in Fig. 3. The regions of sets of $\int r^2 / \int 1$ and $\int i\ \overline{\alpha} \cdot \overline{r} / \int 1$ yielding a good fit to the experimental shape factors, are represented in Fig. 4. It appeared that for curve I of Fig. 3 reasonable confidence levels could only be obtained in the domain I

and for curve III in the domain III: the best fits to
the curve II occur in the same domain but with unacceptable confidence level. Typical theoretical fits to
the curves are also plotted in Fig. 3.

DISCUSSION

In his analysis of the experimental results of
Langer, Bühring arrives at the conclusion that one obtains the best theoretical fit without the introduction
of the second forbidden matrix elements[7]. One should
note however that the discrepancies between this simplified treatment and the results of Langer (though small)
remain systematic.

As for our spectrum shape results, inspection
of Fig. 4 shows that $\int r^2 = \int i \, \bar{\alpha} \cdot \bar{r} = 0$ does not yield
a good fit, and so we have to take into account the
second forbidden matrix elements.

We introduce now the parameters found from the
spectrum shape analysis into the expression of the
ft-value:

$$\frac{1}{ft} = \frac{1}{2\pi^3 \ln 2} \, c_V^2 \, \left(\int 1\right)^2 \, G(Z,W_o)$$

where

$$G(Z,W_o) = \frac{\int C(W)p \, W \, F(Z,W) \, (W_o - W)^2 \, dW}{\int L_o p \, W \, F(Z,W) \, (W_o - W)^2 \, dW}$$

and $C(W)$ is defined by Eq. 1.

Using the experimental value, log ft = 7.9[2],
we can now compute the absolute value of the nuclear
matrix elements $\int 1$, $\int i \, \bar{\alpha} \cdot \bar{r}$ and $\int r^2$ for both domains

682

I and III of Fig. 4. The ratios of domain I yield $| \int i \, \bar{\alpha} \cdot \bar{r} | \simeq \frac{10}{M}$, where M stands for the proton mass; this value seems too high and the solutions of domain I have to be rejected as non-physical. The ratios of domain III, yield the more credible results $| \int i \, \bar{\alpha} \cdot \bar{r} | \simeq \frac{1}{M}$ and $| \int r^2 | < R^2$ (R = nuclear radius) for values of $| \int 1 | \simeq 1.3 \times 10^{-2}$, which can now be used to evaluate the isobaric spin impurity of the Ga^{66} ground state.

CONCLUSIONS ABOUT ISOBARIC SPIN IMPURITY

The admixture of the T = 3 state into the T = 2 Ga^{66} ground state can now be computed using the experimental ft-value of a super-allowed decay (O^{14}):

$$|\alpha^2| = \frac{(ft)_O{}^{14} \, (T - T_z) \, (T + T_z + 1)}{(ft)_{Ga}{}^{66} \, (T' - T'_z) \, (T' + T'_z + 1) \, G(Z, W_o)}$$

where T and T_z are the isobaric spin and its third component for the corresponding states and $G(Z, W_o)$ is the same expression as above.

Extreme values of the solutions of domain III for the second forbidden matrix elements lead to corresponding limits for $|\alpha|^2$: $1.9 \times 10^{-5} < |\alpha|^2 < 4.3 \times 10^{-5}$. This is to be compared to the result 1.4×10^{-5} obtained in Ref. 1 without the consideration of the second forbidden matrix elements. This result is in agreement with the general trend found in other nuclei (cfr. Ref. 8). It emphasizes however the inaccuracy of the isobaric spin impurity determination if one takes into account properly the contribution of the second forbidden matrix elements to the isobaric spin forbidden beta transitions.

The accuracy may be somewhat increased using accurate longitudinal polarization measurements to determine more precisely the second forbidden contributions.

The existing results[9,10] are, however, conflicting and no definite conclusion can be drawn from them.

REFERENCES

1) W. P. Alford and J. B. French, Phys. Rev. Letts. $\underline{6}$ (1961) 119.

2) D. C. Camp and L. M. Langer, Phys. Rev. $\underline{129}$ (1963) 4.

3) Mededelingen van de Kon. Vl. Academie, Ontwerp en opstelling van magnetische spektrometer met korte lens, L. Van Neste (to be published).

4) Verhandelingen van de Kon. Vl. Academie, XXV (1963) 74, R. Coussement.

5) M. Morita, Phys. Rev. $\underline{113}$ (1959) 1584.

6) D. Tadic, (private communication).

7) W. Bühring, Nucl. Phys. $\underline{49}$ (1963) 190.

8) S. D. Bloom, Nuovo Cimento, $\underline{32}$ (1964) 1023.

9) H. Frauenfelder, et al. Phys. Rev. $\underline{107}$ (1957) 910.

10) M. Deutsch, et al. Phys. Rev. $\underline{107}$ (1957) 1733.

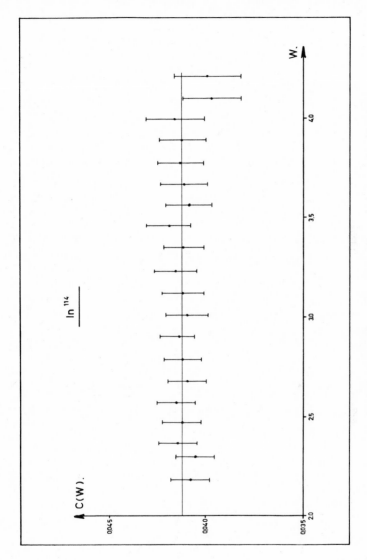

Fig. 1. Shape correction factor of the beta spectrum for In^{114}m plotted as a function of the energy (n.u.).

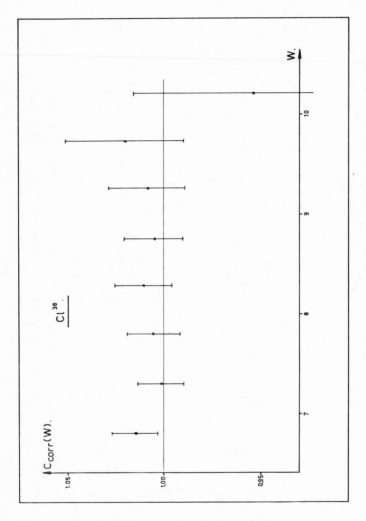

Fig. 2. Shape correction factor of the (2−) − (0+) beta-transition of Cl38 as function of the energy after correction for the unique first forbidden character.

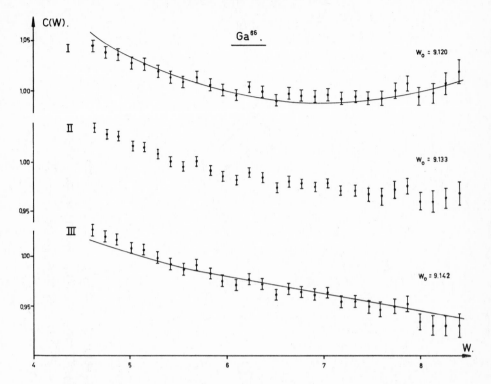

Fig. 3. Plot of the shape factor of the positron spectrum of Ga^{66}, showing the effect of a change in the end point: I corresponds to $W_o = 9.120$, II to $W_o = 9.133$ and III to $W_o = 9.142$ (mc^2). Theoretical fits to I and III, corresponding to the domain of solutions seen in Fig. 4, are also drawn.

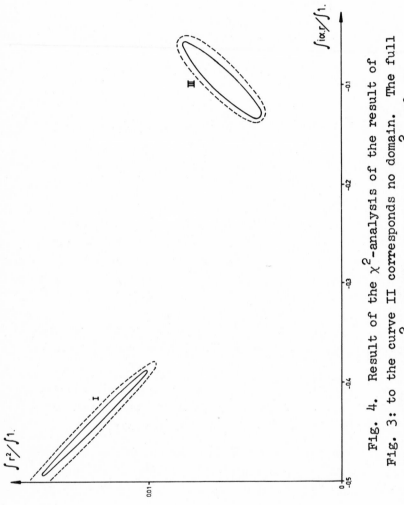

Fig. 4. Result of the χ^2-analysis of the result of Fig. 3: to the curve II corresponds no domain. The full line represents $\chi^2 = 25$, the dashed line $\chi^2 = 28$, for thirty experimental points.

S6. ISOBARIC ANALOGUE STATES OF Sn^{119} AND Sn^{121}

D. L. Allan, G. A. Jones, G. C. Morrison,
R. B. Taylor and R. B. Weinberg

A. E. R. E.
Harwell, England

The study of isobaric analogue states of the Sn isotopes is doubly interesting. The even tin isotopes are good examples of vibrational nuclei so that the use of these isotopes as target nuclei and looking at the inelastic proton scattering to the strong collective states one gains information about states which are isobaric analogues of single particle plus phonon states not obtainable by either elastic proton scattering or the (d,p) reaction. Sn also has a large number of stable isotopes permitting an investigation of the effects of filling neutron shells. Since results have only been obtained for two different target nuclei (Sn^{118} and Sn^{120}) it is mainly the information that can be obtained from the inelastic scattering to the collective states that will be presented here. Both Sn^{118} and Sn^{120} have a strong 2^+ collective state at approximately 1.2 MeV and a strong 3^- collective state at approximately 2.35 MeV. The elastic scattering and inelastic scattering to these 2 states have been studied in the proton range of 7.3 to 11.1 MeV, (10.3 MeV for Sn^{120}). The data are given in the Figs. 1, 2 and 3. Table I and II show a list of the resonances together with those seen by Florida State[1] and the results of .

the (d,p) reactions measured by Cohen et al.[2] and Allan et al.[3].

In both Sn^{119} And Sn^{121} the ground state and first excited state are both very strong single-particle states[2] and therefore their analogues in Sb^{119} and Sb^{121} should be observed as resonances in all three proton channels. In the case of Sb^{121} where the two states are resolved (Fig. 3) both are observed in all three proton channels. The $s^{1/2}$ first excited state does not resonate strongly in the 2^+ and 3^- inelastic channels due to the statistical factor $2J + 1$ and barrier penetration. A measurement of a 0^+ inelastic group (E = 1.87 MeV) in Sn^{120} (not shown) shows the $s^{1/2}$ is stronger than the $d^{3/2}$ ground state for the (p,p') leading to this 0^+ state. For Sb^{119} the two levels are not resolved. At 150° the elastic scattering cross section shows an anomaly which can be interpreted as due to the effect of two close levels. The sum of the two resonances decays strongly to all the proton channels.

About 1.1 MeV above the ground state analogue resonance the 2^+ channel shows 3 strong resonances in both Sb^{119} and Sb^{121}. Only two of these resonances are seen in the elastic channel. The 3^- channel resonates weakly in the case of Sb^{119} for the two higher resonances while in Sb^{121} none were observed. The resonance at 8.35 MeV in Sb^{119} and 8.61 MeV in Sb^{121} are both analogues of weak single particle states and are expected to show in all proton channels. It is therefore a little surprising not to see it in the decay of the 8.61 MeV resonance in Sb^{121} via the 3^- level in Sn^{120}. Since we have only preliminary data on the 3^- for Sn^{120} at this stage the possibility of a very weak

690

resonance cannot be ruled out. One does not expect
this resonance to be as strong in the 3^- channel as
the Sn^{118} + p at 8.35 MeV because the $Sn^{120}(p,n)$ has a
lower threshold. The other two resonances in the region of 1.1 MeV above the g.s. which are strongly resonant only in the 2^+ channel are predominantly due to
resonances in the outgoing channel rather than the ingoing channel.

Above the triplet of states clustered about
8.4 MeV there are many resonances observed in Sn^{118} + p
in all three proton channels. Of these higher resonances those seen in the elastic channel are generally
seen also in both the 2^+ and 3^- channel, while resonances not seen in the elastic channel are usually resonant in only one or other of the inelastic channels.
These latter resonances are considered to be only resonant in the outgoing channel. In Sn^{120} + p there are
very few resonances above the 9.0 MeV resonance. Again
we have the situation of a resonance (10.17 MeV) resonating in the elastic and 2^+ channel but not the 3^-
channel. The (d,p) data[2] would indicate that this
resonance should be a good $(7/2^-)$ single particle state
and penetrability arguments would favor a decay via the
3^- level.

Since the even mass Sn isotopes have strong
collective states then one expects to find states in
the odd mass Sn isotope which look like a single particle attached to an excited core (single particle +
phonon states) and these states should appear at an
energy equal to the single particle energy plus the
excitation energy of the core. B ecause of the selec-
tive nature of the (d,p) mechanism these single particle + phonon states may not be observed or only

weakly. But the isobaric analogue of these states will
decay strongly by emitting the single particle leaving
the core in the same excited configuration. The two
resonances at 8.21 MeV and 8.63 MeV in Sn^{118} + p can
be interpreted as being isobaric analogues of the $s^{1/2}$
ground state neutron + 2^+ excited state of Sn^{118}. The
center of gravity of the two resonances is 1.2 MeV
above the ground state analogue which is approximately
the excitation of the 2^+ state in Sn^{118}. On this model
the spins of these states should be $3/2^+$ and $5/2^+$.
These two resonances could also be interpreted as the
coupling of the 2^+ excited state in Sn^{118} to the $s^{1/2}$
and $d^{3/2}$ single particle states to give $5/2^+$ resonances.
Both interpretations are consistent with Cohen et al.
results[2] which show that the corresponding states in
Sn^{119} are d wave. These states are only very weakly
resonant in the 3^- channel and only weakly resonant in
the elastic channel. Similarly the resonances in Sn^{118}
+ p at about 9.7 MeV decaying strongly to the 3^- state
are consistent with being analogues of states formed
by the coupling of the $s^{1/2}$ ground state neutron to the
3^- excited core of Sn^{118}. In the case of Sn^{120} + p
the resonances at 8.41 MeV and 8.91 MeV decaying strongly to the 2^+ state are consistent with a single particle plus 2^+ phonon states of Sn^{120}. In Sn^{120} + p
there are, however, no resonances observed which correspond to the coupling of the 3^- phonon to a single-
particle. In fact the two large resonances at 8.41 MeV
and 8.91 MeV and a weak resonance of 9.76 MeV observed
in the 2^+ are the only resonances observed in Sn^{120} + p
which are not analogues of single-particle states in
Sn^{121}. No explanation can be given why the more complex configuration states are seen in Sb^{119} but not

Sb^{121}.

To obtain a complete picture of the single particle + phonon states one must couple all the single particle states to the excited core. This makes the interpretation of the resonances in Sb^{119} and Sb^{121} difficult because the ground state and first excited states of the analogue nucleus are both strong single particle states and their separation is less than 100 keV.

The reaction $Sn^{118}(p,p')Sn^{118*}$ has also been studied as a function of incident proton energy using a charged particle magnetic spectrograph to resolve the many proton groups corresponding to levels in Sn^{118} [4]) with excitation energies in the range 2 - 5 MeV. In this way transitions to about 50 levels have been observed simultaneously at more than 100 different incident proton energies between 9 and 12 MeV. Many of these Sn^{118} groups resonate strongly at one or more incident energies, including one group corresponding to an excitation energy $\overset{\sim}{-}$ 5 MeV. In several cases the intensity of a group at the resonance energy is 10 - 15 times greater than its off-resonance intensity. So far, excitation curves of 15 of the levels have been plotted at 10 - 20 keV intervals over the range 9.8 - 11.1 MeV. As in the case of the excitation curves for the 2^{+} and 3^{-} levels, most of the resonance energies correspond to excited states of Sn^{119}, which identifies them as being caused by the presence of analogues of Sn^{119} states in the Sb^{119} compound nucleus.

The excitation curves are of two kinds: those exhibiting only a single strong resonance in the range of energies studied and those exhibiting several strong resonances (3, 4, or more). At some resonance energies

only one or two Sn^{118} levels resonate; at other energies many levels (15 or more) resonate simultaneously.
For the first type of resonance the trend noted earlier
in Ref. 4, namely the higher the excitation energy of
the level in Sn^{118} the higher the energy of the resonance (and so the higher the excitation energy of the
corresponding level in Sn^{119}), has been confirmed.
This observation shows that a simple connection exists
between the analogues of the Sn^{119} levels and the Sn^{118}
levels to which they decay (exit channel resonances).
The occurrence of only one resonance affecting only
one or two levels in Sn^{118} suggests that these states
possess complex and therefore relatively uncommon configurations. Where a resonance affects many levels
simultaneously, we are probably concerned with a resonance in the ingoing channel or single particle plus
ground state configuration.

REFERENCES

1) P. Richard, C. F. Moore, J. A. Becker and J. D. Fox,
   (to be published in Phys. Rev.).

2) E. J. Schneid, A. Prakash and B. L. Cohen, (to be
   published).

3) D. L. Allan, G. A. Jones, R. B. Taylor and R. B.
   Weinberg, (to be published).

4) D. L. Allan, Phys. Letts. 14 (1965) 311.

TABLE I.   Analogue resonances in Sn^{118} + p.

$Sn^{118}(p,p)Sn^{118}$			$(E_p^{cm} \cong 7.28$ MeV)	$Sn^{118}(d,p)Sn^{119}$	
Elastic	2^+	3^-	Elastic(FSU)	Allan et al.	Cohen et al.
0	0	0	0	0.0	0.0
				0.07	0.08
				0.30	
				0.35	
	0.76			0.77	0.79
0.93	0.93			0.90	0.93
1.07	1.07	1.07	1.07	1.07	1.10
				1.17	
				1.22	1.22
				1.29	
1.35	1.35	1.35	1.34	1.34	1.37
		1.55		1.54 } 1.62 }	1.59
	1.67			1.70 } 1.78 }	1.74
		1.80			
1.90	1.90	1.90		1.91 } 1.98 }	1.95
				2.02	
2.12	2.12	2.12		2.10	
		2.27			
		2.37			
	2.41				
2.56	2.56	2.56		2.54	2.58
2.65	2.65	2.65		2.64	2.68
				2.76	

TABLE I (cont.)

Sn^{118}(p,p)Sn^{118} (E$_p^{cm}$≅7.28 MeV)			Sn^{118}(d,p)Sn^{119}		
Elastic	2$^+$	3$^-$	Elastic (FSU)	Allan et al.	Cohen et al.
			2.87		
			2.90 ⎫		2.92
2.93	2.93		2.94 ⎭		
3.09	3.09	3.09	3.08		
			3.13		3.13
			3.16		
	3.19		3.21		3.23
3.39	3.39		3.38		3.33
		3.47	3.49		
3.59	3.59		3.57		3.54
			3.61		
			3.65		3.67
			3.69		
3.77	3.77		3.76		

TABLE II. Analogue resonances in Sn^{120} + p.

$Sn^{120}(p,p)Sn^{120}$			$(E_p{\stackrel{cm}{=}}7.49$ MeV)	$Sn^{120}(d,p)Sn^{120}$
Elastic	2^+	3^-	Elastic (FSU)	Cohen <u>et al</u>.
0	0	0	0	0.0
0.07	0.07	0.07	0.07	0.05
	0.92			0.93
1.12	1.12		1.13	1.12
1.42	1.42		1.44	1.40
				1.71
				1.91
				2.06
	2.27			2.25
				2.45
2.58	2.58	2.58		2.59
2.68	2.68			2.69

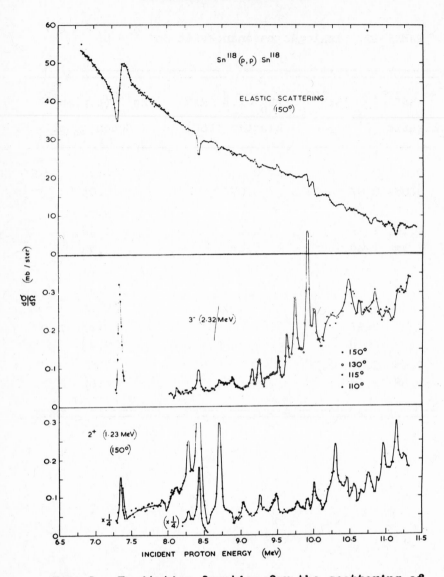

Fig. 1. Excitation function for the scattering of protons from Sn[118].

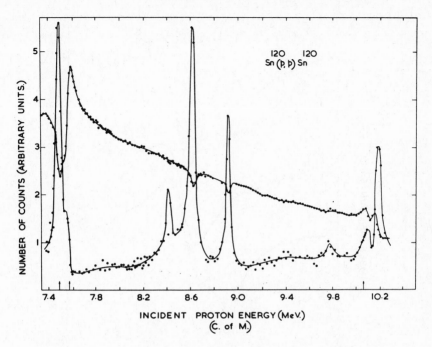

Fig. 2. Excitation function for the scattering of protons from Sn^{120}. The arrows indicate resonances observed in the $Sn^{120}(p,p')Sn^{120}$ (3^-) reaction.

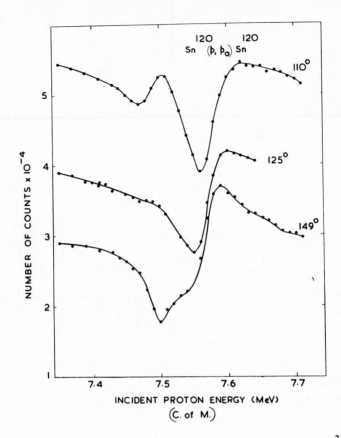

Fig. 3. Elastic scattering of protons from Sn^{120} showing the isobaric analogue resonances corresponding to the $d^{3/2}$ ground state and $s^{1/2}$ excited state in Sn^{119}.

T = 3/2 ANALOGUE LEVELS IN MASS 25 AND 29

J. C. Hardy[*] and D. J. Skyrme

Nuclear Physics Laboratory
Oxford, England

A T = 3/2 isobaric quartet at mass 25 comprises
states in the nuclei $Si^{25}(T_z = -3/2)$, $Al^{25}(-1/2)$,
$Mg^{25}(+1/2)$ and $Na^{25}(+3/2)$; at mass 29, the nuclei involved are $S^{29}(-3/2)$, $P^{29}(-1/2)$, $Si^{29}(+1/2)$ and
$Al^{29}(+3/2)$. In recent work[1-3], the decays of Si^{25}
and S^{29} have been studied by observing the protons
emitted following positron decay to proton-unstable
excited states of Al^{25} and P^{29}, and approximate log ft
values have been measured for the observed decay
branches[4]. In particular, one branch in each decay
has been observed to be superallowed and, on that basis,
the level to which it proceeds, identified as the analogue (T = 3/2) level. However, in addition to this
level, only one other member of each quartet had a
measured mass: the ground state of Na^{25} and Al^{29}. A
determination of the mass of another member of either
quartet would be sufficient to evaluate the coefficients
in the isobaric mass formula[5] which, in turn, could be
used to calculate the mass of the fourth member, such
a calculation having been shown to be remarkably
accurate[6,7]. Calculation of the mass of Si^{25} or S^{29}
by this method would be considerably more accurate than

[*]National Research Council (Canada) Postdoctorate
Overseas Fellow

the previous estimates[1-3], which were based on semi-empirical Coulomb energy differences, and would provide a better value for the superallowed log $\underline{ft}$ values.

We wish to report a study of the following reactions: $Al^{27}(p,t)Al^{25}$, $Al^{27}(p,He^3)Mg^{25}$, $P^{31}(p,t)P^{29}$ and $P^{31}(p,He^3)Si^{29}$. These reactions were induced by 40.3 MeV protons from the Proton Linear Accelerator at the Rutherford Laboratory, and the emitted particles were detected by means of a semi-conductor counter telescope consisting of two silicon surface barrier transmission counters, one 100μ in thickness (dE/dx) and the other 1.7 mm(E), operated in coincidence, followed by a lithium drifted silicon detector in anti-coincidence with the first two. The last counter served to reject particles too energetic to be stopped in the first two. For the remainder, the dE and E pulses were fed separately into a mass analyzer[8] which produced a pulse characteristic of one of the reaction products, and the total energy pulse (dE + E) was routed accordingly into one of the four quarters of a 4096 channel pulse height analyzer. In this way, energy spectra corresponding to deuterons, tritons, He^3, and alphas were recorded simultaneously.

If one assumes spatially symmetric wave functions for the bound states of the captured nucleons then for the (p,t) reaction, where the picked up pair must have T = 1, the transferred spin S is restricted to being zero, while for the (p,He^3) reaction, both T = 1, S = 0 and T = 0, S = 1 are possible. But, if the isobaric spin of the final mirror states differs from that of the target by one unit, only T = 1, S = 0 nucleon pairs can be picked up in either case. As has been pointed out[9], this results in identical angular distributions,

and relative intensities that are simply related by
isobaric spin and momentum factors; such will not, in
general, be the case for reactions to those mirror
states with the same isobaric spin as the target nucleus. The targets used in these experiments both had
$T = 1/2$, so this unique relationship between cross-
sections provided the means of identifying $T = 3/2$
levels.

Figure 1 gives the energy spectra of tritons
and He^3 obtained from an aluminium target; the resolution is ~200 keV. Angular distributions for the three
peaks marked in each spectrum are shown in Fig. 2,
where the upper part of the figure shows in solid lines
the (p,t) distributions to states whose spin-parities
are known. Since only spin transfer $S = 0$ is possible,
these exhibit "pure" shapes characteristic of $L = 0$ and
$L = 2$, and are useful as reference. In the case of
(p, He^3), since both $S = 0$ and $S = 1$ are possible and,
for the transitions involved, $\Delta J \leq 1$, therefore the
distributions shown dashed in the figure have mixed
shapes, i.e. including both $L = 0$ and $L = 2$. The lower
part of the figure shows angular distributions to the
levels identified as the lowest with $T = 3/2$; they are
seen to agree very closely, after suitable correction
has been made for the previously mentioned factors.
A $5/2^+$ assignment to the final states, indicated by the
$L = 0$ shape of the distribution, further strengthens
their identification as analogues to the ground state
of Na^{25} whose spin-parity is known to be $5/2^+$.

The first excited state of Na^{25} is at 90 keV
and, although unmeasured, its spin-parity is most likely
$3/2^+$. Even if this is not so, the level's analogue in
Mg^{25} and Al^{25} would almost certainly be excited by

L = 2 transfer, but at **any rate** not by L = 0. Consequently, if it were unresolved from the analogue ground state and contributed significantly to the observed peak, the apparent excitation energy corresponding to that peak would be expected to vary with angle. However, the energies measured at six angles showed no systematic variation and it was concluded that any contribution must be small. The measured excitation energies were then taken to be that of the ground state analogues, and the two values so obtained are given in Table I. In this connection it should be mentioned that for energy calibration in the region of the analogue levels, the reactions $C^{12}(p,t)C^{10}$ (g.s.) and $C^{12}(p,He^3)B^{10}$ were used. The result for Al^{25} may be compared with $(7.91 + 0.03)$ MeV obtained from delayed proton measurements[3].

In addition, two other states were observed in each spectrum to which a probable T = 3/2 assignment could be made. This identification was based upon observation of similar differential cross sections, and the fact that their energy separation from the analogue ground state agrees with the excitation of known levels in Na^{25}. The energies of these levels also appear in the Table.

Figure 3 shows the energy spectra observed from a nickel-backed phosphorus target. As indicated in the figure, a number of peaks have been attributed to oxygen and carbon impurities in the target. Angular distributions for the three phosphorus peaks marked in each spectrum are shown in Fig. 4. At laboratory angles greater than 25° the peak due to production of the analogue level in Si^{29} is not resolved from the larger peak which arises from production of the T = 1

704

level at 2.31 MeV in N^{14}. However, the contribution
of the latter may be subtracted since the differential
cross-sections for the $O^{16}(p,He^3)N^{14*}$ (2.31 MeV, T = 1)
reaction are known[9] to be related to those for
$O^{16}(p,t)O^{14}$ (g.s., T = 1) in the ratio 1:1.88. The
resultant angular distribution to the T = 3/2 analogue
levels is shown at the bottom of the figure. Although
the statistics are poor, the shapes appear to be characteristic of L = 2 transfer. A $5/2^+$ assignment to
the final states is consistent with this result and
agrees with the known $5/2^+$ spin-parity of the Al^{29}
ground state.

The measured excitation energy of the T = 3/2
analogue state in P^{29} is (8.361 $\pm$ 0.035), while in Si^{29}
it is (8.340 $\pm$ 0.045) MeV. The former value is to be
compared with the value (8.36 $\pm$ 0.03) MeV obtained
from the delayed proton measurements[1].

Within an isobaric multiplet, masses are related
by the formula[5]:

$$M = a + bT_z + cT_z^2;$$

and this relationship may now be used to calculate the
mass excess of Si^{25} from the known masses of Na^{25} and
its analogues in Mg^{25} and Al^{25}. Similarly the known
masses of Al^{29} and its analogues in Si^{29} and P^{29} yield
the mass excess of S^{29}. The results are (+3.72 $\pm$ 0.10)
MeV, for Si^{25} and (-3.31 $\pm$ 0.15) MeV for S^{29}. In these
calculations, the energies of the analogue levels in
Al^{25} and P^{29} were taken to be averages of the present
measurements with those of the delayed proton work. ·
The errors quoted are based entirely upon the experimental errors and assume complete accuracy for the
mass formula itself.

The partial half lives of the decay branches from Si^{25} and S^{29} to their respective analogues in Al^{25} and P^{29} have been measured[4] by comparison with decay branch intensities from Ne^{17}. Using the masses just evaluated, the corresponding log $\underline{ft}$ values are calculated to be (2.90 ± 0.25) for the superallowed branch from Si^{25} and (2.95 ± 0.25) for that from S^{29}. These values differ slightly from those given in Ref. 4 since only less accurate estimates of the two $Q_\beta +$ were possible at that time. Calculations[10] of these log $\underline{ft}$ values give 3.27 for both decays and, although the measured values still have large errors attached to them, the discrepancy appears to be significant. However, still more precise measurements of the partial half lives, both for the two cases considered here and for similar ones throughout the (2s,1d) shell, are needed before firm conclusions can be drawn. It is of interest, though, that any $T = 1/2$ admixture in the levels would tend to increase the calculated log $\underline{ft}$ values; the present measurements may be regarded as evidence for the $T = 3/2$ purity of these states.

An analysis of the dependence on A and T of the coefficients of the mass formula has been carried out for multiplets in the 1p shell[11], but unfortunately results in the (2s,1d) shell are not expected to yield such a simple interpretation. Qualitatively, the coefficients evaluated from the results of this experiment are somewhat smaller than those evaluated from $T = 1$ triplets in the same region, and remain so even if the effect of Coulomb pairing is removed (using the same model as Ref. 11). Such a suggestion of T dependence in the coefficients, however, must be substantiated by measurements on other $T = 3/2$ multiplets in this shell, and a more detailed account of the Coulomb pairing effect.

We should like to thank Dr. R. Hanna for making available the facilities of the Rutherford Laboratory and for his interest in the work. We are also very grateful to Drs. P. S. Fisher, D. K. Scott and N. S. Chant for their assistance, and as well to Prof. D. H. Wilkinson and Dr. R. Rook for a number of valuable discussions. One of us (DJS) wishes to acknowledge the Scientific Research Council for a graduate Studentship.

REFERENCES

1) J. C. Hardy and R. I. Verrall, Phys. Letts. $\underline{13}$ (1964) 148.

2) R. McPherson and J. C. Hardy, Can J. Phys. $\underline{43}$ (1965) 1.

3) J. C. Hardy and R. E. Bell, Can J. Phys. $\underline{43}$ (1965) 1671.

4) J. C. Hardy, R. I. Verrall and R. E. Bell, Nucl. Phys., (to be published).

5) D. H. Wilkinson, Phys. Letts. $\underline{12}$ (1964) 348.

6) J. Cerny, R. H. Pehl, F. S. Goulding and D. A. Landis, Phys. Rev. Letts. $\underline{13}$ (1964) 726.

7) J. Cerny, R. H. Pehl, G. Butler, D. G. Fleming, C. Maples and C. Detraz, Phys. Letts. $\underline{20}$ (1966)35.

8) P. S. Fisher and D. K. Scott, PLA Progress Report 1964, (NIRL/R/81), p. 90.

9) J. Cerny and R. H. Pehl, Phys. Rev. Letts. $\underline{12}$ (1964) 619.

10) J. C. Hardy and B. Margolis, Phys. Letts.$\underline{15}$ (1965) 276.

11) D. H. Wilkinson, Phys. Rev. Letts. $\underline{13}$ (1964) 571.

TABLE I. Comparison of known levels in Na^{25} with observed (T = 3/2) levels in Al^{25} and Mg^{25}.

T=3/2 Levels in Al^{25}		T=3/2 Levels in Mg^{25}		Levels in Na^{25}
Excitation Energy, E_x (MeV)	$E_x - E_{xo}$ (MeV)	Excitation Energy, E_x (MeV)	$E_x - E_{xo}$ (MeV)	
7.914 ± 0.025 ($=E_{xo}$)	0.0	7.812 ± 0.025 ($=E_{xo}$)	0.0	0.0
9.17 ± 0.050	1.26	8.98 ± 0.080	1.17	1.07
10.40 ± 0.070	2.49	10.27 ± 0.070	2.46	$\left\{ \begin{array}{l} 2.42 \\ 2.20 \end{array} \right.$

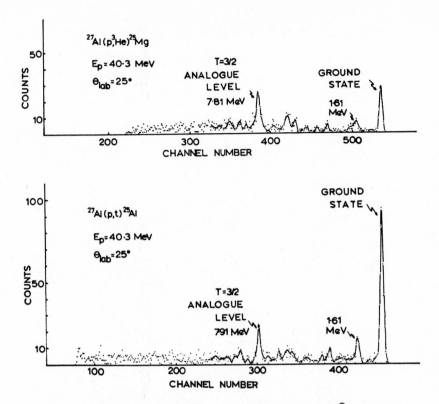

Fig. 1. Energy spectra of tritons and He^3, observed at a laboratory angle of 25°, from proton induced reactions on aluminium.

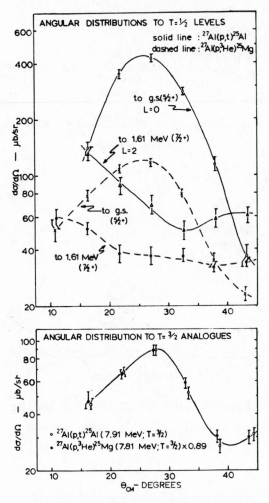

Fig. 2. Angular distributions for those triton and He^3 peaks marked in Fig. 1. In the lower part of the figure, the (p,He^3) cross-sections to the T = 3/2 analogue level in Mg^{25} have been multiplied by 0.89, the computed factor which corrects for differences in isobaric spin coupling and momentum between the two cases. Error bars in the figure are entirely statistical; the absolute uncertainty is approximately ± 15%.

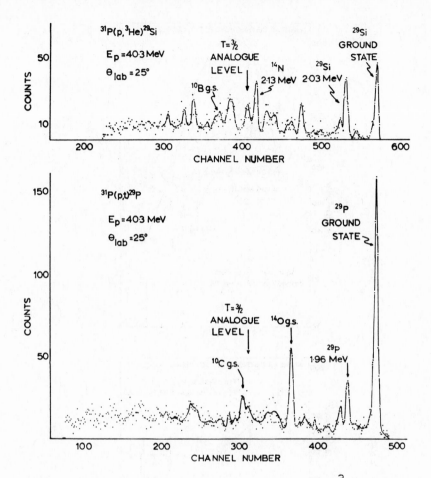

Fig. 3. Energy spectra of tritons and He³, observed at a laboratory angle of 25°, from proton induced reactions on a phosphorus target which includes oxygen and carbon impurities.

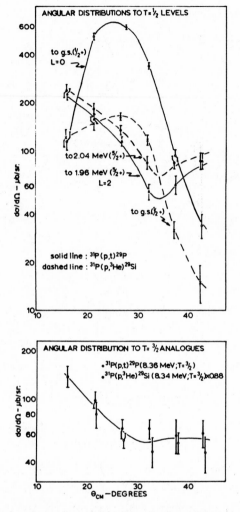

Fig. 4. Angular distributions for those triton and He³ peaks marked in Fig. 3 as being due to reactions on phosphorus. In the lower part of the figure the (p,He³) cross sections to the T = 3/2 analogue level in Si²⁹ have been multiplied by 0.88, the computed isobaric spin coupling and momentum factor. Statistical error bars are shown; the absolute uncertainty is ±25%.

712

S8. ANALOGUE STATES IN Mo^{94} STUDIED BY THE $Nb^{93}(p,n)Mo^{93}$ REACTION

E. Finckh, U. Jahnke, J. Wirsich

Hahn-Meitner-Institut für Kernforschung
Berlin, Germany

Using the (p,n) reaction and proton scattering, analogue resonances in the compound nucleus were investigated for target nuclei with low spin values. A study of the $Nb^{93}(p,n)Mo^{93}$ reaction should prove, whether the resonances can also be detected in the case of high spin values, since the lower levels in the analogue nucleus Nb^{94} have spin values of 6^{+}, 3^{+}, 4^{+}, 7^{+} and 5^{+} [1]. The Coulomb energies are known for the neighboring Zr- and Mo-nuclei [2]. One expects the 6^{+} resonance in the compound nucleus Mo^{94} at a laboratory proton energy of 4.8 MeV.

The level structure of Mo^{93} is known from measurements of the (d,p) reaction [3], the beta-decay [4] and the gamma-decay of the isomeric level [5]. Also theoretical calculations have recently been published [6]. Due to the spin selectivity of each process, only 3 out of 15 states are seen in at least two different processes. Since, for the (p,n) reaction, the spin selection should be less stringent, a measurement of the energy of the neutrons will give additional confirmation of the level scheme.

Nb targets of thicknesses between 0.2 and 0.5 mg/cm^{2} were made by evaporation onto Ta backings.

Yield curves were taken detecting the neutrons with a modified long counter. The proton energy was varied between 4.5 and 5.3 MeV. At the ground state analogue resonance (E_p = 4.82 MeV) the neutron spectrum was measured by time-of-flight technique using the 1 ns pulse from our Van de Graaff.

Figure 1 shows the yield curve measured at 120° to the direction of the proton beam. Maxima are seen at 4.82, 4.88, 4.90, 4.93 and 5.16 MeV. The small shoulders at 4.86 and 5.14 MeV are also seen at other angles. If one assumes that the first line corresponds to the ground state of Nb^{94} the energies of the other lines agree with the energies of the excited states in this nucleus.

If one subtracts from the yield an evenly rising background, one sees that the shape of the line at 4.82 MeV is hardly influenced by the other lines. This line has a full width at half maximum of 25 keV and nearly Lorentz shape. The experimental points can be fitted by a sum of five curves of this shape and width, as shown in Fig. 2. From such fits the energies of the higher analogue states, referred to the lowest one, were deduced to 42 ± 5, 61 ± 3, 79 ± 3, 112 ± 3 keV in agreement with the Nb^{94} level scheme[1].

One of the measured neutron time-of-flight spectra is shown in Fig. 3, in which 14 groups are seen. The excitation energies in Mo^{93} corresponding to the neutron groups are given in Fig. 3 and compared with published values in Table I. It was not possible to separate the levels at 1.49 MeV and 2.44 MeV. The neutron group to the level J^{π}= 1/2$^+$ at 0.93 MeV is very weak, but the groups to levels with higher spins are clearly seen. We assume that the level found by us at

714

2.24 MeV is identical with the 2.186 MeV level found in the (d,p) reaction[3].

REFERENCES

1) Sheline, Jernigan, Ball, Bhatt, Kim and Vervier, Nucl. Phys. 61 (1965) 342. Gruber, Koch, Maier, Schult, Ball, Bhatt, and Sheline, Nucl. Phys. 67 (1965) 433.
2) Fox, ANL - 6878 (1964) 231.
3) Hjorth and Cohen, Phys. Rev. 135 (1964) B920.
4) Vingiani, Monaro, Ricci and van Lieshout, Nuovo Cimento, XXIII, (1962) 729.
5) Nuclear Data Sheet 60 - 5 - 91.
6) Bhatt and Ball, Nucl. Phys. 63 (1965) 286; Auerbach and Talmi, Nucl. Phys. 64 (1965) 458; Vervier, Nucl. Phys. 75 (1966) 17.

TABLE I. Excited levels in Mo^{93}. PROCESS: Process by which the levels have been found. β: β-decay of Tc^{93} 4), γ: γ-decay of $J^{\pi} = 21/2^+$ in Mo^{93} 5), d: Mo^{92}(d,p) Mo^{93} 3). ℓ_n: Orbital angular momentum measured in the (d,p) reaction. SPIN: Established and proposed spin assignments. EXCITATION ENERGY: Column β, γ, (d,p): Values taken from references as quoted under "process"; column (p,n) - our results.

process	ℓ_n	spin	Excitation Energy in MeV	
			β, γ, (d,p)	(p,n)
β γ d	2	$5/2^+$	0	0
d	0	$1/2^+$	0.944	(0.93)
β		$(9/2^+)$	1.35	1.36
β γ		$9/2^+$	1.479 }	1.49
d	2	$3/2^+$	1.486	
d	2	$5/2^+$	1.695	1.70
β		$(7/2^+, 9/2^+)$	2.03	
γ		$13/2^+$	2.164	2.16
d	(2)	$3/2^+$	2.186	2.24
d	4	$7/2^+$	2.300	2.30
γ		$21/2^+$	2.428 }	
β		$(7/2^+, 9/2^+)$	2.44	2.44
d	0	$1/2^+$	2.445	

TABLE I continued

process	ℓ_n	spin	Excitation Energy in MeV	
			β, γ, (d,p)	(p,n)
				2,53
				2,56
(β) d	0	$1/2^+$	2,700	2,66
d	2	$3/2^+$	2,850	2,75
				2,82

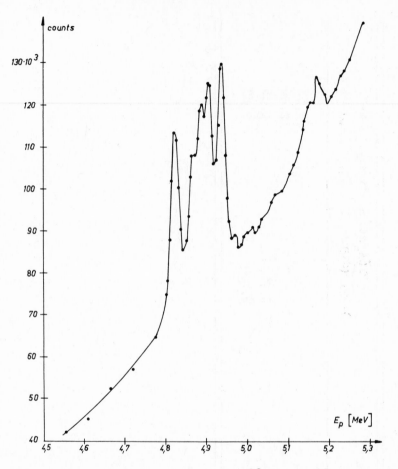

Fig. 1. Neutron yield of the $Nb^{93}(p,n)Mo^{93}$ reaction, measured with a modified long counter at 120° to the direction of the proton beam.

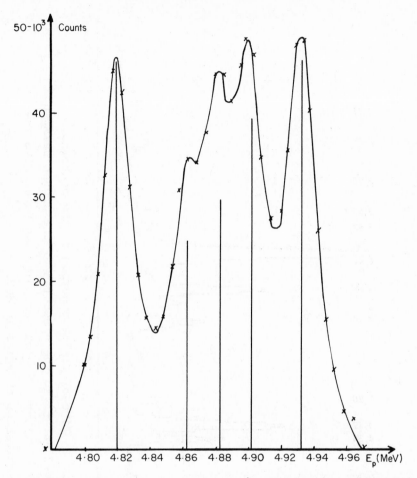

Fig. 2. Analogue resonances (background subtracted) fitted by five lines with Lorentz shape. The vertical bars give position and height of the single lines.

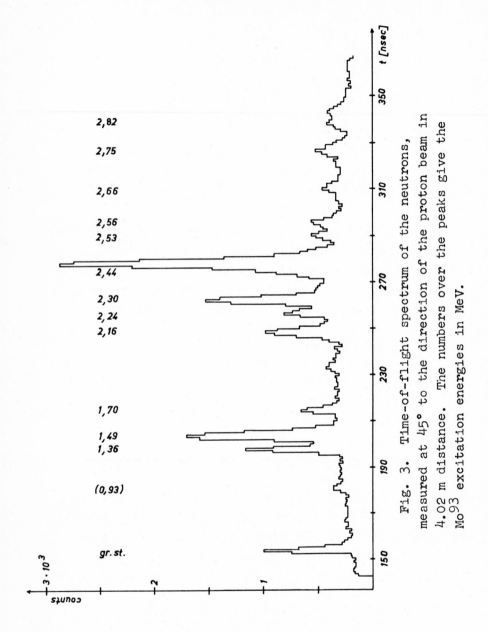

Fig. 3. Time-of-flight spectrum of the neutrons, measured at 45° to the direction of the proton beam in 4.02 m distance. The numbers over the peaks give the Mo93 excitation energies in MeV.

S9. A SEARCH FOR GIANT RESONANCES BUILT ON ANALOGUE STATES[*]

J. S. Allen, M. K. Brussel and A. I. Yavin

University of Illinois
Urbana, Illinois

We wish to describe a search for photonuclear giant dipole resonances built upon isobaric analogue states of nuclei. Our experiment is in a preliminary stage, and therefore conclusive results have not yet been established. However, the data obtained so far do serve to suggest that the approach we have used to investigate the giant dipole reaction may prove useful in future studies of analogue states and nuclear spectroscopy in general.

It is well known that in the (γ,nucleon) reaction, a resonance-like peak occurs for γ-ray energies between 12 and 20 MeV, having a width of a few MeV. This peak, which is associated with the absorption of electric dipole radiation, was first explained by Goldhaber and Teller[1] as a collective oscillation of the protons in the nucleus with respect to the neutrons. Theories based upon hydrodynamical models and shell models have been reasonably successful in predicting the excitation energy, the width, and various details

[*]Supported in part by the United States Office of Naval Research, and by the BUILD program of the University of Colorado and the University of Illinois.

of the structure of this giant dipole resonance. The
resonance state itself is perceived as being built upon
a nucleon ground state, in the sense that absorption of
a γ-ray (via an electric dipole transition) stimulates
a transition from the ground state to the resonance
state.

Similar enhancements of electromagnetic transitions between a highly excited nucleus and some of its
low-lying excited states have been reported for several
nuclei. Such transitions have been investigated via
the inverse reactions to (γ,nucleon) reactions. For
example, excitation functions for the $Al^{27}(p,\gamma_o)Si^{28}$
and $Al^{27}(p,\gamma_1)Si^{28*}$ reactions have revealed giant resonances with considerable structure for both transi-
tions[2].

Since the investigation of (p,γ_1) transitions
to excited states is made difficult by the inherent
difficulties in detecting energetic γ-rays, an alternative method for studying these transitions is desirable. The method we have employed depends upon the
possibility of particle decay from an excited state
following the emission of the γ-ray. Specifically, we
wish to study the γ-ray transition to a proton unstable
state by observing the proton decay of this state. The
process thus has the symbolic form, $(p,\gamma\overline{p})$. The advantages accruing to this method arise from the ease and
precision with which protons may be detected.

It was the purpose of the measurements reported
here to investigate whether the $(p,\gamma\overline{p})$ process is
feasible to observe. If so, by performing an excitation function of this process, one could search for a
giant resonance built upon a particle unstable, excited
state. Suitable candidates for excited states upon

which these resonances could be formed are analogue
states such as those observed by Fox, Moore and
Robson[3].

Consider the reaction: $p + Zr^{90} \rightarrow Nb^{91}(G*) \rightarrow Nb^{91*} + \gamma$, $Nb^{91*} \rightarrow Zr^{90} + \bar{p}$. (G*) denotes the region
of excitation where the giant resonance is expected to
occur. Richard <u>et al</u>.[4] in their elastic scattering
experiments, found that at a proton energy of 5.9 MeV a
state in Nb^{91*} was excited which was the isobaric analogue of a $j^{\pi} = 1/2^+$ excited state of Zr^{91}. If this
state is the analogue of the first excited state of
Zr^{91}, the corresponding energy for the analogue of the
ground state of Zr^{91} is expected to be 5.0 MeV. (In
another paper submitted to this conference[+], this energy
was determined to be 4.7 ± 0.1 MeV, and may indicate
that Richard <u>et al</u>. excited the analogue to the $j^{\pi} = 1/2^+$
second excited state of Zr^{91}. In the following discussion, however, the analogue to the ground state is
taken to be 5.0 MeV above the proton separation energy
of Nb^{91}.)[‡] One might expect that if a giant resonance
were built upon this state at an excitation 17 MeV
higher in energy, then the above reaction would occur,
and one could express it as:

$(p + 22 \text{ MeV}) + Zr^{90} \rightarrow Nb^{91}(G*) \rightarrow Nb^{91*} + \gamma_0 + 17 \text{ MeV})$

$\qquad\qquad\qquad\qquad\qquad\qquad\qquad \rightarrow Zr^{90} + (\bar{p} + 5 \text{ MeV})$

[+]See paper E6.

[‡]Editorial Note: The excitation of the analogue of the
ground state of Zr^{91} was not reported in the abstract
(Ref. 4) but was measured at 4.74 MeV. The 5.9 MeV
resonance is the analogue of the 1.2 MeV excited state
of Zr^{91}. This is reported in more detail elsewhere
(C.F. Moore, Ph.D. Disst., F. S. U., 1964, unpublished)

Figure 1 displays the relevant energy relationships. It is perhaps worthwhile to remark that this particular process is directly akin to the reaction upon the ground state of Y^{90}: $p + Y^{90} \rightarrow Zr^{91}(G) \rightarrow Zr^{90} + \gamma_o$.

This experiment was performed with the proton beam of the University of Colorado cyclotron. Protons coming from the Zr target ($\sim 99\%$ Zr^{90} and $\sim 1\%$ Zr^{91}) were detected in an E - ΔE telescope composed of solid state detectors. The telescope was usually placed at $90°$ with respect to the beam direction. The overall energy resolution of the system was about 150 keV.

A proton spectrum resulting from the bombardment of the target with protons is expected to show the presence of elastic and inelastic scattering in peaks which are correlated in energy with the incident proton energy. In addition, one expects to observe a background of unresolved inelastic proton groups and a large amorphous background of evaporation protons. We hoped to observe, superimposed on the evaporation background, a proton peak having an energy of $\sim$ 5 MeV and a width of between 10 and 100 keV. (Our energy resolution unfortunately would not permit us to observe this expected natural width.) The essential feature which would distinguish this proton group from ordinary inelastic protons is that its energy and width are essentially independent of the incident beam energy and width. In seeking this proton group, we therefore made runs at beam energies of 21.85, 22.0 and 23.0 MeV. Figures 2, 3 and 4 show the spectra obtained. The high energy portions of these spectra have been suppressed. The insets in the figures emphasize the energy region of primary interest - near 5 MeV. The energy scale is accurate to $\pm$ 200 keV. If the $(p, \gamma_o \bar{p})$ process were occurring, each of these spectra would show a small peak at ~ 5 MeV. An indication of such a peak may be discerned. To emphasize the nature of this peak, the spectra were added together channel by channel as shown in Fig. 5. A peak at ~ 5 MeV persists, whereas other structures of the spectra tend to become washed out. The magnitude of the observed peak at 5 MeV accords with a total cross section for its formation of 50 to 100 μb.

Despite the apparently positive result, a cautious appraisal seems in order. First, the energy of the observed peak is consistent with the analogue state appearing at 5.0 MeV, not at 4.7 MeV. The objection, however, is not taken as serious due to the uncertainties in the quoted energies and in our energy calibration. Secondly, it should be noticed that the observed cross section, if indeed due to a $(p, \gamma \bar{p})$ reaction, appears unexpectedly large. We can estimate a cross section for this process by extrapolating from (p, γ) cross sections obtained upon light nuclei.

If, for example, we use the cross section obtained from the $K^{39}(p, \gamma)Ca^{40}$ work of Hafele, Bingham and Allen[5] of ~ 100 μb, and apply a ZN/A correction (a factor of 2.2), and an isobaric spin correction (a factor of $(2T + 1)^{-1} = 0.09$), we obtain an estimated cross section for the $Zr^{90}(p, \gamma)$ reaction of approximately 20 μb. It seems probable that this figure should be considered an upper limit and certainly well below the cross section we have measured.

Since we do not observe the γ-ray directly, we must consider competing processes which could produce a monoenergetic proton group at 5 MeV. Consider then, the following reactions:

725

(a) $p + Zr^{90} \rightarrow Zr^{90*} + p$; $Zr^{90*} \rightarrow Y^{89} + \bar{p}_1 + 5$ MeV.

(b) $p + Zr^{91} \rightarrow Nb^{91*} + n$; $Nb^{91*} \rightarrow Zr^{90} + \bar{p} + 5$ MeV.

Process (a) may be observed. It is energetically possible, and a resonance for 5 MeV protons has been observed by the Florida State group in the reaction $p + Y^{89} \rightarrow Zr^{90*} \rightarrow Y^{89} + p$. The state in Zr^{90*} excited is the analogue of the first excited state of Y^{90}. However, since $\Delta T = 1$ for process (a), the cross section is expected to be small. Moreover, we have seen no evidence for formation of other states in Zr^{90*} which are isobaric analogues to Y^{90} states. This seems to indicate that though process (a) is a possible process for us to have observed, we probably have not observed it.

Process (b) could result from the 1% Zr^{91} impurity in our target, and is a likely explanation for our large cross section. It involves an excitation of the same proton-emitting state (Nb^{91*}) as in the $(p,\gamma p)$ process. Anderson et al.[6] determined a cross section for the (p,n) process of approximately 4 mb, which, considering our 1% Zr^{91} abundance, could account for approximately 40 - 80% of our observed yield.

Finally, it is apparent that no conclusive determination of the specific effect we have observed has been made here. Such a determination can, however, be made. For example, if in fact the $(p,\gamma\bar{p})$ process occurs and is observable, it should be possible to detect the γ-ray as well as the protons, $\bar{p}$. Similarly for the $(p,p'\bar{p})$ process, it should be possible to detect the two emerging protons in coincidence. Another

profitable approach in probing further the likelihood
of these processes would be through the use of magnetic spectrometers of high momentum resolution. The
use of a magnetic spectrometer to detect the protons,
$\overline{p}$ or $\overline{p}_1$, has two beneficial effects. The first is that
it allows higher counting rates to be achieved. All
particles without the correct momentum do not present
themselves to the detector - there is no difficulty
from the effects of high gross counting rates.
Secondly, from kinematic considerations, it should be
possible with such a spectrometer to distinguish the
$(p,\gamma\overline{p})$ process from the $(p,n\overline{p})$ or $(p,p'\overline{p})$ processes,
the latter two producing a larger energy spread for
the emerging protons, $\overline{p}$.

  Although by no means conclusive, our preliminary
measurements suggest the following fascinating possibilities: (1) If the $(p,\gamma\overline{p})$ reaction is occurring,
then a rather precise method is available for investigating giant resonance phenomena built upon excited
nuclear states of a special kind, namely, proton unstable analogue states. One could vary the incident
proton energy, and by measuring the yield of $\overline{p}$, trace
out the structure of the giant resonance; (2) If, in
fact, we have observed the $(p,n\overline{p})$ or $(p,p'\overline{p})$ reactions
then again our methods provide a precise, alternative
method for studying these processes. One might, for
example, observe the decay of the analogue states excited, and so obtain branching ratios for this decay
as well as precise energy determinations of these
states. Other reactions may also be so studied. For
example, (He^3,t) reactions to proton unstable states
could be investigated. It is perhaps the primary purpose of this report to stimulate more detailed experi-

mentation along these lines.

We wish to thank Professor D. Lind for allowing us to use the University of Colorado cyclotron and research facility. We are deeply indebted to Professor M. E. Rickey for his generous help in carrying out the experiment. We are also grateful to Mr. R. Hoffswell for his help.

REFERENCES

1) M. Goldhaber and E. Teller, Phys. Rev. 74 (1948) 1046.

2) P. P. Singh, R. E. Segel, L. Meyer-Schützmeister, S. S. Hanna, and R. G. Allas, Nucl. Phys. 65 (1965) 577.

3) J. D. Fox, C. F. Moore and D. Robson, Phys. Rev. Letts. 12 (1964) 198.

4) P. Richard, D. Robson and J. D. Fox, Bull. Am. Phys. Soc. 10 II (1965) 52.

5) J. C. Hafele, F. W. Bingham and J. S. Allen, Phys. Rev. 135 (1964) B365.

6) J. D. Anderson, C. Wong, J. W. McClure and B. D. Walker, Phys. Rev. 136 (1964) B118.

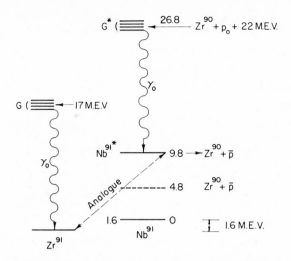

Fig. 1. Energy level diagram of Nb^{91} relative to the ground state of Zr^{91}. G^* is used to denote the giant resonance built upon Nb^{91*}. G is used to denote the giant resonance built upon the ground state of Zr^{91}.

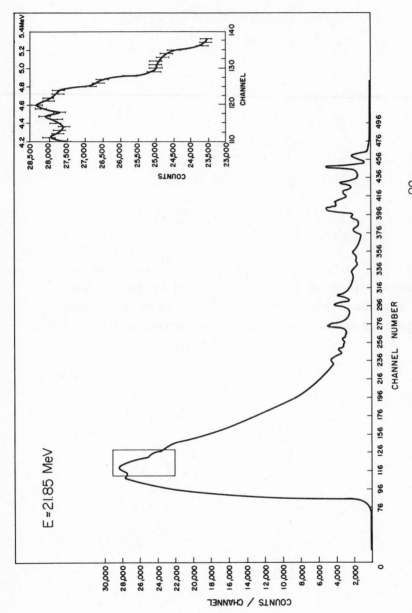

Fig. 2. Proton spectrum from the p + Zr^{90} reaction, taken at an incident proton energy of 21.85 MeV.

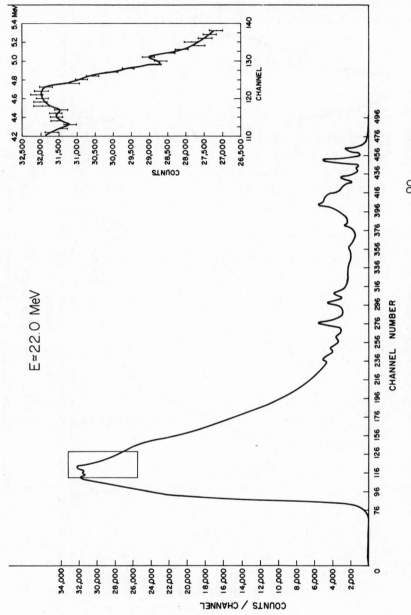

Fig. 3. Proton spectrum from the p + Zr^{90} reaction, taken at an incident proton energy of 22.0 MeV.

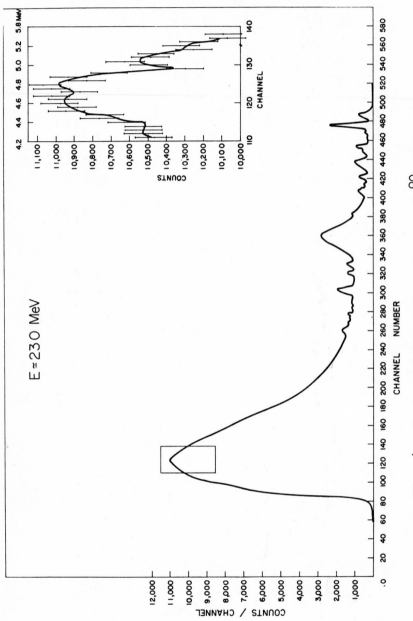

Fig. 4. Proton spectrum from the p + Zr^{90} reaction, taken at an incident proton energy of 23.0 MeV.

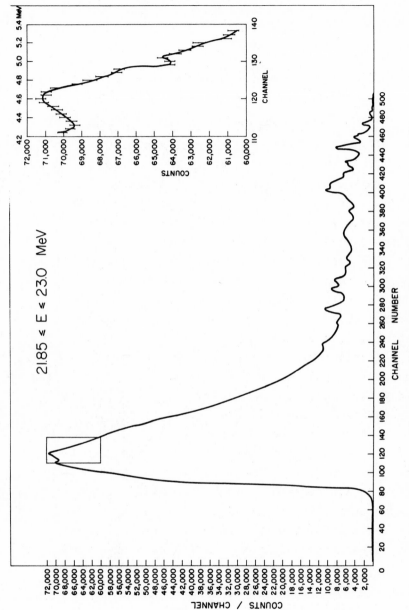

Fig. 5. The summed spectra of Figs. 2, 3 and 4.

S10. STUDY OF THE ISOBARIC-SPIN
FORBIDDEN REACTION $N^{14}(\alpha,\alpha_1)N^{14*}$(2.31 MeV)

Coral M. Chesterfield and B. M. Spicer
University of Melbourne, Australia

Following the observation of isobaric spin forbidden transitions in a number of (d,α) reactions in
light nuclei, a similar violation has been sought in the
inelastic scattering of α-particles by N^{14}.

The reaction $N^{14}(\alpha,\alpha_1)N^{14*}$ (2.31 MeV) was chosen
largely because of its similarity to the $O^{16}(d,\alpha_1)$ reaction, which was already known to exhibit an isobaric
spin forbidden transition. These two reactions have
identical channel spins, and the former cannot proceed
via a direct interaction mechanism. Furthermore, they
can populate only a limited selection of compound states,
namely those of spin and parity 1^-, 2^+, 3^-, 4^+, etc.
Thus identical levels of F^{18} should be excited in the
two reactions, and measurements of angular distributions
of the α_1 group at isolated levels should indicate their
spins and parities. The total cross section for the
isobaric spin forbidden transition will, in principle,
give an indication of the isobaric spin impurity in the
intermediate F^{18} states. However, any interpretation
along these lines will be complicated by the facts that
the (α,α_o) and (α,α_2) reactions may populate compound
states having any spin and parity, and can also proceed
via a direct interaction mechanism.

The beam of 10-13 MeV He^{++} - particles was obtained from the Melbourne variable energy cyclotron. The absolute beam energy calibration is relative to the $C^{12}(\alpha,n)$ and $Al^{27}(p,n)$ thresholds and its resolution is better than $\pm$ 0.1%.

The targets were of melamine evaporated on to very thin (8×10^{-6} cm) gold foil, and were normally approximately 200 keV thick to 11 MeV α-particles. No evidence was found for the evaporation of the melamine under bombardment by up to 0.2μA beams.

Narrow depletion layer surface barrier detectors followed by conventional electronics detected the α-particles. The angular resolution was $\pm$ 1° and absolute angles were known to $\pm$ 1/2° for the angular distribution measurements.

Excitation functions were measured in 50 keV steps at center-of-mass angles of 67°, 80° and 90°. These are shown in Fig. 1, and the energies at which partial angular distributions were measured are marked by arrows. The angular range was limited by the swamping of the forbidden group by the elastic scattering groups at forward angles, and by kinematics and the $N^{14}(\alpha,d_o)$ reaction deuteron group at large angles. Excitation functions over the resonances near 12 MeV and 12.5 MeV were remeasured with a much thinner target ($\sim$50 keV thick) at center-of-mass scattering angles of 67° and 90° respectively, in an effort to resolve any structure in them (See Fig. 2).

The 90° excitation function is particularly useful for locating negative parity resonances because the angular distributions for these resonances all peak at 90°, whereas those for positive parity resonances are zero at 90°.

Nine partial angular distributions were measured (See Figs. 3 and 4) and, on the basis of these, tentative spin and parity assignments have been made for several resonances. Only two of the measured angular distributions fit well to the theoretical forms, and on the basis of these the 12.47 MeV state of F^{18} is assigned as 4^+, and the 13.32 MeV state 5^-. The other seven distributions exhibit interference effects and, from analysis of four of these, tentative assignments are made for F^{18} levels at 12.67 MeV, $(5)^-$; 14.16 MeV, $(5)^-$ and 14.33 MeV, $(4)^+$. The remaining analysis is incomplete as yet.

The forbidden group was observed clearly in a large number of spectra. In the energy and angular range investigated the differential cross section of the α_1 group reached a maximum of 18% of that of the α_0 group and 40% of that of the α_2 group, although it was normally much smaller than this.

Because of the restrictions imposed on the (α, α_1) reaction by angular momentum and parity conservation laws (See above), one can make at best very rough guesses as to the intensity of isobaric spin impurity in the states excited in this reaction. An attempt has been made to estimate the compound nucleus contribution to the (α, α_0) cross section, and this leads to a lower limit for the intensity of impurity in the 12.47 state of 5%, and in the 13.32 MeV state of 2%. Since the inelastic scattering reaction is incapable of distinguishing between predominantly $T = 0$ and $T = 1$ states, one must look to other data for information regarding whether the major component of isobaric spin is 0 or 1.

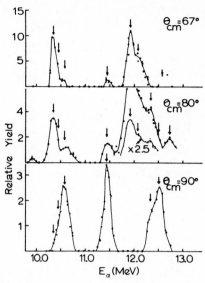

Fig. 1.   Excitation functions for the $N^{14}(\alpha,\alpha_1)$ reaction.

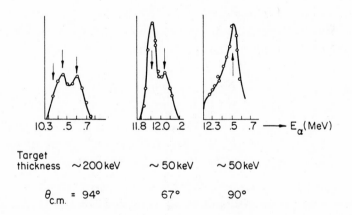

Fig. 2.   Partial excitation functions measured.

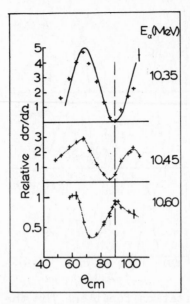

Fig. 3. Angular distributions of α-particles over 2 interfering levels. The solid curve is the theoretical curve for a 4^+ state.

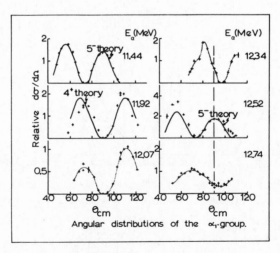

Angular distributions of the α_1-group.

Fig. 4. Angular distributions of the α_1 group.

S11. EXCITATION OF ISOBARIC ANALOGUE STATES BY THE (d,n) REACTION

B. Lawergren, G. C. Morrison[*], and A. T. G. Ferguson

A. E. R. E.
Harwell, England

We wish to report on a high-resolution study of the $Na^{23}(d,n)Mg^{24}$ and $Al^{27}(d,n)Si^{28}$ reactions, which has been carried out at a deuteron energy of 3 MeV by use of the Harwell pulsed Van de Graaff and time-of-flight spectroscopy. The work is part of a wider study of the excitation of isobaric analogue states by the (d,n) reaction on nuclei in the 2s - 1d shell. In order to reach the region of high excitation energies where isobaric analogue states are expected in the final nucleus, the bias on the neutron detector[1] was set such that neutrons down to 150 keV energy could be detected. With this setting, a range of excitation up to 2 - 3 MeV above the ground state analogue could be examined in the above reactions. The ground state Q-values of the two reactions are 9.47 and 9.36 MeV, respectively.

A spectrum of neutrons at $0°$ from the $Na^{23}(d,n)$ Mg^{24} reaction is shown in Fig. 1. A flight path of 6 m was maintained throughout this work. The advantage of using neutron time-of-flight spectroscopy to provide an expanded energy scale in the region of high excited states is clearly shown in Fig. 1

[*]Present address: Argonne National Laboratory, Illinois

Angular distributions were measured at 10° inter-vals in the forward direction and at larger intervals elsewhere. The shapes of the angular distributions were used to determine ℓ values. Isobaric analogue states have been identified by comparing with the posi-tions, ℓ values, and intensities of levels excited in the (d,p) reaction to the analogue nucleus. In this report only the results for states excited with $\ell = 0$ angular momentum transfer will be presented. Such states observed in the $Na^{23}(d,n)Mg^{24}$ reaction are iden-tified in Fig. 1. The extraction of spectroscopic factors for such states should be most reliable since any compound nucleus effects should be small compared with the large forward peaking observed in the case of $\ell = 0$ transfer.

Relative spectroscopic factors which have been extracted from the data by DWBA theory are shown in Table I. Reasonable distortion parameters for this mass region were used, and the variation of separation energy for the bound-state wave function was taken into account in the conventional manner. A cut-off radius of 3 F was used in the calculations. Uncertainty with regard to the value chosen might result in a 20 - 30% uncertainty in the values of the spectroscopic factors so obtained. The upper three states listed in each reaction are isobaric analogues of the states whose excitation energies are listed for the (d,p) reaction. Their excitation energies relative to the ground state analogue are also given. In the case of the Na^{23} tar-get, the unlisted ground state analogue ($\ell = 2$) is ob-served at an excitation energy of 9.52 MeV. In the case of the Al^{27} target, the state listed at 9.33-MeV excitation in Si^{28} is the analogue doublet of the ground state and first excited state of Al^{28}. The combined spectroscopic factor is listed. The peak cross sections, also shown in Table I, illustrate the marked dependence on Q-value of the (d,n) reaction for $\ell = 0$ transfer. This has an obvious practical consequence for the observation of isobaric analogue states by the (d,n) reaction.

Relative spectroscopic factors derived from the (d,p) reactions[2,3] to the corresponding states in the analogue nucleus are also given in Table I, where they have been normalized to those from the (d,n) reaction at the largest value in each case. The values listed for Al^{27}(d,p)Al^{28} have been extracted by PWBA, but over the limited range of excitation energy covered in Al^{28} their ratios are not expected to differ much from those extracted by DWBA. Good agreement in the ratios of spectroscopic factors is observed in both cases.

A further point of interest, not obvious from Table I, should be mentioned. The (d,p) reaction leading to the 1.02-MeV state in Al^{28} has a predominantly $\ell = 2$ pattern with an estimated $\ell = 0$ component of only 10 - 15%. However, in the (d,n) reaction to the analogue of this state, the $\ell = 2$ component is expected to be suppressed relative to the $\ell = 0$ component by a factor of 30 at this high excitation. Experimentally, only the $\ell = 0$ contribution is observed. Thus the (d,n) reaction to the analogue state served to confirm the presence of the small $\ell = 0$ component in the (d,p) reaction.

In addition to comparing the spectroscopic factors for the (d,n) and (d,p) reactions to individual states with $T = 1$, one can also compare the total strength for proton transfer to the $2s_{1/2}$ orbital in

741

$T = 0$ and $T = 1$ states in the same final nucleus. The sum rule of French and Macfarlane[4] predicts that the total strength should be equally divided between the two T states, if it can be assumed that the $2s_{1/2}$ orbitals for neutrons and protons in the target nucleus are both unfilled or partially filled to the same extent. The sum of the relative spectroscopic factors to $T = 0$ and $T = 1$ states is shown in Table II. The sum for $T = 1$ states has been increased by the amount shown, which takes account of transitions to higher excited states unobserved in the (d,n) reaction. The additional strength was estimated from the corresponding (d,p) reactions. It can be seen from Table II that the sum rule appears to be well confirmed in both reactions studied. This would indicate little or no $2s_{1/2}$ configuration in the target ground state. Confirmation of this result is being sought from a determination of the absolute spectroscopic factors.

The mean values of the single-particle energies for the $2s_{1/2}$ configurations in Mg^{24} and Si^{28} have also been calculated and are shown in Table II. The centroids of the $T = 1$ states again take into account the small amount of $2s_{1/2}$ strength in higher excited states. From these centroid energies, a value of about 4.9 MeV for the isobaric spin splitting of the $2s_{1/2}$ orbital is found for both Mg^{24} and Si^{28}. This value is considerably larger than that of about 3 MeV found[5] in O^{16}.

In conclusion, we have sought to demonstrate some of the advantages of the (d,n) reaction in the study of isobaric analogue states - particularly with regard to $\ell = 0$ transitions. Such advantages do much to compensate for the experimental difficulties involved in the detection of neutrons as compared with detection of charged particles in the analogous (He^3,d) reaction. Extension of the work reported here to higher mass values, and of necessity to higher deuteron energies, will be particularly useful.

REFERENCES

1) J. M. Adams, E. Barnard, A. T. G. Ferguson, W. R. McMurray, and I. J. van Heerden, Nucl. Instr. Methods 31 (1965) 21.

2) C. Daum, Nucl. Phys. 51 (1964) 244.

3) P. M. Endt and C. van der Leun, Nucl. Phys. 34 (1962) 1.

4) J. B. French and M. H. Macfarlane, Nucl. Phys. 26 (1961) 168.

5) A. M. Lane, Nucl. Phys. 35 (1962) 676.

TABLE I. Relative spectroscopic factors from (d,n) and (d,p) reactions on Na^{23} and Al^{27} targets for $\ell = 0$ angular momentum transfer.

| | (d,n) | | | (d,p)[a] | |
Excitation (MeV)	Excitation above g.s. analogue (MeV)	$d\sigma/d\Omega$ at 0° (rel.)	$(2J + 1)S$	Excitation (MeV)	$(2J + 1)S$ normalized to (d,n)
			Na^{23} target		
4.23		64	18		
7.33		13.2	1.6		
7.80		102	9		
8.65		146	7.9		
10.08	0.56	134	4.2	0.564	3.7
10.74	1.22	791	23.3	1.341	23.3
11.22	1.70	180	6.7	1.844	7.5
			Al^{27} target		
1.77		26	12.4		
6.27		37	5.4		
7.93		49	3.5		

TABLE I continued

(d,n)				(d,p)[a]	
Excitation (MeV)	Excitation above g.s. analogue (MeV)	$d\sigma/d\Omega$ at 0° (rel.)	$(2J + 1)S$	Excitation (MeV)	$(2J + 1)S$ normalized to (d,n)
			Al^{27} target		
8.59		130	7		
9.33	0.0	507	19.7	0.0	19.7
10.38	1.05	39	1.2	1.018	1.4
11.42	2.09	58	4.8	2.147	4.2

a   The results of Refs. 2 and 3 have been used to obtain normalized spectroscopic factors.

TABLE II. Summary of relative spectroscopic information about $2s_{1/2}$ levels in Mg^{24} and Si^{28}.

Excitation (MeV)	T	$(2J+1)S$	$\sum (2J+1)S$	Centroid energy $\overline{E}$ (MeV)
		Mg^{24}		
4.23	0	18	36.5	6.20
7.33		1.6		
7.80		9		
8.65		7.9		
10.08	1	4.2	41.0	11.10
10.74		23.3		
11.22		6.7		
Higher States		~7.0		
		Si^{28}		
1.77	0	12.4	28.3	5.08
6.27		5.4		
7.93		3.5		
8.59		7		
9.33	1	19.7	28.3	10.0
10.38		1.2		
11.42		4.8		
Higher States		~2.6		

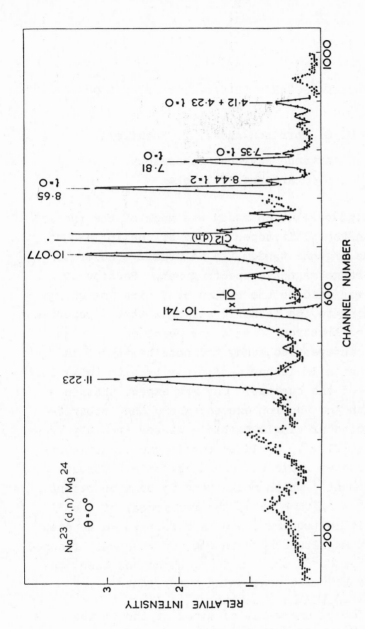

Fig. 1. Spectrum of neutrons at 0° from the reaction
$Na^{23}(d,n)Mg^{24}$. Only the energies of $\ell = 0$ transitions
are listed.

S12. A STUDY OF ISOBARIC SPIN PURITY OF ANALOGUE STATES IN Cu^{59}*

G. C. Morrison and J. P. Schiffer

Argonne National Laboratory
Argonne, Illinois

A high-resolution study was made of the (He^3,d) reaction on the Ni isotopes by use of the 18 MeV He^3 beam of the Argonne tandem Van de Graaff accelerator and broad-range magnetic spectrograph. Particular attention was paid to the region of excitation energy corresponding to the isobaric analogue states reported by Blair and Armstrong[1] in these reactions. It was of special interest to study the possibility of an expected change in isobaric-spin purity with total isobaric spin of the nucleus. One may expect that in a nucleus with low neutron excess, where the isobaric-spin splitting of single-particle states (roughly proportional to $2T + 1$) would be small, the isobaric-spin purity of states would be relatively poor. Mixtures must be present[2] which would tend to be proportional to $[1/(\Delta E)^2 \sim 1/(2T + 1)^2]$, the reciprocal of the energy splitting squared, and therefore would be about an order of magnitude more in the Cu^{59} nucleus, reached by $Ni^{58}(He^3,d)Cu^{59}$, than in Cu^{65}, which had been studied in the $Ni^{64} + p$ scattering experiment[3]

* Work performed under the auspices of the United States Atomic Energy Commission

A composite spectrum showing the region of excitation for the analogue states is shown in Fig. 1. Our results are summarized in Table I. It is clear that a large number of levels are present, many more than the number of expected analogue states, as shown in Fig. 2. Unfortunately, we do not have enough data (because of lack of sufficient beam intensity) to make ℓ-value assignments to more than the strongest transitions in the spectrum. While the very strongest levels do seem to correspond to analogue states, as was found in Ref. 1 there are many somewhat weaker states which could easily contain some appreciable fraction of the analogue strength. Taking the energies of the principal components for the analogue states, we get a mean-square deviation between analogue and normal energies of ~ 40 keV which is to be compared with ~ 35 keV for Ni^{64} found in Ref. 3. This deviation may be attributed in part to differences in Coulomb energies for various states[4]. Such differences would be expected to be about 1/3 as great in this case as in Ni^{64} + p. The results then, are not very clearcut. A similar case exists in the $Fe^{54}(He^3,d)Co^{55}$ reaction reported by Rosner et al.[5]. This is also a T = 1 target, as is Ni^{58}; the mean square-deviation is ~ 35 keV.

One may alternatively consider the possibility of the T = 3/2 analogue states mixing with states of T = 1/2 in the same region of excitation energy. There are, in fact, three ℓ = 1 states around 3.9 MeV which may contain the ground state analogue strength and three ℓ = 3 states around 4.3 MeV. The corresponding weighted mean energies for the analogue states and summed spectroscopic factors are given in Table II. These "center of gravity" energies are in much better

agreement with those in Ni^{59}; in fact, the mean-square
deviation is less than 10 keV. The agreement for $\ell = 1$
spectroscopic factors is also greatly improved for the
$\ell = 1$ states. The fact that the $\ell = 3$ strength is too
high could be caused by the fact that these yields are
low and poorly determined in the present measurement.
The mixing width of these analogue states would then
be $\sim$ 170 keV, and provide a measure of such effects in
a nucleus where the states are almost stationary. Perhaps the type of admixture here is a special variety
of that suggested in Ref. 2. This is illustrated in
Fig. 3. The top part (a) of this figure shows a general giant-resonance-like admixture of the analogue
state while the second one (b) indicates schematically
the fact that admixtures would be greatest between
states having the same shell-model quantum numbers and
differing only in isobaric spin. In the case of low
T_z(c) the analogue state occurs at an energy which
coincides with the tail of the "giant resonance" of the
$T = T_z$ single-particle state and mixes strongly with
the component states of this giant resonance, but over
a limited energy region. This is what we propose as a
possible description of Cu^{59}. The lowest part of the
figure (d) illustrates the case where T_z is relatively
large, as in Ni^{64}, and the analogue state is far removed from "similar" configurations of lower T. It
should be emphasized that the considerations of this
paragraph hinge on some rather tentative ℓ-values and
guessed spin assignments. One should also take into
consideration the type of "external" mixing suggested
by Robson[6] before considering the "internal" mixing
discussed here.

A study of the $Ni^{60,62,64}(He^3,d)$ reaction has

yielded little new information. Two analogue states were seen in Cu^{61} and none in Cu^{63} and Cu^{65}. The reaction seems to be difficult to observe at high excitation energies. This is undoubtedly caused in part by the large continuum yield of deuterons from the C^{12} foils used as target backings and from the O^{16} contamination, and in part by the relatively smaller yield leading to analogue states with these targets. Information on lower excited states from these targets will be reported elsewhere.

REFERENCES

1) A. G. Blair and D. D. Armstrong, Phys. Letts. 16 (1965) 57.

2) C. Bloch and J. P. Schiffer, Phys. Letts. 12 (1964) 22.

3) L. L. Lee, Jr., A. Marinov and J. P. Schiffer, Phys. Letts. 8 (1964) 352.

4) K. W. Jones, J. P. Schiffer, L. L. Lee, Jr., A. Marinov, and J. Lerner, Phys. Rev. (to be published).

5) B. Rosner, C. H. Holbrow, and R. Middleton, Bull. Am. Phys. Soc. 11 (1966) 98.

6) D. Robson, Phys. Rev. 137 (1965) B535.

TABLE I. Energy levels from $Ni^{58}(He^3,d)Cu^{59}$.

Energy (MeV)[a]	ℓ	$(2J + 1)S$[b]
0.0	1	2.3
0.495	1	1.1
0.918	3	3.7
1.407		
2.279		
2.336	1	0.05
3.055	4	4.6
3.140	1	0.33
(3.33)		
(3.56)		
3.592	2	0.76
3.63		
3.758	(1)	0.16
3.899	1	0.44
3.916	2	0.40
4.012	(1)	0.35
4.065	(3)	0.3
4.123	(3)	0.5
4.318	3	1.6
4.365	1	0.42
6.857		
6.930		

[a] Excitation energies are accurate to 10 keV or less.

[b] Spectroscopic factors were normalized by requiring 12 holes in the f-p shell. No absolute cross sections were measured. Also, states above 3.5 MeV excitation are unbound against proton emission and the DWBA analysis is of questionable meaning.

TABLE II. Spectroscopic factors for analogue states.

Ni^{59} excit. (MeV)	ℓ	$(2J+1)S$	Cu^{59} excit. (MeV)	Energy above g.s. (MeV)	$(2T+1)X(2J+1)S$	Cu^{59} excit. (MeV)	Weighted mean energy (MeV)	Energy above g.s. (MeV)	$(2T+1)X(2J+1)S$
0.0	1	2.77	3.899	0.0	1.32	3.758 3.899 4.012	3.917	0.0	2.85
0.341	3	5.19	4.318	0.419	5.0	4.065 4.123 4.318	4.250	0.333	7.3
0.466	1	1.24	4.365	0.466	1.26	4.365	4.365	0.448	1.26

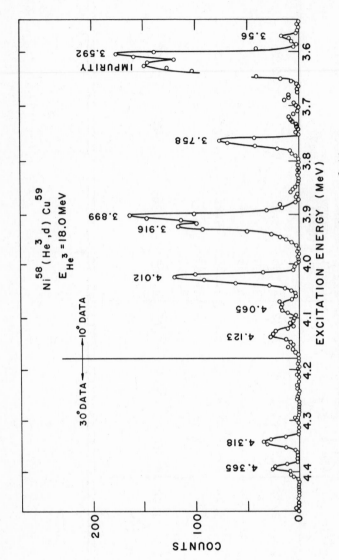

Fig. 1. Composite deuteron spectrum of the Ni58(He3,d)Cu59 reaction in the region of the expected analogue states. Peaks labeled "impurity" were from the C backing or O surface contaminants. The 10° and 30° sections of the spectrum are not normalized to each other.

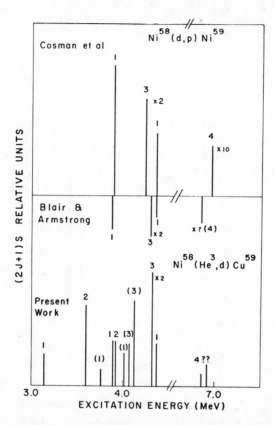

Fig. 2. Line diagram showing the reduced strengths [(2J + 1)S] from the $Ni^{58}(He^3,d)Cu^{59}$ reaction. The states reported by Ref. 1 and the states seen in $Ni^{58}(d,p)Ni^{59}$ by Cosman, Paris, Sperduto, and Enge [Phys. Rev. 142 (1966) 673] are also shown.

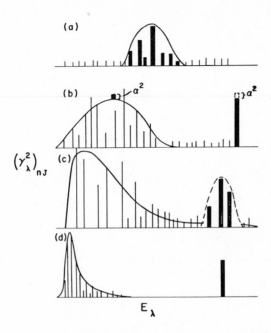

Fig. 3. Schematic representation of different modes of admixture of isobaric analogue states (heavy bars) into the $T = T_z$ states (light lines) taken partially from Ref. 2. Curve (a) shows a "microgiant" resonance, (b) shows the mixture of an analogue state with a giant resonance of the same shell-model quantum numbers but different T, (c) shows, what may be happening in Cu^{59}, a microgiant resonance of the analogue state built on the tail of the giant resonance nearby, and (d) shows that in a nucleus with larger T the energy splitting may be too large for such effects to take place.

S13. INELASTIC PROTON SCATTERING FROM ANALOGUE RESONANCES IN $Zr^{94} + p$

J. C. Legg, M. A. Crosby and G. Roy

Rice University
Houston, Texas

The observation of analogue resonances in heavy nuclei offers the nuclear spectroscopist an important new tool for the study of these nuclei. If the resonances were pure, unmixed isobaric analogue states, one could extract from the proton elastic scattering reduced widths analogous to those obtained from (d,p) experiments and from the inelastic scattering reduced widths between excited states of neighboring nuclei. This last information is available from no other experiment.

Unfortunately a theory capable of analyzing the results of inelastic scattering from real, mixed analogue resonances has not yet been devised. Thus one must use a reaction formulation, such as the Breit-Wigner (B-W), which is really appropriate for resonances which are not strongly mixed. If one uses such a reaction formula, one wants to restrict his attention to those resonances where both incoming and outgoing channel reduced widths with the analogue state are large.

We have suggested two tests of the experimental data in order to prevent the application of such a

757

formula to unfavorable cases[1]. First, a resonance
must be observed in both elastic and inelastic scattering. Second, the inelastic resonance must be symmetric, with the peak occurring at the resonant energy
determined from the elastic scattering. If both these
conditions are satisfied, then it may be reasonable
to hope that the analogue state is dominating the reaction in both the entrance and exit channels and that
analysis using a B-W formula may yield meaningful
widths.

We have studied inelastic proton scattering to
the 0.92 MeV 2+ state of Zr^{94}, using a 65 cm. conver-
tible spectrograph in spectrometer mode. An excitation curve for this reaction is shown in Fig. 1. The
spacing of the resonances agrees quite well with the
levels observed in the $Zr^{94}(d,p)Zr^{95}$ reaction[2].
Elastic scattering of protons has been studied by Fox[3],
and resonances are observed at 5.2, 6.1, 6.9 and 7.6
MeV.

Angular distributions were taken for the inelastic scattering on the 5.2, 6.1, 6.6 and 6.9 MeV resonances. Of these four resonances, the 5.2 and 6.9 MeV
resonances satisfy our two conditions for application
of a B-W formula. Of the two resonances which do not
satisfy our conditions, the 6.1 MeV resonance is dominated by the elastic channel and the 6.6 MeV resonance
is dominated by the inelastic channel.

The angular distributions are shown in Figs. 2
and 3. Since the angular distributions at 6.1 and 6.6
MeV contain a large non-resonant background angular
distributions were taken off resonance and an average
non-resonant background was subtracted from the experimental angular distributions. The results of this

subtraction may be seen in Fig. 4. The resultant distribution for the 6.1 MeV resonance is isotropic giving us some confidence in this procedure since this resonance is an s-wave resonance.

The Legendre polynomial fits to the angular distributions from the other three resonances indicate that they are $d_{5/2}$ resonances. This assignment is particularly surprising for the 6.9 MeV resonance since the 1.63 MeV state of Zr^{95}, to which the 6.9 MeV resonance is an analogue, was assigned by Cohen as a $d_{3/2}$ state and contains about half of the assumed $d_{3/2}$ single particle strength seen in the (d,p) experiments[2]. Accordingly, data is being taken on this resonance using silicon particle detectors to study the large angle inelastic scattering. This is being done in an attempt to determine whether the resonance angular distribution is possibly asymmetric about 90°. If this is indeed the case, it would be of considerable interest to determine which states of opposite parity are interfering with this analogue resonance.

The magnetic spectrometer data on the 5.2 and 6.9 MeV resonances were analyzed using a B-W formula modified to consider the j of the outgoing proton rather than channel spin. In addition, it was assumed that the $d_{3/2}$ and $g_{7/2}$ widths were zero. In other words, it was assumed that the reaction possessed nonzero widths for emission of $s_{1/2}$, $d_{5/2}$ and $g_{9/2}$ protons only. Even under this restrictive assumption, there still remain three quadratic equations in three unknowns. Thus up to four independent sets of widths may be obtained which fit the results of the experiment.

The results of this analysis are shown in Table I. The elastic widths used are the results of preliminary

analysis of the elastic scattering which were kindly
supplied by J. D. Fox.

REFERENCES

1) J. C. Legg, M. A. Crosby, and G. Roy, Phys. Letters,
   (to be published).
2) B. L. Cohen and O. V. Chubinsky, Phys. Rev. $\underline{131}$
   (1963) 2184.
3) J. D. Fox, Proceedings of Conference on Nuclear
   Spectroscopy with Direct Reactions, ANL-6878
   (1964) 231.

TABLE I.   Results of analysis of inelastic scattering data (All widths in keV).

Resonant Energy	ELASTIC WIDTHS				INELASTIC PROTON WIDTHS					
	Γ	Γ_p	γ^2_p	$\Gamma_{p'}$	$\Gamma s_{1/2}$	$\Gamma d_{5/2}$	$\Gamma g_{9/2}$	$\gamma^2 s_{1/2}$	$\gamma^2 d_{5/2}$	$\gamma^2 g_{9/2}$
5.2 MeV	25	2.1	6.3	5.5	0.3	5.2	.02	0.9	60	3
					3.8	0.5	1.1	12	6	300
					.003	1.6	3.9	.009	19	1000
6.9 MeV	40	10	7.3	16.5	9.8	2.3	4.4	5.9	3.2	69
					1.5	3.9	11	.89	5.6	170
					0.1	9.0	7.4	.06	13	120
					2.6	.02	13.8	1.5	.03	220

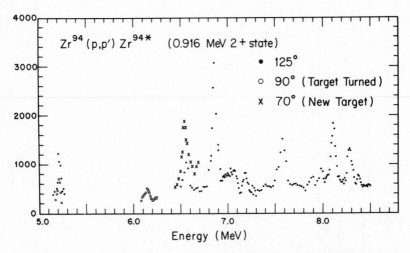

Fig. 1. Excitation curve for inelastic scattering of protons to the 2+ state of Zr^{94}. Many more resonances are seen in the inelastic scattering than in the elastic scattering.

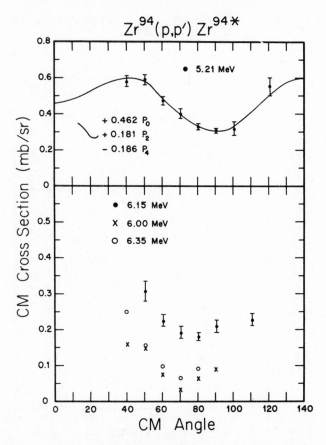

Fig. 2. Angular distributions on the 5.2 and 6.1 MeV resonances. Also shown are non-resonant angular distributions. In this and the following figures, the curve is the result of a weighted least-squares fit with Legendre polynomials.

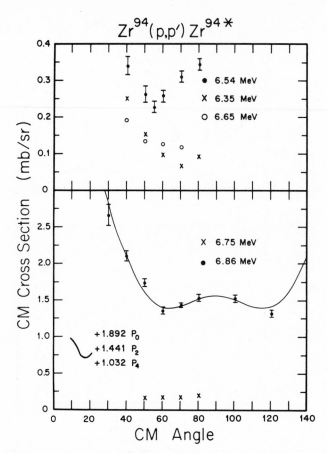

Fig. 3. Angular distributions on 6.5 and 6.9 MeV resonances. Also shown are non-resonant angular distributions.

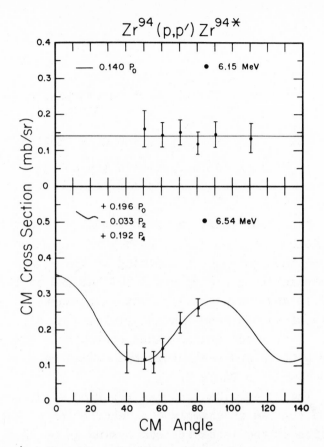

Fig. 4. Results of subtraction of non-resonant angular distribution from resonance angular distribution
for the 6.1 and 6.5 MeV resonances.

S14. FURTHER SPECULATIONS CONCERNING THE STRUCTURE OF Be^8 *

G. J. Stephenson, Jr. and J. B. Marion[+]

California Institute of Technology
Pasadena, California

In recent years, a large amount of experimental information has been collected bearing upon the structure and the isobaric spin mixing of the 2^+ and 1^+ doublets in Be^8 at 16.63 and 16.93 MeV and at 17.64 and 18.15 MeV, respectively. At last count, 16 different reactions had been studied yielding 31 distinct pieces of data concerning these four states. The various reactions and the information which each yields are presented in Table I.

The B^{10}(d,α)Be^8 studies reported by Browne and Erskine[1] gives an unambiguous description of the intensities of the isobaric spin mixing in each of these doublets, and the observed destructive interference between the 16.63 and 16.93 MeV levels reported by Browne elsewhere in these proceedings[2] fixes the relative phase of the T = 0 components. The phases within the states must be determined from other experiments, principally Li^7(d,n)Be^{8*} and Be^9(p,d)Be^{8*}, and

---
* Supported in part by the Office of Naval Research - Nonr-220(47).

[+] John Simon Guggenheim Fellow; on leave of absence from the University of Maryland.

766

consequently are somewhat model dependent, involving the coefficients of fractional parentage.

For the 2^+ doublet, all of these experiments as well as the measured α-particle widths are consistent with the description

$$\psi_{16.63} = 0.68 \, \phi_{T \, = \, 1} - 0.73 \, \phi_{T \, = \, 0},$$

$$\psi_{16.93} = 0.73 \, \phi_{T \, = \, 1} + 0.68 \, \phi_{T \, = \, 0},$$

(1)

where we use the convention that $T_z = + 1/2$ for neutrons, and the assumption that the parentage of the $A = 7$ ground state in both isobaric spin states is the same. This reproduces the well-known result that the 16.63 MeV level has a very large proton reduced width and a negligibly small neutron reduced width, and conversely for the 16.93 MeV level.

A model for these states has been proposed[3,4] in which the 16.63 MeV level is described as a proton coupled to a Li^7 core in its ground state whereas the 16.93 MeV level is described as a neutron coupled to a Be^7 core in its ground state. Dalton and Robson[5] have recently utilized this model to explain the large energy separation between the two states, a factor of two greater than one would expect from a calculation of the off-diagonal Coulomb matrix element in intermediate coupling[6]. While this model works very nicely to explain the reactions listed above, which probe only the $A = 7$ core ground state parentage and the isobaric spin mixing which is independent of parentage, it is clear that some account must be taken of higher core configurations, especially in view of the fact that the 18.15 MeV level is observed in both $Li^7(p,p)Li^7$ and

$Li^7(p,p')Li^{7*}$ reactions.

An attempt has been made to extend the model to include configurations corresponding to both the ground state and the first excited state and to include both $j = 3/2$ and $j = 1/2$ nucleons coupled to this core. To keep the model tractable, the assumption was made that both the $T = 0$ and $T = 1$ members of each doublet had the same parentage, differing only in the isobaric spin coupling. This leads to immediate difficulty in the case of the 1^+ doublet. Both the calculations of Dalton and Robson[5] and the intermediate coupling calculations[6] indicate an off-diagonal matrix element for the 1^+ pair which is smaller but of the same sign as that for the 2^+ doublet. This would again lead to the lower state of the pair having a larger percentage of $Li^7 + p$ and hence a larger proton reduced width than the upper member and, of course, vice versa for the neutron reduced width. On the other hand, the reactions $Be^9(p,d)Be^{8*}$, $Li^7(p,p)Li^7$, and $Li^7(d,n)Be^{8*}$ are all consistent with a proton reduced width ratio of about two favoring the 18.15 MeV level over the 17.64 MeV level. This, coupled with the $B^{10}(d,\alpha)Be^{8*}$ ratios to these two states, implies a description

$$\psi_{17.64} = 0.96 \ \phi_{T = 1} + 0.28 \ \phi_{T = 0},$$

$$\psi_{18.15} = \pm (0.28 \ \phi_{T = 1} - 0.96 \ \phi_{T = 0}). \qquad (2)$$

The possibility that the assumption of equal parentage for the two isobaric-spin states is incorrect was investigated using Barker's intermediate coupling wave functions[6]. According to these calculations, the nucleon reduced width for the $T = 1$ member is about

1.5 times that for the $T = 0$ member, heightening the disagreement.

The M1 transitions between these pairs of states measured by Paul and Kohler[7] and by Marion and Wilson[4] were then considered. Using the isobaric-spin mixing specified in Eqs. 1 and 2 and assuming a negligible contribution from the $\Delta T = 0$ terms, it was impossible to fit all four transitions. The $\Delta T = 0$ terms were included and solutions were obtained for the four matrix elements between the basis states of sharp isobaric spin. These solutions require that one of the 1^+ states of sharp T have an $|M|^2$ for the $\Delta T = 0$ decay which is inhibited by at most a factor of 10 compared to that for the $\Delta T = 1$ decay, where $|M|^2$ for the $\Delta T = 1$ decay is slightly larger than 1. This is in strong disagreement with the known systematics of M1 transitions discussed by Warburton in an invited paper at this conference[8].

If the Morpurgo rule is assumed to hold and the decay of the 17.64 MeV level is taken as input, the decay of the 18.15 MeV level may then be predicted. The results are presented in Table II. As may be seen there is substantial agreement for the $18.15 \rightarrow 16.93$ transitions and complete disagreement for the $18.15 \rightarrow 16.63$ transition.

Be^8 is a nucleus in which the isobaric spin is generally a good quantum number and for which model calculations are possible. It is, therefore, an ideal testing ground for our theories of charge dependence and isobaric-spin mixing in the cases discussed here. The calculations of Dalton and Robson[5] need to be extended to a model which gives a more complete account of the parentage of the states. The 3^+ doublet predicted by any model of Be^8 to lie slightly above the 1^+ doublet needs to be positively identified and studied.

Most particularly, however, the 1^+ doublet demands much further attention. The data regarding these states appear to be at variance with our understanding of the isobaric spin mixing expected and with the dependence of the M1 operator on isobaric spin. Both additional experimental data and more extensive theoretical work must be brought to bear on this problem.

REFERENCES

1) C. P. Browne and J. R. Erskine, Phys. Rev. 143 (1966) 683; and private communication.

2) C. P. Browne, Paper B2.

3) J. B. Marion, Physics Letts. 14 (1965) 315.

4) J. B. Marion and M. Wilson, Nucl. Phys., (in press).

5) B. J. Dalton and D. Robson, Phys. Letts. 20 (1966) 405.

6) F. C. Barker, Nucl. Phys., (in press).

7) P. Paul and D. Kohler, Bull. Am. Phys. Soc. 11 (1966) 26; and private communication.

8) E. K. Warburton, Paper A4.

TABLE I. Reactions used to study the 2^+ and 1^+ doublets in Be^8

REACTION	INFORMATION OBTAINED
$He^4(\alpha,\alpha)He^4$	Definite 2^+ assignments for 16.63 and 16.93
$Li^6(He^3,p)Be^8$	Γ for the 16.63 and 16.93
$Li^6(\alpha,d)Be^8$	σ (16.63)/σ (16.93)
$Li^6(Li^6,\alpha)Be^8$	σ (16.63)/σ (16.93)
$Li^7(p,p)Li^7$	θ_p^2 and channel spin ratios for 17.64 and 18.15
$Li^7(p,p')Li^{7*}$	$\theta_{p'}^2$ for 18.15
$Li^7(p,\gamma\alpha)He^4$	$|M|^2$ for 17.64, 18.15 → 16.63, 16.93; θ^2 for 16.63 from direct capture; E2/M1 for 17.64 → 16.63
$Li^7(d,n)Be^8$	Spectroscopic factors for 16.63, 17.64, 18.15; Limit for 16.93.
$Li^7(He^3,d)Be^8$	Spectroscopic factor for 16.63; Limit for 16.93; Γ for 16.63 and 16.93
$Be^9(p,d)Be^8$	Spectroscopic factors for 16.93, 17.64, 18.15; Limit for 16.63

TABLE I continued

REACTION	INFORMATION OBTAINED
$Be^9(d,t)Be^8$	$\sigma\,(16.93)/\sigma\,[Be^9(d,He^3)\,Li^8(g.s.)]$ $\sigma\,(17.64)/\sigma\,[Be^9(d,He^3)\,Li^8\,(0.98)]$
$Be^9(He^3,\alpha)Be^8$	$\sigma\,(16.63)/\sigma\,(16.93);\ \Gamma\ \text{for}\ 16.63$ and 16.93
$B^8(\beta^+,\nu)Be^8$	Log ft for 16.63 (and 16.93)
$B^{10}(d,\alpha)Be^8$	Cross section ratios for 16.63, 16.93, 17.64, 18.15; Γ for 16.63 and 16.93
$B^{11}(p,\alpha)Be^8$	$\sigma\,(16.63)/\sigma\,(16.93)$
$C^{12}(\gamma,\alpha)Be^8$	Identification of T = 1 strength near 16.8 MeV

TABLE II. $|M|^2$ in Weisskopf units.

From	$17.64 \ (exp)^{4)}$	$18.15 \ (exp)^{7)}$	18.15 (predicted)
To			
16.63	1.05 ± 0.10	1.43 ± 0.16	0.32
16.93	0.22 ± 0.015	1.27 ± 0.70	1.17

S15. T = 1 ANALOGUE STATES IN O^{16}

A. R. Barnett*
Nuclear Physics Laboratory, Oxford, England

Energy levels in O^{16} have been studied with the $N^{15}(p,n)O^{15}$ reaction over the proton energy range 3.8 - 12 MeV. The excitation function of the total cross-section was measured by bombarding a transmission gas target with the proton beam from the Harwell Tandem generator and detecting the residual β^+ - activity from O^{15}. The positrons have maximum energy 1.7 MeV and they traveled through a thin window in the target chamber walls to a nearby plastic scintillator.

Figure 1 shows two decay curves of the O^{15} activity. The scintillator pulses were biased at 1.3 MeV to exclude the background activities C^{11} and N^{13}. The slope of the solid line is equal to the known 124 sec half-life of O^{15} and fits the decay very well. The activation technique gave very clean spectra, the first (at 6.30 MeV) being linear for more than two decades. The initial activity in the second curve is the decay of 4.2 sec Si^{27} from the reaction $Al^{27}(p,n)Si^{27}$. Both this decay and the long lived background were more prominent at the higher energy. The relative yields were obtained by summing eight channels ($0.7\ \tau_{1/2}$) for each spectrum; numerous check runs showed the yields were reproducible to a few percent.

---

*Present Address: Crocker Nuclear Laboratory, Davis, Calif.

In Fig. 2 the upper portion shows total cross-section yield curve from the threshold at 3.78 MeV to 9 MeV (21 MeV excitation). From 21 - 24 MeV the cross-section was smooth and is not given here. The resolution of the experiment was chosen to be 20 keV below about 19 MeV while at higher energies the energy intervals and target thickness were 40 - 50 keV. The quoted energy has been corrected for the proton energy loss in the entrance foil and in one half the target.

It is the sharp states revealed in this curve which are of interest for the present discussion. These appear on a broad background expected to arise from direct reaction contributions and also from the overlapping of broad T = 0 resonances, evident in the $C^{12}(\alpha,\alpha)C^{12}$ work of Carter, Mitchell and Davis.[1] All the sharp states below 18.2 MeV were also obtained by Jones, Lidofsky and Weil[2] in a differential cross-section study of the (p,n) reaction; the energy agreement of the six resonances is to 10 keV and the deduced widths also agree closely. The absolute energy of these resonances is probably known to $\pm$ 15 keV while at higher excitations the maximum uncertainty is $\pm$ 25 keV.

The remainder of Fig. 2 presents a comparison of states in O^{16} and in N^{16}. The N^{16} levels are taken from recent work by Hewka, Middleton and Holbrow[3] who analyzed the $N^{14}(t,p)N^{16}$ reaction up to 8 MeV excitation. A sketch of their 20° spectrum from 3 - 8 MeV is given in which a number of proton groups above 6 MeV from other reactions have been omitted. Hewka et al.[3] also studied the $N^{15}(d,p)N^{16}$ and $O^{18}(d,\alpha)N^{16}$ reactions at several angles; the resulting N^{16} levels generally agree to within 10 keV from the three reactions.

In Fig. 2 the N^{16} states have been adjusted relative to the O^{16} states in order to make analogous levels agree in position; from the correspondence of the eight levels shown, an isobaric mass difference N^{16} - O^{16} = 12.83 $\pm$ 0.02 MeV can be deduced. (An O^{16} state, very probably the analogue of the sharp 6.17 MeV N^{16} state, is known at 19.00 $\pm$ 0.03 MeV - the difference again is 12.83 MeV. It was observed in recent Oxford work (unpublished) on the $N^{15}(p,\gamma_1 + \gamma_2)O^{16}$ reaction[4) and has a width $\leq$ 50 keV, the target thickness.) Two pairs of levels have a difference of about 100 keV and no other differs by more than 30 keV from this mass difference. This is remarkable at an excitation of more than 15 MeV in a light nucleus. The widths of the states in O^{16} are consistent with their identification as T = 1 analogues, they generally agree with the N^{16} widths within a factor 2.5. Exact agreement is not to be expected; apart from experimental uncertainties such as the correct background subtraction, it is the reduced width $\gamma_n^2(N^{16})$, which is equal to $\gamma_p^2(O^{16}) + \gamma_n^2(O^{16})$ for a pure T = 1 system and not the actual widths. Little is known about the spins and parities of these states or hence about the nucleon penetrabilities. In only one case to date has an unambiguous J^π determination been made on these analogous states in both N^{16} and in O^{16}; the 4.39 and 17.30 MeV states are both $J^\pi = 1^-$.

It is interesting to note this isobaric mass difference, $N^{16} - O^{16}$ = 12.83 $\pm$ 0.02 MeV, implies that all the members of the lowest T = 1 odd parity quartet in O^{16} are altered in energy with respect to the N^{16} quartet. The 0^-, 1^- pair (described by the configuration $p_{1/2}^{-1}s_{1/2}$ move downward by 0.14 $\pm$ 0.04 MeV and the 2^-, 3^- pair ($p_{1/2}^{-1}d_{5/2}$) upwards by 0.13 $\pm$ 0.04 MeV.

Thus, while the common assumption[5,6] that the $d_{5/2}$ - states have a negligible Thomas-Erhman shift relative to the $s_{1/2}$ - states may be valid, it appears that this is not the only effect to be considered. Details of the differing s- and d- orbital Coulomb interaction with the core, for example, may be of comparable importance. Furthermore, it is known[1,7] that at least two of these 0^{16} states ($J^{\pi}1^-,3^-$) have appreciable isobaric spin mixing with neighboring $T = 0$ states and it is doubtful if any member of the quartet should be considered to have pure isobaric spin. Hence values of the $b(A,T)$ and $c(A,T)$ coefficients appearing in the isobaric mass formula,[6,8] derived from the 3^- states in N^{16} and 0^{16} are likely to be in error; the value using the present mass difference is

$$b(16,1) + c(16,1) = -2.42 \pm 0.03 \text{ MeV}$$

compared with -2.54 ± 0.03 MeV using the 3^- states.[6] (The larger errors quoted in Ref. 6 come from the uncertainties on F^{16} levels which are needed to obtain b and c separately.)

The nine analogue states leading to the value $N^{16} - 0^{16} = 12.83$ MeV are all narrow (<100 keV), implying small nucleon reduced widths. Many of the N^{16} states are not seen in the (p,n) reaction, however these generally have very narrow widths, ≤ 10 keV. In these states even a small admixture (a few percent) of α-width from $T = 0$ states by the Coulomb force is enough to increase the width to the point where the state will not be resolved in the (p,n) reaction. Finite target thickness effects also make a very narrow state difficult to resolve. The states do have a measurable nucleon reduced width since they are observed[9] in the

777

$N^{15}(n,n)N^{15}$ and[3] $N^{15}(d,p)N^{16}$ reactions as well as the $N^{14}(t,p)N^{16}$ reaction[3] and so they are not "pure" two-nucleon states.

REFERENCES

1. E. B. Carter, G. E. Mitchell and R. H. Davis, Phys. Rev. $\underline{133}$ (1964) B1421; G. E. Mitchell, E. B. Carter and R. H. Davis, Phys. Rev. $\underline{133}$ (1964) B1434.

2. K. W. Jones, L. J. Lidofsky and J. L. Weil, Phys. Rev. $\underline{112}$ (1958) 1252.

3. P. V. Hewka, R. Middleton and C. H. Holbrow, Bull. Am. Phys. Soc. $\underline{10}$ (1965) 1125; private communication.

4. N. W. Tanner and A. R. Barnett, to be published.

5. C. D. Zafiratos, F. Ajzenberg-Selove and F. S. Dietrich, Phys. Rev. $\underline{137}$ (1965) B1479.

6. R. H. Pehl and J. Cerny, Phys. Letts. $\underline{14}$ (1965) 137.

7. D. F. Hebbard, Nuclear Phys. $\underline{15}$ (1960) 289.

8. G. T. Garvey, J. Cerny and R. H. Pehl, Phys. Rev. Letts. $\underline{13}$ (1964) 548.

9. D. B. Fossan, R. A. Chalmers, L. F. Chase, Jr. and S. R. Salisbury, Phys. Rev. $\underline{135}$ (1964) B1347.

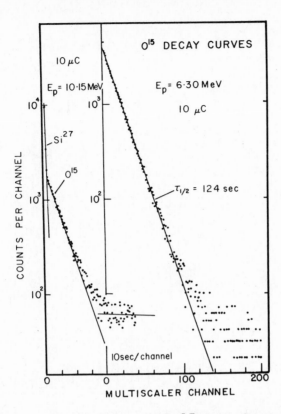

Fig. 1. Decay curves of the O^{15} β^+ - activity at two bombarding energies. The multiscaler time interval was 10 sec per channel. The decay curve is drawn with the known 124 sec half-life of O^{15}.

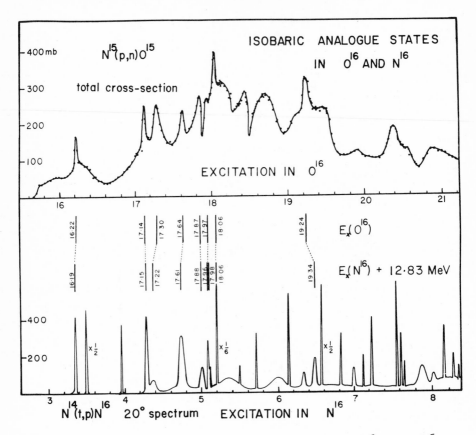

Fig. 2.   Comparison of excited states in O^{16} and N^{16}.
The total cross-section data has a relative accuracy of
about $\pm$ 5%; the absolute scale is accurate to $\pm$ 15%.
Probable T = 1 analogue states in the two nuclei are
shown between the curves.   The N^{16} energy scale has
been shifted to give agreement between these states and
the resulting $N^{16} - O^{16}$ isobaric mass difference is
12.83 $\pm$ 0.02 MeV.

S16. ISOBARIC SPIN SELECTION RULE IN THE $Si^{28}(d,\alpha)Al^{26}$ REACTION

P. G. Bizzeti[*] and A. M. Bizzeti-Sona[**]

Max-Planck-Institut für Kernphysik
Heidelberg, Germany

INTRODUCTION

This paper presents some preliminary results of a systematic investigation on the $Si^{28}(d,\alpha)Al^{26}$ reaction, involving the isobaric spin forbidden transition to the first (0^+, $T = 1$) excited state of Al^{26}. The effect of the isobaric spin selection rule has been studied in the overlapping level region, where the dynamic criterion[1] for the isobaric spin conservation can be expected to hold.

Present measurements extend from $E_d = 6.98$ to $E_d = 9.86$ MeV, corresponding to an excitation energy between 18.3 and 21 MeV for the compound nucleus P^{30}. The fact, not obvious in principle, that also $T = 1$ states of P^{30} overlap in our energy region, is supported by a comparison with the corresponding states in Si^{30} which appear to overlap above 17 MeV, as shown by a recent analysis[2] of the $Si^{29}(n,\alpha)Mg^{26}$ reaction.

EXPERIMENTAL PROCEDURE

Measurements have been made at the Tandem Accelerator of the Max-Planck-Institut, using the 20"

[*]
[**] Euratom fellow, on leave from Universita di Firenze
Istituto Nazionale di Fisica Nucleare, Firenze

scattering chamber and six standard semiconductor detectors. A self supporting SiO target was used, > 99% enriched in Si^{28}. The target thickness was about 70 $\mu g/cm^2$, corresponding to an energy loss < 15 keV for the incoming deuterons. A typical alpha particle spectrum is shown in Fig. 1. The energy resolution resulted ~ 70 keV, mainly due to target thickness and kinematic spread. The deuteron energy was varied from 6.98 to 8.50 MeV in 20 keV steps and up to 9.86 MeV in 40 keV steps. Some more points have been taken up to 10.94 MeV in 120 keV steps.

Only transitions α_0, α_1 and α_2 have been analyzed until now. The excitation functions, taken at different angles, are shown in Fig. 2. Results at 30° and $E_d \leq 7.5$ MeV agree with earlier measurements by Browne[3]. All excitation functions show strong fluctuations, with a coherence width of about 60 keV. Fluctuations are more pronounced for the α_1 transition, as expected from its single channel character[4].

DISCUSSION

Average values of the relative cross section for the transitions α_0, α_1 and α_2 at various angles are shown in Table I and compared with calculated values from the statistical model[5]. The two sets of cross sections are normalized on the average values of $\sigma(\alpha_0)$. Transmission coefficients for deuterons, used in the calculation, were taken from an optical model fit of scattering data[6] and those for alphas have been calculated following Huizenga and Igo[7].

The experimental cross sections for α_1 are found about a factor 4 lower than the calculated ones, while experimental and theoretical values roughly agree

for α_0 and α_2. To these, the experimental uncertainties have to be added. In particular, the comparison
of cross sections at different angles can be affected
by errors. In order to reduce this source of uncertainty, and also that coming from the possible contribution of direct reactions at forward angles, experimental and theoretical ratios $\sigma(\alpha_1)/\sigma(\alpha_0)$ and
$\sigma(\alpha_1)/\sigma(\alpha_2)$ for each angle are compared in Table II.

The comparatively smaller cross section for the
α_1 transition can be interpreted either as the result
of the selection rule or as a consequence of direct
contributions to α_0 and α_2 transitions. In order to
test this point, a statistical analysis of cross section fluctuations[5] has been performed. The average
squared amplitudes of fluctuations agree with theoretical values, calculated assuming pure statistical reactions (see Table III). Therefore, the difference between experimental and calculated values in Table II
cannot be accounted for only assuming a large direct
contribution to α_0 and α_2. In fact, the expected amplitude of fluctuations would be reduced in this case
by more than a factor 2 at all angles, and this is not
consistent with the experimental results. However,
direct effects for a smaller amount, or limited to
some angles, cannot be excluded on this basis. In
effect, direct contributions at least at forward angles
can be inferred from the asymmetry in the angular distributions. The experimental ratio of the cross sections at 32° and 148° in the c.m.s., averaged in the
whole 3 MeV interval, results in 1.35 for α_0 and 1.2 for
α_2. This ratio rises to 1.5 and 1.7 respectively, in
the upper 1 MeV interval (8.90 - 9.86 MeV) and tends to
increase at higher energies ($\sim$ 2 from 9.90 to 10.94 MeV;

see also Ref. 9). We observe, however, that all these
ratios are subject to large statistical uncertainties
(up to 20%), due to finite sample effects.

In conclusion, direct effects, though not predominant at all energies and angles, seem to contribute
to the α_0 and α_2 transitions at forward directions.
The comparison of the experimental cross sections with
the statistical model estimates is therefore significant only at backward angles.

Finally, if we tentatively assume no direct
effects at angles $> 90°$, the α_1 transition appears to
be hindered approximately for a factor 3.5 by the
effect of the isobaric spin selection rule.

ACKNOWLEDGMENTS
It is a pleasure to thank Professor W. Gentner
for the excellent opportunity to work in his Laboratory. We want also to express our sincere thanks to
Professor H. Morinaga, Dr. P. von Brentano, Dr. M.
Boehning and Dr. C. Wiedner for discussions, and to
Dr. C. Signorini and Mr. R. Messlinger for their valuable help during the measurements. One of us (P.G.B.)
is indebted to EURATOM for a grant.

REFERENCES

1) H. Morinaga, Phys. Rev. $\underline{97}$ (1955) 444; D. H. Wilkinson, Phil. Mag. $\underline{1}$ (1956) 379; A. M. Lane and R. G. Thomas, Revs. Mod. Phys. $\underline{30}$ (1958) 257.

2) E. Roessle, (private communication).

3) C. P. Browne, Phys. Rev. $\underline{114}$ (1955) 807.

4) Since for the α_1 transition the ingoing channel spin is S = 1 and the outgoing one is S' = 0, three channels corresponding to the 3 possible orientations of the spin S can in principle contribute to it; but the transition amplitudes for ν = +1 and ν = -1 are not independent and that for ν = 0 vanishes owing to parity conservation.

5) T. Ericson, Advanc. in Phys. $\underline{9}$ (1960) 425; Annals of Phys. $\underline{23}$ (1963) 390.

6) W. Lorentz, C. Mayer-Böricke, R. Santo and U. Schmidt-Rohr, Nucl. Phys. $\underline{46}$ (1963) 25.

7) J. R. Huizenga and G. I. Igo, Nucl. Phys. $\underline{29}$ (1962) 462.

8) M. Boehning, (preprint).

9) R. Jahr, K. Kayser, A. Kostka and J. Wurm, Nucl. Phys. $\underline{76}$ (1966) 79.

TABLE I. Average cross section (arbitrary units).

θ c.m.s.	α_0				α_1				α_2			
	σ_{exp}	σ_{th}	$\frac{\delta\sigma}{\sigma}$	$\frac{\sigma_{exp}}{\sigma_{th}}$	σ_{exp}	σ_{th}	$\frac{\delta\sigma}{\sigma}$	$\frac{\sigma_{exp}}{\sigma_{th}}$	σ_{exp}	σ_{th}	$\frac{\delta\sigma}{\sigma}$	$\frac{\sigma_{exp}}{\sigma_{th}}$
32°	5122	4325	10%	1.18	245	904	25%	0.27	5852	5672	9%	1.03
64°	4912	5034	7%	0.98	92	440	25%	0.21	5602	4538	8%	1.23
90°		4999			134	440	25%	0.30	4622	4077	8%	1.13
148°	3771	4325	10%	0.87	221	904	25%	0.24	5126	5672	9%	0.90
163°	4418	4538	14%	0.97	211	851	25%	0.25	4852	6098	13%	0.80

786

TABLE II. Experimental and theoretical cross section ratios.

θ c.m.s.	$\sigma(\alpha_1)/\sigma(\alpha_0)$			$\sigma(\alpha_1)/\sigma(\alpha_2)$		
	exp.	theor.	th/exp.	exp.	theor.	th/exp.
32°	0.048	0.209	4.3	0.042	0.159	3.8
64°	0.019	0.087	4.6	0.016	0.097	5.9
90°		0.088		0.029	0.108	3.7
148°	0.059	0.209	3.5	0.043	0.159	3.7
163°	0.048	0.187	3.9	0.044	0.140	3.2

TABLE III. Average ratio of the observed squared amplitude of fluctuations to the expected values for pure statistical reactions. Finite sample errors are shown and the expected[8] bias is taken into account.

	α_0	α_1	α_2
$C_{exp}/C_{theor.}$	1.03 ± 0.11	0.90 ± 0.16	1.15 ± 0.11

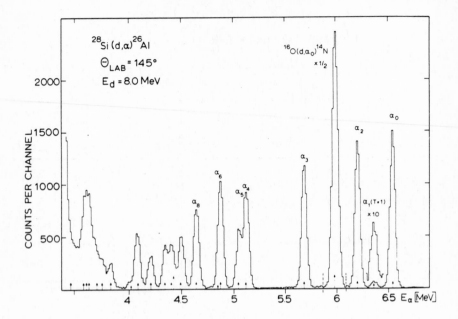

Fig. 1. Alpha particle spectrum from $Si^{28}(d,\alpha)Al^{26}$. Alpha particle groups corresponding to the Al^{26} levels are indicated by arrows. Shorter arrows indicate $T = 1$ states. The strong group at $\sim$ 6 MeV (dotted arrow) is due to $O^{16}(d,\alpha_0)N^{14}$ transition.

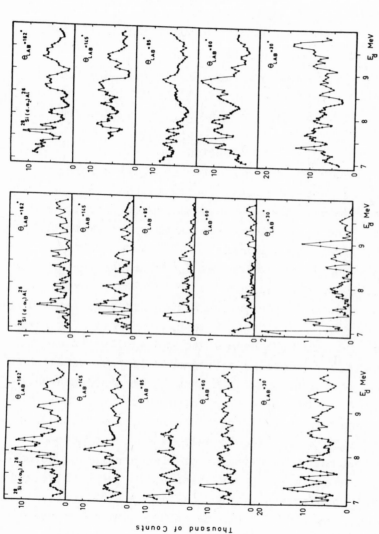

Fig. 2. Excitation functions for the $Si^{28}(d,\alpha)Al^{26}$ transitions to the ground, first and second excited states of Al^{26}. At some angles the curves do not extend over the whole energy interval because of the overlapping line from $O^{16}(d,\alpha)N^{14}$ reaction.

S17. EXCITATION OF ISOBARIC ANALOGUE STATES BY ELASTIC PROTON SCATTERING FROM TARGET NUCLEI WITH N = 82

J. P. Wurm, P. von Brentano, E. Grosse, H. Seitz,
C. A. Wiedner and S. A. A. Zaidi
Max-Planck-Institut für Kernphysik, Heidelberg

INTRODUCTION

The study of proton elastic scattering through analogue resonances in heavy nuclei is shown by the experimental results to give valuable spectroscopic information. Level spacings compare very well with differences of resonance energies. The bound state ℓ_n values are easily determined as ℓ_p values of the analogue resonances. A relation between the partial proton widths and bound state neutron widths has been derived and discussed.[1,2] Different methods of obtaining spectroscopic factors have been given and applied to experimental data.[3-5] These spectroscopic factors were found in rather good agreement with those from distorted-wave-analyses of the corresponding (d,p) reactions. Our interest was to investigate these and similar methods systematically as applied to well isolated and pronounced resonances in a region of high density of "normal" compound states, as they are observed in the elastic and inelastic[6] scattering of protons from N = 82 target nuclei. As the position of the resonances, the penetration factors and (p,n) threshold energies change considerably from the compound system of Ba+p to that of

Sm+p we expect gain consistency checks on the methods used to determine reduced widths.

EXPERIMENTAL METHOD

At the Heidelberg tandem Van de Graaff, excitation functions of the differential cross section for elastic proton scattering from the target nuclei Ce^{140}, Nd^{142}, and Sm^{144} were measured in the following energy intervals:

$9.5 \leqslant E_p \leqslant 12$ MeV   (Ce)

$9 \ \ \leqslant E_p \leqslant 11.4$ MeV (Nd)

$8.6 \leqslant E_p \leqslant 11.7$ MeV (Sm)

The region below the first resonance was covered with several steps of 100 keV in each case in order to fix the nonresonant background. The scattering chamber was equipped with up to ten Si(Li)-detectors set mostly to backward scattering angles. Energy steps were taken in intervals of 10-20 keV between resonances and in 5 keV steps near resonances. The targets consisting of highly enriched material were less than 3 keV thick. Absolute cross sections were measured to an accuracy of $\pm$ 10%, by comparison with Rutherford scattering at 4 and 5 MeV.

RESULTS AND ANALYSIS

Excitation functions measured at different laboratory scattering angles as shown for $Nd^{142}(p,p)$ in Fig. 1 are very typical for the other nuclei investigated as well. The interference between resonant and background scattering is the dominant feature at those scattering angles which are off the zeroes of the Legendre polynomials of the order of the resonating partial wave.

791

The analysis of these excitation functions has to take into account a background scattering which deviates considerably from Coulomb scattering. We split the collision matrix into a resonant part U^R and a part U^D describing the background scattering. On the assumption, that U^D causes no spin-flip of the proton, we have, in the channel spin representation, $\left\{\alpha s \mu\right\}$ [7]

$$U^D_{\alpha s \mu';\alpha s \mu} = U^D_{\alpha s \mu} \delta_{\mu'\mu}$$

In defining the elastic scattering amplitude by

$$\frac{\sqrt{\pi}}{k} <f|U^D|i> \equiv \rho(\theta)e^{i\phi(\theta)}$$

we dispense with a decomposition into partial waves. In the one-level approximation for U^R of definite J^π the differential cross section for the scattering of spin 1/2 particles from spin zero target nuclei is

$$\frac{d\sigma}{d\Omega}(\theta) = 1/2\ \lambdabar^2(\Gamma_p/\Gamma)^2\cos^2\beta \sum_{k=0}^{2J-1} [Z(\ell J \ell J;1/2K]^2 P_K(\cos\theta)$$

$$+ \rho^2 - \rho\lambdabar(2J+1)(\Gamma_p/\Gamma)\cos\beta\sin(\beta+\alpha_\ell)P_\ell(\cos\theta)$$

The phase angle β is related to the resonance energy E_o and the total width Γ by $\tan\ \beta = 2(E-E_o)/\Gamma$. α_ℓ is a phase, defined by $\alpha_\ell = \phi-2\xi_\ell-\pi/2$. ξ_ℓ denotes the phase shift of the background amplitude. The Z-coefficients are those given in Ref. 7. The influence of the nearby resonances of different J was taken into account by coherent superposition of Breit-Wigner terms. The interference terms contain no additional parameters. For the sake of brevity they are omitted from the above expression.

The ℓ-values have been fixed by inspection of the resonances at the zeroes of the Legendre-polynomials.

The parameters E_o, $(2J + 1)$ Γ_p and Γ together with α_ℓ and $\rho^2(E_o)$ were determined in the vicinity of each resonance. This was done either by a computer program by minimizing χ^2 or by the use of graphical methods which proved very reliable. In principle, the formula allows the determination of the spin of the resonance. However, the dependence of the cross section on J is mainly a function of $(2J + 1)$ Γ_p. Because of the experimental error only this combination could be determined.

The errors in the determination of Γ_p and Γ are estimated to be of the order of 5% for the ground state analogues. The use of a one level formula is expected to result in larger errors for the widths of the following two p-wave resonances in the case that their spins are identical. Especially for the higher resonances the values of Γ_p/Γ are more reliable than the width separately. The error of these values should be less than 20%.

Figure 2 shows a "best fit" to the excitation function of $Ce^{140}(p,p)$ measured at the laboratory angle of $\theta = 170°$. The parameters by which this fit had been obtained, agree closely with those from the local fits. For the background scattering $\rho^2(E)$ a short power series in E^{-1} had been used. The curve as determined by the χ^2 condition, which is shown in Fig. 2, is a smooth function of energy.

The parameters as obtained from local fits are listed in Table I. For comparison excitation energies and ℓ_n values from (d,p) experiments on the same target nuclei are given. Some levels have been observed as analogue resonances only in the (p,p') reactions.[6] The ℓ_p values agree with all known ℓ_n values. All

793

deviations of the resonance energy differences from the level spacings are less than 20 keV. This is within the experimental errors. Thus the Coulomb energies are exceedingly constant, which is in favor of the partially collective aspect of the analogue states in these heavy nuclei.

The calculation of Γ_p (single particle) from the optical model including the absorption effects seems to be a successful method[8]. By reproducing the background phase shifts and the (p,n) cross section[9] the optical model parameters should be fairly restricted.

REFERENCES

1) D. Robson, Phys. Rev. <u>137</u> (1965) B535.

2) H. A. Weidenmüller, Nucl. Phys., in press.

3) C. F. Moore, P. Richard, C. E. Watson, D. Robson and J. D. Fox, Phys. Rev. <u>141</u> (1965) B1166.

4) K. W. Jones, A. Marinov, L. L. Lee, Jr., and J. P. Schiffer, Bull. Am. Phys. Soc. <u>10</u> (1965) 479.

5) P. von Brentano, Paper C 2.

6) S. A. A. Zaidi, P. von Brentano, K. Melchior, P. Rauser and J. P. Wurm, Paper S 18.

7) J. M. Blatt and L. C. Biedenharn, Rev. Mod. Phys. <u>24</u> (1952) 258.

8) C. A. Wiedner, P. von Brentano, A. Harney, J. P. Wurm, and S. A. A. Zaidi, submitted to Phys. Letts.

9) H. Morinaga and R. Messlinger, Paper S 19.

TABLE I. Resonance parameters for elastic scattering of protons from the target nuclei Ce^{140}, Nd^{142} and Sm^{144}. Comparison with (d,p) data.

Target nucleus	$E_0-E_0^{g.s}$ (MeV)	(p,p) ℓ_p	J	Γ	Γ_p (keV)	(d,p) E_x (MeV)	ℓ_n
Ce^{140} $E_0^{g.s}=$ 9.75MeV	.0	3	7/2	61	96	.0	3
	.654	1	3/2	86	92	.644	1
	1.131	1	(3/2)	77	40	1.142	1^x
	1.36^b	(5)		(60)		1.360	$(5)^x$
	1.50	3		72	46	1.502	3^x
	1.68^b					1.698	
	1.74	3		110	43	1.745	$(1)^x$
Nd^{142} $E_0^{g.s}=$ 9.50MeV	.0	3	7/2	55	85		
	.735	1	(3/2)	85	100		
	1.31	1	(3/2)	75	44		
	1.43	(5)		45	5		
	1.54	3		69	43		
	1.76^b						
	1.86	1		(40)	(7)		
	1.91	3		45	25		
Sm^{144} $E_0^{g.s.}=$ 9.30MeV	.0	3	7/2	43	64	.0	
	.888	1	3/2	66	96	.895	1
	1.62	1	(3/2)	65	44	1.611	1
	1.67	3		44	24	1.655	3

a)x)The (d,p) data are taken from the following authors: Ce^{140}(d,p): E.E.D. Whiting, MIT preprint(1965);[x] R.H. Fulmer, A.L. McCarthy and B.L. Cohen, Phys. Rev. 128 (1962)1302. Sm^{144}(d,p); excit. energies: R.A.Kenefick and R.K. Sheline, Phys.Rev. 139(1965)B1479; ℓnvalues;C.F. Moore and R.K. Jolly, Phys.Letts. 19(1965)138. Only those levels have been listed in the table, which are observed as resonances in (p,p) or (p,p').

b)Seen as resonance at many scattering angles in the (p,p') reaction (Ref. 6).

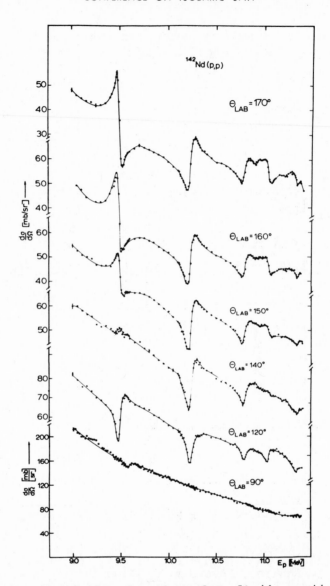

Fig. 1. Excitation functions for elastic scattering of protons from Nd^{142} for different laboratory angles. The ℓ values of the first four prominent resonances are ℓ = 3, 1, 1, 3 respectively.

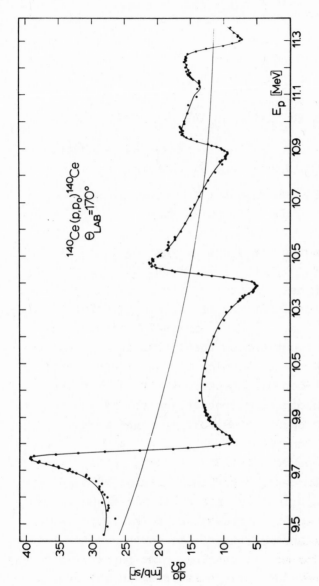

Fig. 2. Fit to the measured excitation function for Ce^{140}(p,p) over the range of five resonances. The smooth curve is the background scattering cross section as determined by the fitting procedure.

S18. ISOBARIC ANALOGUE RESONANCES OBSERVED IN THE INELASTIC SCATTERING OF PROTONS FROM Ba^{138}, Ce^{140}, Nd^{142} and Nd^{144}

S. A. A. Zaidi, P. von Brentano, K. Melchior,
P. Rauser and J. P. Wurm

Max-Planck-Institut für Kernphysik
Heidelberg, Germany

The isobaric analogues of the low lying states of the nuclei Ba^{139}, Ce^{141}, Nd^{143} and Nd^{145} have been observed as resonance states of the compound system in the excitation functions of the elastic proton scattering on Ba^{138}, Ce^{140}, Nd^{142} and Nd^{144} respectively[1]. The excitation functions of the inelastic proton scattering on these nuclei leading to the respective first excited (2^+) states also show very strong resonances at bombarding energies corresponding to the excitation of isobaric analogue states. Figs. 1 and 2 show the excitation functions of $Ce^{140}(p,p_1)$ and $Nd^{142}(p,p_1)$ respectively measured at the scattering angle $\theta_{lab}= 170°$. One sees in both cases 5 prominent peaks and some smaller ones superimposed on a small background. The energies of the peaks agree within 20 keV with those determined from an analysis of the corresponding resonances in the elastic scattering. The rather large cross section for inelastic scattering in the resonances imply large proton widths for this inelastic channel. For the second resonance one obtains in case of Ba^{138}:

$$\frac{\displaystyle\sum_j \Gamma_j^{(in.)}}{\Gamma^{(el.)}} \approx 0.3$$

Here $\Gamma_j^{(in.)}$ are the various partial widths for decay into the first excited (2^+) state and $\Gamma^{(el.)}$ the width for the elastic channel. One obtains similar numbers for the nuclei Ce^{140} and Nd^{142}. The reduced proton widths of the analogue states for decay into the (2^+) state of the target nucleus are related to the reduced neutron widths of the corresponding low lying states with respect to the same (2^+) state[2,3]. Neglecting isobaric spin mixing one obtains simply

$$\gamma^2_{p,C}{}^* = \frac{1}{2T + 1} \quad \gamma^2_{n,C}{}^*$$

Here C^* denotes the first excited (2^+) state of the target nucleus. The possibility of determining these neutron reduced widths makes the study of analogue resonances in inelastic channels a valuable tool for spectroscopy. To be able to determine the various partial widths that are involved in the decay of each analogue resonance into the first excited (2^+) state of the nucleus one must know the angular distribution of the emitted proton.

We have measured the excitation functions of the inelastic proton scattering using a scattering chamber in conjunction with the Heidelberg tandem Van de Graaff accelerator. The scattering chamber was equipped with 8 to 12 solid state counters, which were distributed over the range of scattering angles between

799

40° and 170°. Using a number of multichannel analyzers we measured the excitation functions simultaneously at the various angles. Data points were taken
in 5 - 10 keV steps in the resonances and 20 keV steps
otherwise Figs. 3 and 4 show the angular distributions
of the peak cross sections of the first three resonances observed in the inelastic scattering from Ce^{140}
and Nd^{142} respectively. Unfortunately it was not
always possible to measure the cross section to the
first excited state for scattering angles between 80°
and 120° as in the spectra of scattered protons at
these angles the inelastic line coincided with the
line originating from the elastic scattering of protons from O^{16} and C^{12}. The absolute values of the inelastic scattering cross sections were determined by
comparison with the elastic scattering cross sections
in each case[1]. The measurements were carried out over
the following ranges of proton bombarding energies for
the various nuclei:

1) Ba^{138} (9.7 MeV - 11.4 MeV)
2) Ce^{140} (9.5 MeV - 11.7 MeV)
3) Nd^{142} (9.4 MeV - 11.4 MeV)
4) Nd^{144} (9.2 MeV - 11.1 MeV)

The angular distributions of the peak cross sections
are not symmetric about 90°. However, since all the
resonances are known to have the same parity the observed asymmetry of the angular distribution must be
ascribed to the presence of an appreciable amount of
direct inelastic scattering. This agrees with the
observation that the background between the resonances
rises quite considerably at forward angles. The non-

resonant inelastic scattering interferes with the resonance scattering and the analysis is in general
rather complicated. We shall however show that under
certain conditions the expression for the differential
cross section can be considerably simplified. If the
analogue states with the same spin and parity are well
separated so that a single level approximation is justified the collision matrix can be written,

$$U_{c'c} = U_{c'c}^{(R)} + U_{c'c}^{(D)}$$

Here $U_{c'c}^{(R)}$ describes the resonance scattering from a
single level and $U_{c'c}^{(D)}$ the non-resonant background. The
expressions for the differential cross section simplify
if the following assumptions are made regarding the
background:

1) The spin of the proton does not take part in
   the scattering process;
2) The recoiling nucleus in the excited (2^+)
   state has no spin projection along its
   recoil direction.

The first assumption implies that the amplitude for the
inelastic scattering of a proton through an angle θ
leaving the residual nucleus in the magnetic substate m
can be written $f_m(\theta)$. The second assumption is that
if the direction of recoil is chosen as the axis of
quantization then $f_m(\theta) = 0$ for $m \neq 0$. The validity
of these assumptions in PWBA is well known. It seems
to be a good approximation in the case of distorted
waves[4]. We now obtain for the reaction cross section,

$$\frac{d\sigma_{2^+-0^+}}{d\Omega} = -\frac{\lambda^2 \Gamma_{0JJ}}{2\Gamma^2} (2J+1) \, \text{Cos}^2\beta \; x \sum_{k=0}^{2J-1} P_k(\text{Cos }\theta) \cdot$$

$$\bar{Z}(\ell J \ell J; 1/2 \; k) \; x \sum_{j_1 j_2} \text{Cos}(\xi_{j_1} - \xi_{j_2})(\pm \, \Gamma_{2j_1 J}^{1/2})(\pm \, \Gamma_{2j_2 J}^{1/2})$$

$$\bar{Z}(\ell_1 j_1 \ell_2 j_2; 1/2 \; k) \; W(j_1 J j_2 J; 2k) + 4\pi^2 \lambda^2 d^2 - $$

$$2\pi\lambda^2(2J+1) \cdot \frac{(\pm \, \Gamma_{0JJ}^{1/2})}{\sqrt{10} \cdot \Gamma} \cdot d \cdot G^{1/2} \cdot \cos\beta \cdot P_\ell (\cos\theta)$$

$$\text{with } G^{1/2} = \sum_j (\pm \, \Gamma_{2jJ}^{1/2}) \cdot \bar{Z}(\ell \; 1/2 \; 2 \; j; J\ell')$$

$$\cdot \; \text{Cos} \; [(\xi_\ell + \xi_{\ell'} - \delta) + \beta \;]$$

We have set $< \vec{k}_f | U^{(D)} | \vec{k}_i > \, = d \; e^{i\delta}$ and chosen an angular momentum coupling for the channel wave functions which is appropriate to a shell model description of the analogue state. It is characterized by the equations $1/2 \; \vec{\sigma}_p + \vec{\ell}_p = \vec{j}_p$, $\vec{j}_p + \vec{z} = \vec{J} \cdot \vec{\ell}_p$ and $1/2 \; \vec{\sigma}_p$ denote the orbital angular momentum and spin of the proton and $\vec{J}$ the spin of the resonance. The notation is that of Refs. 5 and 6. A striking prediction of the above expression is that the background amplitude vanishes at the zeros of the Legendre polynomials of the order of the resonating partial wave in the entrance channel. At these angles the resonances will assume Lorentz shapes if they are well isolated and if the background is slowly varying. Experimental evidence is in favor of this prediction. The excitation

functions measured at the different scattering angles
are being analyzed simultaneously using the above formula to determine the various partial widths of the
resonances.

REFERENCES

1) J. P. Wurm, P. von Brentano, E. Grosse, H. Seitz
   and S. A. A. Zaidi, Paper S 17.
2) D. Robson, Phys. Rev. 137 (1965) B535.
3) P. von Brentano, Paper C 2.
4) M. K. Banerjee and C. A. Levinson, Annals of
   Physics 2 (1957) 499.
5) A. M. Lane and R. G. Thomas, Rev. Mod. Phys. 30
   (1958) 257.
6) S. A. A. Zaidi, P. von Brentano, D. Rieck and
   J. P. Wurm, Phys. Letts. 19 (1965) 45.

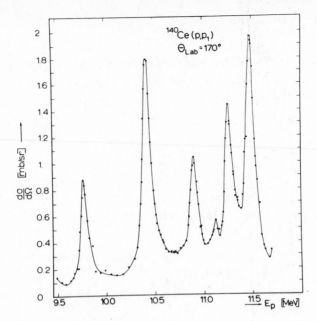

Fig. 1. Excitation functions of the inelastic scattering Ce^{140}(p,p$_1$) measured at θ_{lab} = 170°

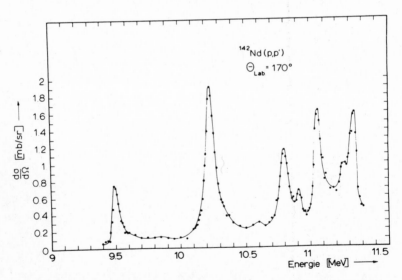

Fig. 2. Excitation functions of the inelastic scattering Nd^{142}(p,p$_1$) measured at θ_{lab} = 170°.

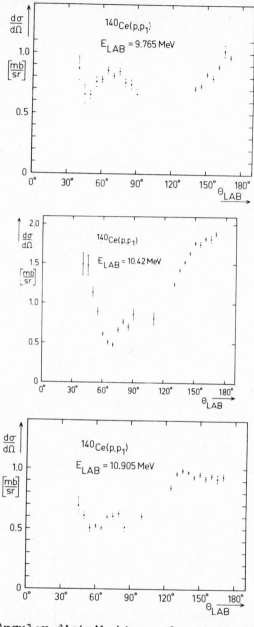

Fig. 3. Angular distributions of peak cross sections
of the first three analogue resonances observed in the
inelastic scattering $Ce^{140}(p,p_1)$.

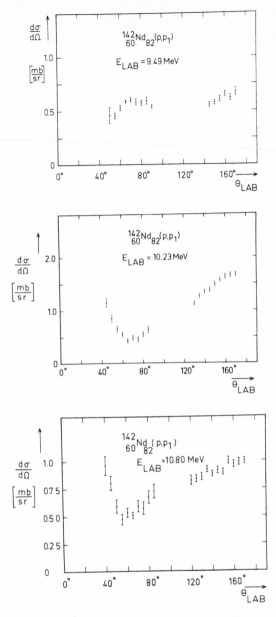

Fig. 4. Angular distributions of peak cross sections of the first three analogue resonances observed in the inelastic scattering $Nd^{142}(p,p_1)$.

S19. (p,n) - TOTAL CROSS SECTION ON Sm^{144} AND Nd^{142}

R. Messlinger and H. Morinaga[+]

Max-Planck-Institut für Kernphysik
Heidelberg, Germany

INTRODUCTION

A series of systematic studies on the properties of analogue states around N = 82 nuclei has been carried out in this laboratory[1]. As one of such studies total cross sections for (p,n) reactions on Sm^{144} and Nd^{142} were undertaken. The point of interest of these reactions is the isobaric spin forbiddeness of the neutron transition from the analogue state in the compound nucleus to the residual nucleus which is seen from Fig. 1. The measurements were made by counting the positron activities of the product nuclei, i.e. Eu^{144} and Pm^{142}. The half lives of those activities were 10.5 sec for Eu^{144} [2] and 40.5 sec for Pm^{142}. The shortness of these half lives were convenient for the cross section measurements. An advantage of this method in comparison to direct neutron counting is the fact that activity measurement is free from angular distributions of neutrons and energy dependence of counter response for neutrons. The energy ranges of our interest have practically only two channels, i.e. (p,p) and (p,n).

[+]On leave of absence from the Department of Physics, University of Tokyo

EXPERIMENTAL PROCEDURE AND APPARATUS

The excitation functions were measured in a scattering chamber with the proton beam of the Tandem van de Graaff accelerator in the energy range of $E_p = 9.20 - 11.10$ MeV for Sm^{144} and $E_p = 9.35 - 10.35$ MeV for Nd^{142}. The energy was varied in steps of 30 keV and, near resonances, in steps of 15 keV. Our targets were carbon backed foils of highly enriched Nd^{142} and Sm^{144} with an effective thickness of 95 $\mu g/cm^2$ and 360 $\mu g/cm^2$, respectively. The beam intensity was measured by integrating the charge of the Faraday cup behind the scattering chamber. The integrator was also used to effect a pneumatic valve in the beam tube, which stopped the beam when a certain charge was reached. After a well known time interval, in order to wait for the decay of background activities with very short half lives, the measurement of Eu^{144} or Pm^{142} activity was started. Lithium drifted silicon detectors were used. Their pulses were amplified and discriminated against background. Although the positrons of Eu^{144} and Pm^{142} were not entirely stopped in the depleted regions of the silicon detectors, their pulse was higher than most of the background pulses which therefore could be discriminated. The pulses above a certain threshold were counted by fast scalers which were gated one after the other in time intervals equal to the half life of the activity. Thereby the purity of the activity and the background could be controlled. The counting rates of all scalers were added and the small background was subtracted.

In order to avoid the counting rate to be dependent on variations of the beam intensity, the charge integrating capacitance of the current integrator was

modified by adding additional capacitances and resis-
tors in such a way that the RC of this combination was
equal to the mean life of the activity to be measured.
To normalize for inhomogeneities of target thickness
the elastically scattered protons were also measured
at each energy in a part of the activation time of the
target and compared with known (p,p) data. Curves proportional to absolute cross sections were obtained in
this way.

For measuring absolute (p,n) - cross sections
at several energies the target was driven by a motor
device through a narrow slit into the center of a plastic scintillator, after being activated by the proton
beam. This set-up made it possible to get an approximate 4π-geometry. The scintillator pulses produced by
the positrons inside the scintillator were amplified
and analyzed in 15 consecutive times, each equal to the
half life again, in a multichannel analyzer. The β^+-
spectra were fitted, at these parts of the spectra where
the Fermi plots were straight lines, with theoretical
curves to get the parts of the spectra below the pulse
height which deviates from linear Fermi plot. After
normalization for the analyzer dead time the sum of all
positrons of one spectrum was obtained. The sum of all
these 15 counting rates minus background gave the angle
integrated counting rate of our β^+-activity. Corrections i.e. for K-capture and deviation from 4π-geometry
were made. For target thickness control the scattered
protons were also measured.

The results for the absolute cross section for
$Sm^{144}(p,n)Eu^{144}$ and $Nd^{142}(p,n)Pm^{142}$ are shown in Fig. 2
and Fig. 3 respectively. The errors are about $\pm$ 10%.

DISCUSSION

The general behavior of the cross section for Sm^{144} resembles the curve obtained by C. F. Moore and R. K. Jolly[3] at Florida State University by measuring neutrons at 90°, but the resonances in comparison with background are not so prominent there.

The cross section for Sm^{144} is considerably smaller than that of Nd^{142}. This is qualitatively understood by the fact that the (p,n) threshold of -7.2 MeV for Sm^{144} is not so far from the barrier for protons. In Nd^{142} case the threshold for (p,n) reaction (-5.5 MeV) is smaller, so (p,p) reactions will compete to a lesser extent.

In both curves the first two analogue states are clearly seen, which correspond to the ground state and first excited state of Sm^{145} and Nd^{143}, respectively. Three other bumps in the Sm^{144} curve could correspond also to higher excited states of Sm^{145}. A characteristic feature of some resonances is their definite asymmetries, which seem to have dips on the high energy side.

ACKNOWLEDGEMENTS

We are grateful to Professor W. Gentner for the support and the interest he took in this work. We are also indebted to Dr. P. von Brentano and Dr. P. G. Bizzeti for discussions.

REFERENCES

1) S. A. A. Zaidi, P. von Brentano, D. Rieck and J. P. Wurm, Phys. Letts. 19 (1965) 45.
P. von Brentano, N. Marquardt, J. P. Wurm and S. A. A. Zaidi, Phys. Letts. 17 (1965) 124.

2) R. Messlinger, H. Morinaga and C. Signorini, Phys. Letts. 19 (1965) 133.

3) C. F. Moore and R. K. Jolly, Phys. Letts. 19 (1965) 138.

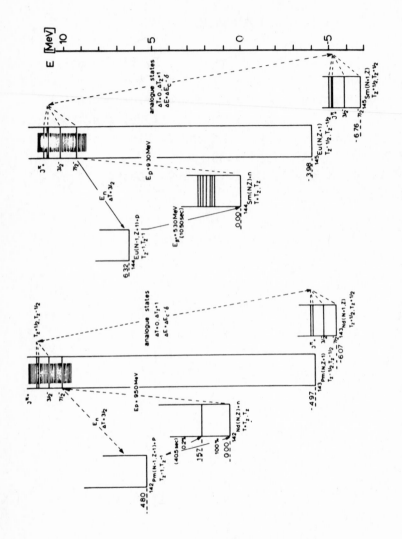

Fig. 1. Level schemes for the reactions
Sm^{144}(p,n)Eu^{144} and Nd^{142}(p,n)Pm^{142}.

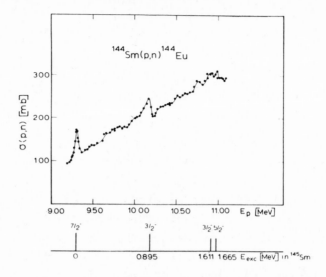

Fig. 2. Total cross section for Sm^{144}(p,n)Eu^{144}. Below the levels of Sm^{145} corresponding to the resonances.

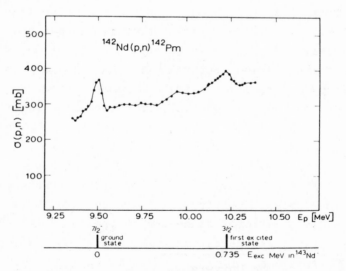

Fig. 3. Total cross section for Nd^{142}(p,n)Pm^{142}. Below the ground state and first excited state of Nd^{143}.

813

S20. T-SPIN VIOLATIONS IN $O^{16}(d,\alpha_1)N^{14*}$

S. Messelt[+]

University of Wisconsin[++]

Madison, Wisconsin

Differential cross sections for the $O^{16}(d,\alpha_1)N^{14*}$ reaction to the first T-spin forbidden T = 1 state of N^{14} have recently been measured by Jobst.[1] Measurements were taken at six different angles and covered the energy range 5 to 9 MeV in 20 keV steps. At several energies, corresponding to peaks in the excitation curves, the angular distributions were studied in more detail.

This investigation has now been extended down to 3 MeV using the same differentially pumped gas scattering chamber. Electrolytic oxygen was continuously fed in through a temperature regulated capillary controlled by a pressure sensitive servomechanism. A dry ice-acetone trap was used to remove the water vapor.

The alpha-particles were detected by a 65μ thick totally depleted silicon detector connected to a 512 channel pulse-height analyzer. Protons and deuterons with energy higher than 2.3 MeV and 3.2 MeV respectively would penetrate this detector and be detected by another thick silicon detector connected to the anticoincidence input of the pulse-height analyzer. When the protons or

---

[+] On leave from the University of Oslo, Norway.

[++] Work supported in part by the U. S. Atomic Energy Commission.

deuterons had too low energy to penetrate the thin
detector, it was often found advantageous to operate
the thin detector with a very low bias.

Excitation curves for the α_1 group to the T-spin
forbidden first excited state of N^{14} were measured at
$\theta_{c.m.} = 30°$ and $\theta_{c.m.} = 143°$, while data on the α-groups
to the ground state and second excited state also were
obtained at several other angles. The α_1 data are
shown in Fig. 1. Typical uncertainties of the measurements are indicated by the error bars on some of the
points. The main contribution to the uncertainty is
the statistical uncertainty. The energy resolution is
approximately $\pm$ 5 keV, and the uncertainty of the bombarding energy is $\pm$ 10 keV.

Considerable resonance structure is apparent in
the energy region $E_d = 3.2$ MeV to 4.5 MeV. Since this
transition to the $T = 1$ state of N^{14} is forbidden by
T-spin conservation, the resonances must correspond to
F^{18} states with an appreciable $T = 1$ admixture. The
strongest violations were seen at $\theta_{c.m.} = 30°$,
$E_d = 4.06$ MeV, and at $\theta_{c.m.} = 143°$, $E_d = 4.24$ MeV with
peak cross sections 1.6 mb/sr and 2.9 mb/sr respectively. At 30° this is 11% and 18% of the correspond-
ing α_0 and α_2 values, and at 143° it is 22% and 35% of
the α_0 and α_2 values. In general the α_1 cross sections
are roughly 6% and 10% of the α_0 and α_2 values at the
same angles.

Due to the difference in the angular distribution
of the groups, these values might be too high for the
total cross sections. Remembering, however, the statistical factor of $(2J + 1) = 3$ and the serious spin and
parity restrictions of available states in F^{18} for the
α_1-group this represents a very large T-spin violation.

At the energies indicated by arrows, corresponding to most of the peaks in the excitation curves, the angular distribution of the alpha particles was measured. It is easy to show that if the levels corresponding to α_1 peaks are well isolated, the entrance and exit orbital angular momentum are unique, and have the same value. The allowed states in F^{18} are therefore 1^-, 2^+, 3^-, etc., corresponding to ℓ = 1, 2, 3, etc., and some theoretical angular distributions are shown in Fig. 2. All curves go to zero at $\theta_{c.m.}$ = 0 and 180°, and the number of maxima are equal to the ℓ-value.

The measured angular distributions of the α_1 group are shown in Fig. 3. Where not shown, the uncertainties are of the same size as the points. It is seen that the angular distributions at the four energies from 3.36 MeV to 3.92 MeV are nearly similar with one minimum near 90°. The shape of the distribution resembles an ℓ = 2 distribution indicating J^π = 2^+ states in F^{18}.

At the next three higher energies there are two minima, and a small maximum near 90°. The distributions are, however, quite asymmetric with respect to 90°, indicating interference between levels of different parities. Ignoring the asymmetry, the distributions resemble an ℓ = 3 distribution corresponding to J^π = 3^- states in F^{18}.

At the higher energies the cross sections are much smaller. At the three energies 4.380 to 4.780 MeV the distributions resemble an ℓ = 2 distribution again, with quite large asymmetry. At 4.920 MeV the distribution has changed and does not have any special resemblance to either ℓ = 1, 2 or 3, but perhaps to a mixture of the last two. An angular distribution with 16 points (not illustrated) taken at 4.980 MeV, corresponding to a small peak in the excitation curve at $\theta_{c.m.} = 30°$, have indeed features which indicate a mixture of $\ell = 2$ and 3.

The curves in Fig. 3 are least squares fit to a Legendre polynomial expansion of the form

$$\sigma(\theta) = A_0 [1 + \sum_{L=1}^{n} \frac{A_L}{A_0} P_L (\cos\theta)]$$

and n indicates the highest order of the Legendre polynomial used. The values of the coefficients are given in Table I.

At the lowest energy where there are only seven experimental points and no point between 85° and 143°, no reasonable fit was obtained without giving the computer some extra estimated values. The two curves shown at this energy are the results obtained with estimated values at 47°, 60°, 76° and 94°.

The excitation energies of F^{18}, corresponding to the energies where the angular distributions have been measured, range from 10.498 MeV to 11.884 MeV. Since the angular distributions are very sensitive to interference effects, it is concluded that the peaks seen in the excitation curves correspond to excited states in F^{18}, and at some peaks there is interference with levels of different spin and parity.

REFERENCES

1) J. E. Jobst, Bull. Am. Phys. Soc. 10 (1965) 10.

TABLE I. Coefficients of Legendre Polynomial Expansions Shown in Fig. 3.

E_d (MeV)	A_0	A_1/A_0	A_2/A_0	A_3/A_0	A_4/A_0	A_5/A_0	A_6/A_0	A_7/A_0	A_8/A_0
3.360	0.638	0.055	0.132	1.719	-2.249				
3.360	0.468	0.432	0.904	0.688	-1.921	0.090	-1.124		
3.500	0.790	-0.703	1.219	0.211	-1.258				
3.500	0.700	-0.664	1.474	-0.194	-0.991	0.014	-0.654		
3.850	0.534	-0.191	0.963	-0.313	-1.367				
3.850	0.552	-0.299	1.150	-0.607	-0.957	-0.348	0.040		
3.920	0.603	-0.076	0.876	-0.280	-1.421				
3.920	0.617	-0.149	0.997	-0.465	-1.162	-0.212	0.044		
4.060	0.445	0.375	1.146	0.243	-0.553	-0.703	-1.903		
4.180	0.497	1.781	2.008	-1.612	0.839	0.268	-0.755		
4.240	0.612	-1.632	1.129	-0.835	-0.127	1.908	-2.000		
4.240	0.611	-1.565	1.123	-0.756	-0.162	1.784	-2.007	0.773	-0.180
4.380	0.100	0.650	0.340	-0.100	-1.850				
4.580	0.069	-1.652	1.246	-0.116	-0.710				
4.780	0.097	-1.124	0.237	1.165	-0.907				
4.920	0.108	0.259	-0.611	-0.981	0.435				

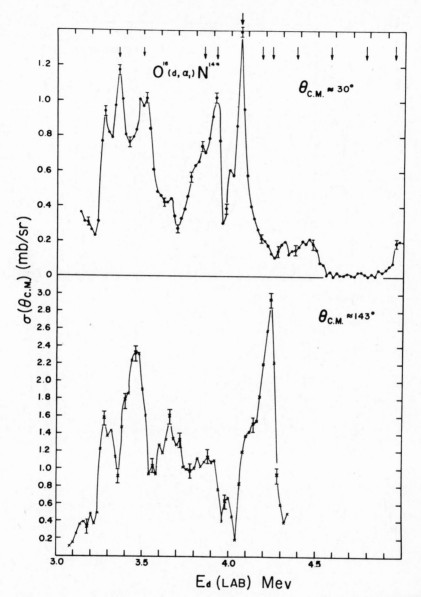

Fig. 1. Center of mass differential cross sections for $O^{16}(d,\alpha_1)N^{14*}$ (first excited state) as a function of deuteron bombarding energy.

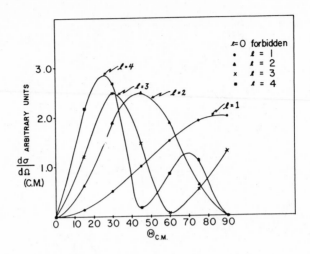

Fig. 2.   Calculated angular distributions of the α_1 group.

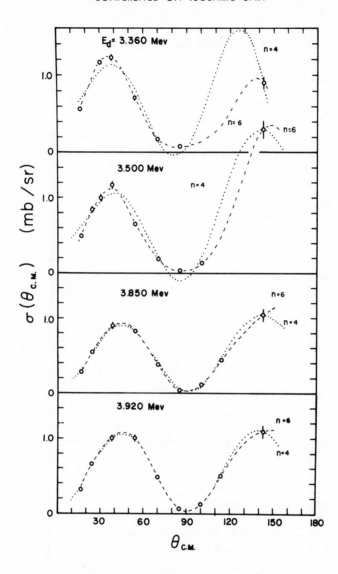

Fig. 3. Center-of-mass differential cross sections vs. center-of-mass scattering angle. The curves are least squares fit to a Legendre polynomial expansion with maximum order n. (See following page)

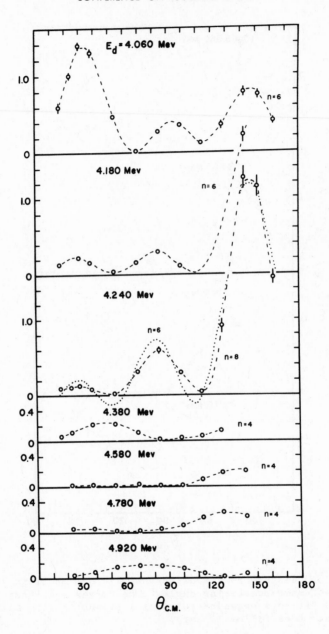

S21. ON THE A, T - DEPENDENCE OF COULOMB ENERGIES[*]

K. T. Hecht

University of Michigan
Ann Arbor, Michigan

Recent studies of Coulomb energy systematics throughout the periodic table have made it possible to make a detailed examination of the A (nucleon number) and T (isobaric spin) dependence of the iso-vector and tensor coefficients[1] of the Coulomb energy. The Coulomb interaction between nucleons can be written as

$$\sum_{i<j} \frac{e^2}{r_{ij}} \left\{ 1/3(3/4 + \vec{t}_i \cdot \vec{t}_j) - 1/2(t_{zi} + t_{zj}) \right.$$

$$\left. + 1/3(3\, t_{zi}t_{zj} - \vec{t}_i \cdot \vec{t}_j) \right\} \qquad (1)$$

and in first order perturbation theory leads to the Coulomb energy (or isobaric mass) formula

$$E_{Coul.} = E^{(0)} - E^{(1)}T_z + E^{(2)}\left[3T_z^2 - T(T + 1) \right] \quad (2)$$

where the coefficients, $E^{(i)}$, are functions of A and T and the details of the nuclear configuration, but are independent of T_z. Equation 2 is a simple application of the Wigner-Eckart theorem in isobaric spin space

---
[*] This work was supported in part by the United States Office of Naval Research under Contract Number Nonr 1224(59)

which makes it possible to factor out the T_z-dependence
of the Coulomb energy after the interaction has been
classified according to its irreducible tensor character in isobaric spin space, (Eq. 1). In the same way
the A, T- dependent factors of the Coulomb energy can
be separated out through an application of a generalized Wigner-Eckart theorem in 5-dimensional quasispin
space[2] by further classifying the interaction according to its irreducible tensor character under the 5-
dimensional quasispin group. Although the method can
in principle be applied to arbitrary configurations
and states of mixed seniority, the 5-dimensional quasispin group is closely tied to the seniority scheme and
in practice can yield general algebraic expressions
easily only in simple configurations and in states of
good seniority v, and particularly in states of low
reduced isobaric spin t. Expressions for the Coulomb
energy of Z protons in a configuration j^Z and states
of lowest possible seniority are very simple in form[3].
Similarly, expressions giving the n, T- dependence of
a charge independent (iso-scalar) interaction of n
nucleons in a configuration j^n and states with v = 0
or 1 are also well-known[4]. Corresponding expressions
for the iso-vector and tensor parts of the Coulomb
energy are seemingly not part of the literature and
will be derived in this note by the techniques outlined
above. It is known that the seniority scheme is a
poor approximation for nuclei where neutrons and protons
are filling the same shell. Nevertheless, Coulomb
energy formulae for the simple configuration j^n and
states of lowest possible seniority may at least be
a guide, to the true n, T-dependence of the Coulomb
energy.

824

To classify the terms of the Coulomb interaction according to their irreducible tensor character under the 5-dimensional quasispin group it is convenient to write the interaction (restricted to a simple configuration j^n) in the form:

$$H_{Coul.} = 1/2 \sum_{\alpha\beta\gamma\delta} < \alpha\beta | V_{ij} | \gamma\delta > a_\alpha^+ a_\beta^+ a_\delta a_\gamma$$

$$=1/2 \sum_{J \text{ even}(T=1)M_J M_T} <(j)^2 J1M_T | V_{ij} | (j)^2 J1M_T > \left[a^+ a^+ \right]_{T=1M_T}^{JM_J}$$

$$\left[aa \right]_{T=1M_T}^{JM_J} \qquad (3)$$

The four single nucleon creation and annihilation operators with fixed j, m, $a_{jm,m_t=\pm 1/2}^+$, $(-1)^{J-m}$ $a_{j,-m,m_t = \pm 1/2}$ transform according to the 4-dimensional irreducible representation (1/2 1/2) of the 5-dimensional quasispin group. The pairs $[a^+a^+]_{TM_T}^{JM_J}$, coupled to definite total angular momentum J and isobaric spin T, therefore transform according to the product (1/2 1/2) x (1/2 1/2) = (11) + (10) + (00). Since the Coulomb interaction acts only in two-nucleon states coupled to T = 1, only the pair operators coupled to T = 1 need be considered. These transform according to the 10-dimensional representation (11). The Coulomb interaction thus transforms according to the terms of the Kronecker product

$$(11) \text{ x } (11) = (22) + (20) + (10) + (00) + (21) + (11) \qquad (4)$$

which contains two 35-dimensional representations, (22) and (21), the 14-dimensional representation (20), the 10-dimensional (regular) representation (11), the 5-dimensional (5-vector) representation (10), and the 1-dimensional (scalar) representation (00); where the first four terms in the Kronecker product correspond to a symmetric, the last two to an antisymmetric coupling of the two identical representations (11). Equation 3 can be rewritten $H_{Coul.} = H^{(s)} + H^{(a)}$ with

$$H^{(s)}(H^{(a)}) = 1/4 \sum_{\substack{J \text{ even}, M_J M_T}} < j^2 J 1 M_T | V_{ij} | j^2 J 1 M_T > \quad \times$$

$$\left\{ [a^+ a^+]_{1M_T}^{JM_J} [aa]_{1M_T}^{JM_J} \underset{(-)}{+} [aa]_{1M_T}^{JM_J} [a^+ a^+]_{1M_T}^{JM_J} \right\} . \qquad (5)$$

The symmetrically coupled part, $H^{(s)}$, contains only the representations (22), (20), (10) and (00), while the antisymmetrically coupled part, $H^{(a)}$, reduces via the anticommutation properties of a^+ and a to

$$H^{(a)} = \left\{ \frac{3}{2j+1} \sum_{J \text{ even}} V_J (2J+1) \right\} \left\{ 1/2 \, N_{op.} - T_z - (j + 1/2) \right\}$$

$$\qquad (6)$$

where

$$V_J = < (j)^2 J | \frac{e^2}{3r_{ij}} | (j)^2 J >.$$

Since the matrix elements of Eq. 6 are given by the trivial eigenvalues of the number operator and T_z, (the operators $H_1 = 1/2 \, N_{op.} - j - 1/2$, and $H_2 = T_z$ belong to the 10-dimensional representation (11)), only symmetrically coupled tensor operators need be considered. With the use of the Wigner coefficients[5] for the product (11) x (11) the specific tensor character of $H^{(s)}$ is found to be

$$H^{(s)} = \left\{ \sqrt{2/3}\, \mathcal{J}^{(22)}_{000} + \sqrt{2/3\sqrt{5}}\, \mathcal{J}^{(20)}_{000} + \sqrt{2/\sqrt{5}}\, \mathcal{J}^{(00)}_{000} \right\} +$$

$$\left\{ -1/\sqrt{3}\, \mathcal{J}^{(22)}_{010} + \sqrt{2}/\sqrt{3}\, \mathcal{J}^{(10)}_{010} \right\} +$$

$$\left\{ 1/3\, \mathcal{J}^{(22)}_{020} + \sqrt{2/3}\, \mathcal{J}^{(20)}_{020} \right\}. \tag{7}$$

The tensor operators $\mathcal{J}^{(\omega_1 \omega_2)}_{H_1 T T_z}$ are characterized by the irreducible representation labels $(\omega_1 \omega_2)$ of the 5-dimensional quasispin group; the labels $H_1 = 0$ and $T_z = 0$ indicate that the tensor components are those which conserve nucleon number and z-component of isobaric spin, while the $T = 0$, 1 and 2 components represent the iso-scalar, vector, and tensor parts of the Coulomb interaction, Eq. 1. Note that the iso-tensor part transforms only according to (22) and (20), the iso-vector part only according to (22) and (10).

The states of a configuration j^n belong to the irreducible representations $(\omega_1 \omega_2) = (j + 1/2 - v/2, t)$ of the 5-dimensional quasispin group, and are further characterized by n, T, T_z, and a fourth quantum number[6] $\mathcal{K}$, as well as the spatial quantum numbers J, M_J, and additional α's if there is more than one independent state of a given J and definite v and t. Straightforward application of a generalized Wigner-Eckart theorem makes it possible to factor the matrix elements of the irreducible tensor operators of the Coulomb interaction according to

$$< j \ (vt); \ n \ T \ T_z \ \mathcal{K}; \ J \ \alpha \ |\mathcal{J}^{(\omega_1 \omega_2)}_{OT'O}| \ j(vt); n \ T \ T_z \mathcal{K}; J\alpha >$$

$$= C[(j + 1/2 - 1/2 \ v, \ t); n \ T \ T_z \mathcal{K}; T']<j(vt)J\alpha| \ |\mathcal{J}^{(\omega_1 \omega_2)}| \ |$$

$$j(vt) \ J\alpha >. \qquad (8)$$

The first factor, C, is the Wigner coefficient of the 5-dimensional quasispin group which contains all of the dependence on nucleon number and isobaric spin, while the double-barred or reduced matrix element is independent of n, T, T_z, and $\mathcal{K}$. (Since the group is not simply reducible, some products $(j + 1/2 - v/2, \ t) \times (\omega_1 \omega_2)$ may contain the representation $(j + 1/2 - v/2, t)$ more than once. In this case, Eq. 8 becomes a sum over the several independent Wigner coefficients multiplied by their appropriate double-barred partners).

Since the tensor operators $\mathcal{J}^{(\omega_1 \omega_2)}_{OTO}$ include the relatively complicated 35 and 14-dimensional representations, (22) and (20), algebraic expressions for the n, T- dependent factors in states of arbitrary v, t can be very complicated and difficult to calculate; but in states with low reduced isobaric spin, in particular in states with t = 0 and t = 1/2, (arbitrary v), the factors are quite simple[5]. In the irreducible representations $(\omega_1 \omega_2) = (j + 1/2 - v/2, \ t = 0)$ the Coulomb energy (diagonal matrix element) has the form

$$\left\{ a^{(00)} + \omega_1 (\omega_1 + 3) [4/5 \ a^{(20)} - 4a^{(22)}] + a^{(11)} (n-2j-1) \right.$$

$$\left. + (4a^{(22)} + a^{(20)})(n-2j-1)^2 + (8a^{(22)} - 4a^{(20)})T(T + 1) \right\}$$

$$- T_z \left\{ a^{(11)} + 18a^{(22)}(n-2j-1) \right\}$$

$$+ [3T_z^2 - T(T+1)] \left\{ (5a^{(22)} + 2a^{(20)}) \right.$$

$$+ \frac{(a^{(22)} - 2a^{(20)})}{(2T-1)(2T+3)} \left. [(n-2j-1)^2 - (2\omega_1 + 3)^2] \right\} \qquad (9)$$

where the coefficients $a^{(\omega_1 \omega_2)}$ are, except for trivial j-dependent normalization factors, the double-barred reduced matrix elements of Eq. 8 and hence functions only of j, v, J, and α. Similarly, in the irreducible representation $(\omega_1 \omega_2) = (j + 1/2 - v/2, t = 1/2)$ the Coulomb energy has the form

$$\left\{ a'^{(00)} + [\omega_1(\omega_1 + 3) + 3/4] [4/5 \, a'^{(20)} - 4a'^{(22)}] \right.$$

$$+ 3(2\omega_1 + 3)b'^{(22)} + a^{(11)}(n-2j-1)$$

$$+ (4a'^{(22)} + a'^{(20)})(n-2j-1)^2 + (8a'^{(22)} - 4a'^{(20)})T(T+1)$$

$$+ 6(-1)^{n/2 - T}b'^{(22)}(n-2j-1)(2T+1) \Big\}$$

$$- T_z \left\{ a^{(11)} + [18a'^{(22)} - \frac{(a'^{(10)} + 3a'^{(22)}}{2T(T+1)}] (n-2j-1) \right.$$

$$+ (-1)^{n/2 - T}(a'^{(10)} + 3a'^{(22)}) \frac{(2T+1)(2\omega_1 + 3)}{2T(T+1)}$$

$$+ \frac{3b'^{(22)}}{4T(T+1)} [(-1)^{n/2 - T}(2T+1)[3(n-2j-1)^2 + 12T(T+1)$$

$$- (2\omega_1 + 3)^2] - 2(2\omega_1 + 3)(n-2j-1)] \Big\}$$

$$+ [3T_z^2 - T(T + 1)] \left\{ (5a'^{(22)} + 2a'^{(20)}) \right.$$

$$+ \frac{(a'^{(22)} - 2a'^{(20)})}{4T(T + 1)} [(n-2j-1)^2 - (2\omega_1 + 3)^2]$$

$$\left. - b'^{(22)} \frac{[(2\omega_1 + 3) - (-1)^{n/2 - T}(n-2j-1)(2T + 1)]}{2T(T + 1)} \right\}$$

$$\tag{10}$$

Since the Kronecker product $(\omega_1 \ 1/2) \times (22)$ contains the irreducible representation $(\omega_1 \ 1/2)$ twice, there are two independent double-barred matrix elements, (denoted by $a'^{(22)}$ and $b'^{(22)}$), and corresponding Wigner coefficients[5] for this coupling.

The evaluation of the double-barred matrix elements is particularly simple for states with $v = 0$ ($J = 0$; $A = 4k$, T even; $A = 4k + 2$, T odd; $k =$ integer), and $v = 1$ ($J = j$)[7]. In this case, $b'^{(22)} = 0$, $a'^{(22)} = a^{(22)}$, $a'^{(20)} = a^{(20)}$, and $(3a'^{(22)} + a'^{(10)}) = 3(a^{(22)} - 2a^{(20)})$. The expression for the Coulomb energy for states with $v = 0$ ($t = 0$), $v = 1$ ($t = 1/2$) in the configuration j^n can therefore be combined into one formula

$$E_{Coul.} = \left\{ E_o + 3/2 \ a_{core} \ n + \frac{n(n-1)}{2} (3/2 \ b + c) \right.$$

$$+ [T(T + 1) - 3/4 \ n](b-2c) + [n/2] \ 8c \ (j + 1) \Big\}$$

$$- T_z \left\{ 3(a + a_{core}) + [3b + \frac{\delta_{v1}3c}{2T(T+1)}](n-2j-1) \right.$$

$$\left. - (-1)^{[n/2 - T]}\delta_{v1} \ 3c \ \frac{(2T + 1)(2j + 3)}{2T(T + 1)} \right\}$$

$$+ [3T_z^2 - T(T + 1)] \left\{ (b + c) - c \frac{[(n-2j-1)^2 - (2j+4-v)^2]}{[(2T-1)(2T+3)+4t(t+1)]} \right\}$$

$$(11)$$

where

$$a = \frac{1}{2j + 1} \sum_{J \text{ even}} (2J + 1) V_J,$$

$$a_{core} = \frac{3}{8(2j + 1)} \sum_{J, j_{core}} (2J + 1) V_J^{jj_{core}},$$

$$b = \frac{2(j + 1) \overline{V}_2 - V_o}{2(2j + 1)},$$

$$c = \frac{V_o - \overline{V}_2}{4(2j + 1)}$$

with

$$(2j - 1)(j + 1) \overline{V}_2 = \sum_{J \text{ even} \geq 2} (2J + 1) V_J$$

and

$$V_J = < (j)^2 J| \frac{e^2}{3r_{ij}} | (j)^2 J >.$$

The Coulomb "pairing coefficient", c, carries the whole burden of the T-dependence of the iso-vector and tensor coefficients. Since it is small compared to a or b, the T-dependence of the Coulomb energy is weak. (With harmonic oscillator wave functions, for example, the predicted ratios b/c are typically of the order of 40/1 or 50/1). Since the coefficient c is small, the exact calculations of the T-dependence of Coulomb energies will have to take into account other small effects. Quite apart from the undoubtedly important effects of seniority admixtures, the electromagnetic spin-orbit interaction among nucleons can make a significant contribution to c. This interaction can be written as

$$H_{e.m.s.o.} = \sum_{i < j} [W_{ij} \left\{ 1/3 \ (g_p + 1/2 \ g_n)(3/4 + \vec{t}_i \cdot \vec{t}_j) \ - \right.$$

$$1/2 \ g_p(t_{zi} + t_{zj}) + 1/3 \ (g_p - g_n)(3t_{zi}t_{zj} - \vec{t}_i \cdot \vec{t}_j)$$

$$\left. + 1/2 \ g_n(1/4 - \vec{t}_i \cdot \vec{t}_j) \right\} + 1/2 \ g_n \ U_{ij}(t_{zi} - t_{zj})]$$

$$(12)$$

where
$$W_{ij} = - \left(\frac{e\hbar^2}{Mc} \right) \frac{(\vec{s}_i + \vec{s}_j) \cdot \ell_{ij}}{r_{ij}^3} \ ,$$

$$U_{ij} = - \left(\frac{e\hbar^2}{Mc} \right) \frac{(\vec{s}_i - \vec{s}_j) \cdot \ell_{ij}}{r_{ij}^3}$$

The last term, proportional to $(t_{zi} - t_{zj})$ has no two-body matrix elements; (it must be off-diagonal in T but diagonal in J). The neutron term proportional to $(1/4 - \vec{t}_i \cdot \vec{t}_j)$ acts only in two-body T = 0 states and makes a contribution only to the iso-scalar part of the interaction. The remaining terms have the same form as the Coulomb interaction between nucleons, Eq. 1, and can be included in the results of Eq. 11 if the following replacements are made in the two-body matrix elements, V_J:

$$\frac{e^2}{r_{ij}} \longrightarrow \frac{e^2}{r_{ij}} + (g_p + 1/2\, g_n)W_{ij}$$
$$\text{in } H(\text{iso-scalar})$$

$$\frac{e^2}{r_{ij}} \longrightarrow \frac{e^2}{r_{ij}} + g_p\, W_{ij} \quad \text{in } H(\text{iso-vector})$$

$$\frac{e^2}{r_{ij}} \longrightarrow \frac{e^2}{r_{ij}} + (g_p - g_n)\, W_{ij}$$
$$\text{in } H(\text{iso-tensor})$$

$$(13)$$

The electromagnetic spin-orbit interaction gives an insignificant contribution to the coefficients a and b, but may increase the coefficient c by as much as 20% in the iso-vector part of the electromagnetic interaction and by as much as 30 to 40% in the iso-tensor part.

Although Eq. 11 is valid only under rather restrictive assumptions, and much more accurate calculations have been performed for the Coulomb energy of specific nuclei, the results of this study do perhaps give an indication of the overall A, T-dependence of the Coulomb energy. In particular, the isobaric spin dependence of the vector and tensor parts is weak and decreases with T in general agreement with the experimentally observed facts[1].

ACKNOWLEDGMENTS

The author would like to acknowledge many valuable discussions with J. Jänecke whose interests in Coulomb energy systematics were the stimulus for this work.

REFERENCES

1) See, e.g., J. Jänecke, Paper A3.

2) For a description of the 5-dimensional quasispin group and earlier references see K. T. Hecht, Phys. Rev. 139 (1965) B794; the notation will follow this reference.

3) A. de-Shalit and I. Talmi, Nuclear Shell Theory, New York and London, 1963, p. 345.

4) A. de-Shalit and I. Talmi, Nuclear Shell Theory, New York and London, 1963, p. 465.

5) Details to be published elsewhere.

6) In most of the simple irreducible representations of the 5-dimensional quasispin group actually needed in nuclear spectroscopy, this fourth quantum number, related to the nucleon number and isobaric spin structure of the wave function, is either redundant or it can be replaced by a simple symmetry label, (see Ref. 2).

7) Equation 9 may also be useful in the simple case $v = 2$ (J odd; $A = 4k$, T odd; $A = 4k + 2$, T even; k = integer).

S22. ISOBARIC ANALOGUE RESONANCES IN LIGHT NUCLEI

A. A. Jaffe and M. Harchol

The Hebrew University
Jerusalem, Israel

Recently, many isobaric analogue states have been identified in medium weight nuclei by the observation of resonances in the excitation functions of (p,p), (p,p'), (p,γ) and (p,n) reactions, the measurements being restricted to target nuclei no lighter than Ca^{48} [1]. These resonances are the analogues of levels observed in the (d,p) reaction on the same target nucleus which have a large reduced width for neutrons. As is well known there is much accurate information, on (p,γ) and (p,p) excitation functions and on (d,p) reactions available in the literature. The aim of this contribution is to show that these data may be used to identify analogue resonances in light nuclei $(A \leqslant 40)$.

In light nuclei the density of normal states (i.e. states of isobaric spin $T = T_z$) is lower, in the energy range where analogue states are expected to appear, than in heavier nuclei. Mixing of the configurations of normal states is therefore lower and hence many normal states are observed as resonances in the proton excitation function. However, the lower-lying states with isobaric spin $T = T_z + 1$ are widely spaced and mixing with normal states, which results from the Coulomb interaction, is very weak. Thus the lower-lying analogue states should have, generally, much purer configurations than normal states and in cases of single particle configurations, higher reduced width for the incoming proton. This was observed experimentally by Calvert, Jaffe, Litherland and Maslin[2], via the reaction $Al^{27}(d,n)Si^{28}$, where the state at 9.3 MeV excitation in Si^{28} was found to have a reduced width much larger than that of any neighboring level and was identified as the analogue of the ground state of Al^{28}.

We present here just a few examples of the identification of resonances observed in proton induced reactions corresponding to analogue states to illustrate the method which should have general application.

The condition that the analogue of the ground state of the nucleus $(A + 1, Z, T_z)$ could in principle be observed as a proton resonance using the target $(A, Z, T_z - 1/2)$ is that the neutron separation energy of $(A + 1, Z)$ be smaller than the Coulomb displacement energy, which is not usually the case in light nuclei. In the following examples only resonances corresponding to analogues of excited states have been identified. The Coulomb displacement energies from the identification of the analogues were compared with values obtained from a plot of the known Coulomb displacement energies[3] which allows this quantity to be estimated to within $\sim$ 50 keV.

$$Ar^{41} - K^{41}$$

In Table I a comparison is made between all the levels observed in the $Ar^{40}(d,p)Ar^{41}$ reaction, corresponding to excitation of from 1.35 to 2.74 MeV in Ar^{41} and all the resonances of the reaction $Ar^{40}(p,p)$ in the range 0.80 MeV $< E_p <$ 3.50 MeV. Identification of

the level at 9.61 MeV in K^{41} as the analogue of the
1.354 MeV level in Ar^{41} corresponds to a Coulomb energy
of 6.65 MeV in good agreement with the value expected
from the systematics. Additional analogues corresponding to the levels at 1.871 and 3.740 MeV in Ar^{41} are
identified but the resonance corresponding to the
2.402 MeV level has not been observed though one might
be expected.

$$Al^{28} - Si^{28}$$

The levels in Al^{28} having $(2J + 1)\theta_n^2 > 30 \times 10^{-3}$
for the reaction $Al^{27}(d,p)Si^{28}$ are shown in Table II,
together with the resonances of the reaction $Al^{27} + p$
with $\Gamma \geqslant 1$ keV. Analogues of the levels of Al^{28} at
3.461, 3.591 and 4.685 MeV are identified. The $Al^{27}(p,\alpha)$
resonances aid in the identification. The analogue of
the level at 3.591 MeV in Al^{28} may be split between the
two levels in Si^{28} at 12.911 and 12.918 MeV. It may
be seen that the analogue resonances usually have large
values of Γ_γ in keeping with our original assumption
that prominent analogue resonances have single particle character.

$$S^{35} - Cl^{35}$$

The 1.99 MeV level in S^{35}, which has the largest
value of $(2J + 1)\theta_n^2$ observed in the reaction
$S^{34}(d,p)S^{35}$ and for which $\ell_n = 3$, is evidently the analogue of the 7.545 MeV level of Cl^{35} having $J_\pi = 7/2^-$
which appears as a resonance in the reaction $S^{34}(p,\gamma)$
for $E_p = 1.214$ MeV[4]. This resonance is narrow (< 4.5
keV) which is not surprising since $\ell_p = 3$. It has a
very high cross section compared with neighboring resonances and therefore a large value of Γ_γ, which

suggests (as for some levels of Al^{28} - Si^{28} discussed above) that this level has a single particle nature. The assignment yields a Coulomb displacement energy of 6.17 MeV in excellent agreement with the systematics. The level decays mainly to the $7/2^-$ level at 3.163 MeV, which we tentatively take as its configuration state. The energy splitting of 4.38 MeV corresponds to an isobaric spin interaction V_1 = 101 MeV in agreement with values for this parameter found by Sherr et al.[7].

$$Mg^{27} - Al^{27}$$

The isobaric analogue of the ground state of Mg^{27} has been identified by Lawergren[8] from the reaction $Mg^{26}(d,n)Al^{27}$, to be the 6.76 MeV level in Al^{27}. The levels of Mg^{27} at 3.47 MeV ($J^\pi = 1/2^+$) and at 3.56 MeV ($J^\pi = 3/2^-$) have ℓ_n = 0 and ℓ_n = 1 respectively in the reaction $Mg^{26}(d,p)Al^{27}$ and have large reduced widths[9]. They are therefore expected to have analogues with large proton widths and indeed the reaction $Mg^{26}(p,\gamma)$ has a resonance at E_p = 2.03 MeV with Γ = 40 keV (5 times larger than for any other resonance) and a very high cross section[10]. This resonance, which corresponds to an excitation of $\sim$ 10.24 MeV in Al^{27}, is 3.48 MeV above the analogue of the ground state of Mg^{27} and is known to be a doublet with components having $J^\pi = 1/2^+$ and $3/2^-$ [11].

REFERENCES

1) K. W. Jones, L. L. Lee, Jr., A. Marinov and J. P. Schiffer, Bull. Am. Phys. Soc. 10 (1965) 479.

2) J. M. Calvert, A. A. Jaffe, A. E. Litherland and E. E. Maslin, Proc. Phys. Soc. A68 (1955) 1008.

3) M. Harchol, S. Cochavi, A. A. Jaffe and Ch. Drory, (submitted for publication in Nucl. Phys.).

4) P. M. Endt and C. Van der Leun, Nucl. Phys. 34 (1962) 1.

5) A. K. Valter, I. Ya. Malakhov, P. V. Sorokin and A. Ya. Taranov, Izvest, Akad. Nauk SSSR, Ser. Fiz. 23 (1959) 846.

6) G. P. Plain, R. G. Herb, C. M. Hudson and R. E. Warren, Phys. Rev. 57 (1940) 187.

7) R. Sherr, B. F. Bayman, E. Rost, M. E. Rickey and C. G. Hoot, Phys. Rev. 139 (1965) B1272.

8) B. Lawergren, Phys. Letts. 13 (1964) 61.

9) B. Cujec, Phys. Rev. 136 (1964) B1305.

10) C. Van der Leun and P. M. Endt, Physica 29 (1963) 990.

11) M. C. Mertz, Thesis (private communication from P. M. Endt).

TABLE I. Isobaric analogue resonances in K^{41}. All data for this table, except the values of ℓ_p, are from Ref. 4. The values of ℓ_p are from Ref. 5. The extrapolated position of the analogue of the ground state of Ar^{41} is at an excitation of 8.26 MeV in K^{41}.

Levels in Ar^{41} from $Ar^{40}(d,p)Ar^{41}$			Levels in K^{41} from $Ar^{40}(p,p)Ar^{40}$			
E_{ex} (MeV)	ℓ_n	$(2J+1)\theta_n^2 \times 10^3$	E_p (MeV)	E_{ex} (MeV)	ℓ_p	$E_{ex} - 8.26$ (MeV)
1.354	1	68	1.88	9.61	1	1.35
1.636		weak				
1.871	0	3.4	2.45	10.19	0	1.93
1.988		weak				
2.4C2	1	11.2				
2.701	1	1.3				
2.740	1	11.3	3.4	11.1		2.8

TABLE II. Isobaric analogue resonances in Si^{28}. The analogue of the ground state of Al^{28} is known to be at an excitation of 9.31 MeV in Si^{28}. All data for this table, except the data on the 14.03 MeV excited level in Si^{28}, are from Ref. 4. The data on this level are from Ref. 6. The level at 12.895 MeV excitation in Si^{28} has presumably T = 0 since it decays very strongly via α_0, and has very small Γ_γ.

Levels in Al^{28} from Al^{27}(d,p)Al^{28}			Levels in Si^{28} from Al^{27}(p,γ)Si^{28}					Al^{27}(p,α_0) data
E_{ex} (MeV)	ℓ_n	$(2J+1)\theta_n^2 \times 10^3$	E_p (MeV)	E_{ex} (MeV)	$E_{ex}-9.31$ (MeV)	Γ (keV)	$(2J+1)\dfrac{\Gamma_p \Gamma_\gamma}{\Gamma}$ (eV)	$(2J+1)\dfrac{\Gamma_p \Gamma_\alpha}{\Gamma}$ (eV)
2.663	2	110						
3.461	1	80	1.198	12.736	3.426	6.3	9	no α_0 group
			1.363	12.895	3.585	1.1	0.2	1640
3.591	1	130	1.380	12.911	3.601	0.7	65	no α_0 group
			1.387	12.918	3.608	0.3	50	206
4.685	1	150	2.53	14.03	4.72	10	$\approx$ 300	

841

S23. (He^3,t) INVESTIGATIONS OF IRON, NICKEL, AND ZIRCONIUM[*+]

A. I. Yavin, R. A. Hoffswell,
L. H. Jones, and T. M. Noweir

University of Illinois
Urbana, Illinois

The study of isobaric analogue states in non-mirror nuclei via charge exchange reactions has stimulated experiments by several investigators of recent years. Anderson et al.[1,2] have used the (p,n) reaction on medium-weight nuclei to demonstrate the existence of analogues to the ground state and a few excited states of the target nuclei. They have also used their results to calculate Coulomb displacement energies. Blair and Wegner[3] and Sherr et al.[4] have shown that the (He^3,t) reaction gives similar information with the attendant advantages of a charged product particle and relatively low evaporation background from compound nucleus decay. The main difficulty with a (He^3,t) reaction is that the low cross section for tritons compared with deuterons necessitates efficient particle identification.

In the present experiment the (He^3,t) reaction was studied with 17.7- MeV He^3 ions obtained from the University of Illinois 43 inch isochronous cyclotron.

[*]Supported in part by the United States Office of Naval Research
[+]Partially presented following paper E6

Self-supporting isotopically enriched targets of Fe, Ni and Zr with thicknesses of 600 - 800 $\mu g/cm^2$ were used. All spectra were taken at a laboratory scattering angle of 40° with beam currents of 0.1 - 0.5 μa. Tritons were identified using solid state detectors in a $\Delta E \cdot E$ mass discrimination setup. Energy calibration was carried out by observing spectra for He^3 elastically and inelastically scattered from C^{12}.

Preliminary results are presented for the isotopes $Fe^{54,56,57}$, $Ni^{58,60,61,62,64}$ and $Zr^{90,91,92,94}$. In each spectrum a pronounced triton peak corresponding to the excitation of the isobaric analogue to the ground state of the target nucleus (hereafter called the analogue state) was observed. The energy of this triton group was very nearly constant for each isotope of the elements investigated. Some peaks corresponding to excited analogue states as well as to low-lying "non-analogue" states in the residual nuclei were identified.

A comparison with deuteron spectra taken simultaneously with the triton spectra suggests only a small contribution from strong deuteron groups in most of the observed triton spectra. There is some evidence of weak He^3 peaks from elastic scattering. In all observed spectra the ground state peaks were identified using published values of the Coulomb displacement energies[2] and (p,n) Q values[5]. Table I lists, for some of the pronounced triton groups, the observed excitation energies in the corresponding residual nuclei and, where applicable, the excitations relative to the analogue states, in an attempt to correlate some triton groups to excited analogue states. For each spectrum the triton groups are numbered, with 0

843

always referring to the ground state transition and *
referring to the analogue state transition. Also presented are differential cross sections for the analogue
states. The uncertainty in the cross section is 50%,
mainly due to uncertainty in solid angle. The relative
uncertainty is only 10 - 20%. For simplicity of language in the following discussion we use the terms triton group, peak, level, and state interchangeably.

Figure 1 shows the observed triton spectra for
$Fe^{54,56,57}$, all plotted on the same scale. In the Fe^{54}
spectrum, peak 0 is the ground state of Co^{54}. Peak 1
is apparently a non-analogue low-lying state in Co^{54}.
Peak 2 could be the analogue to the first excited state
(1.41 MeV) of Fe^{54}. Peaks 3 and 4 may be analogues to
states in Fe^{54} at $\approx$ 2.2 MeV and $\approx$ 3.0 MeV respectively.
However, these peaks might also be non-analogue excited
states of Co^{54}. In the Fe^{56} spectrum, peak 0 is the
ground state of Co^{56}. Peak 1 is then identified as the
0.9 MeV state in Co^{56} and peaks 2, 3 and 4 are presumed
to be non-analogue states of Co^{56}. Peaks 5 and 6 are
probably analogues to the excited states in Fe^{56} at
0.845 and 2.085 MeV. For Fe^{57}, peak 0 is assumed to be
the ground state of Co^{57}. Peaks 1 and 2 are probably
analogues of Fe^{57} states at 0.71 MeV and $\approx$ 1.71 MeV.

Figure 2 gives the spectra for $Ni^{58,60,61,62,64}$.
It is of interest here that, unlike the situation in
Fe, some non-analogue states are as strongly excited
as the analogue states. For Ni^{58}, the analogue state
and the ground state of Cu^{58} are not resolved. The
ground state is assumed to be 0.2 MeV below the analogue state[6]. Peak 1 is probably a non-analogue excited state of Cu^{58}. Peaks 2 and 3 are consistent
with being analogues of the Ni^{58} states at 1.45 MeV

and 2.46 MeV, while peak 4 may be the analogue of a group of Ni^{58} states at $\approx$ 3 MeV. For Ni^{60}, we identify peak 0 as the Cu^{60} ground state and peaks 1, 2 and 3 as low-lying levels in Cu^{60}. Peaks 4 and 5 might be analogues of the excited states in Ni^{60} at 1.33 MeV and 3.12 MeV. In the Ni^{61} spectrum peak 0 is identified as the ground state and peaks 1 - 5 as low-lying excited states of Cu^{61}. Peak 6 may be an excited analogue state; however, no definite conclusion can be reached because of the high density of levels in Ni^{61}. For the spectra of $Ni^{62,64}$ we are not able to unambiguously identify the ground state transitions of the residual nuclei. These two spectra show an apparent structure for excitations of non-analogue states but because of the difficulty in the identification of the ground states and possible deuteron contamination in the spectra, we cannot definitely determine excitation energies. However, we tentatively identify two excited analogue states from these spectra. Peak 1 in the Ni^{62} spectrum is assumed to be the analogue of the 1.17 MeV state in Cu^{62}. Similarly peak 1 in the Ni^{64} spectrum is probably the analogue of the 1.34 MeV state in Cu^{64}.

Figure 3 gives the spectra for $Zr^{90,91,\ 92,94}$. Non-analogue states seem to be strongly excited for all these isotopes. In each spectrum the prominent peak of highest energy is tentatively taken as the ground state of the corresponding residual nucleus. The reason for our hesitancy is that the computation of Coulomb displacement energies, assuming that these peaks are ground states, yields an average value of 12.2 $\pm$ 0.2 MeV in apparent disagreement with the measured value of 11.75 $\pm$ 0.15 MeV for Zr reported by

Anderson et al. It is interesting to note that there are one or two wide groups of states in all the Zr spectra. Anderson et al. also observed such groups and suggested that they correspond to isobaric configuration states[7] (with $\Delta T = 1$). For Zr^{91}, peak 1 may be the analogue to the Nb^{91} states at ≈ 1.4 MeV. In the case of Zr^{92} it is curious that peak 1, which is as strong as the analogue state peak, cannot be correlated to any known state in Zr^{92}. It might correspond to the 1.39 MeV state of Nb^{92} but this identification is by no means clear.

The observed energy of triton groups corresponding to analogue states of isotopes of the same elements is constant to better than 300 keV. Due to possible fluctuations in the incident He^3 energy we are able to suggest only that the Coulomb displacement energy for the investigated isotopes of the same element does not vary by more than 400 - 500 keV. Since we did not make an accurate measurement of the He^3 incident energy, we had to calculate each Coulomb displacement energy from the observed energy difference between the analogue state and the ground state, whenever the ground state peak could be clearly identified. In Table II, comparison is made of our calculated Coulomb displacement energies E_c with those of Anderson et al.[2]. Our data are presented in several forms: (a) measured values of E_c for all isotopes investigated, (b) average values for the isotopes studied weighted according to isotopic abundance ($\bar{E}_{c1}$), (c) averages over isotopes for which identification of the ground state is clear ($\bar{E}_{c2}$), and (d) reduced Coulomb displacement energies $E_c A^{1/3}$, normalized to 1.00 for the lowest A for each element. Our values of Coulomb displacement energies for Fe and

Ni are consistent (within estimated experimental error
of $\pm$ 200 keV) with the values given by Anderson et al.,
which are also shown in Table II. Our measured values
for the Coulomb displacement energy of Zr are higher
than Anderson's value by $\approx$ .45 MeV and are higher by
$\approx$ 0.3 MeV than the value for Zr^{91} measured in a $(p,n\bar{p})$
experiment which is reported in another paper in this
conference[8]. We feel that our values for Zr are somewhat doubtful since the value of E_c, as measured by
Anderson et al., was used to identify the ground state
peaks, but led in turn to a different E_c. There is
no supporting evidence that the peaks labeled (0) are
indeed the ground state peaks, except possibly, the
appearance of the spectra. The approximate constancy
of the derived values of E_c for the Zr isotopes suggests that either our values are correct, or that our
calibration for Zr changed. Further experiments are
needed to resolve this difficulty. From a study of the
reduced Coulomb displacement energies presented in
Table II, it is evident that the isotopic shift of E_c
is fairly consistent with an $A^{-1/3}$ dependence. A
slight monotonic decrease for $E_c A^{1/3}$ is apparent for
Fe and Ni, but it is impossible to draw strong conclusions on the basis of this experiment.

We wish to point out in conclusion that although
we present here only preliminary results, it is already
possible to suggest that the (He^3,t) reaction can
serve as an accurate tool for the investigation of
Coulomb displacement energy and its dependence for any
element on the number of neutrons (isotope shift).
When excited isobaric analogues are observed it should
also be possible to investigate the dependence of the
Coulomb displacement energy on the details of indivi-

dual states, especially when states cannot be reached in proton capture reactions. Since (He^3, t) reactions also seem to excite states for which $\Delta T = 1$ relatively more strongly than (p,n) reactions, it is expected that (He^3, t) studies would favorably compete with (p,n) studies of those states.

It is a pleasure to acknowledge the assistance of Mr. L. E. Ernest and the cyclotron crew in obtaining the data. We also wish to thank Professor P. Axel for stimulating discussions, and Professor R. Sherr and Dr. A. G. Blair for making available unpublished data.

TABLE I. Excitation energies and differential cross sections. The columns labeled Ex and Ex(*) list measured excitation energies relative to the ground states and to the analogue states, respectively. ? signifies that the state is apparently not an excited analogue state. The last column gives approximate differential cross sections for the analogue states.

Target	Peak	Ex (MeV)	Ex(*) (MeV)	$\sigma(40°)$ $\mu b/sr$
Fe^{54}	0,*	0.0	0.0	18
	1	0.9	0.9?	
	2	1.4	1.4	
	3	2.1	2.1	
	4	3.1	3.1	
Fe^{56}	0	0.0		
	1	0.9		
	2	1.6		
	3	2.1		
	4	2.5		
	*	3.3	0.0	40
	5	$\approx$ 4.2	0.9	
	6	$\approx$ 5.2	1.85	
Fe^{57}	0	0.0		
	*	7.0	0.0	52
	1	7.7	0.7	
	2	8.75	1.75	

TABLE I (continued)

Target	Peak	Ex (MeV)	Ex(*) (MeV)	$\sigma(40°)$ μb/sr
Ni^{58}	0	0.0		
	*	0.2	0.0	8
	1	1.1	0.9?	
	2	1.6	1.4	
	3	2.8	2.6	
	4	3.3	3.1	
Ni^{60}	0	0.0		
	1	0.5		
	2	1.6		
	*	2.2	0.0	10
	3	3.0	0.8?	
	4	3.7	1.5	
	5	≈ 5.6	3.4	
Ni^{61}	0	0.0		
	1	1.2		
	2	2.8		
	3	3.7		
	4	4.4		
	5	5.4		
	*	6.1	0.0	10
	6	7.0	0.9	
Ni^{62}	(0)	(0.0)		
	*	(4.0)	0.0	26

TABLE I (continued)

Target	Peak	Ex (MeV)	Ex(*) (MeV)	$\sigma(40°)$ μb/sr
	1	(5.2)	1.2	
Ni^{64}	(0)	(0.0)		
	*	(5.9)	0.0	35
	1	(7.3)	1.4	
Zr^{90}	(0)	(0.0)		
	*	(5.4)	0.0	10
Zr^{91}	(0)	(0.0)		
	*	(10.3)	0.0	9
	1	(11.7)	1.4	
Zr^{92}	(0)	(0.0)		
	*	(9.3)	0.0	10
	1	(10.5)	1.2?	
Zr^{94}	(0)	(0.0)		
	*	(10.5)	0.0	7

TABLE II. Coulomb displacement energies E_c in MeV.
Values labeled $\bar{E}_{c1}$ are averages over the isotopes investigated, weighted according to isotopic abundance.
Values labeled $\bar{E}_{c2}$ are averages over isotopes for
which our identification of the ground state is unambiguous. The errors are estimated to be $\pm$ 0.20 MeV.
Reduced Coulomb displacement energies $E_c A^{1/3}$ are normalized to 1.00 for the lowest A for each element, with
estimated error $\pm$ 0.02. For comparison, values of E_c
reported by Anderson et al.[2], which have uncertainties of $\pm$ 0.15 MeV, are given in the last column.

| Target | Present Experiment | | | Anderson, et al. | |
	E_c	$\bar{E}_{c1}$	$\bar{E}_{c2}$	$E_c A^{1/3}$	E_c
Fe^{54}	9.05			1.00	
Fe^{56}	8.70			0.98	8.9
Fe^{57}	8.60			0.975	
Fe		8.70	8.85		
Ni^{58}	9.55			1.00	
Ni^{60}	9.10			0.97	
Ni^{61}	9.15			0.965	
Ni^{62}	(8.75)			(0.925)	
Ni^{64}	(8.40)			(0.895)	
Ni		9.40	9.25		9.5
Zr^{90}	(12.30)			1.00	
Zr^{91}	(12.20)			1.00	
Zr^{92}	(12.10)			0.99	
Zr^{94}	(12.20)			1.01	
Zr		(12.25)	(12.15)		11.75

REFERENCES

1) J. D. Anderson, C. Wong, J. N. McClure, and B. D. Walker, Phys. Rev. $\underline{136}$ (1964) B118.

2) J. D. Anderson, C. Wong, and J. N. McClure, Phys. Rev. $\underline{138}$ (1965) B615.

3) A. G. Blair and H. E. Wegner, Phys. Rev. Letts. $\underline{9}$ (1962) 168.

4) R. Sherr, A. G. Blair, D. D. Armstrong, (private communication).

5) H. E. Mattauch, W. Thiele, and A. H. Wapstra, Nucl. Phys. $\underline{67}$ (1965) 32.

6) M. Harchol, A. A. Jaffe, C. H. Drory, and J. Zioni, Phys. Letters $\underline{20}$ (1966) 302.

7) A. M. Lane and J. M. Soper, Nucl. Phys. $\underline{37}$ (1962) 506.

8) A. I. Yavin, R. A. Hoffswell, and T. M. Noweir Paper E6.

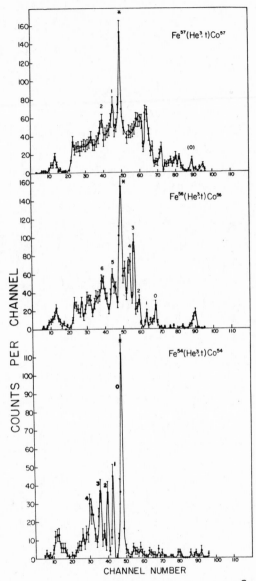

Fig. 1. Spectra of tritons from the (He^3, t) reaction on $Fe^{54,56,57}$. The analogue state and ground state peaks are labeled * and O, respectively. Other prominent peaks are numbered.

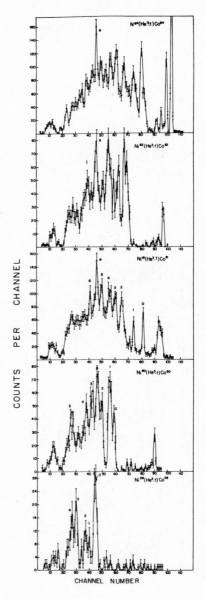

Fig. 2. Spectra of tritons from the (He³,t) reaction on Ni⁵⁸,⁶⁰,⁶¹,⁶²,⁶⁴. The analogue state and ground state peaks are labeled * and O, respectively. Other prominent peaks are numbered.

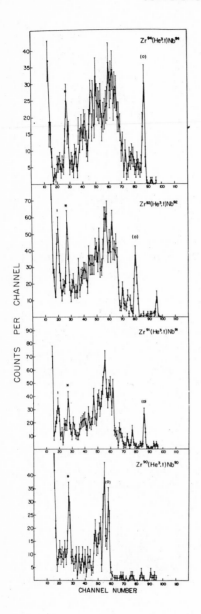

Fig. 3. Spectra of tritons from the (He^3,t) reaction on Zr^{90,91,92,94}. The analogue state and ground state peaks are labeled * and 0, respectively. Other prominent peaks are numbered.

S24. THE ANALYSIS OF ISOBARIC ANALOGUE RESONANCES AS BREIT-WIGNER TYPE RESONANCES

G. A. Jones

A. E. R. E.

Harwell, England

The experimental physicist is familiar with the method of analysis of resonances using the Breit-Wigner expression. The excitation functions arising from proton bombardment of medium and heavy nuclei in the range $E_p \sim 4$ to 10 MeV look like typical Breit-Wigner type resonances superimposed on a continuous background. Careful measurement may reveal asymmetry in the shapes of resonances, but the measurements are generally not sufficiently precise and analysis is usually made by subtracting out the background and applying the Breit-Wigner formula. Indeed, a simple approach to the reaction mechanism, due to Lane[1], does give a Breit-Wigner shape to the resonance, but a more thorough approach - by Robson[2] - gives an expression for the cross-section, under approximations which may not hold, which has a built-in asymmetry and does not appear to be a function of the same parameters which describe the Breit-Wigner type resonance. A question therefore arises: for a reaction when Robson's conditions are likely to hold, if the resonance shape is sufficiently near symmetrical to justify a Breit-Wigner fit, do the two methods of analysis give similar results?

The total-reaction cross-sections for the appropriate J in the two cases are:

(1) <u>B-W</u> $\sigma_p(tot) = \sigma_{p'}(tot) + \pi\lambda^2 \dfrac{2J+1}{(2I+1)(2S+1)}$

$$x \ \dfrac{\Gamma_p \ W}{(E_o - E_p)^2 + 1/4 \ (\Gamma_p + W)^2}$$

where W is the sum of all outgoing widths, and, in Lane's picture, is identified with the spreading width of the Coulomb perturbation; and $\sigma p'(tot)$ is the background contribution for the given J.

(2) <u>Robson</u> $\sigma_p(tot) = \sigma_p{}'(tot) \dfrac{(E_o - E_p - \Delta_p)^2}{(E_o - E_p) + 1/4 \ (\Gamma_p + W)^2}$

where $\sigma_p{}'(tot)$ is again the background contribution for the given J, Δ_p is the resonance shift and W is again the spreading width.

Robson's expression passes through a peak value of $\sigma_p{}'(1 + x^2)$, where $x = 2\Delta_p(\Gamma_p + W)^{-1}$, at an energy removed from the resonance energy of the resonance denominator by an amount $(\Gamma_p + W)^2 (4\Delta_o)^{-1}$. Defining the half-width by the energy spacing between the two energies at which $\sigma_p = \sigma_p{}' (1 + 1/2 \ x^2)$, which corresponds to subtracting out the non-resonant background, then the half-width has the approximate value $(\Gamma_p + W)$ $(1 + x^{-2})$. Thus the conventional way of extracting the half-width yields the correct result provided that $x^2 \gg 1$. The ratio between respective values of cross-section minus background at two energies removed from the peak energy by half a half-width up and down is approximately $(1 + 2x^{-1})$. When the half-width is accurate to 4%, this expression indicates a 40% departure from symmetry (a more accurate expression places it at 50%), so the width measurement yields a reasonably accurate result even when the resonance is quite visibly asymmetric.

The Breit-Wigner expression for the peak cross-section minus background is

$$\frac{\pi \lambda^2 (2J + 1)}{(2I + 1)(2S + 1)} \cdot \frac{4 \, \Gamma_p \, W}{(\Gamma_p + W)^2}$$

whilst Robson's expression is

$$\sigma_p' \cdot 4\Delta_p^{\,2}(\Gamma_p + W)^{-2}.$$

Equating these two expressions gives

$$\sigma_p' = \frac{\pi \lambda^2 (2J + 1)}{(2I + 1)(2S + 1)} \cdot \frac{\Gamma_p \, W}{\Delta_p^{\,2}} .$$

Now Robson defines

$$\Delta_p^{\,2} = \frac{(\mathrm{Re} \; L^o_p)^2}{4 \, P_p^{\,2}} \; \Gamma_p^{\,2}$$

and

$$W = \frac{\pi \mathcal{S}_p}{P_p} \; | \, L^o_p \, |^2 \; \Gamma_p$$

where $\mathcal{S}_p$ is the strength function appropriate to the given J, and $L^o_p = S^+_p - B_c + iP_p$ where the real term is the shift function relative to the neutron shift and the imaginary term is the penetrability (ρ/A_ℓ^2).

Therefore for agreement we require

$$\sigma_p' = \frac{\pi \lambda^2 (2J + 1)}{(2I + 1)(2S + 1)} \cdot 4\pi \, P_p \mathcal{S}_p \, \frac{|L|^2}{(\text{Re } L)^2}$$

But the contribution to the total cross-section from a given J is

$$\sigma_p' = \frac{\pi \lambda^2 (2J + 1)}{(2I + 1)(2S + 1)} \cdot \frac{2\pi < \Gamma_p >}{< D >}$$

and Robson has in addition defined his strength function by

$$2P_p \mathcal{S}_p = \frac{< \Gamma_p >}{< D >}$$

so the condition for agreement is simply $|L|^2 \approx (\text{Re } L)^2$ that is that the square of the penetrability be fairly small compared with the square of the shift function. This condition is in fact less stringent than the one required to determine the correct total width, namely $x^2 \gg 1$, and this in turn is less stringent than the condition for looking symmetric, namely $|x| \gg 2$. This means that under conditions where the resonance may not look symmetric, analysis ignoring the asymmetry will often yield the same values of the parameters defining the resonance as does the more accurate analysis. In fact all resonances so far observed can be analyzed using the Breit-Wigner formula since the condition $|L|^2 \approx (\text{Re } L)^2$ holds well up the Coulomb barrier.

Finally, an interesting feature emerges from looking at the Breit-Wigner formula which is not so

immediately apparent from Robson's expression. The
expression for the peak cross-section contains the
term $\Gamma_p W(\Gamma_p + W)^{-2}$, and since W is usually much greater
than Γ_p, this is approximately Γ_p/W. Resonances are
therefore larger for smaller values of W. But,

$$\Gamma_p/W = \frac{P_p}{\pi \mathcal{J}_p} \quad \frac{1}{|L^o_p|^2} \quad ,$$

so we expect to see sharper, more intense isobaric
analogue resonances in a region well away from the
size resonances for the ingoing proton. This was deduced using Robson's theory of external mixing, but it
feeds back upon itself to assert that external mixing
is more important than internal mixing when one is
seeing well defined resonances, for the reason that,
when $\mathcal{J}_p$ is small, the nucleus is looking like a hard
sphere for the background states and so the wave-func-
tion for these states, averaged over a suitable energy
interval, will indeed be small within the nucleus.
The dominant contribution to the mixing will then arise
from outside the nucleus.

Furthermore the parameter x, which determines
the departure from symmetry, takes on the value 5
for the 5.0 MeV resonance in $Y^{89} + p$[3] when one inserts
for the strength function the black nucleus value
$(\pi K R)^{-1} \approx (10\ \pi)^{-1}$. Johnson[4] has measured the shape
of this resonance using the (p,n) reaction and deduces
a value of $x > 10$. Other resonances using this target
appear equally symmetric[5]. Thus the strength function
must be quite a bit smaller than the black nucleus
value confirming the above remarks. It would be of
interest to look at the intensity and shape of isobaric

analogue resonances in a region close to a size resonance - for example targets of A $\sim$ 70 for s-wave resonances.

REFERENCES

1) G. A. Jones, A. M. Lane and G. C. Morrison, Phys.
   Letts. 11 (1964) 329.
2) D. Robson, Phys. Rev. 137 (1965) B535.
3) J. D. Fox, C. F. Moore and D. Robson, Phys. Rev.
   Letts. 12 (1964) 198.
4) C. H. Johnson, (private communication).
5) J. Black, M. M. Islam, G. A. Jones, G. C.
   Morrison and R. B. Taylor, Paper S 25.

S25. ISOBARIC ANALOGUE STATES IN Zr^{90}

J. Black[+], M. M. Islam[++]

Nuclear Physics Laboratory

Oxford, England

G. A. Jones, G. C. Morrison[+++] and R. B. Taylor

A. E. R. E.

Harwell, England

INTRODUCTION

Fox, Moore and Robson[1] have reported two sharp resonances in the $Y^{89}(p,n)Zr^{89}$ excitation function just above threshold. Their proton elastic scattering excitation function also showed sharp anomalies at the same energies. These resonances were interpreted as corresponding to the lowest $T = 6$ (i.e. $T_z + 1$) states of the compound nucleus Zr^{90} and hence as analogues of the ground state and the first excited state of Y^{90} ($T_z = 6$) with $J = 2^-$ and 3^-. They have also observed other similar doublets in elastic scattering.

This paper describes detailed studies of the excitation functions for the following reactions: $Y^{89}(p,\gamma_0)Zr^{90}$, $Y^{89}(p,n)Zr^{89}$, $Y^{89}(p,n)^{89m}Zr$, $Y^{89}(p,p')$ Y^{89m} and $Y^{89}(p,\gamma)Zr^{90m}$. The proton beam was supplied by the A.E.R.E. or the Oxford Tandems, ranging from 4.7 to approximately 6.4 MeV for all reactions. The

[+] Now at University of Stanford, California
[++] Now at Atomic Energy Center, Dacca, Pakistan
[+++] Now at Argonne National Laboratory, Illinois

results for $Y^{89}(p,\gamma_0)Zr^{90}$ and preliminary results for $Y^{89}(p,p')Y^{89m}$ have been reported in brief elsewhere[2,3] but they are included here again with further discussion for the sake of clarity and completeness.

It is demonstrated in this paper that the study of the proton elastic scattering excitation function alone is not sufficient as a tool for investigating low-lying excited states of the analogue nucleus. The elastic scattering reaction is the analogue of the (d,p) stripping reaction in which a neutron instead of a proton is added to the same target; and there is a direct relationship between the stripping reduced width and the proton reduced width for the resonant state[2]. On the other hand, analogues of states which are not good shell model states with a configuration based on the ground state configuration of the target nucleus are not expected to show up well in the elastic scattering experiments. It has been found that the (p,n) and (p,p') reactions are especially useful as additional tools and that these reactions should always be investigated in conjunction with the (p,p) reaction.

EXPERIMENTAL PROCEDURE AND RESULTS

The Reaction $Y^{89}(p,\gamma_0)Zr^{90}$

The γ-radiation was detected with a 5" dia. by 6" thick NaI (Tl) crystal with circuitry for reducing pulse pile up and gain shifts. The excitation function as shown in Fig. 1 in which it is seen that two strong resonances occur at E_p = 6.15 and 8.04 MeV, of width $\approx$ 70 keV. Angular distributions were taken at the peaks of the resonances and are shown in Fig. 2, which also shows the least squares fits. They were:

$W(\theta) = 1 - (0.05 \pm 0.03)P_1 + (0.03 \pm 0.04)P_2$ for the

6.15 MeV resonance and

$W(\theta) = 1 + (0.04 \pm 0.04)P_1 - (0.68 \pm 0.04)P_2$ for the

8.04 MeV resonance.

By comparison of the peak intensities with that of the peak of the 5.115 MeV resonance[3] of $F^{19}(p,\gamma_o)Ne^{20}$, an absolute cross section for the 6.15 MeV peak at 90° is 14.8 ± 6.5 μb/ster. Assuming that we are dealing with a simple Breit-Wigner resonance and that the intermediate state spin is 1 then it is possible to make a lower estimate of the radiation widths if the simplifying assumption that $\Gamma_p = \Gamma$ is made. The results obtained are $\Gamma_\gamma > 30$ eV and $\Gamma_\gamma > 60$ eV for the 6.15 and 8.04 MeV resonances. The Weisskopf estimate for an El transition of 14.4 MeV (the excitation of the 6.15 MeV resonance) is 4.1 keV so that our measured strength $|M|^2 > 0.0075$ Weisskopf units. Since the isobaric spin factor[2], $(2T + 1)^{-1}$, which suppresses Γ_p will also suppress Γ_γ, this is sufficiently large a fraction of the Weisskopf unit to ensure that the transition is El and therefore the two states at $E_p = 6.15$ and 8.04 MeV have $J^\pi = 1^-$. Analysis of the angular distributions then indicate that the 6.15 MeV resonance is formed by s-wave with less then 0.1% by intensity of d-wave, with an alternative solution of 95% d-wave and 5% s-wave. For the 8.04 MeV resonance the two solutions are 95% d-wave plus 5% s-wave and 40% d-wave plus 60% s-wave.

The Reactions $Y^{89}(p,n)Zr^{89}$ and $Y^{89}(p,n)Zr^{89m}$

The former reaction was investigated with a long counter placed at 90° to the beam and close to the

865

target. The latter reaction was investigated by detecting the 0.588 MeV isomeric γ-transition ($t_{1/2}$ = 4.43 min) using a 1 1/2" dia. by 1 1/2" NaI(Tl) crystal. See Fig. 3 for the transition scheme. The two excitation functions have been taken simultaneously to detect shifts in locations of resonance peaks. The excitation function for the (p,n) reaction is shown in Fig. 4.

The Reactions $Y^{89}(p,p')Y^{89m}$ and $Y^{89}(p,\gamma)Zr^{90m}$

These reactions were investigated by detection of the isomeric transitions involved (see Fig. 3). In the former the 0.92 MeV radiation from the $9/2^+$ state ($t_{1/2}$ = 14 secs) was detected and in the latter the 2.3 MeV radiation from the 5^- state ($t_{1/2}$ = 0.8 secs). The excitation functions are shown in Figs. 5 and 6. In addition some runs over resonance peaks were taken from the (p,p') reaction and the (p,n) reaction simultaneously. The results are shown in Figs. 7, 8 and 9.

Summary of Results

The strong resonances observed in all reactions involving Y^{89} + p are listed in Table I. The results of the work of Fox et al.[1] are also included in the Table. There is good agreement between the (p,n) resonances from the Florida work and the work reported here, but several new resonances are reported in the present work.

COMPARISON OF RESONANCES OBSERVED IN DIFFERENT (Y^{89} + p) REACTIONS

(p,n) and (p,n)^m

All resonances in (p,n)^m were also observed at

the same energies in (p,n). The resonance at 5.01 MeV
in (p,n) does not however have its counterpart in $(p,n)^m$.
This result is expected from the work of Lightbody et
al.[4] and Mani and Dutt[5].

(p,n) and (p,p)

The agreement between the resonances observed in
these reactions is quite good except that extra resonances appear in (p,n) which do not appear in (p,p);
they are those at E_p = 5.645, 5.80 and 5.93 MeV. In
addition the doublet at 6.01 and 6.15 MeV in (p,p) has
split up into four levels in (p,n).

(p,n) and $(p,p')^m$

Careful measurement of the 5.0 MeV resonance re-
veals that the resonance in $(p,p')^m$ occurs at 5 ± 2 keV
higher than that in (p,n). The resonance in $(p,p')^m$ at
5.625 MeV appears at 17 ± 3 keV lower than its counterpart in (p,n) - if indeed it is the counterpart; it
seems unlikely that a shift of such a large fraction of
the resonance width can arise. The resonance of
$(p,p')^m$ at 5.805 MeV is 5 ± 2 keV higher than the corresponding (p,n) resonance. The strong resonance at
6.045 MeV in $(p,p')^m$ is 20 keV removed from the nearest
resonance in (p,n) at 6.025 MeV, but these were not
measured simultaneously. The relevant excitation functions for these measurements are shown in Figs. 7, 8
and 9.

DISCUSSION OF MECHANISM

Robson[2] has produced a model for reactions involving isobaric analogue states in which the mixing
between $T_>$ and $T_<$ states arises chiefly from "outside

the nucleus". He has solved the problem only after
making the simplifying assumption that the unmixed $T_>$
state contains width only in the entrance channel, and
his solution is therefore best fitted for the analysis
of resonances which appear strongly in elastic scattering. The most interesting feature of the model is that
it leads to a resonance which is asymmetric in shape
and whose peak cross section in reaction does not correspond with the resonance energy in elastic scattering.
Lane[6] has produced a simpler theory, based on mixing
of the $T_>$ and $T_<$ states arising from inside the nucleus,
which can produce resonances even when there is no
width in the entrance channel for the unmixed $T_>$ state,
provided that this latter state has width in the exit
channel. However Bloch and Schiffer[7] point out that
the mixing produced by the Coulomb perturbation can
be split up into a "local" effect and a "distant"
effect; the former is the mixing considered by Robson
and by Lane, but the latter can be considerable and
could lead to the production of a resonance in a reaction for which the unmixed state $T_>$ had neither width
in the entrance channel, nor in the exit channel. This
effect is covered in Robson's general treatment of the
reaction, but has been neglected by him in arriving at
an expression for the cross section.

The most striking aspect of the data presented
in this paper is the fact that many additional analogue
resonances appear in (p,n) and (p,p') which are not
observed in (p,p). One of these resonances namely that
at $Ep = 5.625$ MeV can be identified with the (2^+) state
in Y^{90} which is known to have very little neutron width
in $Y^{89}(d,p)Y^{90}$ - Sheline[8] puts an upper limit to its
formation in this reaction at less than 0.1% of the

reaction to the ground state. The configuration of this (2^+) state is known[9] and is expected to have a strong single-particle (neutron) connection with the $9/2^+$ state of Y^{89}; the mechanism for the production of the resonance at 5.625 MeV seems therefore to be that in which the $T_>$ state has width only in the outgoing channel*. Since the (2^+) state in Y^{90} belongs to a sextuplet arising from the coupling of a ($d_{5/2}$) neutron with a ($g_{9/2}$) neutron, it seems reasonable to assume that the strong resonances at 5.805 and 6.045 MeV in $(p,p')^m$, which do not appear in (p,p), are also analogue members of the multiplet. The fact that the (7^+) resonance (corresponding to the known position[10] of the 7^+ state in Y^{90}) has not been observed in $(p,p')^m$ can be explained by consideration of penetrability of the $\ell = 7$ wave involved in its formation. Since at least one and possibly all three of these resonances occur quite strongly in the (p,n) reaction, we must invoke some mechanism like that of Bloch and Schiffer since the unmixed $T_>$ state has no proton partial width to the ground state and cannot have neutron width.

Our results on locations of resonance peaks in different reactions is in conflict with Robson's theory which produces a resonance shift but only between the elastic and reaction channels, all such reaction channels having the same peak energy (provided that the background cross sections are not changing too rapidly and this should be the case). Lane's expression for the cross section produces no resonance shifts. The reason for discrepancy between Robson's predictions and

---

*The mechanism for this can however be produced from Robson's model by a detailed-balance argument.

our measurements may arise from the Bloch-Schiffer effect which gives width in the $T_>$ state to a number of channels by weak mixing and so makes the situation more complex than that envisaged by Robson.

SUMMARY

Our measurements on reaction cross sections associated with Y^{89} + p reveal many more isobaric analogue states than do the elastic scattering measurements. We feel that our results demonstrate the need for a mechanism to cope with width in the outgoing channel and also for an effect like that described by Bloch and Schiffer.

REFERENCES

1) J. D. Fox, C. F. Moore and D. Robson, Phys. Rev. Letts. 12 (1964) 198.

2) D. Robson, Phys. Rev. 137 (1965) B535; D. Robson, J. D. Fox, P. Richard and C. F. Moore, Phys. Letts. 18 (1965) 86.

3) N. W. Tanner, G. C. Thomas and E. D. Earle, Nucl. Phys. 52 (1964) 29.

4) D. B. Lightbody, G. E. Mitchell and A. Sayres, Phys. Letts. 15 (1965) 155.

5) G. S. Mani and G. C. Dutt, Phys. Letts. 16 (1965) 50.

6) G. A. Jones, A. M. Lane and G. C. Morrison, Phys. Letts. 11 (1964) 329.

7) C. Bloch and J. P. Schiffer, Phys. Letts. 12 (1964) 22.

8) C. Watson, C. F. Moore and R. K. Sheline, Nucl. Phys. 54 (1964) 519.

9) Y. E. Kim, Phys. Rev. 131 (1963) 1712.

10) W. L. Alford, D. R. Koehler and C. E. Mandeville, Phys. Rev. <u>123</u> (1961) 1365.

TABLE I. Major resonances in $Y^{89} + p$ as determined from the various reaction channels observed.

$(p,n)^*$	$(p,n)^m$	$(p,p')^m$	$(p,n)^{**}$ Florida	$(p,p)^{**}$ Florida	$(p,\gamma)^m$ Florida	$(p,\gamma_0)^*$
4.81	4.81	4.79	4.82	4.82	4.81	
5.01	No resonance	5.015	5.02	5.02	5.01	
5.645	5.645	5.625				
5.80	5.80	5.805				
5.93	5.93					
5.98⎫ 6.025⎭	5.98⎫ 6.025⎭	6.045	6.01	6.01		
6.12⎫ 6.15⎭	6.12⎫ 6.15⎭	6.15	6.16	6.16		6.16
			7.26	7.26		
			7.45	7.45		
						8.04

* Results presented in this paper.
**Work done at Florida State University. Ref. 1.

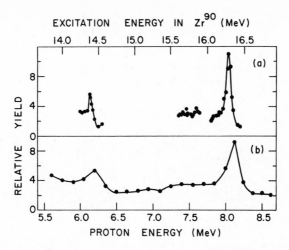

Fig. 1. Excitation function for the reaction $Y^{89}(p,\gamma_0)Zr^{90}$.

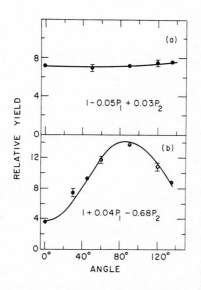

Fig. 2. Upper: Angular distribution of resonance at 6.15 MeV in $Y^{89}(p,\gamma_0)$; Lower: Angular distribution of resonance at 8.04 MeV in $Y^{89}(p,\gamma_0)$.

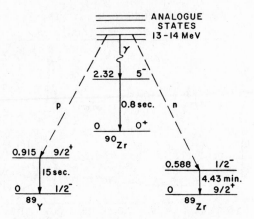

Fig. 3. Isomeric transitions following the decay of
highly excited states in Zr^{90}.

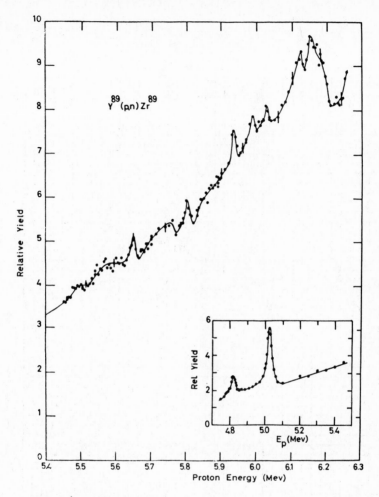

Fig. 4. Excitation function for the reaction $Y^{89}(p,n)Zr^{89}$.

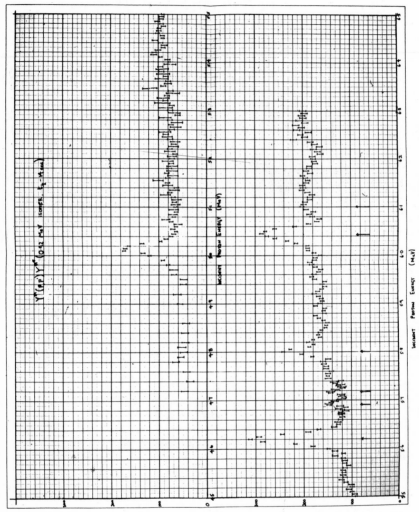

Fig. 5. Excitation function for the reaction
Y[89](p,p')Y[89m].

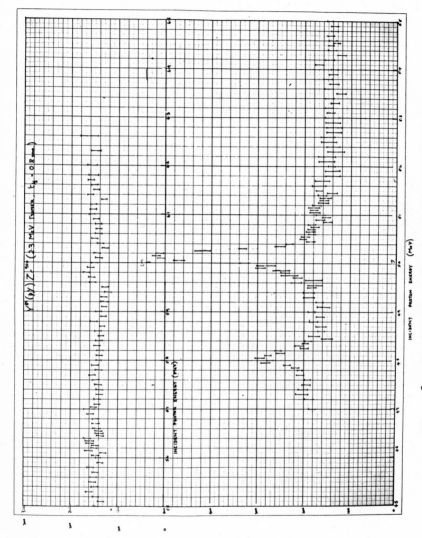

Fig. 6. Excitation function for the reaction
Y[89](p,γ)Zr[90m].

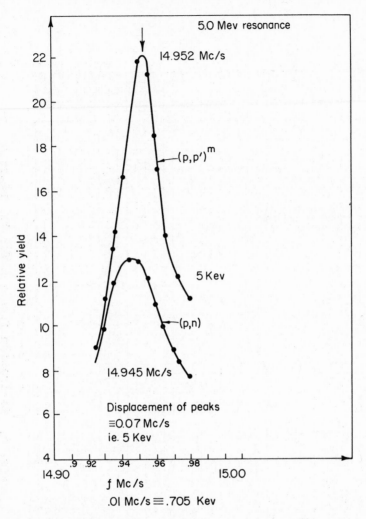

Fig. 7. Comparison of (p,n) and (p,p')^m over the 5.0 MeV peak.

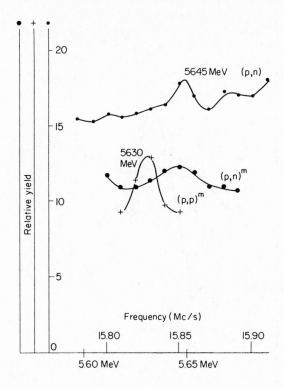

Fig. 8. Comparison of (p,n) and $(p,p')^m$ over the 5.6 MeV peak.

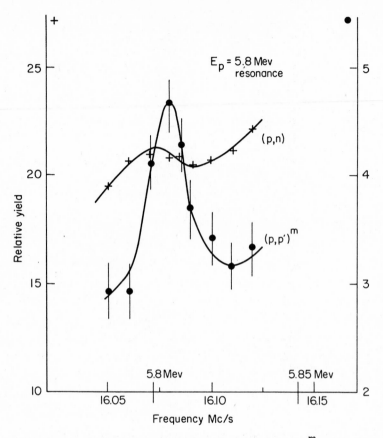

Fig. 9. Comparison of (p,n) and (p,p')^m over the 5.8 MeV peak.

S26. SPIN MEASUREMENT OF $_{31}Ga^{64}$; PRELIMINARY RESULTS[+]

J. P. Deutsch and L. Grenacs[++]

Louvain University
Louvain, Belgium

INTRODUCTION

The Conserved Vector Current Theory of Weak Interactions - rather well established by now (see e.g. Ref. 1) - enables us to ascribe the occurrence of non-vanishing isobaric spin forbidden $\int 1$ matrix-elements in $\Delta T = \pm 1$ beta-transitions to the isobaric spin impurity of the nuclear states involved. The existence of well-defined isobaric states of known energy[2] makes it further possible to evaluate the matrix element responsible for the isobaric spin mixing from the amount of the isobaric spin impurity[3]. Describing the states involved by some model wave functions, this mixing matrix element can be eventually computed in order to check whether Coulomb forces alone suffice to explain their experimental values[4]. If this is not the case, one should introduce charge dependence into the nuclear forces.

This program was actively pursued these last years both in the medium and heavy nuclei[3-7]. It was found, in particular, that the isobaric spin impurities were rather low and systematically corresponded to

---

[+]Work supported by I. I. S. N.

[++]Chercheur agréé I. I. S. N.

mixing matrix elements of 30 keV or lower[3].

   One outstanding exception to this empirical rule
was the ground state of Ga^{64} which seemed to be mixed
with the isobaric analogue of the Zn^{64} ground state
through a matrix element of 73 $\pm$ 2 keV[3]. This figure
is so high because of the unusual rapidity (log ft =
6.6)[8] of the ground state to ground state beta-decay
of Ga^{64}, taking into account the isobaric spin forbid-
denness of this presumably (0^+) - (0^+) transition.
This (0^+)-assignment to the ground state of Ga^{64} is
effectively plausible if one considers the decay-scheme
of Ga^{64} [8], but it was emphasized lately[3,9] that because of the far-reaching consequences of this assignment, the conjectures should be backed by a direct experimental determination. The experiment we describe
was aimed to perform this determination. It consisted
in the measurement of the beta-gamma circular polarization correlation between beta rays emitted by Ga^{64}
and the high energy gamma rays of E$_\gamma \simeq$ 3.3 MeV of the
daughter nucleus. This correlation is sensitive to
the spin-assignment of Ga^{64}.[+]

LAY-OUT, MEASURING PROCEDURE AND RESULTS

   The relative positions and main features of the
detectors and the polarimeter are represented in Fig. 1.
The beta rays, having a direction defined by a plastic
collimator and after their passage through an Al-foil
of 0.5 mm (half-opening angle : 26°) were detected by
a plastic scintillator NE102 5 mm thick and 40 mm in

[+]One may note that the parity-assignment (+) was never
questioned because it would be difficult to construct
a negative parity, low-energy, low-spin state, for an
odd-odd nucleus, from the orbitals available in the
region 28 < N, Z < 50.

diameter. The photomultiplier was an AVP56; a lucite
light-pipe of 20 cm length and heavy magnetic shielding
was used to extract and shield it against the influence
of the magnetic stray-field of the polarimeter. The
inversion of this stray-field had influence less than
0.1% on the number of beta rays effectively detected.

The gamma rays, after their passage through the
polarimeter, were detected by a 4" x 4" NaI(Tl) crystal
coupled through a light-pipe of 50 cm to a 58AVP photomultiplier. The lead collimator had a half opening
angle of 6°; the magnetic shielding was sufficient to
reduce the pulse height shift introduced by the inversion of the stray-field to a negligible amount.

The polarimeter was a soft iron cylinder of
10.4 $\pm$ .5 cm effective length magnetized to 16,800 $\pm$
200 Gauss (polarized fraction of electrons : 6.7%).
Inverting the magnetization of the polarimeter its
transmission changes for polarized gamma rays and this
can serve as measurement of the gamma ray polarization[10].

Impulses from the beta- and gamma- detectors in
fast coincidence (2τ = 5 nanosec) opened the gate of
an RIDL 400-channel pulse height analyzer for the impulses of the gamma-detector. We could distinguish
in this manner between the transmitted fraction of
gamma rays of about 3.3 MeV and Compton-scattered,
respectively lower-energy components. The magnetic
field was regularly inverted and the corresponding impulses directed toward different sub-groups of the
multichannel's memory.

Ga^{64} was obtained bombarding 10 mg/cm^2 self-
sustaining Zn-foils enriched to 98.9% in Zn^{64+} with

[+]Supplied by the Electromagnetic Sep. Group, Harwell.

protons degraded to 13 MeV from the synchrocyclotron of
I. K. O., Amsterdam[++]. The absence of other isotopes
was checked by gamma-spectrum and lifetime measurements.
The linear size of the source was about 8 mm. The
Pr^{144} used in the control measurements was obtained in
equilibrium with its Ce^{144} mother as carrier-free $CeCl_2$.
The linear size of this source was 5 mm. The source
backings were of mylar of 4 mg/cm^2 and zapon of 0.5
mg/cm^2, respectively.

The half-life of Ga^{64} being 2.6 min, alternative
measurements of 20 sec were done with the opposite directions of magnetization. The series of measurements
with one sample begun and ended, however, with a measurement of 10 sec only, corresponding to the same direction of magnetization. It can be shown, that this
procedure minimizes the systematic error introduced
by the decay of the sample to a negligible amount. The
overall measuring time for each sample and each direction of magnetization was 140 sec. Waiting time between the measurements was 1 sec, sufficient to ensure
the effective inversion of the magnetization. In the
control measurements, performed on Pr^{144}, we were able
to show that alternating periods of 2 sec, 20 sec and
200 sec yielded, within statistics, the same results.
For each sample, the measurement was preceeded by the
determination of the rate of chance-coincidences. For
a typical counting rate of 10/sec in the pulse-height
region equivalent to E_γ > 2.6 MeV, the chance rate was
about 15%.

If we denote by N_+ and N_- the number of coinci-
dences obtained after subtraction of the chance-ones,

[++]Particular thanks are due to the cyclotron crew and
the chemistry department of I.K.O. for their efficient
collaboration.

for the magnetic field of the polarimeter pointing toward the sample, and away from it respectively, we may express the result of our experiment as:

$$E = 2 \; \frac{N_+ - N_-}{N_+ + N_-}$$

This effect has to be corrected for the spurious gamma-gamma or annihilation radiation-gamma coincidence (a) and for the influence of the backscattered beta rays (b). Knowing the spin-dependent part of the transmission-coefficient of magnetized iron[10], one computes from E_{corr} the effective circular polarization P_c of the gamma rays detected in coincidence ($E_{corr} = K \, P_c$). The circular polarization P_c is related to the asymmetry coefficient A by the relation:

$$P_c = A(v/c)_m \; (\cos \theta)_m$$

$(v/c)_m$ and $(\cos \theta)_m$ being the mean-velocity of the detected beta rays and the mean of the angle's cosine they form with the detected gamma ray (taking into account also the finite size of the source). The relevant results and correction factors are summarized in Table I.

DISCUSSION

Our preliminary results are compared to the theoretical predictions in Fig. 2. The result of our control-measurement performed on the well-known[11] $(0-)-(1-)-(0+)$ beta-gamma cascade ($E_\gamma = 2.18$ MeV) of Pr^{144} is in good agreement with the expected asymmetry-coefficient for such a cascade and so the instrument and the corrections seem to be under good control.

According to the decay-scheme presented by the authors of Ref. 8, our correlation measurements were performed on the allowed beta-branch (log ft = 4.6) of Ga^{64} feeding an excited state of Zn^{64} around 3.3 MeV; the possible spin-sequences are: (0)-(1)-(0) if Ga^{64} has a ground state of 0-spin and (1)-(1)-(0) or (1)-(2)-(0) if it has a ground state spin of 1. The comparison of the expected asymmetry-coefficients for these cases with our preliminary result indicates that the 0-spin assignment to the Ga^{64} is strongly favored.

One should note, that in the hypothesis of a (1)-(1)-(0) spin sequence a unique asymmetry coefficient could be obtained only because we supposed $\int 1 = 0$, in agreement with the systematics[3,4,5,6,7] and the theoretical arguments invoked in the introduction. If one admits tentatively the (1)-assignment to the ground state of Ga^{64} and a non-vanishing Fermi matrix element for the beta-branch we measured, the asymmetry-coefficient can be expressed as[12]:

$$A = -0.5 \frac{2.8x + 1}{1 + x^2} \quad \text{with } x = \frac{C_V \int 1}{C_A \int \sigma}$$

In this hypothesis, however, our result yields $0.26 < x < 1.65$. Such a great Fermi-contribution would imply a mixing matrix element $|<H_c>|$[3] of 350 keV $< |<H_c>|$ $<$1200 keV, much greater than the already unusual $|<H_c>|$ = 73 keV implied by the 0-spin assignment and the rapidity of the ground state to ground state transition.

One should mention, finally that preliminary results of some recent work done on the decay-scheme of Ga^{64} indicate the partial inadequacy of the one proposed by authors of Ref. 8[13]. These results, however do not change qualitatively our conclusions.

A more detailed description of our measurements and their final results will be published later.

It is a pleasure for us to thank Prof. R. van Lieshout for many valuable discussions, stimulating interest and hospitality at I. K. O. Collaboration of Dr. J. Konijn is also gratefully acknowledged.

REFERENCES

1) C. S. Wu, Rev. Mod. Phys. $\underline{36}$ (1964) 618.

2) J. D. Anderson, C. Wong and J. W. McClure, Phys. Rev. $\underline{126}$ (1962) 2170; $\underline{129}$ (1963) 2718.

3) S. D. Bloom, Nuovo Cimento $\underline{32}$ (1964) 1023.

4) C. C. Bouchiat, Phys. Rev. $\underline{118}$ (1960) 540; P. S. Kelly and S. A. Moszkowski, Z. Phys. $\underline{158}$ (1960) 304; R. J. Blin-Stoyle and L. Novakovic, Nucl. Phys. $\underline{51}$ (1964) 133; J. Damgaerd, (to be published).

5) H. Schopper, Kolloquium über Beta-Zerfall, Heidelberg, 1965.

6) H. Daniel and H. Schmitt, Nucl. Phys. $\underline{65}$ (1965) 481.

7) E. T. Williams, P. G. Hansen, J. Lippert, H. L. Nielsen and K. Wilsky, Phys. Letts. $\underline{15}$ (1965) 143. P. G. Hansen, H. L. Nielsen, K. Wilsky and J. Treherne, Phys. Letts. $\underline{19}$ (1965) 304.

8) T. H. Jacobi, H. A. Howe and J. R. Richardson, Phys. Rev. $\underline{117}$ (1960) 1086.

9) W. P. Alford and J. B. French, Phys. Rev. Letts. $\underline{6}$ (1961) 119.

10) H. Schopper, Nucl. Instr. Meth. $\underline{3}$ (1958) 158.

11) Nuclear Data Sheets, Nat. Acad. Sci., Washington, D. C.; R. Hess, P. Lipnik, J. W. Sunier, Phys. Letts. $\underline{5}$ (1963) 327; W. Collin, H. Daniel, S. Margulies, D. Mekling, P. Schmiellin, H. Schmitt and K. S. Subudlli, Phys. Letts. $\underline{5}$ (1963) 329; R. M. Singru, R. S. Raghavan, R. M. Steffen, Phys. Letts. $\underline{6}$ (1963) 319; E. Creutz, J. de Raedt, J. P. Deutsch, L. Grenacs, D. Siddique, Phys. Letts. $\underline{6}$ (1963) 329.

12) R. M. Steffen, Angular Correlation Handbook, Vol. I, (unpublished), Purdue University, Lafayette, Indiana.

13) J. P. Deutsch, L. Grenacs, J. Konijn and R. van Lieshout, (to be published).

TABLE I. Results of beta-gamma circular polarization correlation measurements (Ga^{64} and Pr^{144}), relevant correction factors and deduced asymmetry coefficients.

	E%	a	b	E_{corr}	k	P_c	$(v/c)_m$	$(cos\theta)_m$	A
$_{31}Ga^{64}$	-5.25 ±0.83	1 +0.02 -0.00	1.11 ±0.07	-5.82 ±1.00	-14.3 ±0.8	0.83 ±0.16	0.953 ±0.004	-0.932	-0.94 ±0.18
$_{60}Pr^{144}$	4.02 ±0.91	-	1.19 ±0.05	4.78 ±1.09	-14.6 ±0.8	-0.70 ±0.16	0.86 ±0.02	-0.942	0.86 ±0.22

E : experimental effect

a = gamma-gamma correction factor

b : backscattering correction factor

E_{corr} : abE

k : inverse of the polarimeter's efficiency

P_c : k E_{corr}

$(v/c)_m$: mean velocity of the beta-rays

$(cos\theta)_m$: mean detection angle

A : experimental value of the asymmetry parameters.

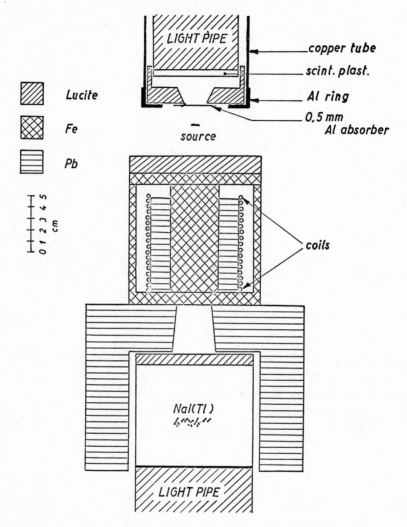

Fig. 1. Scheme of the source-analyzer-detector assembly.

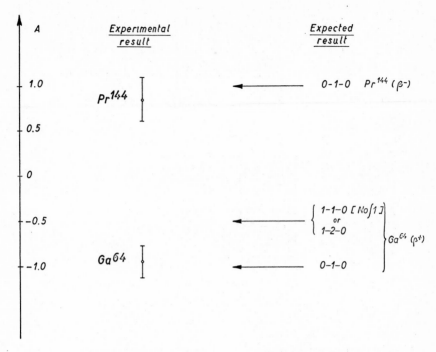

Fig. 2. Comparison of the preliminary values of the asymmetry parameter with the expected ones for different spin attributions to the decaying states.

LIST OF PARTICIPANTS AND AUTHORS

Abdo, K.
Adam, A., 366
Adams, J. L., 333
Adelberger, E. G.
Ahlfeld, C. E.
Ajzenberg-Selove, F.
Aldrich, J.
Aldridge, J. P.
Allan, D. L., 689
Allas, R. G.
Allen, J. S., 721
Anderson, J. D., 530
Armstrong, D. D.
Assousa, G. E.
Axel, P.

Bahnsen, A.
Ball, J. B.
Barnes, C. A.
Barnett, A. R., 774
Barshay, S.
Bassani, G., 366, 373
Bayman, B., 503
Belote, T. A.
Benenson, W.
Bennett, M. J.
Beres, W. P.
Berkowitz, E. H.
Berman, B.
Bilpuch, E. G., 235
Birstein, L., 631
Bisson, A. E.
Bizzeti, P. G., 781
Bizzeti-Sona, A. M., 781
Black, J., 863
Blake, R. B.
Bleuler, E.
Bloom, S., 26, 123
Bock, R.
Bondorf, J., 576
Bonner, B. E.

Borlin, D. D., 605
Boyce, J. R.
Braid, T. H., 605
Bredin, D. J., 472
von Brentano, P., 285, 790, 798
Browne, C. P., 136
Brussel, M. K., 721
Buccino, S. G.
Burch, D.
Burde, J., 631
Buttle, P. J. A.

Cassagnou, Y., 373
Cerny, J.
Chen, S.
Cherubini, J. H.
Chesterfield, C. M., 734
Choppin, G. R.
Cindro, N., 366
Cohen, B. L.
Cosman, E. R., 647
Cosper, S. W.
Courtney, W. J.
Coussement, R., 677
Craig, R. M.
Crawford, G. E.
Crosby, M. A., 757

Daehnick, W. W.
Dalton, B. J.
Davis, R. H.
Dawson, J.
Dehnhard, D.
Deutsch, J. P., 647, 881
Dietrich, F. S.
Dorenbusch, W.
Duhm, H. H.
Dumazet, G.
Dutta, S. K.

893

Edwards, S.
Elwyn, A.
Enge, H. A., 647
Engler, G., 631
Ewbank, W. B.

Fan, C.
Ferguson, A. T. G., 739
Fernald, B.
Fetrow, C. M.
Finckh, E., 713
Fletcher, N. R.
Fortune, H. T.
Fossan, D.
Foster, L.
Fou, C.
Fox, J. D.
Frickey, J. W.
Fuchs, H., 523
Fuller, E. G.
Furubayashi, B., 640

Gabbard, F.
Gantt, D.
Garvey, G. T.
Ginocchio, J.
Ginsburg, A., 631
Glaudemans, P. W. M.
Glendenning, N.
Gorrell, J. E.
Grace, M. A., 357
Gray, M.
Gray, T. J.
Green, A. E. S., 113
Grenacs, L., 881
Grosse, E., 790
Gugelot, P. C.

Hamburger, E. W., 464
Hanna, S. S., 357
Hansen, O., 472
Harchol, M., 230, 835
Hardy, J. C., 701
Harlan, R.
Harris, G. I.
Hayakawa, S. I.
Haynes, S.

Hecht, K. T., 823
Hemsky, J.
Henley, E. M., 3
Hensley, D. C.
Heydenburg, N. P.
Hobbie, R. K.
Hoffswell, R. A., 584, 842
Holbrow, C. H., 595
Hutzelmeyer, H.
Hynes, J. E.

Inglis, D. R.
Islam, M. M., 863

Jaffe, A. A., 230, 631, 835
Jägare, S., 576
Jahnke, U., 713
Jänecke, J. W., 60
Jensen, J. H. D.
John, J.
Johnson, C. H.
Jones, G. A., 689, 857, 863
Jones, K. W.
Jones, L. H., 842

Kahana, S.
Kaufmann, H. C.
Kavaloski, C. D., 307
Kenefick, R. A.
Kennedy, J. W.
Kerman, A. K., 647
Kernell, R. L.
Keyworth, G.
Kim, C. C.
Kim, H. J., 487
Knudson, A. R.
Koshel, R. D.
Kotajima, K.
Kromhout, R. A.
Krone, R. W.
Kurath, D. K.
Kyker, G. G.

Lambert, M.
Lande, A.
Lane, A. M.

894

LIST OF PARTICIPANTS AND AUTHORS

Lane, R. O.
LaSalle, R. A.
Lawson, R. D.
Lawergren, B., 739
Lee, L. L.
Legg, J. C., 757
Legge, G. J. F., 219
Levi, C., 366, 373
Lilley, J. S., 307
Lock, G.
Long, D. D.
Ludemann, C. A.
Lütken, H., 576
Lutz, H. F.

MacDonald, W. M., 173
Macfarlane, M. H., 383
Madsen, B.
Magee, N. H.
Mancusi, M. D.
Manthuruthil, J. C.
Margolis, B.
Marinov, A., 631
Marion, J. B., 766
Martin, M. J.
Maxson, D. R.
McCray, J. A.
McManus, H.
McPherson, R., 162
Melchior, K., 798
Mermaz, M., 366
Messelt, S., 814
Messlinger, R., 807
Meyer-Shützmeister, L., 605
Minor, M.
Mitchell, G. E.
Monahan, J. E.
Moore, C. F., 333
Morinaga, H., 352, 807
Morrison, G. C., 320, 523, 689,
    739, 748, 863
Mulligan, B.

Nelson, J. W.
Nolan, J.
Norbeck, E.
Noweir, T. M., 584, 842

Okamoto, K., 659

Padgett, D. W.
Papineau, L., 366, 373
Parish, L. J.
Park, J. Y.
Park, S. C.
Paul, E. B.
Pearson, J. D.
Pinkston, W. T.
Plendl, H. S.
Prosser, F. W.
Pullen, D. J., 595

Quinton, A. R.

Rauser, P., 798
Richard, P., 307
Richards, H. T.
Rickey, F. A.
Rigby, R. N.
Riley, P.
van Rinsvelt, H. A.
Risser, J. R.
Ritter, R. C.
Robinson, C. P.
Robinson, R. L., 487
Robson, D., 333, 411
Rochleder, E.
Rodney, W. S.
Rose, M. E.
Rosner, B., 595
Roush, M.
Roy, G., 757

Sample, G. T.
Sample, J. T.
Sankey, R. R.
Sawada, T., 113
Schier, W.
Schiffer, J. P., 748
Schult, O.
Segel, R. E., 194, 357
Seitz, H., 790
Shafroth, S., 219

LIST OF PARTICIPANTS AND AUTHORS

Shakin, C.
Shapiro, P.
Sharma, R. D., 113
Sheline, R. K.
Shelton, W. N.
Shida, Y.
Shull, F. B.
Shute, G.
Siemssen, R. H., 523
Singh, P. P., 357
Skyrme, D. J., 701
Sood, P. C.
Soper, J. M., 572
Sperduto, A., 647
Spicer, B. M., 734
Stein, N., 307
Stephen, R. O., 456
Stephenson, G. J., Jr., 766
Stock, R.
Stokes, R. H.
St. Pierre, C.
Sunyar, A.

Talley, T. L.
Talmi, I.
Tamura, T., 447
Taras, P.
Taylor, R. B., 689, 863
Tebor, S.
Temmer, G. M., 472
Teranishi, E. 640
Terrell, G., 333
Thaxton, G. D.
Thompson, W. J.
Trost, W.
True, W. W.

Udagawa, T.
Umbarger, C. J.

Vager, Z., 327
Van Bree, R., 472
Van Neste, L., 677
Vourvopolous, G.

Wallace, J. J.
Warburton, E., 90
Warsh, K. L.
Watson, B.
Watson, C. E.
Watson, D. D.
Way, K.
Weigold, E.
Weil, J. L.
Weinberg, R. B., 689
Weneser, J.
Wesolowski, J.
Wiedner, C. A., 790
Wigner, E. P., 437
Wiley, C.
Wilkinson, D. H., 30, 612
Windham, P. M.
Winter, R. G.
Wirsich, J., 713
Wolicki, E. A.
Wood, L. A.
Wurm, J. P., 798

Yavin, A. I., 584, 721, 842
Yntema, J. L.

Zaidi, S. A. A., 790, 798
Zamick, L., 301
Ziedman, B., 523
Ziegler, J.